McGraw Hill Education create™

Course

Introduction to Business Statistics w/Connect code STAT 201

DREXEL UNIVERSITY
Department of Decision Sciences

create™

http://create.mheducation.com

ISBN-10: 1308881894 ISBN-13: 9781308881898

Contents

Credits

Chapter 1. Overview of Statistics

CHAPTER 1
Overview of Statistics

CHAPTER CONTENTS

CHAPTER LEARNING OBJECTIVES

LO

When you finish this chapter you should be able to

LO 1-1 Define statistics and explain some of its uses.

LO 1-2 List reasons for a business student to study statistics.

LO 1-3 Explain the uses of statistics in business.

LO 1-4 State the common challenges facing business professionals using statistics.

LO 1-5 List and explain common statistical pitfalls.

Prelude

When managers are well informed about a company's internal operations (e.g., sales, production, inventory levels, time to market, warranty claims) and competitive position (e.g., market share, customer satisfaction, repeat sales) they can take appropriate actions to improve their business. Managers need reliable, timely information so they can analyze market trends and adjust to changing market conditions. Better data can also help a company decide which types of strategic information they should share with trusted business partners to improve their supply chain. *Statistics* and *statistical analysis* permit *data-based decision making* and reduce managers' need to rely on guesswork.

Statistics is a key component of the field of *business intelligence,* which encompasses all the technologies for collecting, storing, accessing, and analyzing data on the company's operations in order to make better business decisions. Statistics helps convert unstructured "raw" data (e.g., point-of-sale data, customer spending patterns) into *useful information* through online analytical processing (OLAP) and data mining, terms that you may have encountered in your other business classes. Statistical analysis focuses attention on key problems and guides discussion toward issues, not personalities or territorial struggles. While powerful database software and query systems are the key to managing a firm's data warehouse, relatively small Excel spreadsheets are often the focus of discussion among managers when it comes to "bottom line" decisions. That is why Excel is featured prominently in this textbook.

In short, companies increasingly are using *business analytics* to support decision making, to recognize anomalies that require tactical action, or to gain strategic insight to align business processes with business objectives. Answers to questions such as "How likely is this event?" or "What if this trend continues?" will lead to appropriate actions. Businesses that combine managerial judgment with statistical analysis are more successful.

1.1 WHAT IS STATISTICS?

LO 1-1

Define statistics and explain some of its uses.

Statistics is the science of collecting, organizing, analyzing, interpreting, and presenting data. Some experts prefer to call statistics **data science**, a trilogy of tasks involving data modeling, analysis, and decision making. A **statistic** is a single measure, reported as a number, used to summarize a sample data set. Statistics may be thought of as a collection of methodologies to summarize, draw valid conclusions, and make predictions from empirical measurements. Statistics helps us organize and present information and extract meaning from raw data. Although it is often associated with the sciences and medicine, statistics is now used in every academic field and every area of business.

Plural or Singular?

Statistics The science of collecting, organizing, analyzing, interpreting, and presenting data.

Statistic A single measure, reported as a number, used to summarize a sample data set.

Many different measures can be used to summarize data sets. You will learn throughout this textbook that there can be different measures for different sets of data and different measures for different types of questions about the same data set. Consider, for example, a sample data set that consists of heights of students in a university. There could be many different uses for this data set. Perhaps the manufacturer of graduation gowns wants to know how long to make the gowns; the best *statistic* for this would be the *average* height of the students. But an architect designing a classroom building would want to know how high the doorways should be, and would base measurements on the *maximum* height of the students. Both the average and the maximum are examples of a *statistic*.

You may not have a trained statistician in your organization, but any college graduate is expected to know something about statistics, and anyone who creates graphs or interprets data is "doing statistics" without an official title.

There are two primary kinds of statistics:

- **Descriptive statistics** refers to the collection, organization, presentation, and summary of data (either using charts and graphs or using a numerical summary).
- **Inferential statistics** refers to generalizing from a sample to a population, estimating unknown population parameters, drawing conclusions, and making decisions.

Figure 1.1 identifies the tasks and the text chapters for each.

FIGURE 1.1

Overview of Statistics

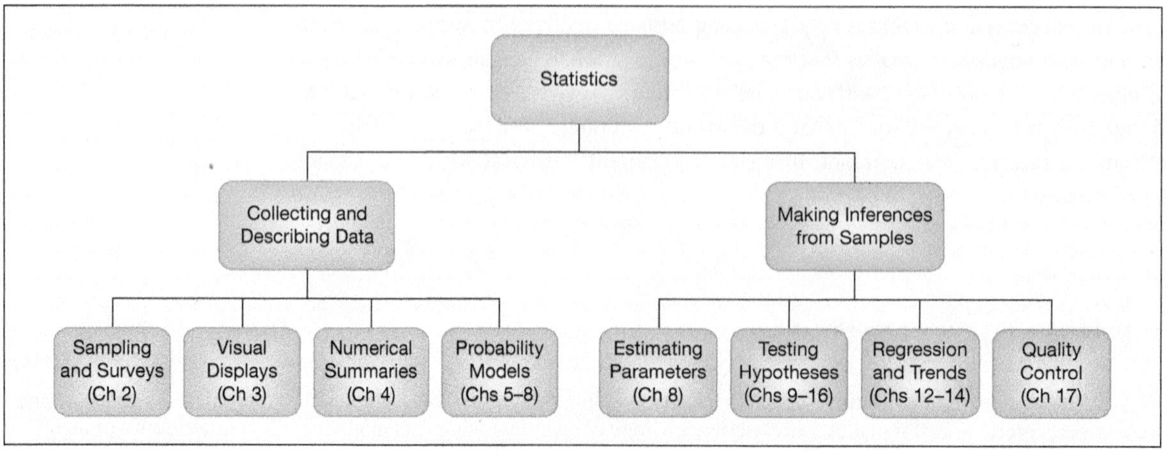

Mini Case 1.1

Vail Resorts

What do the following experiences have in common with *statistics:* an epic ski down a snowy mountain, a superb day of golf, a restful night's sleep, and plentiful clean water for wildlife? Vail Resorts, Inc., has been successfully providing these experiences through the use of rigorous data analysis.

How does Vail Resorts achieve growth? One way is to increase ski lift ticket revenue. Prior to the 2008/2009 ski season, Vail Resorts management asked their marketing group to figure out how to increase the number of annual visits from their destination guests. Customer surveys indicated that having more flexibility around vacation planning would increase the chance that they visited more than once per year. A new season pass of some sort that allowed multiple ski days throughout the ski season was one possible solution. Vail Resorts currently offers The Colorado Pass, which is attractive to in-state guests. But this pass product was not available to out-of-state guests. Vail Resorts needed answers to questions such as: Which resorts should be included on the pass? How many ski days should the pass offer? Should there be blackout dates or not? What price would make the pass attractive?

Four market surveys were sent out to random samples of current and potential guests, including out-of-state guests, in-state guests, and Vail Valley residents. The responses were then used in a statistical analysis to determine relative importance of the various pass features so that the optimal pass product could be offered. What the Vail Resorts marketing team found was that guests were most concerned about the pass price but still wanted to be able to ski at all five ski areas owned by Vail Resorts: Vail, Beaver Creek, Breckenridge, Keystone, and Heavenly. Guests also wanted unlimited days of skiing at Vail and Beaver Creek, and did not want any dates blacked out.

The Epic Pass was first offered for sale on March 18, 2008, for a price of $579. Customers kept their word. By December 9, 2008, over 59,000 Epic Passes had been purchased for total sales revenue of $32.5 million. The number of total passes sold had increased by 18 percent and total pass revenue had increased by 29 percent over the previous pass sales season.

In the following chapters, look for examples and exercises to learn more about how Vail Resorts uses data analysis and statistics to:

- Decrease waiting times to purchase lift tickets.
- Maintain a healthy ratio of out-of-state to in-state guests.

- Help guests feel safe on the mountain.
- Keep hotel rooms booked.
- Increase the percentage of employees who return each season.
- Ensure a healthy environment for wildlife at Grand Teton National Park.

1.2 WHY STUDY STATISTICS?

LO 1-2

List reasons for a business student to study statistics.

A 2006 *BusinessWeek* article called statistics and probability "core skills for businesspeople" in order to know when others are dissembling, to build financial models, or to develop a marketing plan. This same report also said that "B-school grads with strong calculus will find far more opportunities." Each year, *The Wall Street Journal* asks corporate recruiters to rate U.S. business schools on various attributes. In a 2006 *WSJ* survey, recruiters said that the top five attributes were (1) communication and interpersonal skills; (2) ability to work well within a team; (3) personal ethics and integrity; (4) analytical and problem-solving skills; and (5) work ethic. (See "Why Math Will Rock Your World," *BusinessWeek,* January 23, 2006, p. 60; and *The Wall Street Journal,* Sept. 20, 2006.)

Data Skills Count

"We look to recruit and groom leaders in our organization who possess strong quantitative skills in addition to a passion for what we do—delivering exceptional experiences at our extraordinary resorts every day. Knowing how to use and interpret data when making important business decisions is one of the keys to our Company's success."

Rob Katz, chairman and chief executive officer of Vail Resorts

Knowing statistics will make you a better consumer of other people's data analyses. You should know enough to handle everyday data problems, to feel confident that others cannot deceive you with spurious arguments, and to know when you've reached the limits of your expertise. Statistical knowledge gives your company a competitive advantage versus those that cannot understand their internal or external market data. Mastery of basic statistics gives you, the individual manager, a competitive advantage as you work your way through the promotion process, or when you move to a new employer. For specialized training, many universities now offer masters degrees in business analytics. But here are some reasons for anyone to study statistics.

Communication The language of statistics is widely used in science, social science, education, health care, engineering, and even the humanities. In all areas of business (accounting, finance, human resources, marketing, information systems, operations management), workers use statistical jargon to facilitate communication. In fact, statistical terminology has reached the highest corporate strategic levels (e.g., "Six Sigma" at GE and Motorola). And in the multinational environment, the specialized vocabulary of statistics permeates language barriers to improve problem solving across national boundaries.

Computer Skills Whatever your computer skill level, it can be improved. Every time you create a spreadsheet for data analysis, write a report, or make an oral presentation, you bring together skills you already have, and learn new ones. Specialists with advanced training design the databases and decision support systems, but you must handle daily data problems *without* experts. Besides, you can't always find an "expert," and, if you do, the "expert" may not understand your application very well. You need to be able to analyze data, use software with confidence, prepare your own charts, write your own reports, and make electronic presentations on technical topics.

Information Management Statistics can help you handle either too little or too much information. When insufficient data are available, statistical surveys and samples can be used to obtain the necessary market information. But most large organizations are closer to drowning in data than starving for it. Statistics can help summarize large amounts of data and reveal underlying relationships. You've heard of data mining? Statistics is the pick and shovel that you take to the data mine.

Technical Literacy Many of the best career opportunities are in growth industries propelled by advanced technology. Marketing staff may work with engineers, scientists, and manufacturing experts as new products and services are developed. Sales representatives must understand and explain technical products like pharmaceuticals, medical equipment, and industrial tools to potential customers. Purchasing managers must evaluate suppliers' claims about the quality of raw materials, components, software, or parts.

Process Improvement Large manufacturing firms like Boeing or Toyota have formal systems for continuous quality improvement. The same is true of insurance companies and financial service firms like Vanguard or Fidelity, and the federal government. Statistics helps firms oversee their suppliers, monitor their internal operations, and identify problems. Quality improvement goes far beyond statistics, but every college graduate is expected to know enough statistics to understand its role in quality improvement.

Mini Case 1.2

Can Statistics Predict Airfares?

When you book an airline ticket online, does it annoy you when the next day you find a cheaper fare on exactly the same flight? Or do you congratulate yourself when you get a "good" fare followed by a price rise? This ticket price volatility led to the creation of a new company called Farecast that examines over 150 billion "airfare observations" and tries to use the data to predict whether or not the fare for a given ticket is likely to rise. The company's prediction accuracy so far is estimated at 61 percent (in independent tests) and 75 percent (the company's tests). In this case, the benchmark is a coin toss (50 percent). The company offers price rise insurance for a small fee. If you travel a lot and like to play the odds, such predictions could save money. With online air bookings at $44 billion, a few dollars saved here and there can add up. (See *Budget Travel,* February 2007, p. 37; and *The New York Times,* "An Insurance Policy for Low Airfares," January 22, 2007, p. C10.)

1.3 STATISTICS IN BUSINESS

You've seen why statistics is important. Now let's look at some of the ways statistics is used in business.

LO 1-3

Explain the uses of statistics in business.

Auditing A large firm pays over 12,000 invoices to suppliers every month. The firm has learned that some invoices are being paid incorrectly, but they don't know how widespread the problem is. The auditors lack the resources to check all the invoices, so they decide to take a sample to estimate the proportion of incorrectly paid invoices. How large should the sample be for the auditors to be confident that the estimate is close enough to the true proportion?

Marketing A marketing consultant is asked to identify likely repeat customers for Amazon.com, and to suggest co-marketing opportunities based on a database containing records of 5 million Internet purchases of books, CDs, and DVDs. How can this large database be mined to reveal useful patterns that might guide the marketing strategy?

Health Care Health care is a major business (1/6 of the U.S. GDP). Hospitals, clinics, and their suppliers can save money by finding better ways to manage patient appointments, schedule procedures, or rotate their staff. For example, an outpatient cognitive retraining clinic for victims of closed-head injuries or stroke evaluates 56 incoming patients using a 42-item physical and mental assessment questionnaire. Each patient is evaluated independently by two experienced therapists. Are there statistically significant differences between the two therapists' evaluations of incoming patients' functional status? Are some assessment questions redundant? Do the initial assessment scores accurately predict the patients' lengths of stay in the program?

Quality Improvement A manufacturer of rolled copper tubing for radiators wishes to improve its product quality. It initiates a triple inspection program, sets penalties for workers who produce poor-quality output, and posts a slogan calling for "zero defects." The approach fails. Why?

Purchasing A retailer's shipment of 200 DVD players reveals 4 with defects. The supplier's historical defect rate is .005. Has the defect rate really risen, or is this simply a "bad" batch?

Medicine An experimental drug to treat asthma is given to 75 patients, of whom 24 get better. A placebo is given to a control group of 75 volunteers, of whom 12 get better. Is the new drug better than the placebo, or is the difference within the realm of chance?

Operations Management The Home Depot carries 50,000 different products. To manage this vast inventory, it needs a weekly order forecasting system that can respond to developing patterns in consumer demand. Is there a way to predict weekly demand and place orders from suppliers for every item, without an unreasonable commitment of staff time?

Product Warranty A major automaker wants to know the average dollar cost of engine warranty claims on a new hybrid vehicle. It has collected warranty cost data on 4,300 warranty claims during the first six months after the engines are introduced. Using these warranty claims as an estimate of future costs, what is the margin of error associated with this estimate?

Mini Case 1.3

How Do You Sell Noodles with Statistics?

"The best answer starts with a thorough and thoughtful analysis of the data," says Aaron Kennedy, founder of Noodles & Company.

(Visit www.noodles.com to find a Noodles & Company restaurant near you.)

Noodles & Company introduced the *quick casual* restaurant concept, redefining the standard for modern casual dining in the United States in the 21st century. Noodles & Company first opened in Colorado in 1995 and has not stopped growing since. As of June 2014, they had over 400 restaurants all across the United States from Portland and San Diego to Alexandria and Silver Spring with stops in cities such as Omaha and Naperville.

Noodles & Company has achieved this success with a customer-driven business model and fact-based decision making. Their widespread popularity and high growth rate have been supported by careful consideration of data and thorough statistical analysis that provide answers to questions such as:

- Should we offer continuity/loyalty cards for our customers?
- How can we increase the use of our extra capacity during the dinner hours?
- Which new city should we open in?
- Which location should we choose for the new restaurant?
- How do we determine the effectiveness of a marketing campaign?
- Which meal maximizes the chance that a new customer will return?
- Are rice krispies related to higher sales?
- Does reducing service time increase sales?

Aaron Kennedy, founder of Noodles & Company, says that "using data is the strongest way to inform good decisions. By assessing our internal and external environments on a continuous basis, our Noodles management team has been able to plan and execute our vision."

"I had no idea as a business student that I'd be using statistical analysis as extensively as I do now," says Dave Boennighausen, Chief Financial Officer at Noodles & Company. In the coming chapters, as you learn about the statistical tools businesses use today, look for the Noodles logo NOODLES next to examples and exercises that show how Noodles uses data and statistical methods in its business functions.

SECTION EXERCISES

1.1 Give an example of how statistics might be useful to the person in the scenario.

a. An auditor is looking for inflated broker commissions in stock transactions.
b. An industrial marketer is representing her firm's compact, new low-power OLED screens to the military.
c. A plant manager is studying absenteeism at vehicle assembly plants in three states.
d. An automotive purchasing agent is comparing defect rates in steel shipments from three vendors of steel.

1.2 Give an example of how statistics might be useful to the person in the scenario.

a. A personnel executive is examining job turnover by gender in different restaurants in a fast-food chain.
b. An intranet manager is studying e-mail usage rates by employees in different job classifications.
c. A retirement planner is studying mutual fund performance for six different types of asset portfolios.
d. A hospital administrator is studying surgery scheduling to improve facility utilization rates at different times of day.

1.3 (a) Should the average business school graduate expect to use computers to manipulate data, or is this a job better left to specialists? (b) What problems arise when an employee is weak in quantitative skills? Based on your experience, is that common?

1.4 "Many college graduates will not use very much statistics during their 40-year careers, so why study it?" (a) List several arguments for and against this statement. Which position do you find more convincing? (b) Replace the word "statistics" with "accounting" or "foreign language" and repeat this exercise.

1.5 (a) How much statistics does a student need in *your* chosen field of study? Why not more? Why not less? (b) How can you tell when the point has been reached where you should call for an expert statistician? List some costs and some benefits that would govern this decision.

1.4 STATISTICAL CHALLENGES

LO 1-4

State the common challenges facing business professionals using statistics.

Business professionals who use statistics are not mere number crunchers who are "good at math." As Jon Kettenring succinctly said, "Industry needs holistic statisticians who are nimble problem solvers" (www.amstat.org). The ideal data analyst:

- Is technically current (e.g., software-wise).
- Communicates well.
- Is proactive.
- Has a broad outlook.
- Is flexible.
- Focuses on the main problem.
- Meets deadlines.
- Knows his/her limitations and is willing to ask for help.
- Can deal with imperfect information.
- Has professional integrity.

Role of Communication Skills

"Leaders differentiate themselves by *how* they get jobs done. The how is largely about communication. By communication, I mean both written and oral skills, and both listening and presentation skills. Leaders are able to present their ideas and knowledge in complete thoughts that leave no room for guessing. They are able to achieve funding for projects by using data to articulate a strong written business case and return on investment. They effectively engage and listen to others, ultimately gaining buy-in and a comprehensive solution. These tasks are dependent upon excellent communication skills—a core competency for leaders at all levels."

Comments on leadership skills by Mark Gasta, senior vice president and chief human resources officer, Vail Resorts Management Company

Imperfect Data and Practical Constraints

In mathematics, exact answers are expected. But statistics lies at the messy interface between theory and reality. For instance, suppose a new air bag design is being tested. Is the new air bag design safer for children? Test data indicate the design may be safer in some crash situations, but the old design appears safer in others. The crash tests are expensive and time-consuming, so the sample size is limited. A few observations are missing due to sensor failures in the crash dummies. There may be random measurement errors. If you are the data analyst, what can you do? Well, you can know and use generally accepted statistical methods, clearly state any assumptions you are forced to make, and honestly point out the limitations of your analysis. You can use statistical tests to detect unusual data points or to deal with missing data. You can give a range of answers under varying assumptions. Occasionally, you need the courage to say, "No useful answer can emerge from these data."

You will face constraints on the type and quantity of data you can collect. Automobile crash tests can't use human subjects (*too risky*). Telephone surveys can't ask a female respondent whether or not she has had an abortion (*sensitive question*). We can't test everyone for HIV (*the world is not a laboratory*). Survey respondents may not tell the truth or may not answer all the questions (*human behavior is unpredictable*). Every analyst faces constraints of time and money (*research is not free*).

Business Ethics

In your business ethics class, you learned (or will learn) the broad ethical responsibilities of business, such as treating customers in a fair and honest manner, complying with laws that prohibit discrimination, ensuring that products and services meet safety regulations, standing behind warranties, and advertising in a factual and informative manner. You learned that organizations should encourage employees to ask questions and voice concerns about the company's business practices, and give employees access to alternative channels of communication if they fear reprisal. But as an individual employee, *you* are responsible for accurately reporting information to management, including potential sources of error, material inaccuracies, and degrees of uncertainty. A data analyst faces a more specific set of ethical requirements.

Surveys of corporate recruiters show that ethics and personal integrity rank high on their list of hiring criteria. The respected analyst is an honest broker of data. He or she uses statistics to find out the truth, not to represent a popular point of view. Scrutinize your own motives carefully. If you manipulate numbers or downplay inconvenient data, you may succeed in fooling your competitors (or yourself) for a while. But what is the point? Sooner or later the facts will reveal themselves, and you (or your company) will be the loser. Quantitative analyses in business can quantify the risks of alternative courses of action and events. For example, statistics can help managers set realistic expectations on sales volume, revenues, and costs. An inflated sales forecast or an understated cost estimate may propel a colleague's favorite product program from the planning board to an actual capital investment. But a poor analysis may cost both of you your jobs.

Headline scandals such as Bernard L. Madoff's financial pyramid that cost investors as much as $65 billion (*The New York Times,* April 11, 2009, p. B1) or tests of pain relievers financed by drug companies whose results turned out to be based on falsified data (*NewScientist,* March 21, 2009, p. 4) are easily recognizable as willful lying or criminal acts. You might say, "I would never do things like that." Yet in day-to-day handling of data, you may not *know* whether the data are accurate or not. You may not *know* the uses to which the data will be put. You may not *know* of potential conflicts of interest. You and other employees (including top management) will need training to recognize the boundaries of what is or is not ethical within the context of your organization and the decision at hand.

Find out whether your organization has a code of ethics. If not, initiate efforts to create such a code. Fortunately, ideas and help are available (e.g., www.ethicsweb.ca/codes/). Since every organization is different, the issues will depend on your company's business environment. Creating or improving a code of ethics will generally require employee involvement to identify likely conflicts of interest, to look for sources of data inaccuracy, and to update company policies on disclosure and confidentiality. Everyone must understand the code and know the rules for follow-up when ethics violations are suspected.

Upholding Ethical Standards

Let's look at how ethical requirements might apply to anyone who analyzes data and writes reports for management. You need to know the specific rules to protect your professional integrity and to minimize the chance of inadvertent ethical breaches. Ask questions, think about hidden agendas, and dig deeper into how data were collected. Here are some basic rules for the data analyst:

- Know and follow accepted procedures.
- Maintain data integrity.
- Carry out accurate calculations.
- Report procedures faithfully.
- Protect confidential information.
- Cite sources.
- Acknowledge sources of financial support.

Because legal and ethical issues are intertwined, there are specific ethical guidelines for statisticians concerning treatment of human and animal subjects, privacy protection, obtaining informed consent, and guarding against inappropriate uses of data. For further information about ethics, see the American Statistical Association's ethical guidelines (www.amstat.org), which have been extensively reviewed by the statistics profession.

Ethical dilemmas for a nonstatistician are likely to involve conflicts of interest or competing interpretations of the validity of a study and/or its implications. For example, suppose a market research firm is hired to investigate a new corporate logo. The CEO lets you know that she strongly favors a new logo, and it's a big project that could earn you a promotion. Yet, the market data have a high error margin and could support either conclusion. As a manager, you will face such situations. Statistical practices and statistical data can clarify your choices.

A *perceived* ethical problem may be just that—*perceived*. For example, it may appear that a company promotes more men than women into management roles while, in reality, the promotion rates for men and women are the same. The perceived inequity could be a result of fewer female employees to begin with. In this situation, organizations might work hard to hire more women, thus increasing the pool of women who are promotable. Statistics plays a role in sorting out ethical business dilemmas by using data to uncover *real* versus *perceived* differences, identify root causes of problems, and gauge public attitudes toward organizational behavior.

Using Consultants

Students often comment on the first day of their statistics class that they don't need to learn statistics because businesses rely on consultants to do the data analyses. This is a misconception. Today's successful companies expect their employees to be able to perform all types of statistical analyses, from the simple descriptive analyses to the more complex inferential analyses. They also expect their employees to be able to interpret the results of a statistical analysis, even if it was completed by an outside consultant. Organizations have been asking business schools across the nation to increase the level of quantitative instruction that students receive and, when hiring, are increasingly giving priority to candidates with strong quantitative skills.

Jobs for Data Scientists

Many companies hire data scientists. Examples include social networks (Facebook, Twitter, LinkedIn), web service providers (Google, Microsoft, Apple, Yahoo), financial institutions (Bank of America, Citi, JPMorganChase), credit card companies (Visa, American Express), online retailers (Amazon, eBay), computer software and database developers (IBM, SAP, Oracle, Tableau, SAS, Hewlett-Packard, Cisco Systems), accounting firms (KPMG, DeLoitte, Ernst & Young), and retailers (Target, Sears). Governments, defense contractors, and engineering firms also hire data scientists, sometimes calling them operations research analysts.

Here are examples of some recent job postings: Risk Analytics Manager, Data Management Specialist, Analytics Associate, Digital Strategy Consultant, Quantitative Research Analyst, Big Data Enterprise Architect, Software Engineer, Predictive Modeling Consultant, Security Data Analyst, Mobile App Developer, and Cloud Professional. To find out more about analytics jobs and the required skills, see http://www.datasciencecentral.com.

This is not to say that statistical consultants are a dying breed. When an organization is faced with a decision that has serious public policy implications or high cost consequences, hiring a consultant can be a smart move. An hour with an expert at the *beginning* of a project could be the smartest move a manager can make. When should a consultant be hired? When your team lacks certain critical skills, or when an unbiased or informed view cannot be found inside your organization. Expert consultants can handle domineering or indecisive team members, personality clashes, fears about adverse findings, and local politics. Large and medium-sized companies may have in-house statisticians, but smaller firms only hire them as needed. Obtain agreement at the outset on the consultant's rates and duties. Fees should be by the hour or job (never contingent on the findings). If you hire a statistical expert, you can make better use of the consultant's time by learning how consultants work. Read books about statistical consulting. If your company employs a statistician, take him or her to lunch!

Keep It Simple

"When we communicate statistics, there are two things I want to make sure don't happen. One is showing off and using too much statistical jargon to our clients. The second thing is adding too many details . . . I prefer a two-sentence explanation or overview in language that would be clear to our clients."

From an interview with Mary Batcher, executive director of Ernst and Young's Quantitative Economics and Statistics Group. Copyright 2010 by the American Statistical Association. All rights reserved.

Communicating with Numbers

Numbers have meaning only when communicated in the context of a certain situation. Busy managers rarely have time to read and digest detailed explanations of numbers. **Appendix I** contains advice on technical report writing and oral presentations. But you probably already know that attractive graphs will enhance a technical report, and help other managers quickly understand the information they need to make a good decision. Chapter 3 will give detailed directions for effective tables and graphs using Excel.

But how do we present a table or graph in a written report? Tables should be embedded in the narrative (*not* on a separate page) near the paragraph in which they are cited. Each table should have a number and title. Graphs should be embedded in the narrative (*not* on a separate page) near the paragraph in which they are discussed. Each table or graph should have a title and number. A graph may make things clearer. For example, compare Table 1.1 and Figure 1.2. Which is more helpful in understanding U.S. trademark activity in recent years?

TABLE 1.1 U.S. Trademarks, 2004–2010 (thousands)

	2004	*2005*	*2006*	*2007*	*2008*	*2009*	*2010*
Applications Filed	304.5	334.7	362.3	401.0	390.8	351.9	370.2
Trademarks Issued	146.0	154.8	193.7	218.8	233.9	222.1	210.6

Source: U.S. Census Bureau, *Statistical Abstract of the United States, 2012,* p. 778. A trademark (identified with ®) is a name or symbol identifying a product, registered with the U.S. Patent and Trademark Office and restricted by law to use by its owner.

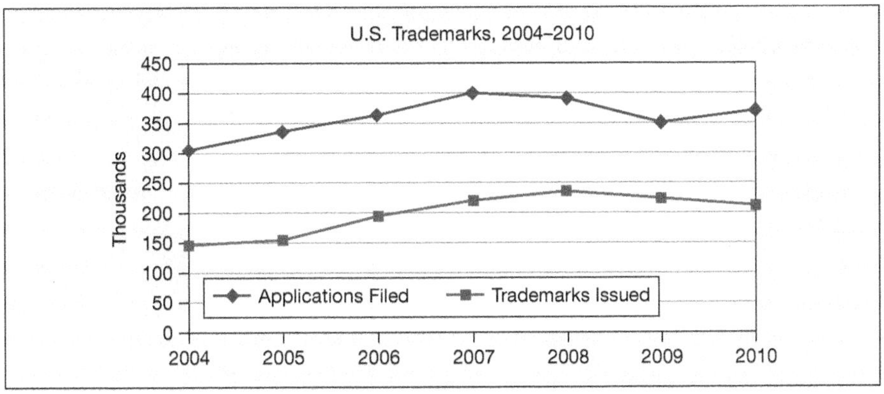

FIGURE 1.2
U.S. Trademarks, 2004–2010

SECTION EXERCISES

1.6 The U.S. Public Interest Research Group Education Fund, USPIRG, recently published a report titled *The Campus Credit Card Trap: A Survey of College Students about Credit Card Marketing*. You can find this report and more information about campus credit card marketing at www.truthaboutcredit.org. Read this report and then answer the following questions about how statistics plays a role in resolving ethical dilemmas.

a. What is the perceived ethical issue highlighted in this report?
b. How did USPIRG conduct their study to collect information and data?
c. What broad categories did their survey address?
d. Did the survey data verify that the issue was a real, instead of a perceived, ethical problem?
e. Do you agree with the study's assessment of the issue? Why or why not?
f. Based on the results of the survey, is the issue widespread? Explain.
g. Describe the report's suggested solutions to confront unethical business practices.

1.7 Using your favorite web browser, enter the search string "business code of ethics." List five examples of features that a business ethics code should have.

Mini Case 1.4

Lessons from NASA

The late President Lyndon Baines Johnson observed, "A President's hardest task is not to *do* what is right, but to *know* what is right." What's missing is wisdom, not courage. Given incomplete or contradictory data, people have trouble making decisions (remember *Hamlet*?). Sometimes the correct choice is obvious in retrospect, as in NASA's space shuttle disasters. On January 28, 1986, *Challenger* exploded shortly after takeoff, due to erosion of O-rings that had become brittle in freezing overnight temperatures at Cape Canaveral. The crux of the matter was a statistical relationship between brittleness and temperature. Data on O-ring erosion were available for 22 prior shuttle flights. The backup O-rings (there were two layers of O-rings) had suffered no erosion in 9 prior flights at launch temperatures in the range 72°F–81°F, but they had suffered significant erosion in 4 of 13 prior flights at temperatures in the range 53°F–70°F. However, the role of temperature was by no means clear. NASA and Morton-Thiokol engineers had debated the erratic data inconclusively, including the night before the launch.

After the *Challenger* accident, it was clear that the risk was underestimated. Two *statistical* issues were the degree to which backup layer O-rings provided redundant protection and the correct way to predict O-ring erosion at the *Challenger* launch temperature of 36°F when the lowest previous launch temperature had been 53°F. Two possible *ethical* questions were whether NASA officials should have postponed the launch until they understood the problem better and whether the astronauts, as participants in a risky mission, had sufficient opportunity for informed consent. NASA's 100 percent previous success record was undoubtedly a factor in everyone's self-confidence, including the astronauts'.

On February 1, 2003, space shuttle *Columbia* burned on reentry. The heat shield failure was apparently due to tiles damaged by falling foam insulation from the fuel tanks, loosened by vibration during launch. Prior to the *Columbia* disaster in 2003, foam-damaged tiles had been noted 70 times in 112 flights. In retrospect, review of the data showed that some previous flights may have come close to *Columbia*'s fate. This is a *statistical* issue because the heat shield had worked 70 times despite being damaged. Is it surprising that NASA officials believed that the tiles were resistant to foam damage? An *ethical* question would be whether organizational inertia and pressure to launch favored a risky interpretation of the data.

These disasters remind us that decisions involving data and statistics are embedded in organizational culture. NASA differs from most businesses due to the dangers inherent in its cutting-edge missions. At the time of the *Challenger* launch, the risk of losing a vehicle was estimated at 1 in 30. At the time of the *Columbia* reentry accident, the risk was estimated at 1 in 145. For nonhuman launches the risk is about 1 in 50 (2 percent) compared with 2 space shuttle losses in 113 flights (1.8 percent). By comparison, the risk of losing a commercial airline flight is about 1 in 2,000,000.

Sources: yahoo.com; www.nasa.gov; *The New York Times*, February 2, 2003.

1.5 CRITICAL THINKING

LO 1-5

List and explain common statistical pitfalls.

Statistics is an essential part of **critical thinking** because it allows us to test an idea against empirical evidence. Random occurrences and chance variation inevitably lead to occasional outcomes that could support one viewpoint or another. But the science of statistics tells us whether the sample evidence is convincing. In this book, you will learn how to use statistics correctly in accordance with professional standards to make the best decision.

> "Critical thinking means being able to evaluate evidence, to tell fact from opinion, to see holes in an argument, to tell whether cause and effect has been established, and to spot illogic."
> *The Wall Street Journal,* October 20, 2006.

We use statistical tools to compare our prior ideas with **empirical data** (data collected through observations and experiments). If the data do not support our theory, we can reject or revise our theory. In *The Wall Street Journal,* in *Money* magazine, and on CNN you see stock market experts with theories to "explain" the current market (bull, bear, or pause). But each year brings new experts and new theories, and the old ones vanish. Logical pitfalls abound in both the data collection process and the reasoning process. Let's look at some.

Pitfall 1: Conclusions from Small Samples "My Aunt Harriet smoked all her life and lived to 90. Smoking doesn't hurt you." Good for her. But does one case prove anything? Five customers are asked if the new product design is an improvement. If three say yes, should the company implement the new design? If 10 patients try a new asthma medication and one gets a rash, can we conclude that the medication caused the rash? How large a sample is needed to make reliable conclusions? Statisticians have developed clear rules about sample sizes. Until you learn them in Chapter 8, it's OK to raise your pennant hopes when your favorite baseball team wins five games in a row.

Pitfall 2: Conclusions from Nonrandom Samples "Rock stars die young. Look at Buddy Holly, Jimi Hendrix, Janis Joplin, Jim Morrison, John Lennon, and Kurt Cobain." But we are looking only at those who *did* die young. What about the thousands who are alive and well or who lived long lives? Similarly, we should be careful about generalizing from retrospective studies of people who have heart attacks, unless we also study those who do not have heart attacks. (From Arnold Barnett, "How Numbers Can Trick You," *Technology Review,* October 1994, p. 40.) In Chapter 2, you will learn proper sampling methods to make reliable inferences.

Pitfall 3: Conclusions from Rare Events Unlikely events happen if we take a large enough sample. In Chapter 5, you will learn about the law of large numbers, which explains unlikely events such as these:

- "Mary in my office won the lottery. Her system must have worked." Millions of people play the lottery. Someone will eventually win.
- "Bill's a sports genius. He predicted every Notre Dame football win last season." Millions of sports fans make predictions. A few of them will call every game correctly.
- "Tom's SUV rolled over. SUVs are dangerous." Millions of people drive SUVs. Some will roll over.

Pitfall 4: Poor Survey Methods Did your instructor ever ask a question like "How many of you remember the simplex method from your math class?" One or two timid hands (or maybe none) are raised, even though the topic was covered. Did the math department not teach the simplex method? Or did students not "get it"? Actually, the instructor has used a poor sampling method and a vaguely worded question. It's difficult for students to respond to such a question in public, for they assume (often correctly) that if they raise a hand, the instructor is going to ask them to explain it, or that their peers will think they are showing off.

An anonymous survey or a quiz on the simplex method would provide better insight. In Chapter 2, you will learn rules for survey design and response scaling.

Pitfall 5: Assuming a Causal Link In your economics class, you may have learned about the **post hoc fallacy** (the mistaken conclusion that if *A* precedes *B* then *A* is the *cause* of *B*). For example, the divorce rate in Mississippi fell in 2005 after Hurricane Katrina. Did the hurricane cause couples to stay together? A little research reveals that the divorce rate had been falling for the previous two years, so Hurricane Katrina could hardly be credited.

The *post hoc fallacy* is a special case of the general fallacy of *assuming causation* anytime there is a *statistical association* between events. For example, there is the "curse of the ballfield," which says that teams who play in named ballparks (e.g., Citi Field for the New York Mets) tend to lose more games than they win (see *The New York Times,* November 15, 2006, p. C16). Perhaps in a statistical sense this may be true. But it is actually the players and managers who determine whether a team wins. Association does not prove causation. You've probably heard that. But many people draw unwarranted conclusions when no cause-and-effect link exists. Consider anecdotes like these:

- "Murder rates were higher during the full moon in Miami last year. I guess the moon makes people crazy." But what about cities that saw a *decrease* in murders during the same full moon?
- "Most shark attacks occur between 12 p.m. and 2 p.m. Sharks must be hungrier then." But more people go swimming near midday. If a causal link exists, it would have to be shown in a carefully controlled experiment.

On the other hand, association may warrant further study when common sense suggests a potential causal link. For example, is there any link between cell phones and cancer (see *Scientific American,* Vol. 305, No. 2, August 2011, p. 96)? In Chapter 12, you will learn tests to decide whether a correlation is within the realm of chance.

Pitfall 6: Generalization to Individuals "Men are taller than women." Yes, but only in a statistical sense. Men are taller *on average,* but many women are taller than many men. "Japanese cars have high quality." Yes, but not all of them. We should avoid reading too much into **statistical generalizations**. Instead, ask how much *overlap* is in the populations that are being considered. Often, the similarities transcend the differences. In Chapter 10, you will learn precise tests to compare two groups.

Pitfall 7: Unconscious Bias Without obvious fraud (tampering with data), researchers can unconsciously or subtly allow bias to color their handling of data. For example, for many years it was assumed that heart attacks were more likely to occur in men than women. But symptoms of heart disease are usually more obvious in men than women and so doctors tend to catch heart disease earlier in men. Studies show that heart disease is the number one cause of death for American women (www.americanheart.org). In Chapter 2, you will learn about sources of bias and error in surveys.

Pitfall 8: Significance versus Importance Statistically significant effects may lack practical importance. A study of over 500,000 Austrian military recruits showed that those born in the spring averaged 0.6 cm taller than those born in the fall (J. Utts, *The American Statistician* 57, no. 2 (May 2003), pp. 74–79). But who would notice? Would prospective parents change their timing in hopes of having a child 0.6 cm taller? Cost-conscious businesses know that some product improvements cannot support a valid business case. Consumers cannot perceive small improvements in durability, speed, taste, and comfort if the products already are "good enough." For example, Seagate's Cheetah 147GB disk drive already has a mean time between failure (MTBF) rating of 1.4 million hours (about 160 years in continuous use). Would a 10 percent improvement in MTBF matter to anyone?

SECTION EXERCISES

connect

1.8 Recently, the same five winning numbers (4, 21, 23, 34, 39) came up both on Monday and on Wednesday in the North Carolina Lottery. "That's so unlikely that it must be rigged," said Mary. Which fallacy, if any, do you see in Mary's reasoning?

1.9 A National Health Interview Survey conducted by the U.S. Centers for Disease Control reported that using a cell phone instead of a landline appeared to double a person's chances of binge drinking. "I guess I'd better give up my cell phone," said Bob. Which fallacy, if any, do you see in Bob's reasoning?

1.10 A study found that radar detector users have lower accident rates, wear their seat belts more, and even vote more than nonusers. (a) Assuming that the study is accurate, do you think there is cause-and-effect? (b) If everyone used radar detectors, would voting rates and seat-belt usage rise?

1.11 A lottery winner told how he picked his six-digit winning number (5-6-8-10-22-39): number of people in his family, birth date of his wife, school grade of his 13-year-old daughter, sum of his birth date and his wife's, number of years of marriage, and year of his birth. He said, "I try to pick numbers that mean something to me." The State Lottery Commissioner called this method "the screwiest I ever heard of . . . but apparently it works." (a) From a statistical viewpoint, do you agree that this method "works"? (b) Based on your understanding of how a lottery works, would someone who picks 1-2-3-4-5-6 because "it is easy to remember" have a lower chance of winning?

1.12 "Smokers are much more likely to speed, run red lights, and get involved in car accidents than nonsmokers." (a) Can you think of reasons why this statement might be misleading? *Hint:* Make a list of six factors that you think would cause car accidents. Is smoking on your list? (b) Can you suggest a causal link between smoking and car accidents?

1.13 An ad for a cell phone service claims that its percent of "dropped calls" was significantly lower than that of its main competitor. In the fine print, the percents were given as 1.2 percent versus 1.4 percent. Is this reduction likely to be *important* to customers (as opposed to being *significant*)?

1.14 What logical or ethical problems do you see in these hypothetical scenarios?

a. Dolon Privacy Consultants concludes that its employees are not loyal because a few samples of employee e-mails contained comments critical of the company's management.
b. Calchas Financial Advisors issues a glowing report of its new stock market forecasting system, based on testimonials of five happy customers.
c. Five sanitation crew members at Malcheon Hospital are asked to try a new cleaning solvent to see if it has any allergic or other harmful side effects.
d. A consumer group rates a new personal watercraft from Thetis Aquatic Conveyances as "Unacceptable" because two Ohio teens lost control and crashed into a dock.

1.15 A recent study of 231,164 New Jersey heart attack patients showed that those admitted on a weekday had a 12.0 percent death rate in the next three years, compared with 12.9 percent for those admitted on a weekend. This difference was statistically significant. (a) "That's too small to have any practical importance," said Sarah. Do you agree with Sarah's conclusion? Explain.

1.16 When Pennsylvania repealed a law that required motorcycle riders to wear helmets, a news headline reported, "Deaths Soar After Repeal of Helmet Law." After reading the story, Bill said, "But it's just a correlation, not causation." Do you agree with Bill's conclusion? Explain.

CHAPTER SUMMARY

Statistics (or **data science**) is the science of collecting, organizing, analyzing, interpreting, and presenting data. A **statistician** is an expert with a degree in mathematics or statistics, while a **data analyst** is anyone who works with data. **Descriptive statistics** is the collection, organization, presentation, and summary of data with charts or numerical summaries. **Inferential statistics** refers to generalizing from a sample to a population, estimating unknown parameters, drawing conclusions, and making decisions. Statistics is used in all branches of business. **Statistical challenges** include imperfect data, practical constraints, and ethical dilemmas. Statistical tools are used to test theories against empirical data. Pitfalls include nonrandom samples, incorrect sample size, and lack of causal links. The field of statistics is relatively new and continues to grow as mathematical frontiers expand.

KEY TERMS

critical thinking
data science
descriptive statistics
empirical data
inferential statistics
post hoc fallacy
statistic
statistics
statistical generalization

CHAPTER REVIEW

1. Define (a) statistic; (b) statistics.
2. List three reasons to study statistics.
3. List three applications of statistics.
4. List four skills needed by statisticians. Why are these skills important?
5. List three *practical* challenges faced by statisticians.
6. List three *ethical* challenges faced by statisticians.
7. List five pitfalls or logical errors that may ensnare the unwary statistician.

CHAPTER EXERCISES

connect

1.17 A survey of beginning students showed that a majority strongly agreed with the statement, "I am afraid of statistics." (a) Why might this attitude exist among students who have not yet taken a statistics class? (b) Would a similar attitude exist toward an ethics class? Explain your reasoning.

1.18 Under a recent U.S. Food and Drug Administration (FDA) standard for food contaminants, 3.5 ounces of tomato sauce can have up to 30 fly eggs, and 11 ounces of wheat flour can contain 450 insect fragments. How could statistical sampling be used to see that these standards of food hygiene are being met by producers? (Source: www.fda.gov)

1.19 A statistical consultant was retained by a linen supplier to analyze a survey of hospital purchasing managers. After looking at the data, she realized that the survey had missed several key geographic areas and included some that were outside the target region. Some survey questions were ambiguous. Some respondents failed to answer all the questions or gave silly replies (one manager said he worked 40 hours a day). Of the 1,000 surveys mailed, only 80 were returned. (a) What alternatives are available to the statistician? (b) Might an imperfect analysis be better than none?

1.20 Ergonomics is the science of making sure that human surroundings are adapted to human needs. How could statistics play a role in the following:

a. Choosing the height of an office chair so that 95 percent of the employees (male and female) will feel it is the "right height" for their legs to reach the floor comfortably.
b. Designing a drill press so its controls can be reached and its forces operated by an "average employee."
c. Defining a doorway width so that a "typical" wheelchair can pass through without coming closer than 6 inches from either side.
d. Setting the width of a parking space to accommodate 95 percent of all vehicles at your local Walmart.
e. Choosing a font size so that a highway sign can be read in daylight at 100 meters by 95 percent of all drivers.

1.21 Analysis of 1,064 deaths of famous popular musicians showed that 31 percent were related to alcohol or drug abuse. "But that is just a sample. It proves nothing," said Hannah. Do you agree with Hannah's conclusion? Explain.

1.22 A recent study showed that women who lived near a freeway had an unusually high rate of rheumatoid arthritis. Sarah said, "They should move away from freeways." Is there a fallacy in Sarah's reasoning? Explain.

1.23 "Lacrosse helmets are not needed," said Tom. "None of the guys on my team have ever had head injuries." Is there a fallacy in Tom's reasoning? Explain.

1.24 A European study of thousands of men found that the PSA screening for prostate cancer reduced the risk of a man's dying from prostate cancer from 3.0 percent to 2.4 percent. "But it's already a small risk. I don't think a difference of less than 1 percent would be of practical importance," said Ed. Do you agree with Ed's conclusion? Explain.

1.25 A research study showed that 7 percent of "A" students smoke, while nearly 50 percent of "D" students do. (a) List in rank order six factors that you think affect grades. Is smoking on your list? (b) If smoking is not a likely cause of poor grades, can you suggest reasons why these results were observed? (c) Assuming these statistics are correct, would "D" students who give up smoking improve their grades? Why or why not?

1.26 A research study showed that adolescents who watched more than 4 hours of TV per day were more than five times as likely to start smoking as those who watched less than 2 hours a day. The researchers speculate that TV actors' portrayals of smoking as personally and socially rewarding were an effective indirect method of tobacco promotion. List in rank order six factors that you think cause adolescents to start smoking. Did TV portrayals of attractive smokers appear on your list?

1.27 The Graduate Management Admission Test (GMAT) is used by many graduate schools of business as one of their admission criteria. GMAT scores for selected undergraduate majors are shown below. Using your own reasoning and concepts in this chapter, criticize each of the following statements.

a. "Philosophy majors must not be interested in business since so few take the GMAT."
b. "More students major in engineering than in English."
c. "If marketing students majored in physics, they would score better on the GMAT."
d. "Physics majors would make the best managers."

GMAT Scores and Undergraduate Major GMAT

Major	*Average GMAT Score*	*Number Taking Test*
Accounting	483	25,233
Computer Science	508	7,573
Economics	513	16,432
Engineering	544	29,688
English	507	3,589
Finance	489	20,001
Marketing	455	15,925
Philosophy	546	588
Physics	575	1,223

Source: Graduate Management Admission Council, *Admission Office Profile of Candidates*, October 1989, pp. 27–30.

1.28 (a) Which of these two displays (table or graph) is more helpful in visualizing the relationship between restaurant size and interior seating for 74 Noodles restaurants? Explain your reasoning. (b) Do you see anything unusual in the data? (*Source:* Noodles & Company) NoodlesSqFt

Number of Restaurants in Each Category (n = 74 restaurants)

	Square Feet Inside Restaurant				
Interior Seats	*1000 < 1750*	*1750 < 2500*	*2500 < 3250*	*3250 < 4000*	**Row Total**
105 < 130	0	0	0	3	3
80 < 105	0	4	17	0	21
55 < 80	0	21	24	0	45
30 < 55	1	4	0	0	5
Col Total	1	29	41	3	74

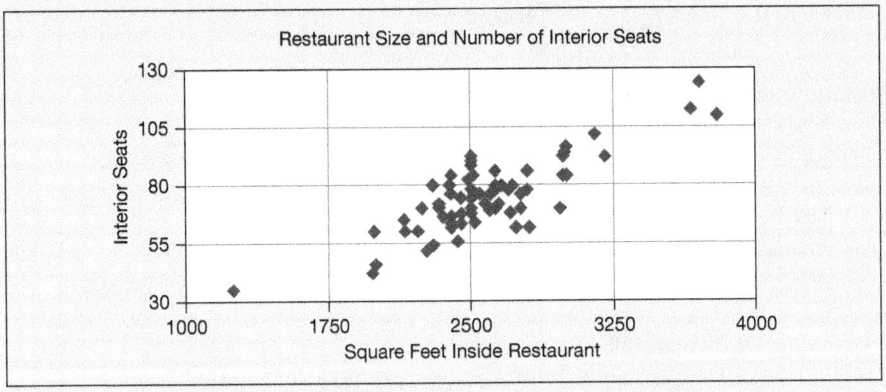

NOODLES & COMPANY

1.29 (a) Which of these two displays (table or graph) is more helpful in describing the salad sales by Noodles & Company? Why? (b) Write a one-sentence summary of the data. (*Source:* Noodles & Company) NoodlesSalad

2005 Average Daily Salads Sold by Month, Noodles & Company

Month	*Salads*	*Month*	*Salads*
Jan	2847	Jul	2554
Feb	2735	Aug	2370
Mar	2914	Sep	2131
Apr	3092	Oct	1990
May	3195	Nov	1979
Jun	3123	Dec	1914

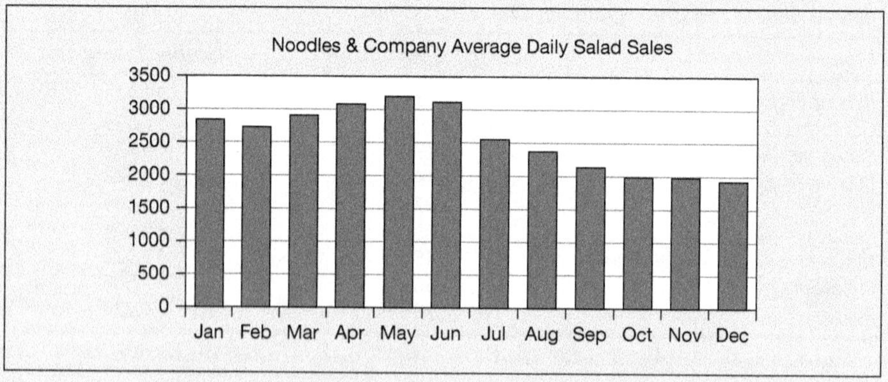

1.30 Choose *three* of the following statisticians and use the web to find out a few basic facts about them (e.g., list some of their contributions to statistics, when they did their work, whether they are still living, etc.).

Florence Nightingale	John Wilder Tukey	Genichi Taguchi
Gertrude Cox	William Cochran	Helen Walker
Sir Francis Galton	Siméon Poisson	George Box
W. Edwards Deming	S. S. Stevens	Sam Wilks
The Bernoulli family	R. A. Fisher	Carl F. Gauss
Frederick Mosteller	George Snedecor	William S. Gosset
William H. Kruskal	Karl Pearson	Thomas Bayes
Jerzy Neyman	C. R. Rao	Bradley Efron
Egon Pearson	Abraham De Moivre	Nate Silver
Harold Hotelling	Edward Tufte	

RELATED READING

Practical Guides

Baker, Stephen. *The Numerati.* Houghton-Mifflin, 2008.

Best, Joel. *Stat-Spotting: A Field Guide to Dubious Data.* University of California Press, 2008.

Davenport, Thomas H.; and Jeanne G. Harris. *Competing on Analytics: The New Science of Winning.* Harvard Business School Press, 2007.

Dodge, Yadolah. *The Concise Encyclopedia of Statistics.* Springer, 2008.

Everitt, B. S. *The Cambridge Dictionary of Statistics.* 2nd ed. Cambridge University Press, 2002.

Fung, Kaiser. *Numbers Rule Your World: The Hidden Influence of Probabilities and Statistics on Everything You Do.* McGraw-Hill, 2010.

John, J. A.; and D. Whitaker. *Statistical Thinking in Business.* 2nd ed. Chapman and Hall, 2005.

Newton, Rae R. *Your Statistical Consultant.* 2nd ed. Sage Publications, 2013.

Sahei, Hardeo; and Anwer Khurshid. *Pocket Dictionary of Statistics.* McGraw-Hill, 2002.

Seife, Charles. *Proofiness: The Dark Arts of Mathematical Deception.* Viking, 2010.

Utts, Jessica. "What Educated Citizens Should Know About Statistics and Probability." *The American Statistician* 57, no. 2 (May 2003), pp. 74–79.

Ethics

Badaracco, Joseph L., Jr. *Defining Moments: When Managers Must Choose between Right and Right.* Harvard Business School Press, 1997.

Gardner, Howard; Mihaly Csikszentmihalyi; and William Damon. *Good Work: When Excellence and Ethics Meet.* Dutton, 2001.

Hartman, Laura P. *Perspectives in Business Ethics.* 2nd ed. McGraw-Hill, 2011.

Nash, Laura L. *Good Intentions Aside: A Manager's Guide to Resolving Ethical Problems.* Harvard Business School Press, 1995.

Seglin, Jeffrey L. *The Right Thing: Conscience, Profit and Personal Responsibility in Today's Business.* Spiro Press, 2003.

Vardeman, Stephen B.; and Max D. Morris. "Statistics and Ethics: Some Advice for Young Statisticians." *The American Statistician* 57 (February 2003), pp. 21–26.

CHAPTER 1 More Learning Resources

connect™

You can access these *LearningStats* demonstrations through McGraw-Hill's Connect® to give you an overview of statistics.

Topic	*LearningStats Demonstrations*
Microsoft® Office	Excel Tips Word Tips PowerPoint Tips
Excel	Excel Functions
Math Review	Math Review Significant Digits
Web Stuff	Web Resources Statistics Software

Key: [PowerPoint icon] = PowerPoint [PDF icon] = PDF

Chapter 2. Data Collection

CHAPTER 2 Data Collection

CHAPTER CONTENTS

CHAPTER LEARNING OBJECTIVES

LO

When you finish this chapter you should be able to

LO 2-1 Use basic terminology for describing data and samples.

LO 2-2 Explain the difference between numerical and categorical data.

LO 2-3 Explain the difference between time series and cross-sectional data.

LO 2-4 Recognize levels of measurement in data and ways of coding data.

LO 2-5 Recognize a Likert scale and know how to use it.

LO 2-6 Use the correct terminology for samples and populations.

LO 2-7 Explain the common sampling methods and how to implement them.

LO 2-8 Find everyday print or electronic data sources.

LO 2-9 Describe basic elements of survey types, survey designs, and response scales.

2.1 VARIABLES AND DATA

In scientific research, data arise from experiments whose results are recorded systematically. In business, data usually arise from accounting transactions or management processes (e.g., inventory, sales, payroll). Much of the data that statisticians analyze were recorded without explicit consideration of their statistical uses, yet important decisions may depend on the data. How many pints of type A blood will be required at Mt. Sinai Hospital next Thursday? How many dollars must State Farm keep in its cash account to cover automotive accident claims next November? How many yellow three-quarter-sleeve women's sweaters will Lands' End sell this month? To answer such questions, we usually look at historical data.

LO 2-1

Use basic terminology for describing data and samples.

LO 2-2

Explain the difference between numerical and categorical data.

LO 2-3

Explain the difference between time series and cross-sectional data.

Data: Singular or Plural?

Data is the plural of the Latin *datum* (a "given" fact). This traditional usage is preferred in Britain, and especially in scientific journals, where over 90 percent of the references use *data* as a plural ("These data show a correlation . . ."). But in the popular press (newspapers, magazines) you will often see "data" used synonymously with "information" and hence as a singular ("The compressed data is stored on a CD . . ."). The singular usage is especially common in the United States and is becoming more common in the United Kingdom, rather to the chagrin of the educated populace.

Data Terminology

An **observation** is a single member of a collection of items that we want to study, such as a person, firm, or region. An example of an observation is an employee or an invoice mailed last month. A **variable** is a characteristic of the subject or individual, such as an employee's income or an invoice amount. The **data set** consists of all the values of all of the variables for all of the observations we have chosen to observe. In this book, we will use **data** as a plural, and data set to refer to a collection of observations taken as a whole. Data usually are entered into a spreadsheet or database as an $n \times m$ matrix. Specifically, each column is a variable (m columns) and each row is an observation (n rows). Table 2.1 shows a small data set with eight observations (8 rows) and five variables (5 columns).

A data set may consist of many variables. The questions that can be explored and the analytical techniques that can be used will depend upon the data type and the number of variables. This textbook starts with **univariate data sets** (one variable), then moves to **bivariate data sets** (two variables) and **multivariate data sets** (more than two variables), as illustrated in Table 2.2.

TABLE 2.1

A Small Multivariate Data Set (5 variables, 8 observations)

SmallData

Obs	Name	Age	Income	Position	Gender
1	Frieda	45	$67,100	Personnel director	F
2	Stefan	32	56,500	Operations analyst	M
3	Barbara	55	88,200	Marketing VP	F
4	Donna	27	59,000	Statistician	F
5	Larry	46	36,000	Security guard	M
6	Alicia	52	68,500	Comptroller	F
7	Alec	65	95,200	Chief executive	M
8	Jaime	50	71,200	Public relations	M

TABLE 2.2

Number of Variables and Typical Tasks

Data Set	Variables	Example	Typical Tasks
Univariate	One	Income	Histograms, basic statistics
Bivariate	Two	Income, Age	Scatter plots, correlation
Multivariate	More than two	Income, Age, Gender	Regression modeling

Categorical and Numerical Data

A data set may contain a mixture of *data types*. Two broad categories are **categorical data** and **numerical data**, as shown in Figure 2.1.

Categorical Data *Categorical* data (also called *qualitative* data) have values that are described by words rather than numbers. For example, structural lumber can be classified by the lumber type (e.g., fir, hemlock, pine), automobile styles can be classified by size (e.g., full, midsize, compact, subcompact), and movies can be categorized using common movie classifications (e.g., action and adventure, children and family, classics, comedy, documentary).

Because categorical variables have nonnumerical values, it might seem that categorical data would be of limited statistical use. In fact, there are many statistical methods that can handle categorical data, which we will introduce in later chapters. On occasion the values

FIGURE 2.1

Data Types and Examples

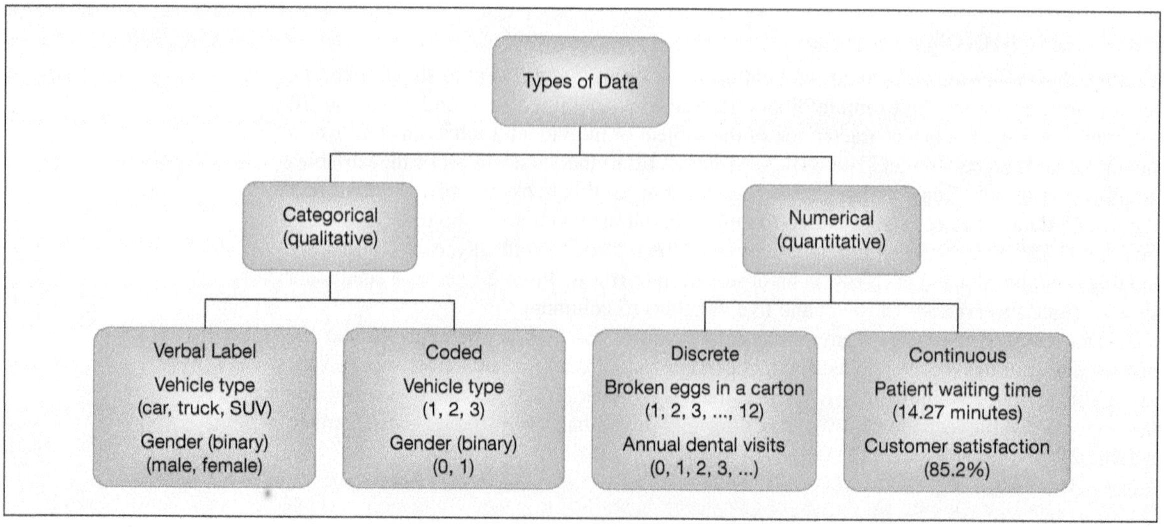

of the categorical variable might be represented using numbers. This is called **coding**. For example, a database might code payment methods using numbers:

1 = cash 2 = check 3 = credit/debit card 4 = gift card

Coding a category as a number does *not* make the data numerical and the numbers do not typically imply a rank. But on occasion a ranking does exist. For example, a database might code education degrees using numbers:

1 = Bachelor's 2 = Master's 3 = Doctorate

Some categorical variables have only two values. We call these **binary variables**. Examples include employment status (e.g., employed or unemployed), mutual fund type (e.g., load or no-load), and marital status (e.g., currently married or not currently married). Binary variables are often coded using a 1 or 0. For a binary variable, the 0-1 coding is arbitrary, so the choice is equivalent. For example, a variable such as gender could be coded as:

1 = female 0 = male

or as

1 = male 0 = female

Numerical Data *Numerical* or *quantitative* data arise from counting, measuring something, or some kind of mathematical operation. For example, we could count the number of auto insurance claims filed in March (e.g., 114 claims) or sales for last quarter (e.g., $4,920), or we could measure the amount of snowfall over the last 24 hours (e.g., 3.4 inches). Most accounting data, economic indicators, and financial ratios are quantitative, as are physical measurements.

Numerical data can be broken down into two types. A variable with a countable number of distinct values is **discrete**. Often, such data are integers. You can recognize integer data because their description begins with "number of." For example, the number of Medicaid patients in a hospital waiting room (e.g., 2) or the number of takeoffs at Chicago O'Hare International Airport in an hour (e.g., 37). Such data are integer variables because we cannot observe a fractional number of patients or takeoffs.

A numerical variable that can have any value within an interval is **continuous**. This would include things like physical measurements (e.g., distance, weight, time, speed) or financial variables (e.g., sales, assets, price/earnings ratios, inventory turns); for example, runner Usain Bolt's time in the 100-meter dash (e.g., 9.58 seconds) or the weight of a package of Sun-Maid raisins (e.g., 427.31 grams). These are continuous variables because any interval such as [425, 429] grams can contain infinitely many possible values. Sometimes we round a continuous measurement to an integer (e.g., 427 grams), but that does not make the data discrete.

Apparent ambiguity between *discrete* and *continuous* is introduced when we round continuous data to whole numbers (e.g., your weight this morning). However, the underlying measurement scale is continuous. That is, a package of Sun-Maid raisins is labeled 425 grams, but on an accurate scale its weight would be a noninteger (e.g., 427.31). Precision depends on the instrument we use to measure the continuous variable. We generally treat financial data (dollars, euros, pesos) as continuous even though retail prices go in discrete steps of .01 (i.e., we go from $1.25 to $1.26). The FM radio spectrum is continuous, but only certain discrete values are observed (e.g., 104.3) because of Federal Communications Commission rules. Conversely, we sometimes treat discrete data as continuous when the range is very large (e.g., SAT scores) and when small differences (e.g., 604 or 605) aren't of much importance. This topic will be discussed in later chapters. If in doubt, just think about how X was measured and whether or not its values are countable.

Time Series Data and Cross-Sectional Data

If each observation in the sample represents a different equally spaced point in time (years, months, days), we have **time series data**. The *periodicity* is the time between observations. It may be annual, quarterly, monthly, weekly, daily, hourly, etc. Examples of *macroeconomic*

FIGURE 2.2
Examples of Time Series versus Cross-Sectional Data

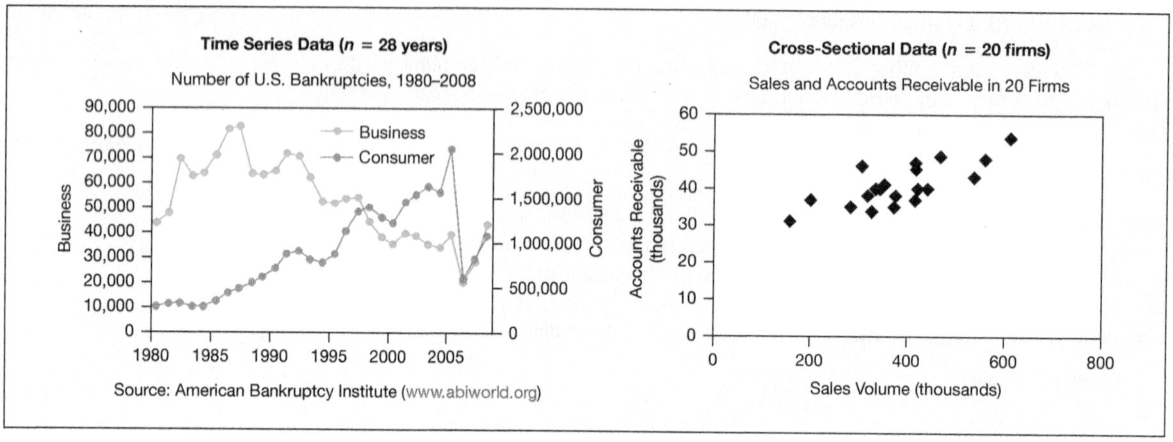

time series data would include national income (GDP, consumption, investment), economic indicators (Consumer Price Index, unemployment rate, Standard & Poor's 500 Index), and monetary data (M1, M2, M3, prime rate, T-bill rate, consumer borrowing, federal debt). Examples of *microeconomic* time series data would include a firm's sales, market share, debt/equity ratio, employee absenteeism, inventory turnover, and product quality ratings. For time series, we are interested in *trends and patterns over time* (e.g., personal bankruptcies from 1980 to 2008 as shown in Figure 2.2).

If each observation represents a different individual unit (e.g., a person, firm, geographic area) at the same point in time, we have **cross-sectional data**. Thus, traffic fatalities in the 50 U.S. states for a given year, debt/equity ratios for the Fortune 500 firms in the last quarter of a certain year, last month's Visa balances for a bank's new mortgage applicants, or GPAs of students in a statistics class would be cross-sectional data. For cross-sectional data, we are interested in *variation among observations* (e.g., accounts receivable in 20 Subway franchises) or in *relationships* (e.g., whether accounts receivable are related to sales volume in 20 Subway franchises as shown in Figure 2.2).

Some variables (such as unemployment rates) could be either time series (monthly data over each of 60 months) or cross-sectional (January's unemployment rate in 50 different cities). We can combine the two (e.g., monthly unemployment rates for the 13 Canadian provinces or territories for the last 60 months) to obtain *pooled cross-sectional and time series data*.

SECTION EXERCISES

connect

2.1 What type of data (categorical, discrete numerical, or continuous numerical) is each of the following variables? If there is any ambiguity about the data type, explain why the answer is unclear.

a. The manufacturer of your car.
b. Your college major.
c. The number of college credits you are taking.

2.2 What type of data (categorical, discrete numerical, or continuous numerical) is each of the following variables? If there is any ambiguity, explain why the answer is unclear.

a. Length of a TV commercial.
b. Number of peanuts in a can of Planter's Mixed Nuts.
c. Occupation of a mortgage applicant.
d. Flight time from London Heathrow to Chicago O'Hare.

2.3 What type of data (categorical, discrete numerical, or continuous numerical) is each of the following variables? If there is any ambiguity about the data type, explain why the answer is unclear.

a. The miles on your car's odometer.
b. The fat grams you ate for lunch yesterday.
c. The name of the airline with the cheapest fare from New York to London.
d. The brand of cell phone you own.

2.4 (a) Give three original examples of discrete data. (b) Give three original examples of continuous data. In each case, explain and identify any ambiguities that might exist. *Hint:* Do not restrict yourself to published data. Consider data describing your own life (e.g., your sports performance, financial data, or academic data). You need *not* list all the data, merely describe them and show a few typical data values.

2.5 Which type of data (cross-sectional or time series) is each variable?

a. Scores of 50 students on a midterm accounting exam last semester.
b. Bob's scores on 10 weekly accounting quizzes last semester.
c. Average score by all takers of the state's CPA exam for each of the last 10 years.
d. Number of years of accounting work experience for each of the 15 partners in a CPA firm.

2.6 Which type of data (cross-sectional or time series) is each variable?

a. Value of Standard & Poor's 500 stock price index at the close of each trading day last year.
b. Closing price of each of the 500 stocks in the S&P 500 index on the last trading day this week.
c. Dividends per share paid by General Electric common stock for the last 20 quarters.
d. Latest price/earnings ratios of 10 stocks in Bob's retirement portfolio.

2.7 Which type of data (cross-sectional or time series) is each variable?

a. Mexico's GDP for each of the last 10 quarters.
b. Unemployment rates in each of the 31 states in Mexico at the end of last year.
c. Unemployment rate in Mexico at the end of each of the last 10 years.
d. Average home value in each of the 10 largest Mexican cities today.

2.8 Give an original example of a time series variable and a cross-sectional variable. Use your own experience (e.g., your sports activities, finances, education).

2.2 LEVEL OF MEASUREMENT

LO 2-4

Recognize levels of measurement in data and ways of coding data.

Statisticians sometimes refer to four levels of measurement for data: *nominal, ordinal, interval,* and *ratio*. This typology was proposed over 60 years ago by psychologist S. S. Stevens. The allowable statistical tests depend on the measurement level. The criteria are summarized in Figure 2.3.

Nominal Measurement

LO 2-5

Recognize a Likert scale and know how to use it.

Nominal measurement is the weakest level of measurement and the easiest to recognize. **Nominal data** (from Latin *nomen,* meaning "name") merely identify a *category*. "Nominal" data are the same as "qualitative," "categorical," or "classification" data. To be sure that the categories are collectively exhaustive, it is common to use **Other** as the last item on the list. For example, the following survey questions yield nominal data:

Did you file an insurance claim last month?

1. Yes 2. No

Which cell phone service provider do you use?

1. AT&T 2. Sprint-Nextel 3. T-Mobile 4. Verizon 5. Other

We usually code nominal data numerically. However, the codes are arbitrary placeholders with no numerical meaning, so it is improper to perform mathematical analysis on them. For example, we would not calculate an average using the cell phone service data (1 through 5).

FIGURE 2.3

Determining the Measurement Level

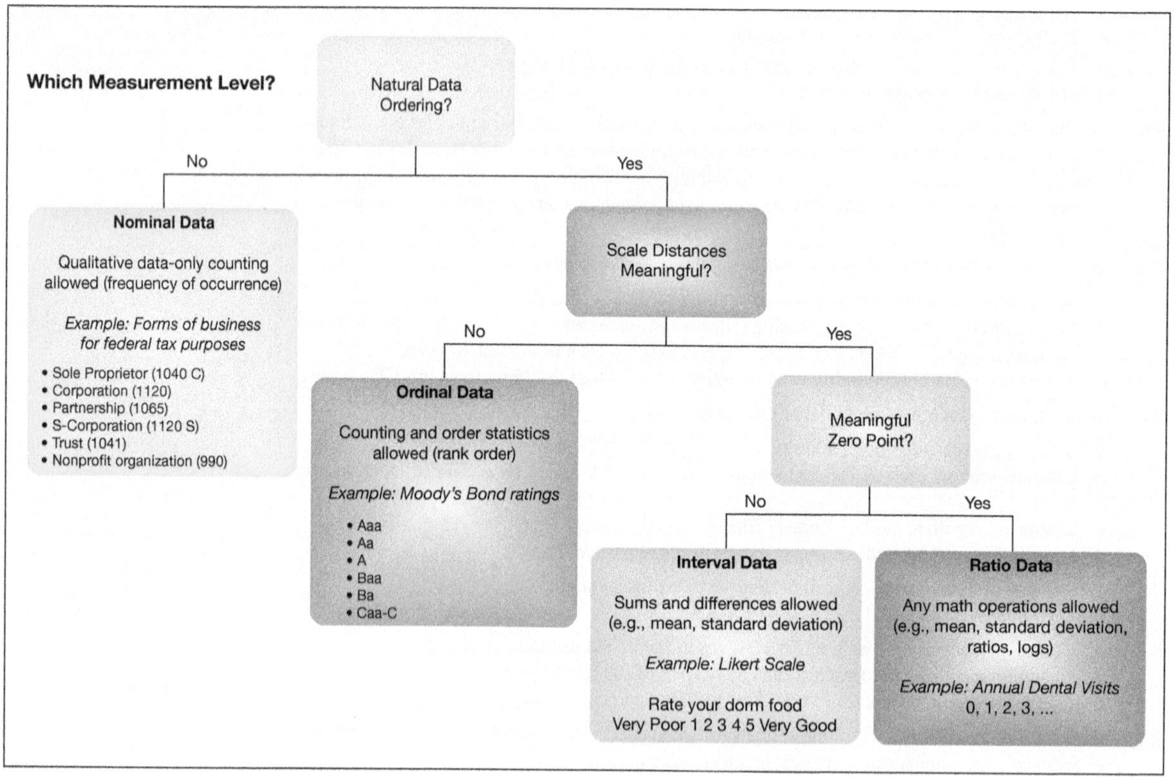

This may seem obvious, yet people have been known to do it. Once the data are in the computer, it's easy to forget that the "numbers" are only categories. With nominal data, the only permissible mathematical operations are counting (e.g., frequencies) and a few simple statistics such as the mode.

Ordinal Measurement

Ordinal data codes connote a *ranking* of data values. For example:

What size automobile do you usually drive?

1. Full-size 2. Compact 3. Subcompact

How often do you use Microsoft Access?

1. Frequently 2. Sometimes 3. Rarely 4. Never

Thus, a 2 (Compact) implies a larger car than a 3 (Subcompact). Like nominal data, these ordinal numerical codes lack the properties that are required to compute many statistics, such as the average. Specifically, there is no clear meaning to the *distance* between 1 and 2, or between 2 and 3, or between 3 and 4 (what would be the distance between "Rarely" and "Never"?). Other examples of ordinal scales can be found in a recruiter's rating of job candidates (outstanding, good, adequate, weak, unsatisfactory), S&P credit ratings (AAA, AA+, AA, AA−, A+, A, A−, B+, B, B−, etc.) or job titles (president, group vice president, plant manager, department head, clerk). Ordinal data can be treated as nominal, but not vice versa. Ordinal data are especially common in social sciences, marketing, and human resources research. There are many useful statistical tests for ordinal data.

Interval Measurement

The next step up the measurement scale is **interval data**, which not only is a rank but also has meaningful intervals between scale points. Examples are the Celsius or Fahrenheit scales of temperature. The interval between 60°F and 70°F is the same as the interval between 20°F and 30°F. Since intervals between numbers represent *distances,* we can do mathematical operations such as taking an average. But because the zero point of these scales is arbitrary, we can't say that 60°F is twice as warm as 30°F, or that 30°F is 50 percent warmer than 20°F. That is, ratios are not meaningful for interval data. The absence of a meaningful zero is a key characteristic of interval data.

Likert Scales The **Likert scale** is a special case that is frequently used in survey research. You have undoubtedly seen such scales. Typically, a statement is made and the respondent is asked to indicate his or her agreement/disagreement on a five-point or seven-point scale using verbal anchors. The *coarseness* of a Likert scale refers to the number of scale points (typically 5 or 7). For example:

"College-bound high school students should be required to study a foreign language." (check one)

❑	❑	❑	❑	❑
Strongly Agree	Somewhat Agree	Neither Agree Nor Disagree	Somewhat Disagree	Strongly Disagree

A neutral midpoint ("Neither Agree Nor Disagree") is allowed if we use an *odd* number of scale points (usually 5 or 7). Occasionally, surveys may omit the neutral midpoint to force the respondent to "lean" one way or the other. Likert data are coded numerically (e.g., 1 to 5), but any equally spaced values will work, as shown in Table 2.3.

TABLE 2.3
Examples of Likert-Scale Coding: "How will deflation affect the investment climate?"

Likert Coding: 1 to 5 scale	*Likert Coding: −2 to +2 scale*
5 = Will help a lot	+2 = Will help a lot
4 = Will help a little	+1 = Will help a little
3 = No effect on investment climate	0 = No effect on investment climate
2 = Will hurt a little	−1 = Will hurt a little
1 = Will hurt a lot	−2 = Will hurt a lot

But do Likert data qualify as interval measurements? By choosing the verbal anchors carefully, many researchers believe that the *intervals* are the same (e.g., the distance from 1 to 2 is "the same" as the *interval,* say, from 3 to 4). However, ratios are not meaningful (i.e., here 4 is not twice 2). The assumption that Likert scales produce interval data justifies a wide range of statistical calculations, including averages, correlations, and so on. Researchers use many Likert-scale variants.

"How would you rate your Internet service provider?" (check one)

❑ Terrible ❑ Poor ❑ Adequate ❑ Good ❑ Excellent

Instead of labeling every response category, many marketing surveys put verbal anchors only on the endpoints. This avoids intermediate scale labels and permits any number of scale points. For example, Vail Resorts includes the following question on their guest satisfaction survey that they administer at their ski resorts. This survey question has a *Likert-type* scale with 11 response points, verbal anchors at each endpoint, and a neutral anchor at the midpoint.

"On a scale of 0 to 10, how likely would you be to recommend this resort to your friends and family?"

0	1	2	3	4	5	6	7	8	9	10
❑	❑	❑	❑	❑	❑	❑	❑	❑	❑	❑
Not likely at all to recommend					Neither likely nor unlikely to recommend					Highly likely to recommend

Likert data usually are discrete, but some web surveys now use a continuous response scale that allows the respondent to position a "slider" anywhere along the scale to produce continuous data (actually the number of positions is finite but very large). For example:

Likert (using scale points)	Likert (using a slider)
Very Poor 1 2 3 4 5 6 7 Very Good	Very Poor ________▼________ Very Good

Ratio Measurement

Ratio measurement is the strongest level of measurement. **Ratio data** have all the properties of the other three data types, but in addition possess a *meaningful zero* that represents the absence of the quantity being measured. Because of the zero point, ratios of data values are meaningful (e.g., $20 million in profit is twice as much as $10 million). Balance sheet data, income statement data, financial ratios, physical counts, scientific measurements, and most engineering measurements are ratio data because zero has meaning (e.g., a company with zero sales sold nothing). Having a zero point does *not* restrict us to positive data. For example, profit is a ratio variable (e.g., $4 million is twice $2 million), yet firms can have negative profit (i.e., a loss).

Zero does *not* have to be observable in the data. Newborn babies, for example, cannot have zero weight, yet baby weight clearly is ratio data (i.e., an 8-pound baby is 33 percent heavier than a 6-pound baby). What matters is that the zero is an absolute reference point. The Kelvin temperature scale is a ratio measurement because its absolute zero represents the absence of molecular vibration, while zero on the Celsius scale is merely a convenience (note that 30°C is not "twice as much temperature" as 15°C).

Lack of a true zero is often the quickest test to defrock variables masquerading as ratio data. For example, a Likert scale (+2, +1, 0, −1, −2) is *not* ratio data despite the presence of zero because the zero (neutral) point does not connote the absence of anything. As an acid test, ask yourself whether 2 (strongly agree) is twice as much "agreement" as 1 (slightly agree). Some classifications are debatable. For example, college GPA has a zero, but does it represent the absence of learning? Does 4.00 represent "twice as much" learning as 2.00? Is there an underlying reality ranging from 0 to 4 that we are measuring? Most people seem to think so, although the conservative procedure would be to limit ourselves to statistical tests that assume only ordinal data.

Although beginning statistics textbooks usually emphasize interval or ratio data, there are textbooks that emphasize other kinds of data, notably in behavioral research (e.g., psychology, sociology, marketing, human resources).

We can recode ratio measurements *downward* into ordinal or nominal measurements (but not conversely). For example, doctors may classify systolic blood pressure as "normal" (under 130), "elevated" (130 to 140), or "high" (140 or over). The recoded data are ordinal, since the ranking is preserved. Intervals may be unequal. For example, U.S. air traffic controllers classify planes as "small" (under 41,000 pounds), "large" (41,001 to 254,999 pounds), and "heavy" (255,000 pounds or more). Such recoding is done to simplify the data when the exact data magnitude is of little interest; however, we discard information if we map stronger measurements into weaker ones.

SECTION EXERCISES

connect

2.9 Which measurement level (nominal, ordinal, interval, ratio) is each of the following variables? Explain.

a. Number of hits in Game 1 of the next World Series.
b. Baltimore's standing in the American League East (among five teams).
c. Field position of a baseball player (catcher, pitcher, etc.).
d. Temperature on opening day (Celsius).
e. Salary of a randomly chosen American League pitcher.
f. Freeway traffic on opening day (light, medium, heavy).

2.10 Which measurement level (nominal, ordinal, interval, ratio) is each of the following variables? Explain.

a. Number of employees in the Walmart store in Hutchinson, Kansas.
b. Number of merchandise returns on a randomly chosen Monday at a Walmart store.
c. Temperature (in Fahrenheit) in the ice-cream freezer at a Walmart store.

d. Name of the cashier at register 3 in a Walmart store.
e. Manager's rating of the cashier at register 3 in a Walmart store.
f. Social Security number of the cashier at register 3 in a Walmart store.

2.11 Which measurement level (nominal, ordinal, interval, ratio) is each of the following variables? Explain.
a. Number of passengers on Delta Flight 833.
b. Waiting time (minutes) after gate pushback before Delta Flight 833 takes off.
c. Brand of cell phone owned by a cabin attendant on Delta Flight 833.
d. Ticket class (first, business, or economy) of a randomly chosen passenger on Delta Flight 833.
e. Outside air temperature (Celsius) when Delta Flight 833 reaches 35,000 feet.
f. Passenger rating (on 5-point Likert scale) of Delta's in-flight food choices.

2.12 Which measurement level (nominal, ordinal, interval, ratio) is the response to each question? If you think that the level of measurement is ambiguous, explain why.
a. How would you describe your level of skill in using Excel? (check one)
❑ Low ❑ Medium ❑ High
b. How often do you use Excel? (check one)
❑ Rarely ❑ Often ❑ Very Often
c. Which version of Excel do you use? (check one)
❑ 2003 ❑ 2007 ❑ 2010 ❑ Other
d. I spend __________ hours a day using Excel.

2.13 Vail Resorts uses various types of scales and questions on their surveys. Here is a question from their guest satisfaction survey that uses a five-point scale. (a) Would the measurement level for the data collected from this question be nominal, ordinal, interval, or ratio? (b) Would it be appropriate to calculate an average rating for the various items? Explain. (c) Would a 10-point scale be better? Explain. (Source: Vail Resorts, Inc.)

"Rate your satisfaction level on numerous aspects of *today's* experience, where 1=Extremely Dissatisfied & 5=Extremely Satisfied."

1. Value for Price Paid:	1	2	3	4	5
2. Ticket Office Line Wait (if went to ticket window):	1	2	3	4	5
3. Friendliness/Helpfulness of Lift Operators:	1	2	3	4	5
4. Lift Line Waits:	1	2	3	4	5
5. Variety of Trails:	1	2	3	4	5
6. Amount of Snow Coverage:	1	2	3	4	5
7. Level of Crowding on Trails:	1	2	3	4	5
8. Clearly Marked Trail Signs:	1	2	3	4	5
9. Attention to Skier Safety:	1	2	3	4	5
10. Ski Patrol Visibility:	1	2	3	4	5

2.14 (a) Would the measurement level for the data collected from this Microsoft® survey question be nominal, ordinal, interval, or ratio? (b) Would a "6" response be considered twice as good as a "3" response? Why or why not? (c) Would a 1–5 scale be adequate? Explain.

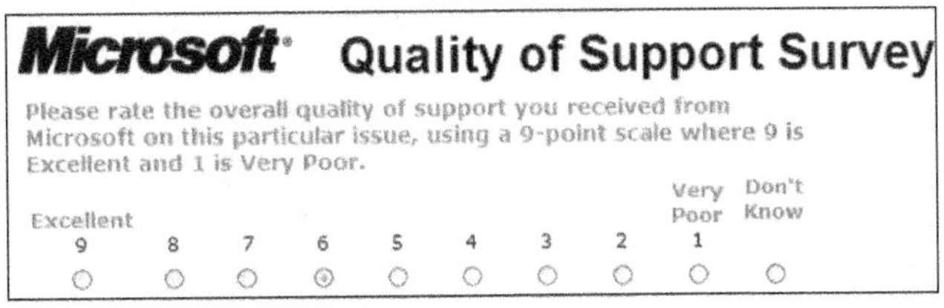
Microsoft® Quality of Support Survey

Please rate the overall quality of support you received from Microsoft on this particular issue, using a 9-point scale where 9 is Excellent and 1 is Very Poor.

Excellent 9	8	7	6	5	4	3	2	Very Poor 1	Don't Know
○	○	○	⊙	○	○	○	○	○	○

2.3 SAMPLING CONCEPTS

LO 2-6

Use the correct terminology for samples and populations.

There are almost 2 million retail businesses in the United States. It is unrealistic for market researchers to study them all or in a timely way. But since 2001, a new firm called ShopperTrak RCT (www.shoppertrak.com) has been measuring purchases at a sample of 45,000 mall-based stores, and using this information to advise clients quickly of changes in shopping trends. This application of sampling is part of the relatively new field of *retail intelligence*. In this section, you will learn the differences between a **sample** and a **population**, and why sometimes a sample is necessary or desirable.

Population or Sample?

Population All of the items that we are interested in. May be either finite (e.g., all of the passengers on a particular plane) or effectively infinite (e.g., all of the Cokes produced in an ongoing bottling process).

Sample A subset of the population that we will actually analyze.

Sample or Census?

A *sample* involves looking only at some items selected from the population, while a **census** is an examination of all items in a defined population. The accuracy of a census can be illusory. For example, the U.S. decennial census cannot locate every individual in the United States (the 1990 census is thought to have missed 8 million people while the 2000 census is believed to have overcounted 1.3 million people). Reasons include the extreme mobility of the U.S. population and the fact that some people do not want to be found (e.g., illegal immigrants) or do not reply to the mailed census form. Further, budget constraints make it difficult to train enough census field workers, install data safeguards, and track down incomplete responses or nonresponses. For these reasons, U.S. censuses have long used sampling in certain situations. Many statistical experts advised using sampling more extensively in the 2000 decennial census, but the U.S. Congress concluded that an actual headcount must be attempted.

When the quantity being measured is volatile, there cannot be a census. For example, The Arbitron Company tracks American radio listening habits using over 2.6 million "Radio Diary Packages." For each "listening occasion," participants note start and stop times for each station. Panelists also report their age, sex, and other demographic information. Table 2.4 outlines some situations where a sample rather than a census would be preferred, and vice versa.

TABLE 2.4 Sample or Census?

Situations Where a Sample May Be Preferred	*Situations Where a Census May Be Preferred*
Infinite Population No census is possible if the population is of indefinite size (an assembly line can keep producing bolts, a doctor can keep seeing more patients).	**Small Population** If the population is small, there is little reason to sample, for the effort of data collection may be only a small part of the total cost.
Destructive Testing The act of measurement may destroy or devalue the item (battery life, vehicle crash tests).	**Large Sample Size** If the required sample size approaches the population size, we might as well go ahead and take a census.
Timely Results Sampling may yield more timely results (checking wheat samples for moisture content, checking peanut butter for salmonella contamination).	**Database Exists** If the data are on disk, we can examine 100% of the cases. But auditing or validating data against physical records may raise the cost.
Accuracy Instead of spreading resources thinly to attempt a census, budget might be better spent to improve training of field interviewers and improve data safeguards.	**Legal Requirements** Banks must count *all* the cash in bank teller drawers at the end of each business day. The U.S. Congress forbade sampling in the 2000 decennial population census.
Cost Even if a census is feasible, the cost, in either time or money, may exceed our budget.	
Sensitive Information A trained interviewer might learn more about sexual harassment in an organization through confidential interviews of a small sample of employees.	

Parameters and Statistics

From a sample of n items, chosen from a population, we compute **statistics** that can be used as estimates of **parameters** found in the population. To avoid confusion, we use different symbols for each parameter and its corresponding statistic. Thus, the population mean is denoted μ (the lowercase Greek letter mu) while the sample mean is $\bar{x}$. The population proportion is denoted π (the lowercase Greek letter pi), while the sample proportion is p. Figure 2.4 illustrates this idea.

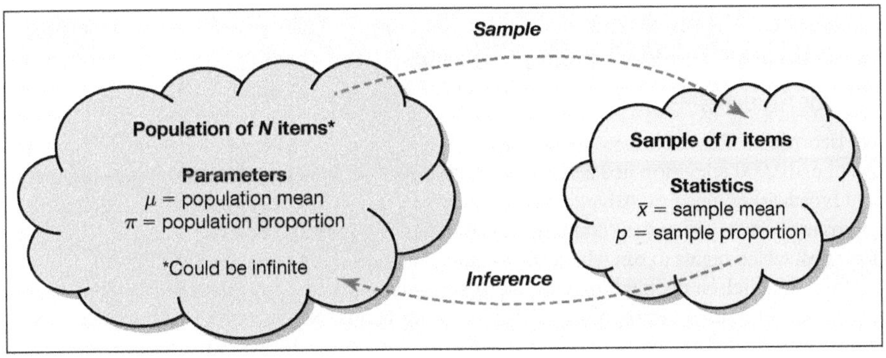

FIGURE 2.4
Population versus Sample

Parameter or Statistic?

Parameter A measurement or characteristic of the population (e.g., a mean or proportion). Usually unknown since we can rarely observe the entire population. Usually (but not always) represented by a Greek letter (e.g., μ or π).

Statistic A numerical value calculated from a sample (e.g., a mean or proportion). Usually (but not always) represented by a Roman letter (e.g., $\bar{x}$ or p).

For example, suppose we want to know the mean (average) repair cost for auto air-conditioning warranty claims, or the proportion (percent) of 25-year-old concertgoers who have permanent hearing loss. Since a census is impossible, these parameters would be estimated using a sample. For the sample statistics to provide good estimates of the population parameters, the population must be carefully specified and the sample must be drawn scientifically so the sample items are representative of the population.

Target Population

A population may be defined either by a list (e.g., the names of the passengers on Flight 234) or by a rule (e.g., the customers who eat at Noodles & Company). The **target population** contains all the individuals in which we are interested. Suppose we wish to estimate the proportion of potential consumers who would purchase a $20 Harley-Davidson desk calendar. Is the target population all drivers? Only male drivers over age 16? Only drivers with incomes over $25,000? Only motorcycle owners? By answering questions such as these, we not only identify the target population but also are forced to define our business goals more clearly. The **sampling frame** is the group from which we take the sample. If the frame differs from the target population, then our estimates might not be accurate. Examples of frames are phone directories, voter registration lists, alumni association mailing lists, or marketing databases. Other examples might be:

- Names and addresses of all registered voters in Colorado Springs, Colorado.
- Names and addresses of all vehicle owners in Ventura County, California.
- E-mail addresses of all L. L. Bean customers who have placed online orders.

EXAMPLE 2.1

Gasoline Price Survey

The sample for the U.S. Energy Information Administration's survey of gasoline prices is drawn from a frame of approximately 115,000 retail gasoline outlets, constructed from purchased private commercial sources and EIA sources, combined with zip codes from private lists. Individual frames are mapped to the county level by using zip codes, and outlets are assigned to standard metropolitan statistical areas from Census Bureau definitions. (For details, see www.eia.doe.gov.)

Mini Case 2.1

College Students—You Have a Voice in TV Ratings!

Nielsen Media Research (see www.nielsenmedia.com) conducts random sampling using a panel of 10,000 television households in order to provide viewing information to advertisers and broadcast companies. Advertising agencies use the viewing ratings to decide which programs are best for airing their commercials. Broadcast companies make decisions on advertising rates, which nights to run which shows, and which shows to keep on the air.

In 2006, Nielsen decided to add college students living in dorms to their National People Meter Sample. After monitoring their viewing habits, Nielsen estimated that 636,000 women age 18–24, living in dorms, viewed *Grey's Anatomy* during November 2006. This implied a 50 percent jump in the program ranking and elevated *Grey's Anatomy* to a top spot in the TV rankings. But to calculate their estimates, Nielsen is extrapolating from the viewing habits of *just 130 students* around the country who have agreed to have electronic monitors installed in their dorm rooms. That means that a handful of students can lead to a huge swing in ratings. For example, an estimated 163,000 jump in viewers for *Drawn Together* was based on only 12 people in the survey group who tuned in to the show. Later in this textbook, you will learn how to estimate the *margin of error* in a sample like this. But advertisers clearly believe that the information is reliable enough to use in making their decisions (for a discussion of Nielson's margin of error, see *The New York Times,* April 8, 2007, p. 10).

Does Nielsen accept volunteers in their National People Meter Sample? No. According to the Nielsen website, the firm draws its samples in a way that offers every American household with a television an equal chance of being selected. They go on to say that "[t]o include volunteers would violate basic laws of random sampling practice and skew our results. A truly representative sample of the population can only be generated using statistical methods of selection."

SECTION EXERCISES

connect

2.15 Would you use a sample or a census to measure each of the following? Why?

a. The model years of the cars driven by each of your five closest friends.
b. The model years of the cars driven by each student in your statistics class.
c. The model years of the cars driven by each student in your university.
d. The model years of the cars driven by each professor whose classes you are taking.

2.16 Would you use a sample or a census to measure each of the following? Why? If you are uncertain, explain the issues.

a. The mean time battery life of your laptop computer in continuous use.
b. The number of students in your statistics class who brought laptop computers to class today.
c. The average price paid for a laptop computer by students at your university.
d. The percentage of disk space available on laptop computers owned by your five closest friends.

2.17 The target population is all stocks in the S&P 500 index. Is each of the following a parameter or a statistic?

a. The average price/earnings ratio for all 500 stocks in the S&P index.
b. The proportion of all stocks in the S&P 500 index that had negative earnings last year.
c. The proportion of energy-related stocks in a random sample of 50 stocks.
d. The average rate of return for 20 stocks recommended by a broker.

2.4 SAMPLING METHODS

LO 2-7

Explain the common sampling methods and how to implement them.

There are two main categories of sampling methods. In **random sampling** items are chosen by randomization or a chance procedure. The idea of random sampling is to produce a sample that is representative of the population. **Non-random sampling** is less scientific but is sometimes used for expediency.

Random Sampling Methods

We will first discuss the four random sampling techniques shown in Table 2.5 and then describe three commonly used non-random sampling techniques, summarized in Table 2.8.

TABLE 2.5 Random Sampling Methods

Simple Random Sample	Use random numbers to select items from a list (e.g., Visa cardholders).
Systematic Sample	Select every *k*th item from a list or sequence (e.g., restaurant customers).
Stratified Sample	Select randomly within defined strata (e.g., by age, occupation, gender).
Cluster Sample	Select random geographical regions (e.g., zip codes) that represent the population.

Simple Random Sample We denote the population size by N and the sample size by n. In a **simple random sample**, every item in the population of N items has the same chance of being chosen in the sample of n items. A physical experiment to accomplish this would be to write each of the N data values on a poker chip, and then to draw n chips from a bowl after stirring it thoroughly. But we can accomplish the same thing if the N population items appear on a numbered list, by choosing n integers between 1 and N that we match up against the numbered list of the population items.

For example, suppose we want to select one student at random from a list of 15 students (see Figure 2.5). If you were asked to "use your judgment," you would probably pick a name in the middle, thereby biasing the draw against those individuals at either end of the list. Instead we rely on a **random number** to "pick" the name. How do we determine the random number? Before computers, statisticians relied on published tables of random numbers. The process is simpler today. Even most pocket calculators have a key to produce a random decimal in the interval [0, 1] which can be converted to a random integer. In this example, we used Excel's function =RANDBETWEEN(1,15) to pick a random integer between 1 and 15. The number was 12, so Stephanie was selected. There is no bias since all values from 1 to 15 are *equiprobable* (i.e., equally likely to occur).

FIGURE 2.5 Picking on Stephanie

Random person **12**

1	Adam	6	Haitham	11	Moira
2	Addie	7	Jackie	12	**Stephanie**
3	Don	8	Judy	13	Stephen
4	Floyd	9	Lindsay	14	Tara
5	Gadis	10	Majda	15	Xander

Sampling without replacement means that once an item has been selected to be included in the sample, it cannot be considered for the sample again. The Excel function =RANDBETWEEN(a,b) uses **sampling with replacement**. This means that the same random number could show up more than once. Using the bowl analogy, if we throw each chip back in the bowl and stir the contents before the next draw, an item can be chosen again. Instinctively most people believe that sampling without replacement is preferred over sampling with replacement because allowing duplicates in our sample seems odd. In reality, sampling without replacement can be a problem when our sample size n is close to our population size N. At some point in the sampling process, the remaining items in the population will no longer have the same probability of being selected as the items we chose at the beginning of the sampling process. This could lead to a bias (a tendency to overestimate or underestimate the parameter we are trying to measure) in our sample results. Sampling with replacement does not lead to bias.

When should we worry about sampling without replacement? Only when the population is finite and the sample size is close to the population size. Consider the Russell 3000® Index, which has 3000 stocks. If you sample 100 stocks, without replacement, you have "used" only about 3 percent of the population. The sample size $n = 100$ is considered small relative to the population size $N = 3000$. A common criterion is that a finite population is *effectively infinite* if the sample is less than 5 percent of the population (i.e., if $n/N \leq .05$). In Chapter 8, you will learn how to adjust for the effect of population size when you make a sample estimate. For now, you only need to recognize that such adjustments are of little consequence when the population is large.

Infinite Population?

When the sample is less than 5 percent of the population (i.e., when $n/N \leq .05$), then the population is effectively infinite. An equivalent statement is that a population is effectively infinite when it is at least 20 times as large as the sample (i.e., when $N/n \geq 20$).

Because computers are easier, we rarely use random number tables. Table 2.6 shows a few alternative ways to choose 10 integers between 1 and 875. All are based on a software algorithm that creates uniform decimal numbers between 0 and 1. Excel's function =RAND( ) does this, and many pocket calculators have a similar function. We call these *pseudorandom* generators because even the best algorithms eventually repeat themselves (after a cycle of millions of numbers). Thus, a software-based random data encryption scheme could conceivably be broken. To enhance data security, Intel and other firms are examining hardware-based methods (e.g., based on thermal noise or radioactive decay) to prevent patterns or repetition. Fortunately, most applications don't require that degree of randomness. For example, the iPod Shuffle's song choices are not strictly random because its random numbers are generated by an algorithm from a "seed number" that eventually repeats. However, the repeat period is so great that an iPod user would never notice. Excel's and MINITAB's random numbers are good enough for most purposes.

TABLE 2.6

Some Ways to Get 10 Random Integers between 1 and 875

Excel—Option A	Enter the Excel function **=RANDBETWEEN(1,875)** into 10 spreadsheet cells. Press **F9** to get a new sample.
Excel—Option B	Enter the function **=INT(1+875*RAND())** into 10 spreadsheet cells. Press **F9** to get a new sample.
Internet	The website www.random.org will give you many kinds of excellent random numbers (integers, decimals, etc).
MINITAB	Use MINITAB's Random Data menu with the Integer option.
Pocket Calculator	Press the **RAND** key to get a random number in the interval [0,1], multiply by 875, then round up to the next integer.

Randomizing a List

To randomize a list (assuming it is in a spreadsheet) we can insert the Excel function =RAND( ) beside each row. This creates a column of random decimal numbers between 0 and 1. Copy the random numbers and paste them in the same column using **Paste Special > Values** to "fix" them (otherwise they will keep changing). Then sort all the columns by the random number column, and *voilà*—the list is now random! The first *n* items on the randomized list can now be used as a random sample. This method is especially useful when the list is very long (perhaps millions of lines). The first *n* items are a random sample of the entire list, for they are as likely as any others.

Systematic Sample

Another method of random sampling is to choose every *k*th item from a sequence or list, starting from a randomly chosen entry among the first *k* items on the list. This is called **systematic sampling**. Figure 2.6 shows how to sample every fourth item, starting from item 2, resulting in a sample of $n = 20$ items.

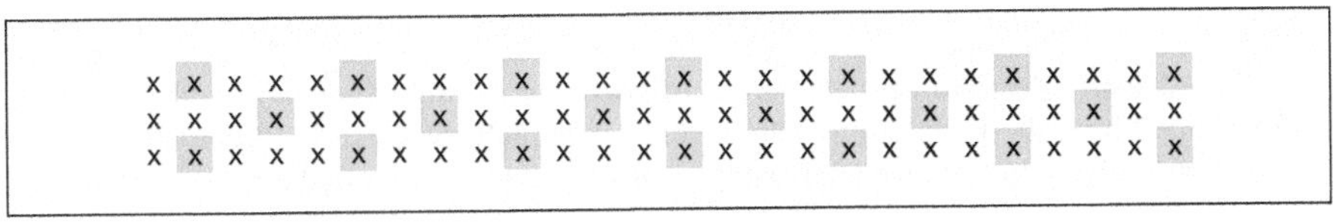

FIGURE 2.6

Systematic Sampling

An attraction of systematic sampling is that it can be used with unlistable or infinite populations, such as production processes (e.g., testing every 5,000th light bulb) or political polling (e.g., surveying every tenth voter who emerges from the polling place). Systematic sampling is also well-suited to linearly organized physical populations (e.g., pulling every tenth patient folder from alphabetized filing drawers in a veterinary clinic).

A systematic sample of *n* items from a population of *N* items requires that periodicity *k* be approximately N/n. For example, to choose 25 companies from a list of 500 companies in Example 2.2 (Table 2.7), we chose every twentieth stock ($k = 500/25 = 20$).

EXAMPLE 2.2

CEO Compensation

To sample the compensation of the CEOs of the 500 largest companies in the United States listed in *Forbes'* annual survey, take every twentieth company in the alphabetized list, starting (randomly) with the thirteenth company. The starting point (the thirteenth company) is chosen at random. This yields the sample of 25 CEOs, shown in Table 2.7. While it would be very time-consuming to examine all 500 executives, this sample should provide a representative cross-section.

TABLE 2.7

CEO Compensation in 25 Large U.S. Firms
CEOComp

Observation	*Firm*	*CEO*	*One-Year Total ($mil)*
1	AK Steel Holding	James L Wainscott	11.82
2	Anadarko Petroleum	James T Hackett	19.65
3	Avnet	Roy Vallee	10.16
4	Bristol-Myers Squibb	James M Cornelius	5.06
5	Charter Communications	Neil Smith	5.63
6	Commercial Metals	Murray R McClean	3.84
7	CVS Caremark	Thomas M Ryan	19.55
8	Dynegy	Bruce A Williamson	8.70
9	Estee Lauder Cos	William P Lauder	5.32
10	FPL Group	Lewis Hay III	14.25
11	Google	Eric E Schmidt	0.48
12	Huntington Bancshares	Thomas E Hoaglin	0.98
13	Johnson Controls	Stephen A Roell	15.69
14	Leucadia National	Ian M Cumming	1.21
15	MBIA	Joseph W Brown	22.20
16	Morgan Stanley	John J Mack	17.65
17	Northeast Utilities	Charles W Shivery	5.91
18	People's United	Philip R Sherringham	2.22
19	Progress Energy	William D Johnson	4.11
20	Rockwell Collins	Clayton M Jones	11.31
21	Sovereign Bancorp	Joseph P Campanelli	2.48
22	TD Ameritrade Holding	Joseph H Moglia	3.76
23	Union Pacific	James R Young	7.19
24	Wal-Mart Stores	H Lee Scott Jr	8.65
25	Wynn Resorts	Stephen A Wynn	11.25

Source: *Forbes.com*, April 30, 2008. Compensation is for 2007.

Systematic sampling should yield acceptable results unless patterns in the population happen to recur at periodicity k. For example, weekly pay cycles ($k = 7$) would make it illogical to sample bank check cashing volume every Friday. A less obvious example would be a machine that stamps a defective part every twelfth cycle due to a bad tooth in a 12-tooth gear, which would make it misleading to rely on a sample of every twelfth part ($k = 12$). But periodicity coincident with k is not typical or expected in most situations.

Stratified Sample Sometimes we can improve our sample efficiency by utilizing prior information about the population. This method is applicable when the population can be divided into relatively homogeneous subgroups of known size (called *strata*). Within each *stratum,* a simple random sample of the desired size could be taken. Alternatively, a random sample of the whole population could be taken, and then individual strata estimates could be combined using appropriate weights. This procedure, called **stratified sampling**, can reduce cost per observation and narrow the error bounds. For a population with L strata, the population size N is the sum of the stratum sizes: $N = N_1 + N_2 + \cdots + N_L$. The weight assigned to stratum j is $w_j = N_j/N$ (i.e., each stratum is weighted by its known proportion of the population).

To illustrate, suppose we want to estimate MMR (measles-mumps-rubella) vaccination rates among employees in state government, and we know that our target population (those individuals we are trying to study) is 55 percent male and 45 percent female. Suppose our budget only allows a sample of size 200. To ensure the correct gender balance, we could sample 110 males and 90 females. Alternatively, we could just take a random sample of 200 employees. Although our random sample probably will not contain *exactly* 110 males and 90 females, we can get an overall estimate of vaccination rates by *weighting* the male and female sample vaccination rates using $w_M = 0.55$ and $w_F = 0.45$ to reflect the known strata sizes.

Mini Case 2.2

Sampling for Safety

To help automakers and other researchers study the causes of injuries and fatalities in vehicle accidents, the U.S. Department of Transportation developed the National Accident Sampling System (NASS) Crashworthiness Data System (CDS). Because it is impractical to investigate every accident (there were 6,159,000 police-reported accidents in 2005), detailed data are collected in a common format from 24 primary sampling units, chosen to represent all serious police-reported motor vehicle accidents in the United States during the year. Selection of sample accidents is done in three stages: (1) The country is divided into 1,195 geographic areas called Primary Sampling Units (PSUs) grouped into 12 strata based on geographic region. Two PSUs are selected from each stratum using weights roughly proportional to the number of accidents in each stratum. (2) In each sampled PSU, a second stage of sampling is performed using a sample of Police Jurisdictions (PJs) based on the number, severity, and type of accidents in the PJ. (3) The final stage of sampling is the selection of accidents within the sampled PJs. Each reported accident is classified into a stratum based on type of vehicle, most severe injury, disposition of the injured, tow status of the vehicles, and model year of the vehicles. Each team is assigned a fixed number of accidents to investigate each week, governed by the number of researchers on a team. Weights for the strata are assigned to favor a larger percentage of higher severity accidents while ensuring that accidents in the same stratum have the same probability of being selected, regardless of the PSU. The NASS CDS database is administered by the National Center for Statistics and Analysis (NCSA) of the National Highway Traffic Safety Administration (NHTSA). These data are currently helping to improve the government's "5 Star" crashworthiness rating system for vehicles.

(Source: www-nrd.nhtsa.dot.gov/Pubs/NASS94.PDF)

Cluster Sample **Cluster samples** are taken from strata consisting of geographical regions. We divide a region (say, a city) into subregions (say, blocks, subdivisions, or school districts). In one-stage cluster sampling, our sample consists of all elements in each of k randomly chosen subregions (or clusters). In two-stage cluster sampling, we first randomly select k subregions (clusters) and then choose a random sample of elements within each cluster. Figure 2.7 illustrates how four elements could be sampled from each of three randomly chosen clusters using two-stage cluster sampling.

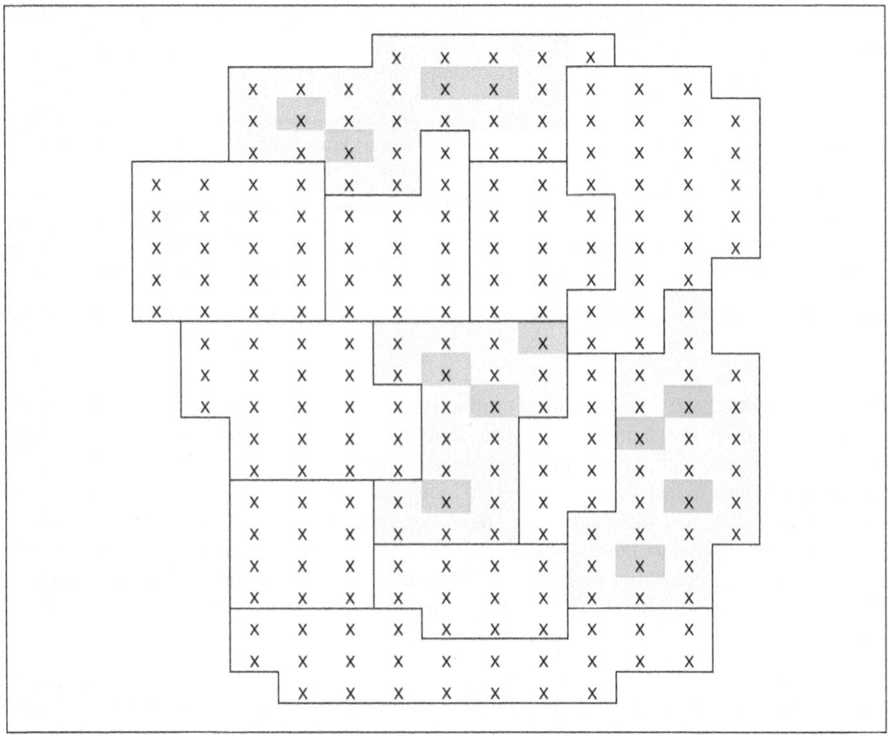

FIGURE 2.7

Two-Stage Cluster Sampling: Randomly choose three clusters, then randomly choose four items in each cluster

Because elements within a cluster are proximate, travel time and interviewer expenses are kept low. Cluster sampling is useful when:

- Population frame and stratum characteristics are not readily available.
- It is too expensive to obtain a simple or stratified sample.
- The cost of obtaining data increases sharply with distance.
- Some loss of reliability is acceptable.

Although cluster sampling is cheap and quick, it is often reasonably accurate because people in the same neighborhood tend to be similar in income, ethnicity, educational background, and so on. Cluster sampling is useful in political polling, surveys of gasoline pump prices, studies of crime victimization, vaccination surveys, or lead contamination in soil. A hospital may contain clusters (floors) of similar patients. A warehouse may have clusters (pallets) of inventory parts. Forest sections may be viewed as clusters to be sampled for disease or timber growth rates.

Cluster sampling is also widely used in marketing and economic surveys. The Bureau of Labor Statistics relies on multistage cluster sampling for estimating economic indicators such as the Consumer Price Index (CPI) and employment rates. The CPI measures the average change in price for a "market basket" of goods and services typically used by urban consumers. The CPI is estimated from a two-stage cluster sampling process. The sampling process begins with 87 urban areas in the United States. Within these urban areas, prices on over 200 categories are gathered from approximately 50,000 housing units and 23,000 retail establishments.

Non-Random Sampling Methods

Table 2.8 describes three commonly used non-random sampling techniques. Businesses often rely on these techniques to quickly gather data that might be used to guide informal decisions or as preliminary data to help design formal studies that use random samples.

TABLE 2.8
Non-Random Samples

Judgment Sample	Use expert knowledge to choose "typical" items (e.g., which employees to interview).
Convenience Sample	Use a sample that happens to be available (e.g., ask co-workers' opinions at lunch).
Focus Groups	In-depth dialog with a representative panel of individuals (e.g., iPod users).

Judgment Sample **Judgment sampling** is a non-random sampling method that relies on the expertise of the sampler to choose items that are representative of the population. For example, to estimate the corporate spending on research and development (R&D) in the medical equipment industry, we might ask an industry expert to select several "typical" firms. Unfortunately, subconscious biases can affect experts, too. In this context, "bias" does not mean prejudice, but rather *non-randomness* in the choice. Judgment samples may be the best alternative in some cases, but we can't be sure whether the sample was random. *Quota sampling* is a special kind of judgment sampling in which the interviewer chooses a certain number of people in each category (e.g., men/women).

Convenience Sample The sole virtue of **convenience sampling** is that it is quick. The idea is to grab whatever sample is handy. An accounting professor who wants to know how many MBA students would take a summer elective in international accounting can just survey the class she is currently teaching. The students polled may not be representative of all MBA students, but an answer (although imperfect) will be available immediately. A newspaper reporter doing a story on perceived airport security might interview co-workers who travel frequently. An executive might ask department heads if they think nonbusiness web surfing is widespread.

You might think that convenience sampling is rarely used or, when it is, that the results are used with caution. However, this does not appear to be the case. Since convenience samples often sound the first alarm on a timely issue, their results have a way of attracting attention and have probably influenced quite a few business decisions. The mathematical properties of convenience samples are unknowable, but they do serve a purpose and their influence cannot be ignored.

Focus Groups A **focus group** is a panel of individuals chosen to be representative of a wider population, formed for open-ended discussion and idea gathering about an issue (e.g., a proposed new product or marketing strategy). Typically 5–10 people are selected, and the interactive discussion lasts 1–2 hours. Participants are usually individuals who do not know each other, but who are prescreened to be broadly compatible yet diverse. A trained moderator guides the focus group's discussion and keeps it on track. Although not a random sampling method, focus groups are widely used, both in business and in social science research, for the insights they can yield beyond "just numbers."

Mini Case 2.3

Pricing Accuracy

Bar code price scanning using the Universal Product Code (UPC) became the standard in most retail businesses following the rapid improvement in scanning technology during the 1970s. Since that time, federal and state agencies have monitored businesses to regulate pricing accuracy at their checkouts. Because a census is impossible for checking price accuracy, sampling is an essential tool in enforcing consumer protection laws. The National Institute for Standards and Technology (NIST) has developed a handbook for inspection agencies that provides guidance on how to conduct a pricing sampling inspection.

Arizona's Department of Weights and Measures (DWM) has set up a UPC scanner pricing sampling inspection process for the retail establishments in their state. A UPC inspection will be based on either a stratified sample (e.g., a cosmetics department) or a simple random sample from throughout the store. The inspector will select between 25 and 50 items based on the sample size recommendation from NIST. The items will be taken to the register for scanning and the inspector will count the number of items that show a difference between the display and scanned price. Arizona requires that the retail store have 98 percent accuracy.

Between 2001 and 2006, in the state of Arizona, Walmart failed 526 price accuracy inspections. The Arizona attorney general filed a lawsuit against Walmart in 2006. The lawsuit was settled when Walmart agreed to a financial settlement of $1 million and modifications of their pricing practices.

Source: http://www.azag.gov/press_releases/may/2009/WM%20Settlement%20Release.pdf, accessed February 10, 2011.

Sample Size

The necessary sample size depends on the inherent variability of the quantity being measured and the desired precision of the estimate. For example, the caffeine content of Mountain Dew is fairly consistent because each can or bottle is filled at the factory, so a small sample size would suffice to estimate the mean. In contrast, the amount of caffeine in an individually brewed cup of Bigelow Raspberry Royale tea varies widely because people let it steep for varying lengths of time, so a larger sample would be needed to estimate the mean. The purposes of the investigation, the costs of sampling, the budget, and time constraints are also taken into account in deciding on sample size. Setting the sample size is worth a detailed discussion, found in later chapters.

Sources of Error

No matter how careful you are when conducting a survey, you will encounter potential sources of error. Let's briefly review a few, summarized in Table 2.9.

In sampling, the word *bias* does not refer to prejudice. Rather, it refers to a systematic tendency to over- or underestimate a population parameter of interest. The word "error" generally refers to problems in sample methodology that lead to inaccurate estimates of a population parameter.

TABLE 2.9
Potential Sources of Survey Error

Source of Error	*Characteristics*
Nonresponse bias	Respondents differ from nonrespondents
Selection bias	Self-selected respondents are atypical
Response error	Respondents give false information
Coverage error	Incorrect specification of frame or population
Measurement error	Unclear survey instrument wording
Interviewer error	Responses influenced by interviewer
Sampling error	Random and unavoidable

Nonresponse bias occurs when those who respond have characteristics different from those who don't respond. For example, people with caller ID, answering machines, blocked or unlisted numbers, or cell phones are likely to be missed in telephone surveys. Since these are generally more affluent individuals, their socioeconomic class may be underrepresented in the poll. A special case is **selection bias**, a self-selected sample. For example, a talk show host who invites viewers to take a web survey about their sex lives will attract plenty of respondents. But those who are willing to reveal details of their personal lives (and who have time to complete the survey) are likely to differ substantially from those who dislike nosy surveys or are too busy (and probably weren't watching the show anyway).

Further, it is easy to imagine that hoax replies will be common to such a survey (e.g., a bunch of college dorm students giving silly answers on a web survey). **Response error** occurs when respondents deliberately give false information to mimic socially acceptable answers, to avoid embarrassment, or to protect personal information.

Coverage error occurs when some important segment of the target population is systematically missed. For example, a survey of Notre Dame University alumni will fail to represent noncollege graduates or those who attended public universities. **Measurement error** results when the survey questions do not accurately reveal the construct being assessed. When the interviewer's facial expressions, tone of voice, or appearance influences the responses, data are subject to **interviewer error**.

Finally, **sampling error** is uncontrollable random error that is inherent in any random sample. Even when using a random sampling method, it is possible that the sample will contain unusual responses. This cannot be prevented and is generally undetectable. It is *not* an error on your part.

Mini Case 2.4

Making Commercials Work Better

A new company has sprung up to offer advertisers help in improving their targeting of commercial messages on various broadcast media, using digital technology. Integrated Media Measurement (IMMI, Inc.) tracks the behavior of 3,000 panel members (including teenagers) by having them carry a special cell phone (the panelists get free cell phone usage for two years). The phones capture samples of audio 24/7 from the surrounding environment. Samples are then analyzed digitally and matched against known ad content to see what the participant is listening to, and where the participant heard the ad (TV, radio, internet, DVD, etc.). This technology has the potential to inform marketers of ways to reach those who watch TV online, a group who tend to be missed through traditional television ads. Another new potential ad content stream being explored is movie theatre ads. Traditional Nielson ratings (see Mini Case 2.1) only cover television viewers, so there is considerable investor interest in this emerging high-tech sampling method. A carefully designed *stratified* sample of panelists is needed to permit estimation of ad exposure of listener populations by age, ethnicity, education, income, and other relevant demographics.

Source: *The New York Times*, September 7, 2007, p. B4; immi.com; www.tradevibes.com.

SECTION EXERCISES

connect

2.18 The target population is all students in your university. You wish to estimate the average current Visa balance for each student. How large would the university student population have to be in order to be regarded as effectively infinite in each of the following samples?

a. A sample of 10 students.
b. A sample of 50 students.
c. A sample of 100 students.

2.19 Suppose you want to know the ages of moviegoers who attend the latest *Hunger Games* movie. What kind of sample is it if you (a) survey the first 20 persons to emerge from the theater, (b) survey every tenth person to emerge from the theater, and (c) survey everyone who looks under age 12?

2.20 Suppose you want to study the number of e-mail accounts owned by students in your statistics class. What kind of sample is it if you (a) survey each student who has a student ID number ending in an odd number. (b) survey all the students sitting in the front row, and (c) survey every fifth student who arrives at the classroom?

2.21 Below is a 6 × 8 array containing the ages of moviegoers (see file **Hunger Games**). Treat this as a population. Select a random sample of 10 moviegoers' ages by using (a) simple random sampling with a random number table, (b) simple random sampling with Excel's =RANDBETWEEN( ) function, (c) systematic sampling, (d) judgment sampling, and (e) convenience sampling. Explain your methods.

32	34	33	12	57	13	58	16
23	23	62	65	35	15	17	20
14	11	51	33	31	13	11	58
23	10	63	34	12	15	62	13
40	11	18	62	64	30	42	20
21	56	11	51	38	49	15	21

2.22 (a) In the previous population, what was the proportion of all 48 moviegoers who were under age 30? (b) For each of the samples of size $n = 10$ that you took, what was the proportion of moviegoers under age 30? (c) Was each sample proportion close to the population proportion?

2.23 In Excel, type a list containing names for 10 of your friends into cells B1:B10. Choose three names at random by randomizing this list. To do this, enter =RAND( ) into cells A1:A10, copy the random column and paste it using Paste Special > Values to fix the random numbers, and then sort the list by the random column. The first three names are the random sample.

2.5 DATA SOURCES

LO 2-8

Find everyday print or electronic data sources.

One goal of a statistics course is to help you learn where to find data that might be needed. Fortunately, many excellent sources are widely available, either in libraries or through private purchase. Table 2.10 summarizes a few of them.

The U.S. Census Bureau and the U.S. Bureau of Labor Statistics are rich sources of data on many different aspects of life in the United States. The publications library supported by the Census Bureau can be found at www.census.gov. The monthly, quarterly, and annual reports published by the Bureau of Labor statistics can be found at www.bls.gov. It should be noted that until 2012, the *Statistical Abstract of the United States* was the largest, most general, and freely available annual compendium of facts and figures from public sources. A 2012 review of publications sponsored by the U.S. Census Bureau concluded with a decision to quit publishing the *Statistical Abstract*. However, you can still access previous years' publications at the U.S. Census website.

For annual and monthly time series economic data, try the *Economic Report of the President* (*ERP*), which is published every February. The tables in the *ERP* can be downloaded for free in Excel format. Data on cities, counties, and states can be found in the *State and Metropolitan Area Data Book,* published every few years by the Bureau of the Census and available on CD-ROM in many libraries.

Annual almanacs from several major publishers are sold at most bookstores. These include data reprinted from the above sources, but also information on recent events, sports, stock market, elections, Congress, world nations, states, and higher education. One of these almanacs should be on every informed citizen's shelf.

TABLE 2.10

Useful Data Sources

Type of Data	*Examples*
U.S. job-related data	U.S. Bureau of Labor Statistics
U.S. economic data	*Economic Report of the President*
Almanacs	*World Almanac, Time Almanac*
Periodicals	*Economist, Bloomberg Businessweek, Fortune, Forbes*
Indexes	*The New York Times, The Wall Street Journal*
Databases	Compustat, Citibase, U.S. Census
World data	*CIA World Factbook*
Web	Google, Yahoo!, MSN

Annual surveys of major companies, markets, and topics of business or personal finance are found in magazines such as *Bloomberg Businessweek, Consumer Reports, Forbes, Fortune,* and *Money*. Indexes such as the *Business Periodical Index, The New York Times Index,* and *The Wall Street Journal Index* are useful for locating topics. Libraries have web search engines that can access many of these periodicals in abstract or full-text form.

Specialized computer databases (e.g., CRSP, Compustat, Citibase, U.S. Census) are available (at a price) for research on stocks, companies, financial statistics, and census data. An excellent summary of sources is F. Patrick Butler's *Business Research Sources: A Reference Navigator*. The web allows us to use search engines (e.g., Google, Yahoo!, MSN) to find information. Sometimes you may get lucky, but web information is often undocumented, unreliable, or unverifiable. Better information is available through private companies or trade associations, though often at a steep price. Related Reading and Web Data Sources are listed at the end of this chapter.

Often overlooked sources of help are your university librarians. University librarians understand how to find databases and how to navigate databases quickly and accurately. Librarians can help you distinguish between valid and invalid Internet sources and then help you put the source citation in the proper format when writing reports.

Copying Data to a Spreadsheet

If your data set contains commas (e.g., 42,586), dollar signs (e.g., $14.88), or percents (e.g., 7.5%), your statistics package (e.g., MINITAB or SPSS) may treat the data as text. A numerical variable may only contain the digits 0–9, a decimal point, and a minus sign. Format the data column as plain numbers with the desired number of decimal places *before* you copy the data to whatever package you are using. Excel can display a value such as 32.8756 as 32.9 if you set only one decimal digit, but it is the *displayed* number that is copied, so your Excel statistics may not agree with the package you are using.

Web Data Sources

Source	*Website*
Bureau of Economic Analysis	www.bea.gov
Bureau of Justice Statistics	www.ojp.usdoj.gov/bjs
Bureau of Labor Statistics	www.bls.gov
Central Intelligence Agency	www.cia.gov
Economic Report of the President	www.gpo.gov/erp
Environmental Protection Agency	www.epa.gov
Federal Reserve System	www.federalreserve.gov
Food and Drug Administration	www.fda.gov
National Agricultural Statistics Service	www.nass.usda.gov
National Center for Education Statistics	www.nces.ed.gov
National Center for Health Statistics	www.cdc.gov/nchs
State and Metropolitan Area Data Book	www.census.gov/statab/www/smadb.html
Statistical Abstract of the United States	www.census.gov/compendia/statab/
Statistics Canada	www.statcan.gc.ca
U.N. Dept of Economic and Social Affairs	www.un.org/depts/unsd
U.S. Census Bureau	www.census.gov
U.S. Federal Statistics	www.fedstats.gov
World Bank	www.worldbank.org
World Demographics	www.demographia.com
World Health Organization	www.who.int/en

2.6 SURVEYS

LO 2-9

Describe basic elements of survey types, survey designs, and response scales.

Most survey research follows the same basic steps. These steps may overlap in time:

- Step 1: State the goals of the research.
- Step 2: Develop the budget (time, money, staff).
- Step 3: Create a research design (target population, frame, sample size).
- Step 4: Choose a survey type and method of administration.
- Step 5: Design a data collection instrument (questionnaire).
- Step 6: Pretest the survey instrument and revise as needed.
- Step 7: Administer the survey (follow up if needed).
- Step 8: Code the data and analyze it.

Survey Types

Surveys fall into five general categories: mail, telephone, interview, web, and direct observation. They differ in cost, response rate, data quality, time required, and survey staff training requirements. Table 2.11 lists some common types of surveys and a few of their salient strengths/weaknesses.

TABLE 2.11 **Common Types of Surveys**

Survey Type	***Characteristics***
Mail	Mail requires a well-targeted and current mailing list (people move a lot). Expect low response rates and nonresponse bias (nonrespondents differ from those who respond). Zip code lists (often costly) are an attractive option to define strata of similar income, education, and attitudes. To encourage participation, a cover letter should explain the uses of the survey data. Plan for follow-up mailings.
Telephone	Random dialing yields low response and is poorly targeted. Purchased phone lists help reach the target population, though a low response rate still is typical (disconnected phones, caller screening, answering machines, work hours, no-call lists). Other sources of nonresponse bias include the growing number of cell phones, non-English speakers, and distrust caused by scams.
Interviews	Interviewing is expensive and time-consuming, yet a trade-off between sample size for high-quality results may be worth it. Interviewers must be well-trained—an added cost. Interviewers can obtain information on complex or sensitive topics (e.g., gender discrimination in companies, birth control practices, diet and exercise).
Web	Web surveys are growing in popularity but are subject to nonresponse bias because they miss those who feel too busy, don't own computers, or distrust your motives (scams and spam). This type of survey works best when targeted to a well-defined interest group on a question of self-interest (e.g., views of CPAs on Sarbanes-Oxley accounting rules, frequent flyer views on airline security).
Direct Observation	Observation can be done in a controlled setting (e.g., psychology lab) but requires informed consent, which can change behavior. Unobtrusive observation is possible in some nonlab settings (e.g., what percentage of airline passengers carry on more than two bags, what percentage of SUVs carry no passengers, what percentage of drivers wear seat belts).

Response Rates Consider the *cost per valid response*. A telephone survey might be cheapest to conduct, but bear in mind that over half the households in some metropolitan areas have unlisted phones, and many have answering machines or call screening. The sample you get may not be very useful in terms of reaching the target population.

Telephone surveys (even with random dialing) do lend themselves nicely to cluster sampling (e.g., using each three-digit area code as a cluster and each three-digit exchange as a cluster) to sample somewhat homogeneous populations. Similarly, mail surveys can be clustered by zip code, which is a significant attraction. Web surveys are cheap, but rather uncontrolled. Nonresponse bias is a problem with all of these. Interviews or observational experiments are expensive and labor-intensive, but they may provide higher quality data. Large-scale national research projects (e.g., mental health status of U.S. household members) offer financial incentives to encourage participants who otherwise would not provide information. Research suggests that adjustments can be made for whatever biases may result from such incentives. Table 2.12 offers some tips to conduct successful surveys.

TABLE 2.12

Survey Guidelines

Planning	What is the survey's purpose? What do you really need to know? What staff expertise is available? What skills are best hired externally? What degree of precision is required? What is your budget?
Design	To ensure a good response and useful data, you must invest time and money in designing the survey. Take advantage of many useful books and references so that you do not make unnecessary errors.
Quality	Care in preparation is needed. Glossy printing and advertising have raised people's expectations about quality. A scruffy questionnaire will be ignored. Some surveys (e.g., web-based) may require special software.
Pilot Test	Questions that are clear to you may be unclear to others. You can pretest the questionnaire on friends or co-workers, but using a small test panel of naive respondents who don't owe you anything is best.
Buy-In	Response rates may be improved by stating the purpose of the survey, by offering a token of appreciation (e.g., discount coupon, free gift), or with endorsements (e.g., from a trusted professional group).
Expertise	Consider hiring a consultant at the early stages, even if you plan to do your own data collection and tabulation. Early consultation is more effective than waiting until you get in trouble.

Questionnaire Design

You should consider hiring a consultant, at least in the early stages, to help you get your survey off the ground successfully. Alternatively, resources are available on the web to help you plan a survey. The American Statistical Association (www.amstat.org) offers brochures *What Is a Survey* and *How to Plan a Survey*. Additional materials are available from the Research Industry Coalition, Inc. (www.researchindustry.org) and the Council of American Survey Research Organizations (www.casro.org). Entire books have been written to help you design and administer your own survey (see Related Reading).

The layout must not be crowded (use lots of white space). Begin with very short, clear instructions, stating the purpose, assuring anonymity, and explaining how to submit the completed survey. Questions should be numbered. Divide the survey into sections if the topics fall naturally into distinct areas. Let respondents bypass sections that aren't relevant to them (e.g., "If you answered no to Question 7, skip directly to Question 15"). Include an "escape option" where it seems appropriate (e.g., "Don't know or Does not apply"). Use wording and response scales that match the reading ability and knowledge level of the intended respondents. Pretest and revise. Keep the questionnaire as short as possible. Table 2.13 lists a few common question formats and response scales.

TABLE 2.13
Question Format and Response Scale

Type of Question	***Example***
Open-ended	Briefly describe your job goals.
Fill-in-the-blank	How many times did you attend formal religious services during the last year? ________ times
Check boxes	Which of these statistics packages have you used? ❑ SAS ❑ Visual Statistics ❑ SPSS ❑ MegaStat ❑ Systat ❑ MINITAB
Ranked choices	Please evaluate your dining experience: (Excellent / Good / Fair / Poor) Food ❑ ❑ ❑ ❑ Service ❑ ❑ ❑ ❑ Ambiance ❑ ❑ ❑ ❑ Cleanliness ❑ ❑ ❑ ❑ Overall ❑ ❑ ❑ ❑
Pictograms	What do you think of the president's economic policies? (circle one) ☺ ☺ 😐 ☹ ☹
Likert scale	Statistics is a difficult subject. Strongly Agree ❑ / Slightly Agree ❑ / Neither Agree nor Disagree ❑ / Slightly Disagree ❑ / Strongly Disagree ❑

Question Wording

The way a question is asked has a profound influence on the response. For example, in a *Wall Street Journal* editorial, Fred Barnes tells of a *Reader's Digest* poll that asked two similar questions:

Version 1: I would be disappointed if Congress cut its funding for public television.

Version 2: Cuts in funding for public television are justified to reduce federal spending.

The same 1,031 people were polled in both cases. Version 1 showed 40 percent in favor of cuts, while version 2 showed 52 percent in favor of cuts. The margin of error was ±3.5 percent (in "How to Rig a Poll," June 14, 1995, p. A18). To "rig" the poll, emotional overlays or "loaded" mental images can be attached to the question. In fact, it is often difficult to ask a neutral question without any context. For example:

Version 1: Shall state taxes be cut?

Version 2: Shall state taxes be cut, if it means reducing highway maintenance?

Version 3: Shall state taxes be cut, if it means firing teachers and police?

An unconstrained choice (version 1) makes tax cuts appear to be a "free lunch," while versions 2 and 3 require the respondent to envision the consequences of a tax cut. An alternative is to use version 1 but then ask the respondent to list the state services that should be cut to balance the budget after the tax cut.

Another problem in wording is to make sure you have covered all the possibilities. For example, how could a widowed independent voter answer questions like these?

Are you married?

❑ Yes

❑ No

What is your party preference?

❑ Democrat

❑ Republican

Avoid overlapping classes or unclear categories. What if the respondent's father is deceased or is 45 years old?

How old is your father?

❑ 35–45 ❑ 45–55 ❑ 55–65 ❑ 65 or older

Data Screening

Survey responses usually are coded numerically (e.g., 1 = male, 2 = female), although many software packages can also use text variables (nominal data) in certain kinds of statistical tests. Most packages require you to denote missing values by a special character (e.g., blank, period, or asterisk). If too many entries on a given respondent's questionnaire are flawed or missing, you may decide to discard the entire response.

Other data screening issues include multiple responses (i.e., the respondent chose two responses where one was expected), outrageous replies on fill-in-the-blank questions (e.g., a respondent who claims to work 640 hours a week), "range" answers (e.g., 10–20 cigarettes smoked per day), or inconsistent replies (e.g., a 25-year-old respondent who claims to receive Medicare benefits). Sometimes a follow-up is possible, but in anonymous surveys you must make the best decisions you can about how to handle anomalous data. Be sure to document your data-coding decisions—not only for the benefit of others but also in case you are asked to explain how you did it (it is easy to forget after a month or two, when you have moved on to other projects).

SECTION EXERCISES

connect

2.24 What sources of error might you encounter if you want to know (a) about the dating habits of college men, so you go to a dorm meeting and ask students how many dates they have had in the last year; (b) how often people attend religious services, so you stand outside a particular church on Sunday and ask entering individuals how often they attend; (c) how often people eat at McDonald's, so you stand outside a particular McDonald's and ask entering customers how often they eat at McDonald's?

2.25 What kind of survey (mail, telephone, interview, web, direct observation) would you recommend for each of the following purposes, and why? What problems might be encountered?

a. To estimate the proportion of students at your university who would prefer a web-based statistics class to a regular lecture.
b. To estimate the proportion of students at your university who carry backpacks to class.
c. To estimate the proportion of students at your university who would be interested in taking a two-month summer class in international business with tours of European factories.
d. To estimate the proportion of U.S. business graduates who have taken a class in international business.

2.26 What kind of survey (mail, telephone, interview, web, direct observation) would you recommend that a small laundry and dry cleaning business use for each of the following purposes, and why?

a. To estimate the proportion of customers preferring opening hours at 7 a.m. instead of 8 a.m.
b. To estimate the proportion of customers who have only laundry and no dry cleaning.
c. To estimate the proportion of residents in the same zip code who spend more than $20 a month on dry cleaning.
d. To estimate the proportion of its seven employees who think it is too hot inside the building.

2.27 What would be the difference in student responses to the two questions shown?

Version 1: I would prefer that tuition be reduced.

Version 2: Cuts in tuition are a good idea even if some classes are canceled.

2.28 What problems are evident in the wording of these two questions?

What is your race?	What is your religious preference?
❑ White	❑ Christian
❑ Black	❑ Jewish

Mini Case 2.5

Roles of Colleges

A survey of public opinion on the role of colleges was conducted by *The Chronicle of Higher Education*. Results of the survey showed that 77 percent of respondents agreed it was highly important that colleges prepare its undergraduate students for a career. The percentage of respondents who agreed it was highly important for colleges to prepare students to be responsible citizens was slightly lower, at 67 percent. The survey utilized 1,000 telephone interviews of 20 minutes each, using a random selection of men and women aged 25 through 65. It was conducted February 25, 2004. The survey was administered by TMR Inc. of Broomall, Pennsylvania. Data were collected and analyzed by GDA Integrated Services, a market research firm in Old Saybrook, Connecticut.

The Likert-type scale labels are weighted toward the positive, which is common when the survey items (roles for colleges in this case) are assumed to be potentially important and there is little likelihood of a strong negative response. Respondents were also asked for demographic information. Fifty-eight percent were women and 42 percent were men, coming from all states except Alaska and Hawaii. Eleven percent were African American (similar to the national average), but only 6 percent were Hispanic (about 8 percent below the national average). The underrepresentation of Hispanics was due to language barriers, illustrating one difficulty faced by surveys. However, the respondents' incomes, religious affiliations, and political views were similar to the general U.S. population. The random selection method was not specified. Note that firms that specialize in survey sampling generally have access to commercial lists and use their own proprietary methods.

CHAPTER SUMMARY

A **data set** consists of all the values of all the variables we have chosen to observe. It often is an array with n rows and m columns. Data sets may be **univariate** (one variable), **bivariate** (two variables), or **multivariate** (three or more variables). There are two basic data types: **categorical data** (categories that are described by labels) or **numerical** (meaningful numbers). Numerical data are **discrete** if the values are integers or can be counted or **continuous** if any interval can contain more data values. **Nominal** measurements are names, **ordinal** measurements are ranks, **interval** measurements have meaningful distances between data values, and **ratio** measurements have meaningful ratios and a zero reference point. **Time series** data are observations measured at n different points in time or over sequential time intervals, while **cross-sectional** data are observations among n entities such as individuals, firms, or geographic regions. Among **random samples, simple random** samples pick items from a list using random numbers, **systematic** samples take every kth item, **cluster** samples select geographic regions, and **stratified** samples take into account known population proportions. **Non-random** samples include convenience or judgment samples, gaining time but sacrificing randomness. **Focus groups** give in-depth information. **Survey design** requires attention to question **wording** and **scale definitions. Survey techniques** (mail, telephone, interview, web, direct observation) depend on time, budget, and the nature of the questions and are subject to various sources of error.

KEY TERMS

binary variable
bivariate data sets
categorical data
census
cluster sample
coding
continuous data
convenience sampling
coverage error
cross-sectional data
data
data set
discrete data
focus group
interval data
interviewer error
judgment sampling
Likert scale
measurement error
multivariate data sets
nominal data
non-random sampling
nonresponse bias
numerical data
observation
ordinal data
parameter
population
random numbers
random sampling
ratio data
response error
sample
sampling error
sampling frame
sampling with replacement

sampling without replacement
selection bias
simple random sample
statistics
stratified sampling
systematic sampling
target population
time series data
univariate data sets
variable

CHAPTER REVIEW

1. Define (a) data, (b) data set, (c) observation, and (d) variable.
2. How do business data differ from scientific experimental data?
3. Distinguish (a) univariate, bivariate, and multivariate data; (b) discrete and continuous data; (c) numerical and categorical data.
4. Define the four measurement levels and give an example of each.
5. Explain the difference between cross-sectional data and time series data.
6. (a) List three reasons why a census might be preferred to a sample. (b) List three reasons why a sample might be preferred to a census.
7. (a) What is the difference between a parameter and a statistic? (b) What is a target population?
8. (a) List four methods of random sampling. (b) List two methods of non-random sampling. (c) Why would we ever use non-random sampling? (d) Why is sampling usually done without replacement?
9. List five (a) steps in a survey, (b) issues in survey design, (c) survey types, (d) question scale types, and (e) sources of error in surveys.
10. List advantages and disadvantages of different types of surveys.

CHAPTER EXERCISES

connect

DATA TYPES

2.29 Which type of data (categorical, discrete numerical, continuous numerical) is each of the following variables?

a. Age of a randomly chosen tennis player in the Wimbledon tennis tournament.
b. Nationality of a randomly chosen tennis player in the Wimbledon tennis tournament.
c. Number of double faults in a randomly chosen tennis game at Wimbledon.

2.30 Which type of data (categorical, discrete numerical, continuous numerical) is each of the following variables?

a. Number of spectators at a randomly chosen Wimbledon tennis match.
b. Water consumption (liters) by a randomly chosen Wimbledon player during a match.
c. Gender of a randomly chosen tennis player in the Wimbledon tennis tournament.

2.31 Which measurement level (nominal, ordinal, interval, ratio) is each of the following variables?

a. A customer's ranking of five new hybrid vehicles.
b. Noise level 100 meters from the Dan Ryan Expressway at a randomly chosen moment.
c. Number of occupants in a randomly chosen commuter vehicle on the San Diego Freeway.

2.32 Which measurement level (nominal, ordinal, interval, ratio) is each of the following variables?

a. Number of annual office visits by a particular Medicare subscriber.
b. Daily caffeine consumption by a six-year-old child.
c. Type of vehicle driven by a college student.

2.33 Below are five questions from a survey of MBA students. Answers were written in the blank at the left of each question. For each question, state the data type (categorical, discrete numerical, or continuous numerical) and measurement level (nominal, ordinal, interval, ratio). Explain your reasoning. If there is doubt, discuss the alternatives.

_____ Q1 What is your gender? (Male = 0, Female = 1)
_____ Q2 What is your approximate undergraduate college GPA? (1.0 to 4.0)
_____ Q3 About how many hours per week do you expect to work at an outside job this semester?
_____ Q4 What do you think is the ideal number of children for a married couple?
_____ Q5 On a 1 to 5 scale, which best describes your parents?
1 = Mother clearly dominant ↔ 5 = Father clearly dominant

2.34 Below are five questions from a survey of MBA students. Answers were written in the blank at the left of each question. For each question, state the data type (categorical, discrete numerical, or continuous numerical) and measurement level (nominal, ordinal, interval, ratio). Explain your reasoning. If there is doubt, discuss the alternatives.

_____	Q6	On a 1 to 5 scale, assess the current job market for your undergraduate major. 1 = Very bad ↔ 5 = Very good
_____	Q7	During the last month, how many times has your schedule been disrupted by car trouble?
_____	Q8	About how many years of college does the more-educated one of your parents have? (years)
_____	Q9	During the last year, how many traffic tickets (excluding parking) have you received?
_____	Q10	Which political orientation most nearly fits you? (1 = Liberal, 2 = Middle-of-Road, 3 = Conservative)

2.35 Below are five questions from a survey of MBA students. Answers were written in the blank at the left of each question. For each question, state the data type (categorical, discrete numerical, or continuous numerical) and measurement level (nominal, ordinal, interval, ratio). Explain your reasoning. If there is doubt, discuss the alternatives.

_____	Q11	What is the age of the car you usually drive? (years)
_____	Q12	About how many times in the past year did you attend formal religious services?
_____	Q13	How often do you read a daily newspaper? (0 = Never, 1 = Occasionally, 2 = Regularly)
_____	Q14	Can you conduct simple transactions in a language other than English? (0 = No, 1 = Yes)
_____	Q15	How often do you exercise (aerobics, running, etc)? (0 = Not at All, 1 = Sometimes, 2 = Regularly)

2.36 Identify the following data as either time series or cross-sectional.

a. The 2014 CEO compensation of the 500 largest U.S. companies.
b. The annual compensation for the CEO of Coca-Cola Enterprises from 2000 to 2014.
c. The weekly revenue for a Noodles & Company restaurant for the 52 weeks in 2014.
d. The number of skiers on the mountain on Christmas Day 2014 at each of the ski mountains owned by Vail Resorts.

2.37 Identify the following data as either time series or cross-sectional.

a. The number of rooms booked each night for the month of January 2014 at a Vail Resorts hotel.
b. The amount spent on books at the start of this semester by each student in your statistics class.
c. The number of Caesar salads sold for the week of April 19, 2014, at each Noodles & Company restaurant.
d. The stock price of Coca-Cola Enterprises on May 1st for each of the last 10 years.

SAMPLING METHODS

2.38 Would you use a sample or a census to measure each of the following? Why? If you are uncertain, explain the issues.

a. The number of cans of Campbell's soup on your local supermarket's shelf today at 6:00 p.m.
b. The proportion of soup sales last week in Boston that was sold under the Campbell's brand.
c. The proportion of Campbell's brand soup cans in your family's pantry.

2.39 Would you use a sample or census to measure each of the following?

a. The number of workers currently employed by Campbell Soup Company.
b. The average price of a can of Campbell's Cream of Mushroom soup.
c. The total earnings of workers employed by Campbell Soup Company last year.

2.40 Is each of the following a parameter or a statistic? If you are uncertain, explain the issues.

a. The number of cans of Campbell's soup sold last week at your local supermarket.
b. The proportion of all soup in the United States that was sold under the Campbell's brand last year.
c. The proportion of Campbell's brand soup cans in the family pantries of 10 students.

2.41 Is each of the following a parameter or statistic?

a. The number of visits to a pediatrician's office last week.
b. The number of copies of John Grisham's most recent novel sold to date.
c. The total revenue realized from sales of John Grisham's most recent novel.

2.42 Recently, researchers estimated that 76.8 percent of global e-mail traffic was spam. Could a census be used to update this estimate? Why or why not?

2.43 A certain health maintenance organization (HMO) is studying its daily office routine. They collect information on three variables: the number of patients who visit during a day, the patient's complaint, and the waiting time until each patient sees a doctor. (a) Which variable is categorical? (b) Identify the two quantitative variables and state whether they are discrete or continuous.

2.44 There are 327 official ports of entry in the United States. The Department of Homeland Security selects 15 ports of entry at random to be audited for compliance with screening procedures of incoming travelers through the primary and secondary vehicle and pedestrian lanes. What kind of sample is this (simple random, systematic, stratified, cluster)?

2.45 The IRS estimates that the average taxpayer spent 3.7 hours preparing Form 1040 to file a tax return. Could a census be used to update this estimate for the most recent tax year? Why or why not?

2.46 The General Accounting Office conducted random testing of retail gasoline pumps in Michigan, Missouri, Oregon, and Tennessee. The study concluded that 49 percent of gasoline pumps nationwide are mislabeled by more than one-half of an octane point. What kind of sampling technique was most likely to have been used in this study?

2.47 Arsenic (a naturally occurring, poisonous metal) in home water wells is a common threat. (a) What sampling method would you use to estimate the arsenic levels in wells in a rural county to see whether the samples violate the EPA limit of 10 parts per billion (ppb)? (b) Is a census possible?

2.48 Would you expect Starbucks to use a sample or census to measure each of the following? Explain.

a. The percentage of repeat customers at a certain Starbucks on Saturday mornings.
b. The number of chai tea latte orders last Saturday at a certain Starbucks.
c. The average temperature of Starbucks coffee served on Saturday mornings.
d. The revenue from coffee sales as a percentage of Starbucks' total revenue last year.

2.49 Would you expect Noodles & Company to use a sample or census to measure each of the following? Explain.

a. The annual average weekly revenue of each Noodles restaurant.
b. The average number of weekly lunch visits by customers.
c. The customer satisfaction rating of a new dessert.
d. The number of weeks in a year that a restaurant sells more bottled beverages than fountain drinks.

2.50 A financial magazine publishes an annual list of major stock funds. Last year, the list contained 1,699 funds. What method would you recommend to obtain a sample of 20 stock funds to estimate the 10-year percent return?

2.51 Examine each of the following statistics. Which sampling method was most likely to have been used (simple random, systematic, stratified, cluster)?

a. A survey showed that 30 percent of U.S. businesses have fired an employee for inappropriate web surfing, such as gambling, watching porn, or shopping.
b. Surveyed doctors report that 59 percent of patients do not follow their prescribed treatment.
c. The Internal Revenue Service reports that, based on a sample of individual taxpayers, 80 percent of those who failed to pay what they owed did so through honest errors or misinterpretation of the tax code.
d. In Spain, per capita consumption of cigarettes is 2,274 compared with 1,230 in the United States.

2.52 The National Claims History (NCH) contains records for 999,645 Medicare patients who were discharged from acute care hospitals in October 2008. The Department of Health and Human Services performed a detailed audit of adverse medical events on a random sample of 780 drawn at random without replacement by assigning a random number to each patient on the list and then choosing random integers between 1 and 999,645. (a) What kind of sample is this (random, systematic, stratified, cluster)? (b) Is this population effectively infinite?

2.53 Prior to starting a recycling program, a city decides to measure the quantity of garbage produced by single-family homes in various neighborhoods. This experiment will require weighing garbage on the day it is set out. (a) What sampling method would you recommend, and why? (b) What would be a potential source of sampling error?

2.54 A university wanted to survey alumni about their interest in lifelong learning classes. They mailed questionnaires to a random sample of 600 alumni from their database of over 30,000 recent graduates. Would you consider this population to be effectively infinite?

2.55 To protect baby scallops and ensure the survival of the species, the U.S. Fisheries and Wildlife Service requires that an average scallop must weigh at least 1/36 pound. The harbormaster at a Massachusetts port randomly selected 18 bags of scallops from 11,000 bags on an arriving vessel. From each bag, agents took a large scoop of scallops, separated and weighed the meat, and divided by the number of scallops in the scoop, finding a mean weight of 1/39 pound. (a) Would the population of 11,000 bags be considered effectively infinite in this case? (b) Which value represents a sample statistic: 1/36 or 1/39? (Data are from *Interfaces* 25, no. 2 [March–April 1995], p. 18.)

2.56 A marketing research group wanted to collect information from existing and potential customers on the appeal of a new product. They sent out surveys to a random sample of 1,200 people from their database of over 25,000 current and potential customers. Would you consider this population to be effectively infinite?

2.57 Households can sign up for a telemarketing "no-call list." How might households who sign up differ from those who don't? What biases might this create for telemarketers promoting (a) financial planning services, (b) carpet cleaning services, and (c) vacation travel packages?

SURVEYS AND SCALES

2.58 Suggest response check boxes for these questions. In each case, what difficulties do you encounter as you try to think of appropriate check boxes?

a. Where are you employed?
b. What is the biggest issue facing the next U.S. president?
c. Are you happy?

2.59 Suggest both a Likert scale question and a response scale to measure the following:

a. A student's rating of a particular statistics professor.
b. A voter's satisfaction with the president's economic policy.
c. An HMO patient's perception of waiting time to see a doctor.

2.60 What level of measurement (nominal, ordinal, interval, ratio) is appropriate for the movie rating system that you see in *TV Guide* (☆, ☆☆, ☆☆☆, ☆☆☆☆)? Explain your reasoning.

2.61 Insurance companies are rated by several rating agencies. The Fitch 20-point scale is AAA, AA+, AA, AA−, A+, A, A−, BBB+, BBB, BBB−, BB+, BB, BB−, B+, B, B−, CCC+, CCC, CCC−, DD. (a) What level of measurement does this scale use? (b) To assume that the scale uses interval measurements, what assumption is required? (Scales are from *Weiss Ratings Guide to HMOs and Health Insurers,* Summer 2003, p. 15.)

2.62 A tabletop survey by a restaurant asked the question shown below. (a) What kind of response scale is this? (b) Suggest an alternative response scale that would be more sensitive to differences in opinion. (c) Suggest possible sources of bias in this type of survey.

Were the food and beverage presentations appealing?

❑ Yes ❑ No

MINI-PROJECTS

2.63 Give *two* original examples of (a) discrete data and (b) continuous data. In each example, explain and identify any ambiguities that might exist. *Hint:* Consider data describing your own life (e.g., your sports performance or financial or academic data). You need *not* list all the data, merely describe them and show a few typical data values.

2.64 Give *two* original examples of (a) time series data and (b) cross-sectional data. *Hint:* Do not restrict yourself to published data. You need *not* list all the data, merely describe them and show a few typical data values.

2.65 Devise a practical sampling method to collect data to estimate each of the following parameters.

a. Percentage of an HMO's patients who make more than five office visits per year.
b. Noise level (measured in decibels) in neighborhoods 100 meters from a certain freeway.
c. Percentage of bank mortgages issued to first-time borrowers last year.

2.66 Devise a practical sampling method to collect data to estimate each of the following parameters.

a. Percentage of peanuts in a can of Planter's Mixed Nuts.
b. Average price of gasoline in your area.
c. Average flight departure delay for Southwest Airlines in Salt Lake City.

2.67 Below are 64 names of employees at NilCo. Colors denote different departments (finance, marketing, purchasing, engineering). Sample eight names from the display shown by using (a) simple random sampling, (b) systematic sampling, and (c) cluster sampling. Try to ensure that every name has an equal chance of being picked. Which sampling method seems most appropriate? **PickEight**

Floyd	Sid	LaDonna	Tom	Mabel	Nicholas	Bonnie	Deepak
Nathan	Ginnie	Mario	Claudia	Dmitri	Kevin	Blythe	Dave
Lou	Tim	Peter	Jean	Mike	Jeremy	Chad	Doug
Loretta	Erik	Jackie	Juanita	Molly	Carl	Buck	Janet
Anne	Joel	Moira	Marnie	Ted	Greg	Duane	Amanda
Don	Gadis	Balaji	Al	Takisha	Dan	Ryan	Sam
Graham	Scott	Lorin	Vince	Jody	Brian	Tania	Ralph
Bernie	Karen	Ed	Liz	Erika	Marge	Gene	Pam

2.68 From the display below pick five cards (without replacement) by using random numbers. Explain your method. Why would the other sampling methods not work well in this case?

A ♠	A ♥	A ♣	A ♦
K ♠	K ♥	K ♣	K ♦
Q ♠	Q ♥	Q ♣	Q ♦
J ♠	J ♥	J ♣	J ♦
10 ♠	10 ♥	10 ♣	10 ♦
9 ♠	9 ♥	9 ♣	9 ♦
8 ♠	8 ♥	8 ♣	8 ♦
7 ♠	7 ♥	7 ♣	7 ♦
6 ♠	6 ♥	6 ♣	6 ♦
5 ♠	5 ♥	5 ♣	5 ♦
4 ♠	4 ♥	4 ♣	4 ♦
3 ♠	3 ♥	3 ♣	3 ♦
2 ♠	2 ♥	2 ♣	2 ♦

2.69 Treating this textbook as a population, select a sample of 10 pages at random by using (a) simple random sampling, (b) systematic sampling, (c) cluster sampling, and (d) judgment sampling. Explain your methodology carefully in each case. (e) Which method would you recommend to estimate the mean number of formulas per page? Why not the others?

2.70 Photocopy the exhibit below (omit these instructions) and show it to a friend or classmate. Ask him/her to choose a number at random and write it on a piece of paper. Collect the paper. Repeat for *at least* 20 friends/classmates. Tabulate the results. Were all the numbers chosen equally often? If not, which were favored or avoided? Why? *Hint:* Review section 2.6. **PickOne**

0	11	17	22
8	36	14	18
19	28	6	41
12	3	5	0

2.71 Ask each of 20 friends or classmates to choose a whole number between 1 and 5. Tabulate the results. Do the results seem random? If not, can you think of any reasons?

2.72 You can test Excel's algorithm for selecting random integers with a simple experiment. Enter =RANDBETWEEN(1,2) into cell A1 and then copy it to cells A1:E20. This creates a data block of 100 cells containing either a one or a two. In cell G1 type =COUNTIF(A1:E20,"=1") and in cell G2 type =COUNTIF(A1:E20,"=2"). Highlight cells G1 and G2 and create a column chart. Click on the vertical axis scale and set the lower limit to 0 and upper limit to 100. You will see something like the example shown below. Then hold down the F9 key and observe the chart. Are you convinced that, on average, you are getting about 50 ones and 50 twos? *Ambitious Students:* Generalize this experiment to integers 1 through 5. **RandBetween**

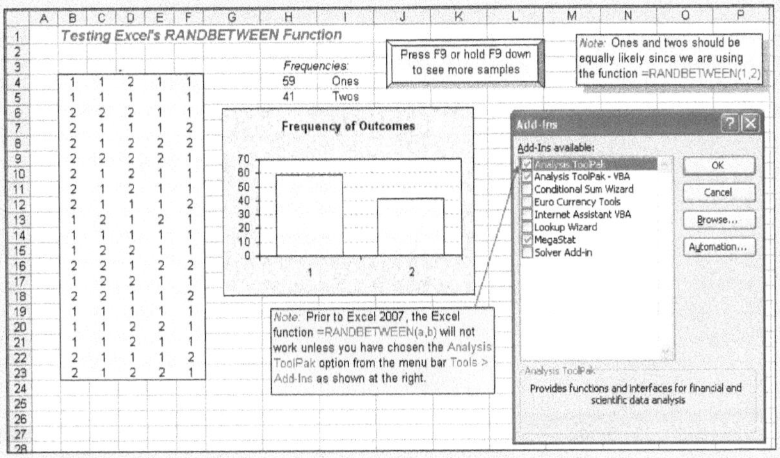

RELATED READING

Guides to Data Sources

Butler, F. Patrick. *Business Research Sources: A Reference Navigator.* http://www.businessresearchsources.com/business-school/.

Clayton, Gary E.; and Martin Giesbrecht. *A Guide to Everyday Economic Statistics.* 7th ed. McGraw-Hill, 2009.

Sampling and Surveys

Cooper, Donald R.; and Pamela S. Schindler. *Business Research Methods.* 11th ed. McGraw-Hill, 2011.

Fowler, Floyd J. *Survey Research Methods.* 4th ed. Sage, 2009.

Groves, Robert M., et al. *Survey Methodology.* 2nd ed. Wiley, 2009.

Levy, Paul S.; and Stanley Lemeshow. *Sampling of Populations.* 4th ed. Wiley, 2008.

Lyberg, Lars; and Paul Blemer. *Introduction to Survey Quality.* Wiley Europe, 2003.

Mathieson, Kieran; and David P. Doane. "Using Fine-Grained Likert Scales in Web Surveys." *Alliance Journal of Business Research* 1, no. 1 (2006), pp. 27–34.

Scheaffer, Richard L.; William Mendenhall; and R. Lyman Ott. *Elementary Survey Sampling.* 7th ed. Brooks/Cole, 2012.

Thompson, Steven K. *Sampling.* 3rd ed. Wiley, 2012.

CHAPTER 2 More Learning Resources

connect™

You can access these *LearningStats* demonstrations through McGraw-Hill's Connect® to help you understand random sampling.

Topic	*LearningStats Demonstrations*
Sampling	Sampling Methods Who Gets Picked? Randomizing a File Pick a Card Excel's RANDBETWEEN Function
Data sources	Web Data Sources Surveys Sampling Plans

Key: = Excel = PowerPoint

Chapter 3. Describing Data Visually

CHAPTER 3 Describing Data Visually

CHAPTER CONTENTS

CHAPTER LEARNING OBJECTIVES

LO

When you finish this chapter you should be able to

LO 3-1 Make a stem-and-leaf or dot plot.

LO 3-2 Create a frequency distribution for a data set.

LO 3-3 Make a histogram with appropriate bins.

LO 3-4 Identify skewness, modal classes, and outliers in a histogram.

LO 3-5 Make an effective line chart.

LO 3-6 Make an effective column chart or bar chart.

LO 3-7 Make an effective pie chart.

LO 3-8 Make and interpret a scatter plot.

LO 3-9 Make simple tables and pivot tables.

LO 3-10 Recognize deceptive graphing techniques.

3.1 STEM-AND-LEAF DISPLAYS AND DOT PLOTS

LO 3-1

Make a stem-and-leaf or dot plot.

Managers need information that can help them identify trends and adjust to changing conditions. But it is hard to assimilate piles of raw data. How can a business analyst convert raw data into useful information? Statistics offers many methods that can help organize, explore, and summarize data in a succinct way. The methods may be *visual* (charts and graphs) or *numerical* (statistics or tables). In this chapter, you will see how visual displays can provide insight into the characteristics of a data set *without* using mathematics. We begin with a set of n observations $x_1, x_2, \ldots, x_n$ on one variable (univariate data). Such data can be discussed in terms of three characteristics: **center**, **variability**, and **shape**. Table 3.1 summarizes these characteristics as *questions* that we will be asking about the data.

TABLE 3.1

Characteristics of Univariate Data

Characteristic	*Interpretation*
Measurement	What are the units of measurement? Are the data integer or continuous? Any missing observations? Any concerns with accuracy or sampling methods?
Center	Where are the data values concentrated? What seem to be typical or middle data values?
Variability	How much dispersion is there in the data? How spread out are the data values? Are there unusual values?
Shape	Are the data values distributed symmetrically? Skewed? Sharply peaked? Flat? Bimodal?

EXAMPLE 3.1

Price/Earnings Ratios

Price/earnings (P/E) ratios—current stock price divided by earnings per share in the last 12 months—show how much an investor is willing to pay for a stock based on the stock's earnings. P/E ratios are also used to determine how optimistic the market is for a stock's growth potential. Investors may be willing to pay more for a lower-earning stock than a higher-earning stock if they see potential for growth. Table 3.2 shows P/E ratios for a random sample of companies (n = 44) from Standard & Poor's 500 index. We are interested in learning how the P/E ratios of the companies in the S&P 500 compare to each other and what the distribution of P/E ratios looks like. Visual displays can help us describe and summarize the main characteristics of this sample.

TABLE 3.2 **P/E Ratios for 44 Companies** PERatios

Company	P/E Ratio	Company	P/E Ratio	Company	P/E Ratio
Amer Tower Corp A	59	FMC Corporation	20	NetApp	37
Analog Devices Inc	16	Gap (The)	12	Occidental Petroleum	19
Applied Materials Inc	20	Hartford Finan Svc Gp	11	O'Reilly Automotive	22
Best Buy Co Inc	10	Hess Corporation	7	PepsiCo Inc	16
Big Lots Inc	11	Hospira Inc	24	PG&E Corp	16
Carefusion Corp	38	Intel Corp	11	PPL Corp	14
Coventry Health Care Inc	10	Invesco Ltd	27	Reynolds Amer Inc	19
Cummins Inc	23	Johnson Controls	17	Roper Industries	26
Dell Inc	13	King Pharmaceuticals	42	Starbucks Corp	26
Dentsply International	18	Kroger Co	13	Sunoco Inc	28
Donnelley (RR) & Sons	31	Macy's Inc	17	Titanium Metals Corp	50
Eastman Chemical	16	Mattel Inc	14	United Health Grp Inc	9
Entergy Corp	10	Medco Health Sols Inc	21	Ventas Inc	37
Exelon Corp	10	MetroPCS Comm Inc	21	Walmart Stores	13
Fiserv Inc	18	Murphy Oil	15		

Source: www.finance.yahoo.com, accessed December 30, 2010. Each of the 500 companies on an alphabetical list was assigned a random number using Excel's =RAND() function. Companies were then sorted on the =RAND() column, and the first 44 companies on the sorted list were chosen as a random sample.

Preliminary Assessment

Before calculating any statistics or drawing any graphs, it is a good idea to *look at the data* and try to visualize how it was collected. Because the companies in the S&P 500 index are publicly traded, they are required to publish verified financial information, so the accuracy of the data is not an issue. Since the intent of the analysis is to study the S&P 500 companies at a *point in time,* these are *cross-sectional* data. (Financial analysts also study time series data on P/E ratios, which vary daily as stock prices change.) Although rounded to integers, the measurements are continuous. For example, a stock price of $43.22 divided by earnings per share of $2.17 gives a P/E ratio (43.22)/(2.17) = 19.92, which would be rounded to 20 for convenience. Since there is a true zero, we can speak meaningfully of ratios and can perform any standard mathematical operations. Because the analysis is based on a sample (not a census), we must allow for *sampling error,* that is, the possibility that our sample is not representative of the population of all 500 S&P 500 firms, due to the nature of random sampling.

As a first step, it is helpful to sort the data. This is a visual display, although a very simple one. From the sorted data, we can see the range, the frequency of occurrence for each data value, and the data values that lie near the middle and ends.

44 Sorted Price/Earnings Ratios

7	9	10	10	10	10	11	11	11	12	13
13	13	14	14	15	16	16	16	16	17	17
18	18	19	19	20	20	21	21	22	23	24
26	26	27	28	31	37	37	38	42	50	59

When the number of observations is large, a sorted list of data values is difficult to analyze. Further, a simple list of numbers may not reveal very much about center, variability, and shape. To see broader patterns in the data, analysts often prefer a *visual display* of the data.

The type of graph you use to display your data is dependent on the type of data you have. Some charts are better suited for quantitative data, while others are better for displaying categorical data. This chapter explains several basic types of charts, offers guidelines on when to use them, advises you how to make them effective, and warns of ways that charts can be deceptive.

Stem-and-Leaf Display

One simple way to visualize small data sets is a **stem-and-leaf plot**. The stem-and-leaf plot is a tool of *exploratory data analysis* (EDA) that seeks to reveal essential data features in an intuitive way. A stem-and-leaf plot is basically a frequency tally, except that we use digits instead of tally marks. For two-digit or three-digit integer data, the *stem* is the tens digit of the data, and the *leaf* is the ones digit. For the 44 P/E ratios, the stem-and-leaf plot would be:

Frequency	Stem	Leaf
2	0	7 9
24	1	0 0 0 0 1 1 1 2 3 3 3 4 4 5 6 6 6 6 7 7 8 8 9 9
11	2	0 0 1 1 2 3 4 6 6 7 8
4	3	1 7 7 8
1	4	2
2	5	0 9
44		

For example, the data values in the fourth stem are 31, 37, 37, 38. We always use equally spaced stems (even if some stems are empty). The stem-and-leaf can reveal *central tendency* (24 of the 44 P/E ratios were in the 10–19 stem) as well as *dispersion* (the range is from 7 to 59). In this illustration, the leaf digits have been sorted, although this is not necessary. The stem-and-leaf has the advantage that we can retrieve the raw data by concatenating a *stem digit* with each of its *leaf digits*. For example, the last stem has data values 50 and 59.

A stem-and-leaf plot works well for small samples of integer data with a limited range but becomes awkward when you have decimal data (e.g., $60.39) or multidigit data (e.g., $3,857). In such cases, it is necessary to round the data to make the display "work." Although the stem-and-leaf plot is rarely seen in presentations of business data, it is a useful tool for a quick tabulation of small data sets.

Dot Plots

A **dot plot** is another simple graphical display of n individual values of numerical data. The basic steps in making a dot plot are to (1) make a scale that covers the data range, (2) mark axis demarcations and label them, and (3) plot each data value as a dot above the scale at its approximate location. If more than one data value lies at approximately the same X-axis location, the dots are piled up vertically. Figure 3.1 shows a dot plot for 44 P/E ratios.

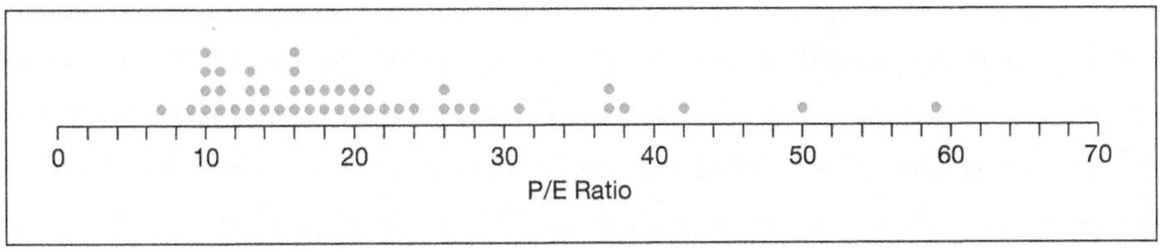

FIGURE 3.1

Dot Plot of 44 P/E Ratios

PERatios

Dot plots are an attractive tool for data exploration because they are easy to understand. A dot plot shows *variability* by displaying the range of the data. It shows the *center* by revealing where the data values tend to cluster and where the midpoint lies. A dot plot can also reveal some things about the *shape* of the distribution if the sample is large enough. For the P/E ratios, the dot plot in Figure 3.1 shows that:

- The range is from 7 to 59.
- All but a few data values lie between 10 and 25.
- A typical "middle" data value would be around 17 or 18.
- The data are not symmetric due to a few large P/E ratios.

You can make a dot plot yourself (if the sample is small) using a straightedge and a pencil. Excel doesn't offer dot plots, but you can get them from most software packages. Figure 3.2 shows menus from MegaStat and MINITAB with marked options to choose a dot plot or stem-and-leaf plot.

FIGURE 3.2

MegaStat and MINITAB Menus for Dot Plot and Stem-and-Leaf Plot

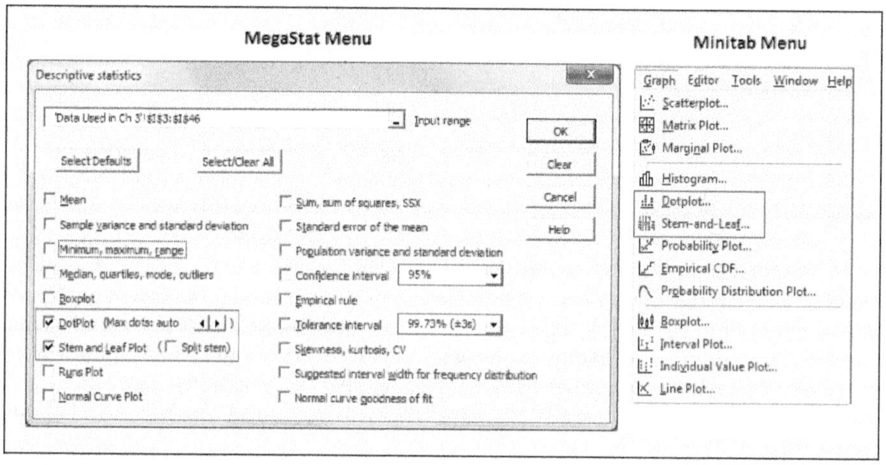

Comparing Groups

A **stacked dot plot** can be used to compare two or more groups. For example, Figure 3.3 shows a stacked dot plot for median home prices for 150 U.S. cities in four different regions. A common *X*-axis scale is used for all four dot plots. This stacked dot plot shows the range of data values and gives an idea of typical home values within each region. Could a table show this amount of information as clearly?

FIGURE 3.3

Stacked Dot Plot For Home Prices (n = 150 cities)

HomePrices

Source: www.realtor.org

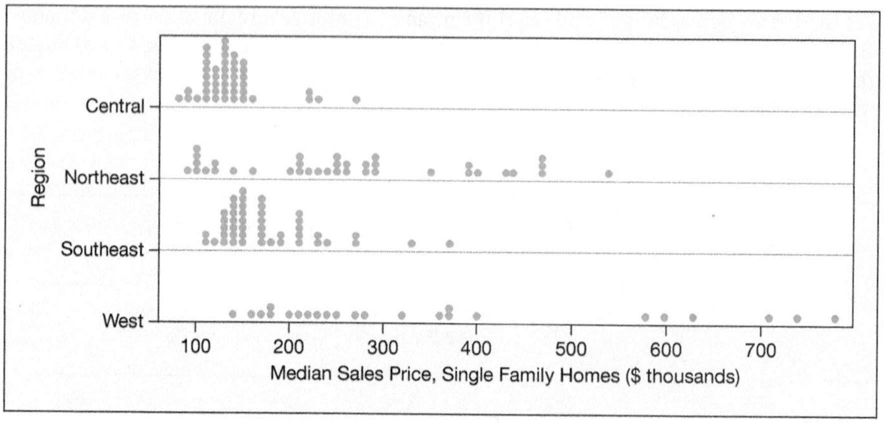

While they are easy to understand, dot plots have limitations. They don't reveal very much information about the data set's shape when the sample is small, and they become awkward when the sample is large (what if you have 100 dots at the same point?) or when you have decimal data. The next section of this textbook explains how to use Excel to create histograms and other visual displays that work for any sample size.

You may download data files indicated by the symbol followed by a file name (e.g., **Housing**) from the problems in McGraw-Hill's Connect® or through your instructor. At the end of each chapter, there are additional learning resources that expand on topics in the textbook (e.g., Excel demonstrations).

SECTION EXERCISES

connect

3.1 (a) Make a stem-and-leaf plot for these 24 observations on the number of customers who used a downtown CitiBank ATM during the noon hour on 24 consecutive workdays. (b) Make a dot plot of the ATM data. (c) Describe these two displays. (*Hint:* Refer to center, variability, and shape.) **CitiBank**

39	32	21	26	19	27	32	25
18	26	34	18	31	35	21	33
33	9	16	32	35	42	15	24

3.2 (a) Make a stem-and-leaf plot for the number of defects per 100 vehicles for these 32 brands. (b) Make a dot plot of the defects data. (c) Describe these two displays. (*Hint*: Refer to center, variability, and shape.) **JDPower**

Defects per 100 Vehicles (alphabetical by brand)

Brand	*Defects*	*Brand*	*Defects*	*Brand*	*Defects*
Acura	86	Hyundai	102	Mini	133
Audi	111	Infiniti	107	Mitsubishi	146
BMW	113	Jaguar	130	Nissan	111
Buick	114	Jeep	129	Porsche	83
Cadillac	111	Kia	126	Ram	110
Chevrolet	111	Land Rover	170	Scion	114
Chrysler	122	Lexus	88	Subaru	121
Dodge	130	Lincoln	106	Toyota	117
Ford	93	Mazda	114	Volkswagen	135
GMC	126	Mercedes-Benz	87	Volvo	109
Honda	95	Mercury	113		

Source: J. D. Power and Associates 2010 Initial Quality Study™.

3.3 Sarah and Bob share a 1,000-minute cell phone calling plan. (a) Make a *stacked dot plot* to compare the lengths of cell phone calls by Sarah and Bob during the last week. (b) Describe what the dot plots tell you. **PhoneCalls**

Sarah's calls: 1, 1, 1, 1, 2, 3, 3, 3, 5, 5, 6, 6, 7, 8, 8, 12, 14, 14, 22, 23, 29, 33, 38, 45, 66

Bob's calls: 5, 8, 9, 14, 17, 21, 23, 23, 24, 26, 27, 27, 28, 29, 31, 33, 35, 39, 41

Mini Case 3.1

U.S. Business Cycles

Although many businesses anticipated the recession that followed the housing price bubble of the early 2000s, they needed to anticipate its probable length to form strategies for debt management and future product releases. Fortunately, good historical data are available from the National Bureau of Economic Research, which keeps track of business cycles. The length of a contraction is measured from the peak of the previous expansion to the beginning of the next expansion based on the real gross domestic product (GDP). Table 3.3 shows the durations, in months, of 33 U.S. recessions.

TABLE 3.3 **U.S. Business Contractions, 1857–2013 (n = 33)** Recessions

Peak	*Trough*	*Months*	*Peak*	*Trough*	*Months*
Jun 1857	Dec 1858	18	May 1923	Jul 1924	14
Oct 1860	Jun 1861	8	Oct 1926	Nov 1927	13
Apr 1865	Dec 1867	32	Aug 1929	Mar 1933	43
Jun 1869	Dec 1870	18	May 1937	Jun 1938	13
Oct 1873	Mar 1879	65	Feb 1945	Oct 1945	8
Mar 1882	May 1885	38	Nov 1948	Oct 1949	11
Mar 1887	Apr 1888	13	Jul 1953	May 1954	10
Jul 1890	May 1891	10	Aug 1957	Apr 1958	8
Jan 1893	Jun 1894	17	Apr 1960	Feb 1961	10
Dec 1895	Jun 1897	18	Dec 1969	Nov 1970	11
Jun 1899	Dec 1900	18	Nov 1973	Mar 1975	16
Sep 1902	Aug 1904	23	Jan 1980	Jul 1980	6
May 1907	Jun 1908	13	Jul 1981	Nov 1982	16
Jan 1910	Jan 1912	24	Jul 1990	Mar 1991	8
Jan 1913	Deç 1914	23	Mar 2001	Nov 2001	8
Aug 1918	Mar 1919	7	Dec 2007	Jun 2009	18
Jan 1920	Jul 1921	18			

Source: U.S. Business Contractions found at www.nber.org.

From the dot plot in Figure 3.4, we see that the 65-month contraction (1873–1879) was quite unusual, although four recessions did exceed 30 months. Most recessions have lasted less than 20 months. Only 7 of 33 lasted less than 10 months. The 8-month 2001 recession was among the shortest. Although the recession that began in December 2007 had unique features (major financial crisis, steep rise in unemployment, sluggish recovery), its duration (18 months) was not extreme.

FIGURE 3.4 **Dot Plot of Business Cycle Duration (n = 33)**

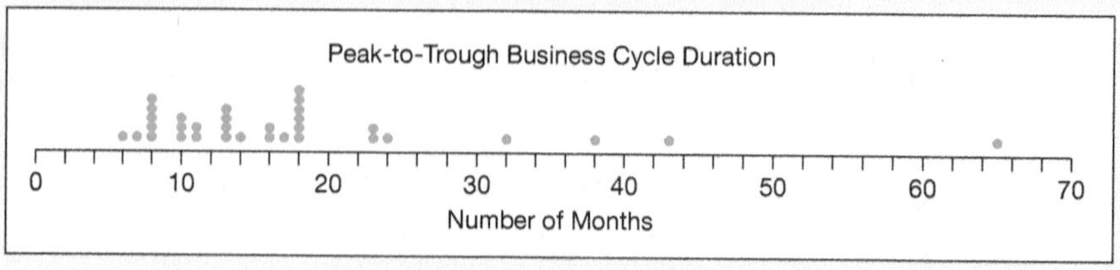

The table supplies information that the dot plot cannot. For example, during the 1930s there were actually *two* major contractions (43 months from 1929 to 1933, 13 months from 1937 to 1938), which is one reason why that period seemed so terrible to those who lived through it. The Great Depression of the 1930s was so named because it lasted a long time and the economic decline was deeper than in most recessions.

3.2 FREQUENCY DISTRIBUTIONS AND HISTOGRAMS

Frequency Distributions

A **frequency distribution** is a table formed by classifying n data values into k classes called *bins* (we adopt this terminology from Excel). The *bin limits* define the values to be included in each bin. Usually, all the bin widths are the same. The table shows the *frequency* of data values within each bin. Frequencies can also be expressed as *relative frequencies* or *percentages* of the total number of observations.

LO 3-2

Create a frequency distribution for a data set.

LO 3-3

Make a histogram with appropriate bins.

LO 3-4

Identify skewness, modal classes, and outliers in a histogram.

Frequency Distribution

A tabulation of n data values into k classes called *bins,* based on values of the data. The *bin limits* are cutoff points that define each bin. Bins generally have equal interval widths and their limits cannot overlap.

The basic steps for constructing a frequency distribution are to (1) sort the data in ascending order, (2) choose the number of bins, (3) set the bin limits, (4) put the data values in the appropriate bin, and (5) create the table. Let's walk through these steps.

Step 1: Find Smallest and Largest Data Values

Sorted Price/Earnings Ratios

7	9	10	10	10	10	11	11	11	12	13
13	13	14	14	15	16	16	16	16	17	17
18	18	19	19	20	20	21	21	22	23	24
26	26	27	28	31	37	37	38	42	50	59

For the P/E data, we get $x_{min} = 7$ and $x_{max} = 59$ (highlighted). You might be able to find x_{min} and x_{max} without sorting the entire data set, but it is easier to experiment with bin choices if you have already sorted the data.

Step 2: Choose Number of Bins Since a frequency distribution seeks to condense many data points into a small table, we expect the number of bins k to be much smaller than the sample size n. When you use *too many* bins, some bins are likely to be sparsely populated, or even empty. With *too few* bins, dissimilar data values are lumped together. Left to their own devices, people tend to choose similar bin limits for a given data set. Generally, larger samples justify more bins. According to **Sturges' Rule**, a guideline proposed by statistician Herbert Sturges, every time we double the sample size, we should add one bin, as shown in Table 3.4.

For the sample sizes you are likely to encounter, Table 3.4 says that you would expect to use from $k = 5$ to $k = 11$ bins. Sturges' Rule can be expressed as a formula:

(3.1) Sturges' Rule: $k = 1 + 3.3 \log(n)$

For the P/E data ($n = 44$), Sturges' Rule suggests:

$$k = 1 + 3.3 \log(n) = 1 + 3.3 \log(44) = 1 + 3.3(1.6435) = 6.42 \text{ bins}$$

Sturges' formula suggests using 6 or 7 bins for the P/E data. However, to get "nice" bin limits, you may choose more or fewer bins. Picking attractive bin limits is often an overriding consideration (not Sturges' Rule).When the data are skewed by unusually large or small data values, we may need more classes than Sturges' Rule suggests.

TABLE 3.4

Sturges' Rule

Sample Size (n)	*Suggested Number of Bins (k)*
16	5
32	6
64	7
128	8
256	9
512	10
1,024	11

Step 3: Set Bin Limits Just as choosing the number of bins requires judgment, setting the bin limits also requires judgment. For guidance, find the approximate width of each bin by dividing the data range by the number of bins:

(3.2)
$$\text{Bin width} \approx \frac{x_{\max} - x_{\min}}{k}$$

Round the bin width *up* to an appropriate value, then set the lower limit for the first bin as a multiple of the bin width. What does "appropriate" mean? If the data are discrete, then it makes sense to have a width that is an integer value. If the data are continuous, then setting a bin width equal to a fractional value may be appropriate. Experiment until you get aesthetically pleasing bins that cover the data range.

For example, for this data set, the smallest P/E ratio was 7 and the largest P/E ratio was 59, so if we want to use $k = 6$ bins, we calculate the approximate bin width as:

$$\text{Bin width} \approx \frac{59 - 7}{6} = \frac{52}{6} = 8.67$$

To obtain "nice" limits, we could round the bin width up to 10 and choose bin limits of 0, 10, 20, 30, 40, 50, 60. As a starting point for the lowest bin, we choose the largest multiple of the bin width smaller than the lowest data value. Here, the bin width is 10 and the smallest data value is 7, so the first bin would start at 0.

Step 4: Count the Data Values in Each Bin In general, the lower limit is *included* in the bin, while the upper limit is *excluded*. MegaStat and MINITAB follow this convention. However, Excel's histogram option *includes* the upper limit and *excludes* the lower limit. There are advantages to either method. Our objective is to make sure that none of the bins overlap and that data values are counted in only one bin.

Step 5: Prepare a Table You can choose to show only the absolute frequencies, or counts, for each bin, but we often also include the relative frequencies and the cumulative frequencies. Relative frequencies are calculated as the absolute frequency for a bin divided by the total number of data values. Cumulative relative frequencies accumulate relative frequency values as the bin limits increase. Table 3.5 shows the frequency distribution we've created for the P/E ratio data. Sometimes the relative frequencies do not sum to 1 due to rounding.

TABLE 3.5

Frequency Distribution of P/E Ratios Using Six Bins PERatios

Bin Limits			*Frequency*	*Relative*		*Cumulative*	
Lower		*Upper*	*(f)*	*Frequency (f/n)*	*Percent*	*Frequency*	*Percent*
0	<	10	2	2/44 = .0455	4.55	2	4.55
10	<	20	24	24/44 = .5455	54.55	26	59.09
20	<	30	11	11/44 = .2500	25.00	37	84.09
30	<	40	4	4/44 = .0909	9.09	41	93.18
40	<	50	1	1/44 = .0227	2.27	42	95.45
50	<	60	2	2/44 = .0455	4.55	44	100.00
			44		100.00		

Histograms

A **histogram** is a graphical representation of a frequency distribution. A histogram is a bar chart whose *Y*-axis shows the number of data values (or a percentage) within each bin of a frequency distribution and whose *X*-axis ticks show the end points of each bin. There should be no gaps between bars (except when there are no data in a particular bin) as shown in Figure 3.5. The appearance of a histogram is identical, regardless of whether the vertical axis displays *frequency, relative frequency,* or *percent.* It is only a matter of scaling the *Y*-axis because a percent is $100f/n$ (the bin frequency divided by the sample size and multiplied by 100).

FIGURE 3.5

Three Histograms for P/E Ratios PERatios

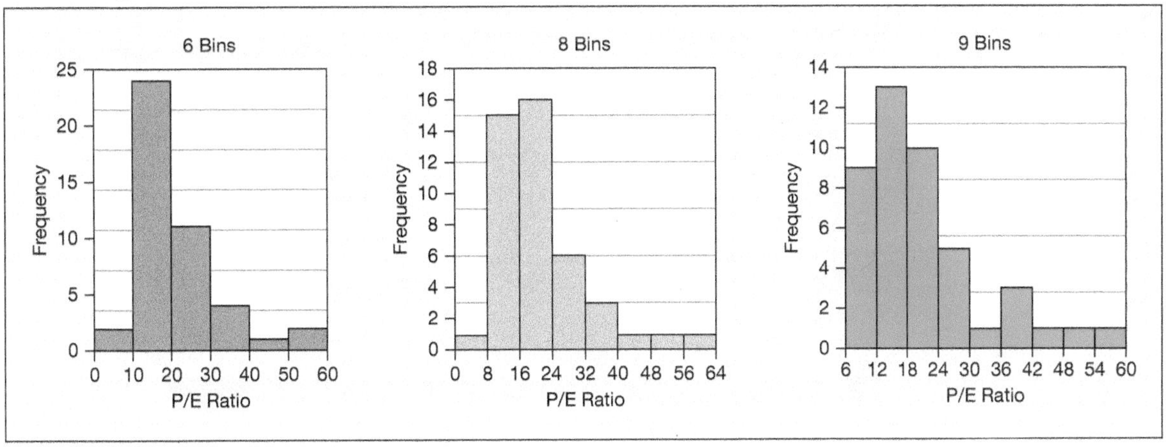

Choosing the number of bins and bin limits requires judgment on our part. Creating a histogram is often a trial-and-error process. Our first choice of bins and limits may not be our final choice for presentation. Figure 3.5 shows histograms for the P/E ratio sample using three different bin definitions.

k	$(x_{max} - x_{min})/k$	*Nice Bin Width*	*Bin Limits*									
6	8.7	10	0	10	20	30	40	50	60			
8	6.5	8	0	8	16	24	32	40	48	56	64	
9	5.8	6	6	12	18	24	30	36	42	48	54	60

Our perception of the shape of the distribution depends on how the bins are chosen. The skewed shape of the distribution becomes more obvious when we use more than six bins. In this example, we might wish to depart from Sturges' Rule to show additional detail. You can use your own judgment to determine which histogram you would ultimately include in a report.

Making an Excel Histogram

Excel will produce histograms. Click on the menu bar **Data** ribbon. If you don't see **Data Analysis** on the **Data** ribbon, click **File** (upper left corner), click the **Excel Options** button at the bottom of the screen, click **Add-Ins**, select **Analysis Tool Pak**, and click **OK**. Once the **Data Analysis** icon appears on the **Data** ribbon, follow these steps to create your histogram:

Step 1: Open an existing data file or key in your own data. Key in the upper bin limits that will cover the data range (smallest through largest data values). Each bin upper limit will be *included* in the bin. Only the *upper* bin limit is used by Excel (both are shown here for clarity). You may wish to experiment with different bin limits, as illustrated in the example shown here. Click on the **Data** ribbon, select the **Data Analysis** icon, choose the **Histogram** option, and click **OK**.

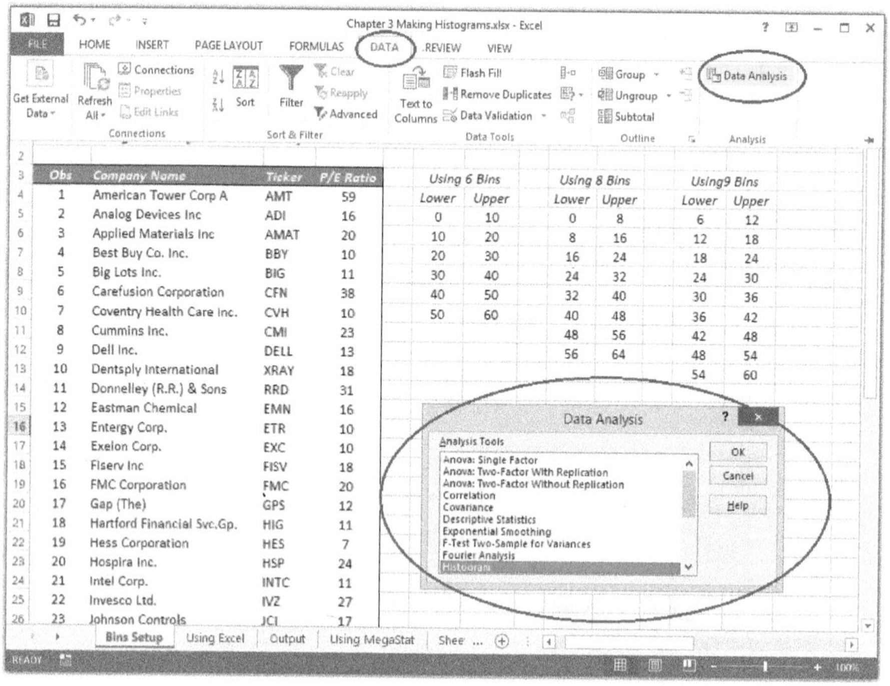

Step 2: Enter the cell range for your data values. Enter the cell range for the upper bin limits. Specify a cell for the upper left corner of the histogram output range (or choose a new worksheet ply). Check **Chart Output** and click **OK**.

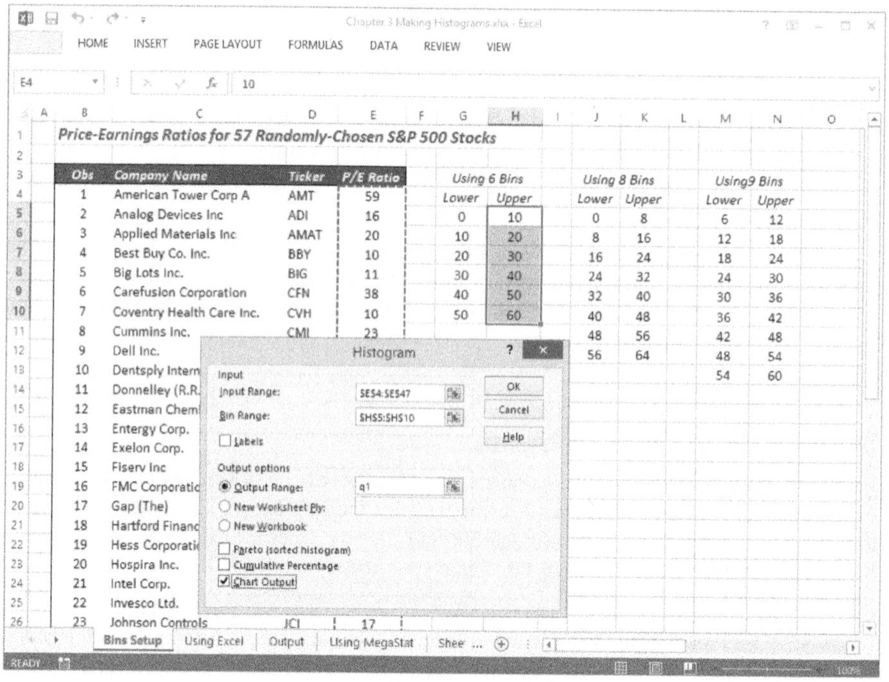

Step 3: Excel's default histogram is quite basic, so you will most likely want to customize it. To do this, click on the chart and use the *Chart Elements* or *Style* tools illustrated here to edit a specific chart feature (e.g., *Chart Title, Axis Titles, Gridlines*). You can also right-click on any feature of the chart (e.g., bars, axis label, chart area, plot area) and choose the edit options you want. For example, to improve Excel's skinny histogram bars, right-click on the histogram bars, choose Format Data Series, and reduce the gap width. Alternatively, you can make a new column chart (highlight the frequency range, click on the Insert ribbon, choose Column, and then customize the resulting chart).

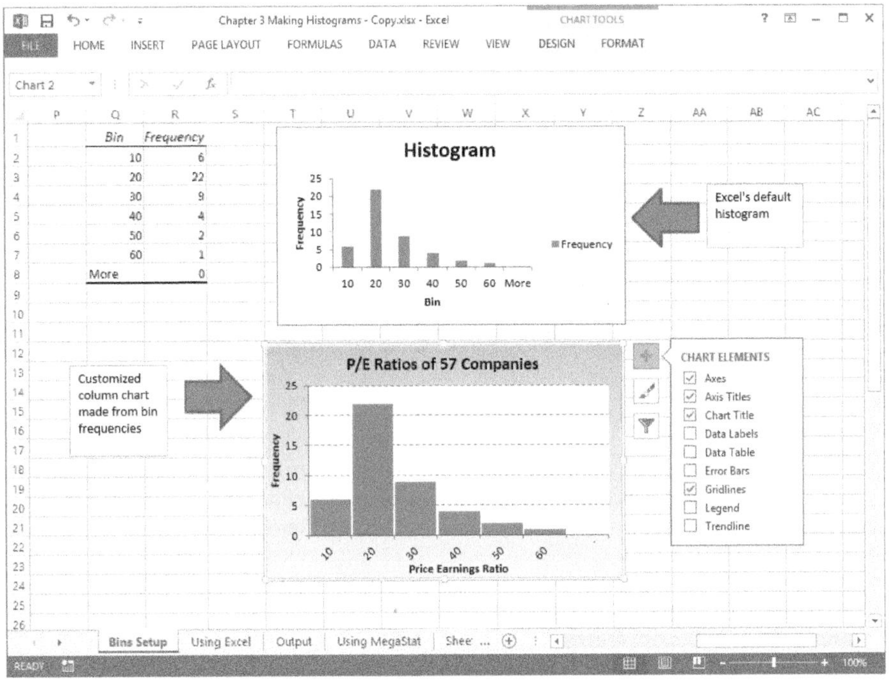

Making a MegaStat Histogram

MegaStat will automatically make a nice histogram, although you can specify your own bins if you wish. It also provides a table of frequencies (including percent and cumulative) for each interval. On the histogram's *Y*-axis, MegaStat shows *percents* (not frequencies), which will give exactly the same view of the data (as you saw in Figure 3.5).

Step 1: Open an existing file or key in the data. Click on Add-Ins and select MegaStat. Select Frequency Distribution. Choose the Input Range for the data. MegaStat will automatically detect the column heading and use it to label the histogram, regardless of whether or not you include it in the input range. You may enter an interval width and lower boundary for the first bin. If you leave them blank, MegaStat will create a nice histogram using its own judgment. As an option, you can create a frequency polygon, ogive, or custom histogram with unequal bins (the default is equal bins).

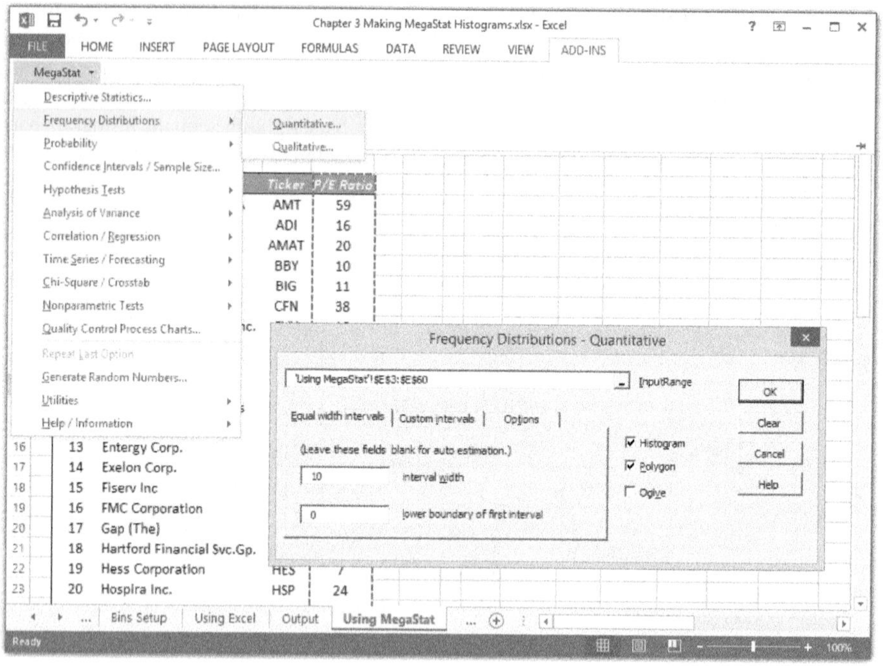

Step 2: MegaStat provides a table with bin limits, frequencies, percent frequencies, and cumulative frequencies. Its nicely labeled histogram shows *percent* (not frequencies) on the vertical axis (the appearance of the histogram is the same either way). The histogram can be edited (e.g., title, colors, axis labels), but if you want different bins, you must revisit the MegaStat menu.

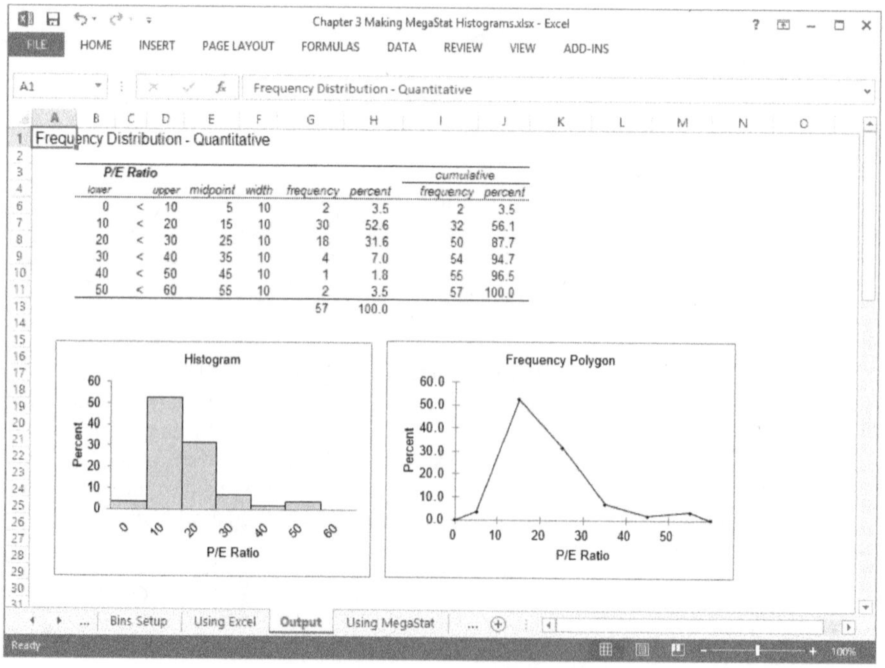
Frequency Distribution - Quantitative

P/E Ratio lower		upper	midpoint	width	frequency	percent	cumulative frequency	cumulative percent
0	<	10	5	10	2	3.5	2	3.5
10	<	20	15	10	30	52.6	32	56.1
20	<	30	25	10	18	31.6	50	87.7
30	<	40	35	10	4	7.0	54	94.7
40	<	50	45	10	1	1.8	55	96.5
50	<	60	55	10	2	3.5	57	100.0
					57	100.0		

MINITAB Histograms

Figure 3.6 shows how MINITAB creates a histogram for the same data. Copy the data from the spreadsheet and paste it into MINITAB's worksheet, then choose Graphs > Histogram from the top menu bar. Let MINITAB use its default options. Once the histogram has been created, you can right-click the *X*-axis to adjust the bins, axis tick marks, and so on.

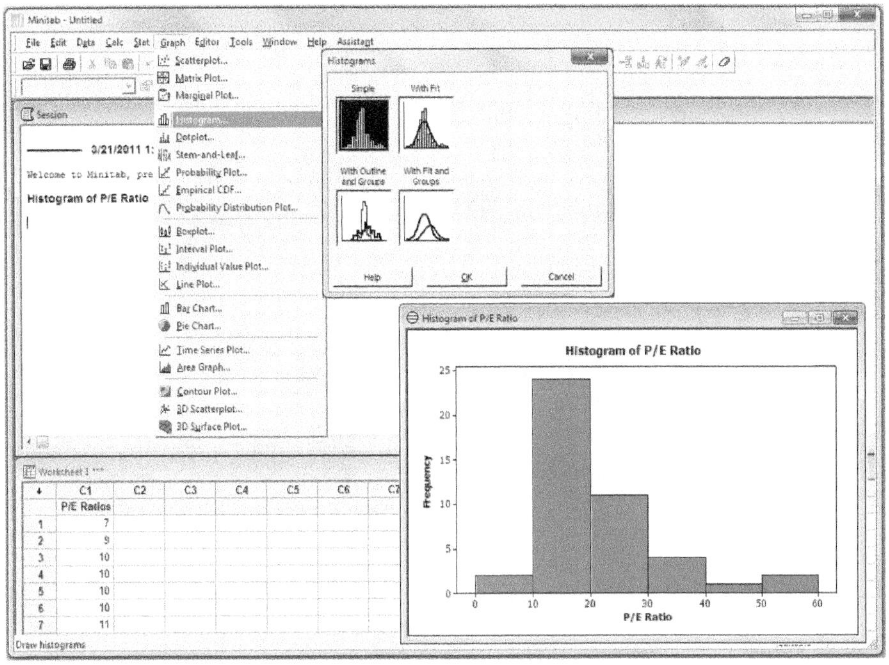

FIGURE 3.6

MINITAB Histogram

PERatios

Shape

A histogram suggests the *shape* of the population we are sampling, but, unless the sample is large, we must be cautious about making inferences. Our perception is also influenced by the number of bins and the way the bin limits are chosen. The following terminology is helpful in discussing shape.

A **modal class** is a histogram bar that is higher than those on either side. A histogram with a single modal class is *unimodal,* one with two modal classes is *bimodal,* and one with more than two modes is *multimodal.* However, modal classes may be artifacts of the way the bin limits are chosen. It is wise to experiment with various ways of binning and to make cautious inferences about modality unless the modes are strong and invariant to binning. Figure 3.6 shows a single modal class for P/E ratios between 10 and 20.

A histogram's *skewness* is indicated by the direction of its longer tail. If neither tail is longer, the histogram is **symmetric.** A **right-skewed** (or positively skewed) histogram has a longer right tail, with most data values clustered on the left side. A **left-skewed** (or negatively skewed) histogram has a longer left tail, with most data values clustered on the right side. Few histograms are exactly symmetric. Business data tend to be right-skewed because they are often bounded by zero on the left but are unbounded on the right (e.g., number of employees). You may find it helpful to refer to the templates shown in Figure 3.7.

An **outlier** is an extreme value that is far enough from the majority of the data that it probably arose from a different cause or is due to measurement error. We will define outliers more precisely in the next chapter. For now, think of outliers as unusual points located in the histogram tails. None of the histograms shown so far has any obvious outliers.

FIGURE 3.7

Prototype Distribution Shapes

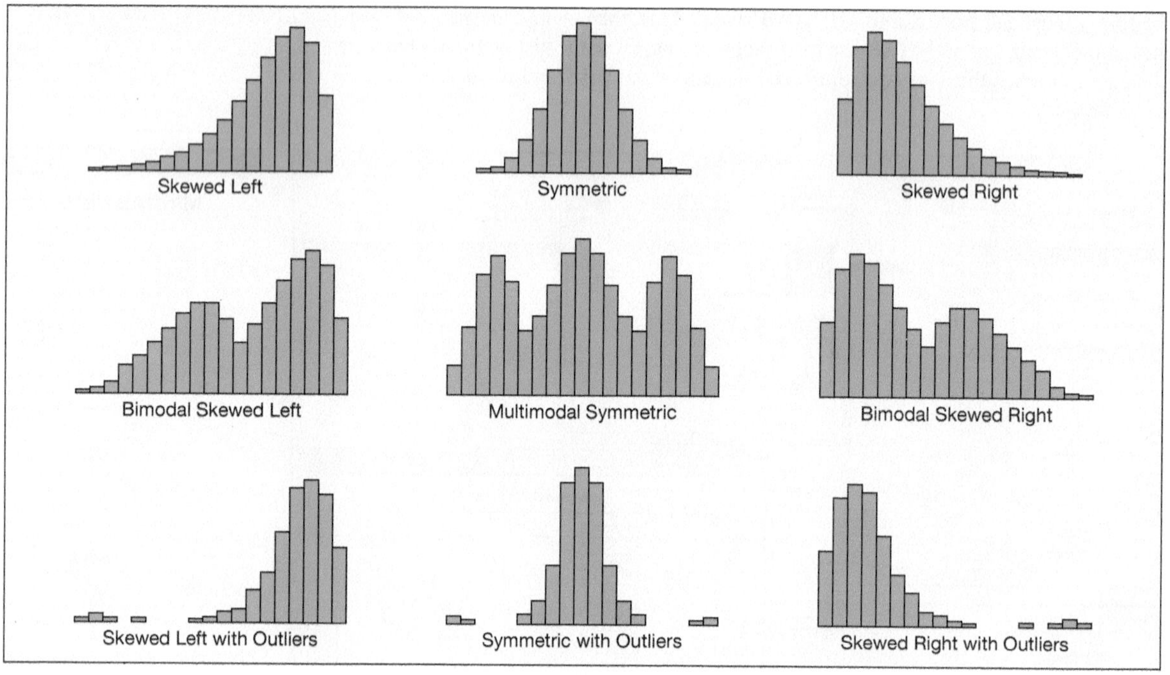

Tips for Effective Frequency Distributions

Here are some general tips to keep in mind when making frequency distributions and histograms.

1. Check Sturges' Rule first, but only as a suggestion for the number of bins.
2. Choose an appropriate bin width.
3. Choose bin limits that are multiples of the bin width.
4. Make sure that the range is covered, and add bins if necessary.
5. Skewed data may require more bins to reveal sufficient detail.

Frequency Polygon and Ogive

Figure 3.8 shows two more graphs offered by MegaStat. A **frequency polygon** is a line graph that connects the midpoints of the histogram intervals, plus extra intervals at the

FIGURE 3.8

MegaStat's Frequency Polygon and Ogive (embellished) PERatios

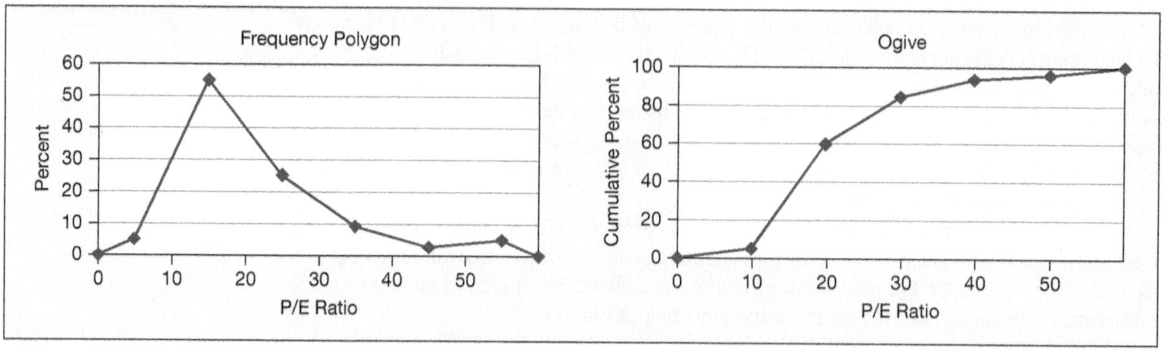

beginning and end so that the line will touch the *X*-axis. It serves the same purpose as a histogram, but is attractive when you need to compare two data sets (since more than one frequency polygon can be plotted on the same scale). An **ogive** (pronounced "oh-jive") is a line graph of the cumulative frequencies. It is useful for finding percentiles or in comparing the shape of the sample with a known benchmark such as the normal distribution (that you will be seeing in the next chapter).

Mini Case 3.2

Duration of U.S. Recessions

Table 3.6 shows two "nice" ways to bin the data on the duration of 33 U.S. recessions (for details, see **Mini Case 3.1**). Sturges would recommend using six bins, i.e., $k = 1 + 3.3 \log(n) = 1 + 3.3 \log(33) = 5.97$. Using six bins works out well, using a bin size of 12 months (one year). However, we also can create a nice histogram using seven bins of width 10 months. You can surely think of other valid possibilities.

TABLE 3.6 **Some Ways to Tabulate 33 Business Contractions** Recessions

Using k = 6 bins			*Using k = 7 bins*		
From	***To (not inclusive)***	***f***	***From***	***To (not inclusive)***	***f***
0	12	12	0	10	7
12	24	16	10	20	19
24	36	2	20	30	3
36	48	2	30	40	2
48	60	0	40	50	1
60	72	1	50	60	0
			60	70	1
	Total	33		Total	33

Both histograms in Figure 3.9 suggest right-skewness (long right tail, most values cluster to the left). Each histogram has a single modal class (e.g., the $k = 7$ bin histogram says that a recession most often lasts between 10 and 20 months). The long recession of 1873–1879 (65 months) can be seen as a possible outlier in the right tail of both histograms.

FIGURE 3.9 **Histograms for 6 and 7 Bins**

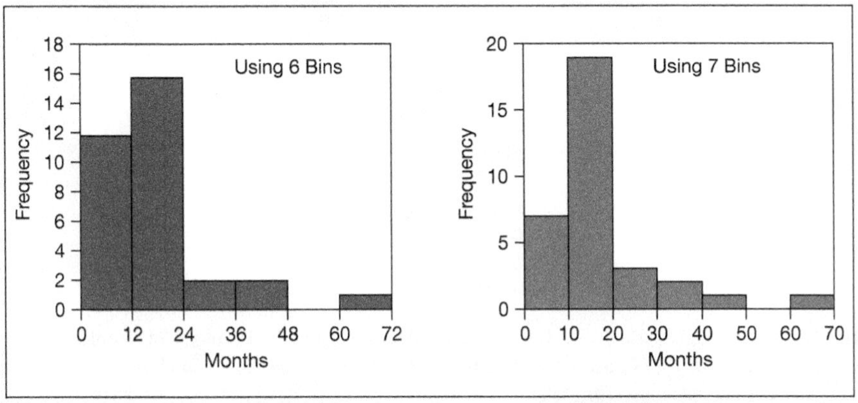

SECTION EXERCISES

connect

3.4 (a) The table shows the number of days on the market for the 36 recent home sales in the city of Sonando Hills. Construct a frequency distribution and histogram, using nice (round) bin limits. (b) Describe the distribution and note any unusual features. Homes

18	70	52	17	86	121	86	3	66
96	41	50	176	26	28	6	55	21
43	20	56	71	57	16	20	30	31
44	44	92	179	80	98	44	66	15

3.5 (a) The table shows raw scores on a state civil service exam taken by 24 applicants for positions in law enforcement. Construct a frequency distribution and histogram, using nice (round) bin limits. (b) Describe the distribution and note any unusual features. Civil

83	93	74	98	85	82	79	78
82	68	67	82	78	83	70	99
18	96	93	62	64	93	27	58

3.6 (a) Make a frequency distribution and histogram (using appropriate bins) for these 28 observations on the amount spent for dinner for four in downtown Chicago on Friday night. (b) Repeat the exercise, using a different number of bins. Which is preferred? Why? Dinner

95	103	109	170	114	113	107
124	105	80	104	84	176	115
69	95	134	108	61	160	128
68	95	61	150	52	87	136

3.7 (a) Make a frequency distribution and histogram for the monthly off-campus rent paid by 30 students. (b) Repeat the exercise, using a different number of bins. Which is preferred? Why? Rents

730	730	730	930	700	570
690	1,030	740	620	720	670
560	740	650	660	850	930
600	620	760	690	710	500
730	800	820	840	720	700

3.8 (a) Make a frequency distribution and histogram for the 2007 annual compensation of 40 randomly chosen CEOs (millions of dollars). (b) Describe the shape of the histogram. (c) Identify any unusual values. (Source: www.forbes.com.) CEOComp40

5.33	18.3	24.55	9.08	12.22	5.52	2.01	3.81
192.92	17.83	23.77	8.7	11.15	4.87	1.72	3.72
66.08	15.41	22.59	6.75	9.97	4.83	1.29	3.72
28.09	12.32	19.55	5.55	9.19	3.83	0.79	2.79
34.91	13.95	20.77	6.47	9.63	4.47	1.01	3.07

3.9 For each frequency distribution, suggest "nice" bins. Did your choice agree with Sturges' Rule? If not, explain.

a. Last week's MPG for 35 student vehicles ($x_{min} = 9.4$, $x_{max} = 38.7$).
b. Ages of 50 airplane passengers ($x_{min} = 12$, $x_{max} = 85$).
c. GPAs of 250 first-semester college students ($x_{min} = 2.25$, $x_{max} = 3.71$).
d. Annual rates of return on 150 mutual funds ($x_{min} = .023$, $x_{max} = .097$).

NOODLES & COMPANY

3.10 Below are sorted data showing average spending per customer (in dollars) at 74 Noodles & Company restaurants. (a) Construct a frequency distribution. Explain how you chose the number of bins and the bin limits. (b) Make a histogram and describe its appearance. (c) Repeat, using a larger number of bins and different bin limits. (d) Did your visual impression of the data change when you increased the number of bins? Explain. *Note:* You may use MegaStat or MINITAB if your instructor agrees. NoodlesSpending

6.54	6.58	6.58	6.62	6.66	6.70	6.71	6.73	6.75	6.75	6.76	6.76
6.76	6.77	6.77	6.79	6.81	6.81	6.82	6.84	6.85	6.89	6.90	6.91
6.91	6.92	6.93	6.93	6.94	6.95	6.95	6.95	6.96	6.96	6.98	6.99
7.00	7.00	7.00	7.02	7.03	7.03	7.03	7.04	7.05	7.05	7.07	7.07
7.08	7.11	7.11	7.13	7.13	7.16	7.17	7.18	7.21	7.25	7.28	7.28
7.30	7.33	7.33	7.35	7.37	7.38	7.45	7.56	7.57	7.58	7.64	7.65
7.87	7.97										

3.3 EFFECTIVE EXCEL CHARTS

Excel has strong graphics capabilities. Once you become proficient at making effective visuals in Excel, you will possess a skill that will make you a valuable team member and employee. Making your own charts in Excel is something you will have to learn by experience. Professionals who use Excel say that they learn new things every day. Excel offers a vast array of charts. While only a few of them are likely to be used in business, it is fun to review the whole list.

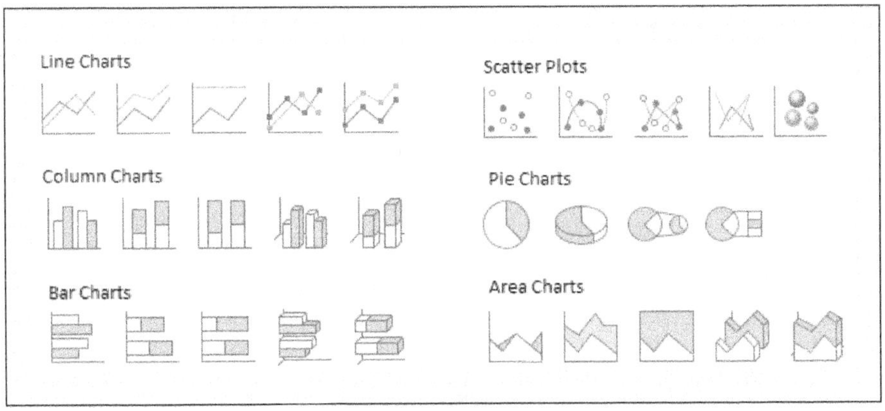

FIGURE 3.10

Excel Chart Types

Excel charts are represented by icons (see Figure 3.10). The icons are designed to be visually self-explanatory. We will discuss those that are most useful in business and economics, paying special attention to line charts (used by analysts to reveal trends) and scatter plots (used by analysts to reveal relationships between two variables).

Excel's default charts tend to be very plain. But business charts need not be dull. You can customize any graph to your taste. For example, you can

- Improve the titles (main, x-axis, y-axis).
- Change the axis scales (minimum, maximum, ticks).
- Display the data values (not always a good idea).
- Add a data table underneath the graph (if there is room).
- Change color or patterns in the plot area or chart area.
- Format decimals to make axis scales more readable.
- Edit the gridlines and borders (dotted or solid, colors).
- Alter the appearance of bars (color, pattern, gap width).
- Change markers and lines on a scatter plot (size, color).

Once you have inserted a chart into your worksheet, click on the chart to select it, and the *Format* and *Design* ribbons will be highlighted at the top of the screen.

FIGURE 3.11

Chart Tool Ribbons

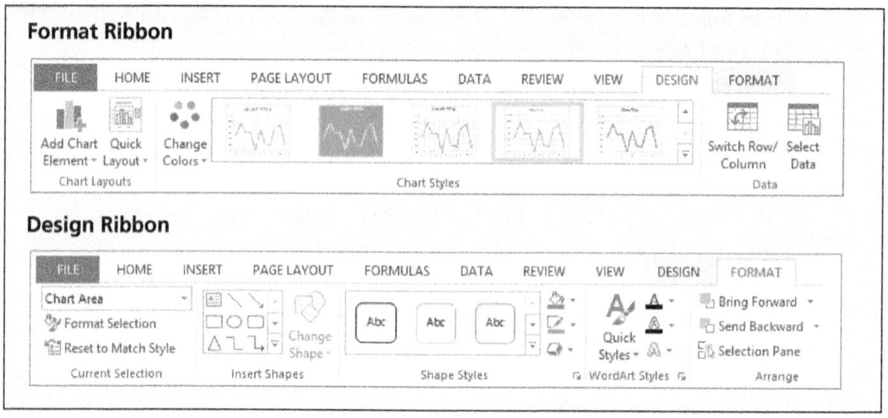

FIGURE 3.12

Chart Elements Menus

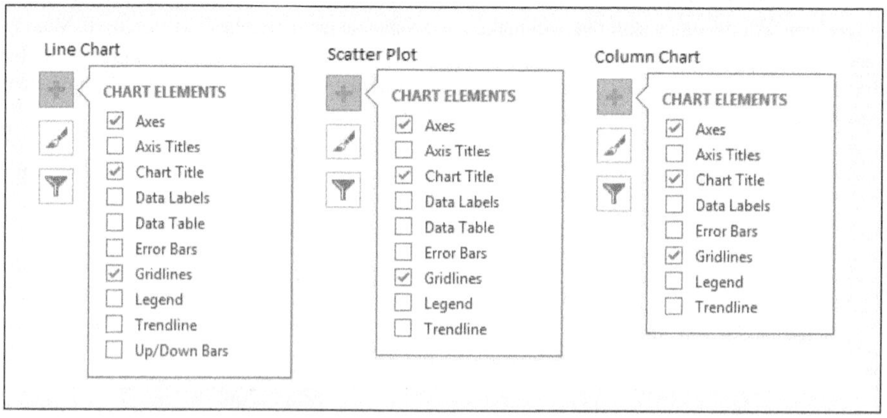

You can customize the chart you have created, as illustrated in Figure 3.11 for a line chart. Although certain features are unique to each chart type, these ribbons are similar for all chart types. If you don't like the result of your edits, just click the Undo icon (or Ctrl-Z).

Alternatively, you can click on the graph and use the *Chart Elements* menus (see Figure 3.12) to edit specific features of your graph (e.g., *Chart Title, Axis Titles, Gridlines*).

3.4 LINE CHARTS

LO 3-5

Make an effective line chart.

A **line chart** like the one shown in Figure 3.13 is used to display a time series, to spot trends, or to compare time periods. Line charts can be used to display several variables at once. If two variables are displayed, the right and left scales can differ, using the right scale for one variable and the left scale for the other. Excel's *two-scale line chart,* illustrated in Figure 3.14, lets you compare variables

FIGURE 3.13

Line Chart CableTV

Source: *Statistical Abstract of the U.S., 2007,* p. 717.

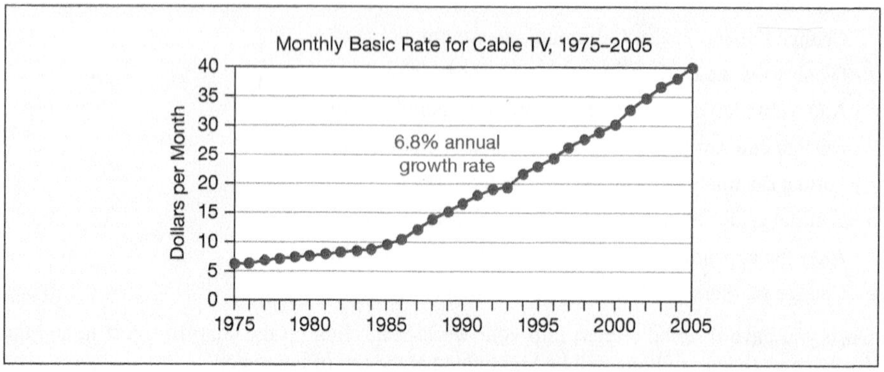

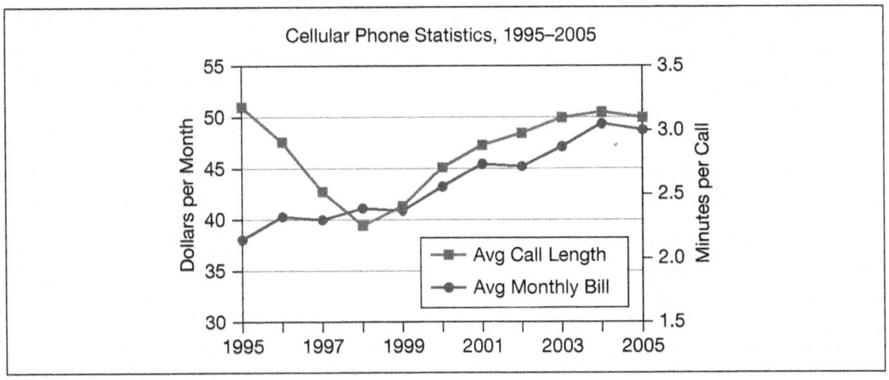

FIGURE 3.14

Two Scales

CellPhones

Source: *Statistical Abstract of the U.S., 2007*, p. 720.

that *differ in magnitude* or are measured in *different units*. But keep in mind that someone who only glances at the chart may mistakenly conclude that both variables are of the same magnitude.

How many variables can be displayed at once on a line graph? Too much clutter ruins any visual display. If you try to display half a dozen time series variables at once, no matter how cleverly you choose symbols and graphing techniques, the result is likely to be unsatisfactory. You will have to use your judgment.

A line graph usually has no vertical gridlines. What about horizontal gridlines? While gridlines do add background clutter, they make it easier to establish the *Y* value for a given year. One compromise is to use lightly colored dashed or dotted gridlines to minimize the clutter, and to increase gridline spacing. If the intent is to convey only a general sense of the data magnitudes, gridlines may be omitted.

Making an Excel Line Chart

Step 1: Highlight the data that you want to display in the line chart, click on the Insert ribbon, click on the Line icon, and choose a line chart style. *Hint:* Do *not* highlight the *X*-axis labels (if any). You can add *X*-axis labels later. The default line plot is quite basic, so you may wish to customize it.

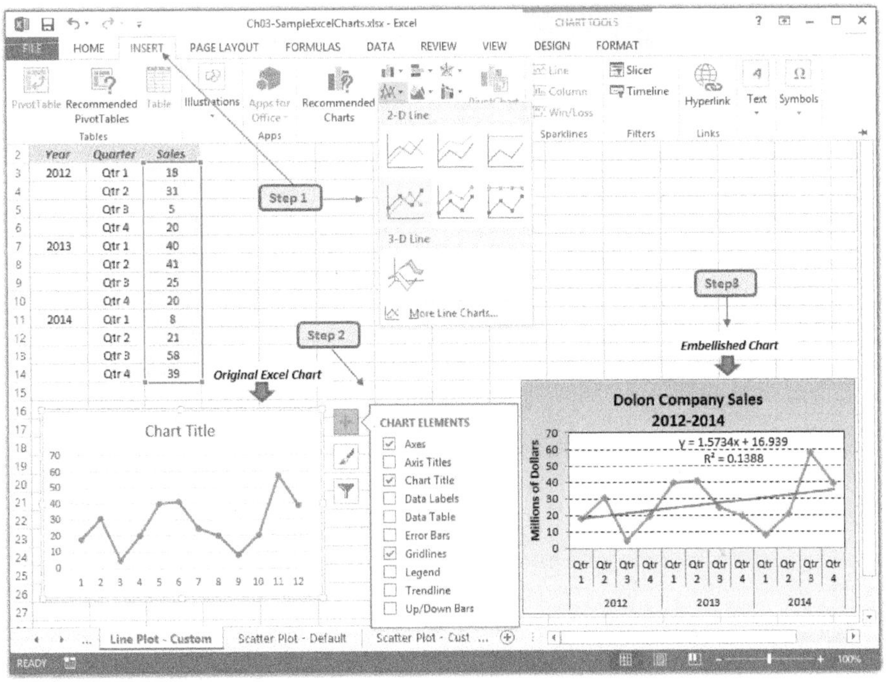

Step 2: To customize your graph, click on it. Its border will change to show that it has been selected, and the *Chart Elements* control will appear (just to the right of the graph). The *Design* and *Format* ribbons will become active (at the top of the screen) to let you edit the chart. Alternatively, you could simply right-click on any feature of your graph (e.g., chart area, plot area, *X*-axis, *Y*-axis, gridlines) and explore the options until you are satisfied with the graph's appearance. To add *X*-axis labels, right-click on the chart, choose Select Data, click on the Edit button for *Horizontal (Category) Axis Labels,* and then enter the cell range for the *X*-axis labels (A3:B14 in this example).

Step 3: If you wish to add a fitted trend, right-click on the data series on the line chart and choose Add Trendline. By default, the fitted trend will be linear. There is an option to display the trend equation and its R^2 statistic (a measure of "fit" of the line).

Log Scales

On the customary **arithmetic scale**, distances on the *Y*-axis are proportional to the magnitude of the variable being displayed. But on a **logarithmic scale**, equal distances represent equal *ratios* (for this reason, a log scale is sometimes called a *ratio scale*). When data vary over a wide range, say, by more than an order of magnitude (e.g., from 6 to 60), we might prefer a *log scale* for the vertical axis, to reveal more detail for small data values. A log graph reveals whether the quantity is growing at an *increasing percent* (convex function), *constant percent* (straight line), or *declining percent* (concave function). On a log scale, *equal distances* represent *equal ratios*. That is, the distance from 100 to 1,000 is the same as the distance from 1,000 to 10,000 (because both have the same 10:1 ratio). Since logarithms are undefined for negative or zero values (try it on your calculator), a log scale is only suited for positive data values.

A log scale is useful for time series data that might be expected to grow at a compound annual percentage rate (e.g., GDP, the national debt, or your future income). Log scales are common in financial charts that cover long periods of time or for data that grow rapidly (e.g., revenues for a start-up company). Some experts feel that corporate annual reports and stock prospectuses should avoid ratio scales, on the grounds that they may be misleading to uninformed individuals. But then how can we fairly portray data that vary by orders of magnitude? Should investors become better informed? The bottom line is that business students must understand log scales because they are sure to run into them.

EXAMPLE 3.2

U.S. Trade

USTrade

Figure 3.15 shows the U.S. balance of trade. The arithmetic scale shows that growth has been exponential. Yet, although exports and imports are increasing in absolute terms, the log graph suggests that the *growth rate* in both series may be slowing because the log graph is slightly concave. On the log graph, the recently increasing trade deficit is not *relatively* as large. Regardless how it is displayed, the trade deficit remains a concern for policymakers, for fear that foreigners may no longer wish to purchase U.S. debt instruments to finance the trade deficit.

FIGURE 3.15

Comparison of Arithmetic and Log Scales USTrade

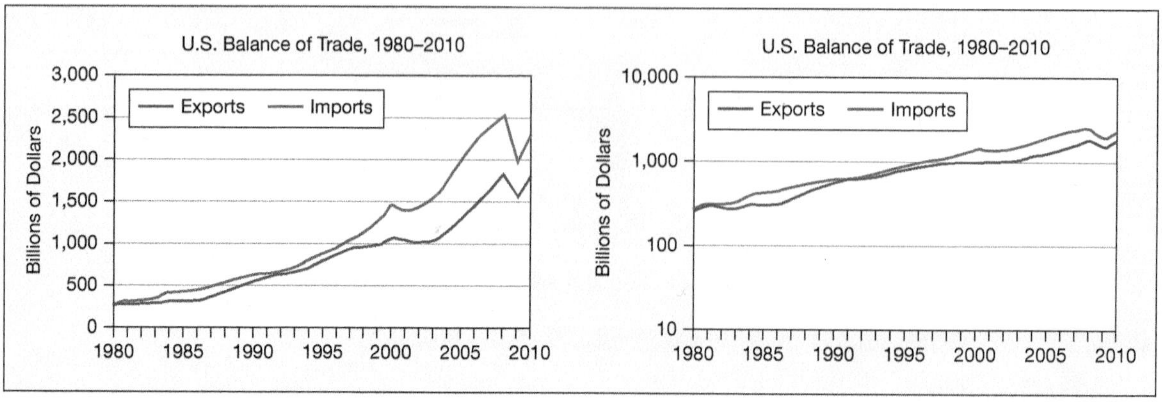

Source: *Economic Report of the President, 2011*, Table B24.

Tips for Effective Line Charts

Here are some general tips to keep in mind when creating line charts:

1. Line charts are used for *time series data* (never for cross-sectional data).
2. The numerical variable is shown on the *Y*-axis, while the time units go on the *X*-axis with time increasing from left to right. Business audiences expect this rule to be followed.
3. Except for log scales, use a zero origin on the *Y*-axis (this is the default in Excel) unless more detail is needed. The zero-origin rule is mandatory for a corporate annual report or investor stock prospectus.
4. To avoid graph clutter, numerical labels usually are *omitted* on a line chart, especially when the data cover many time periods. Use gridlines to help the reader read data values.
5. Data markers (squares, triangles, circles) are helpful. But when the series has many data values or when many variables are being displayed, they clutter the graph.
6. If the lines on the graph are too thick, the reader can't ascertain graph values.

SECTION EXERCISES

connect

3.11 (a) Use Excel to prepare a line chart to display the data on housing starts. Modify the default colors, fonts, etc., to make the display effective. (b) Describe the pattern, if any. Housing

U.S. Housing Starts (thousands), 1990–2013

Year	*Starts*	*Year*	*Starts*	*Year*	*Starts*
1990	895	1998	1,271	2006	1,465
1991	840	1999	1,302	2007	1,046
1992	1,030	2000	1,231	2008	622
1993	1,126	2001	1,273	2009	445
1994	1,198	2002	1,359	2010	471
1995	1,076	2003	1,499	2011	431
1996	1,161	2004	1,611	2012	535
1997	1,134	2005	1,716	2013	615

Sources: www.census.gov and *Statistical Abstract of the U.S., 2012*, p. 610.

3.12 (a) Use Excel to prepare a line chart to display the skier/snowboarder data. Modify the default colors, fonts, etc., to make the display effective. (b) Describe the pattern, if any. Snowboards

U.S. Skier/Snowboarder Visits (Millions), 1984–2007

Season	*Visits*	*Season*	*Visits*	*Season*	*Visits*
1984–1985	51.354	1992–1993	54.032	2000–2001	57.337
1985–1986	51.921	1993–1994	54.637	2001–2002	54.411
1986–1987	53.749	1994–1995	52.677	2002–2003	57.594
1987–1988	53.908	1995–1996	53.983	2003–2004	57.067
1988–1989	53.335	1996–1997	52.520	2004–2005	56.882
1989–1990	50.020	1997–1998	54.122	2005–2006	58.897
1990–1991	46.722	1998–1999	52.089	2006–2007	55.068
1991–1992	50.835	1999–2000	52.198		

Source: www.nsaa.org/nsaa/press/.

3.13 (a) Use Excel to prepare a line chart to display the lightning death data. Modify the default colors, fonts, etc., as you judge appropriate to make the display effective. (b) Describe the pattern, if any.

U.S. Deaths by Lightning, 1940–2010 Lightning

Year	Deaths	Year	Deaths	Year	Deaths
1940	340	1965	149	1990	74
1945	268	1970	122	1995	85
1950	219	1975	91	2000	51
1955	181	1980	74	2005	38
1960	129	1985	74	2010	29

Sources: *Statistical Abstract of the United States, 2007*, p. 228; and www.nws.noaa.gov.

3.14 (a) Use Excel to prepare a line chart to display the following transplant data. Modify the default colors, fonts, etc., to make the display effective. (b) Describe the pattern, if any.

U.S. Organ Transplants, 2000–2010

Year	Heart	Liver	Kidney
2000	2,172	4,816	13,258
2001	2,202	5,177	14,152
2002	2,153	5,326	14,741
2003	2,057	5,673	15,137
2004	2,015	6,169	16,004
2005	2,125	6,443	16,481
2006	2,192	6,650	17,094
2007	2,210	6,493	16,624
2008	2,163	6,318	16,517
2009	2,212	6,320	16,829
2010	2,333	6,291	16,898

Source: *Statistical Abstract of the U.S., 2012*, p. 123.

LO 3-6

Make an effective column chart or bar chart.

3.5 COLUMN AND BAR CHARTS

A **column chart** is a *vertical* display of data and a **bar chart** is a *horizontal* display of data. Figure 3.16 shows simple column and bar charts comparing market shares among tire manufacturers.

FIGURE 3.16

Same Data Displayed Two Ways Tires

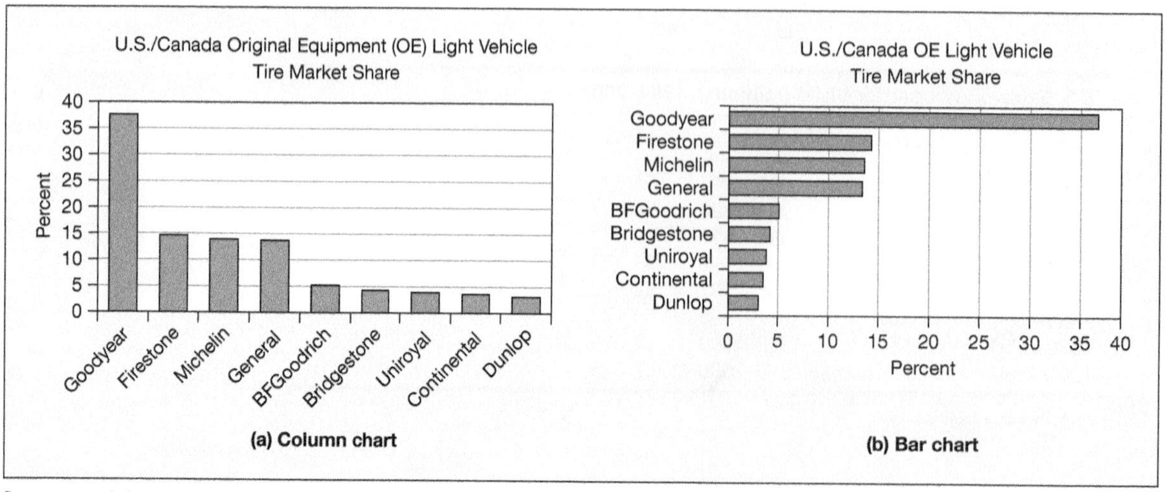

Source: www.mtdealer.com

The column chart is probably the most common type of data display in business. Attribute data are displayed using a column to represent a category or attribute. The *height* of each column reflects a frequency or a value for that category. Each column has a label showing the category name. Excel allows either vertical or horizontal display of categorical data. Each column or bar is separated from its neighbors by a slight gap to improve legibility. You can control gap width in Excel. Most people find a column chart display easier to read, but a bar chart can be useful when the axis labels are long or when there are many categories.

Pareto Charts

A special type of column chart used in business is the **Pareto chart**. A Pareto chart displays categorical data, with categories displayed in descending order of frequency, so that the most common categories appear first. Typically, only a few categories account for the majority of observations. This phenomenon is called the *80/20 Rule*. This rule holds true for many aspects of business. For example, in a sample of U.S. guests responding to a Vail Resorts' guest satisfaction survey, 80 percent of the respondents were visiting from just 20 percent of the states in the United States.

Pareto charts are commonly used in quality management to display the *frequency* of defects or errors of different types. The majority of quality problems can usually be traced to only a few sources or causes. Sorting the categories in descending order helps managers focus on the *vital few* causes of problems rather than the *trivial many*.

Figure 3.17 shows a Pareto chart for complaints collected from a sample of $n = 398$ customers at a concession stand. Notice that the top three categories make up 76 percent of all complaints. The owners of the concession stand can concentrate on ensuring that their food is not cold, on decreasing the time their customers spend in line, and on providing vegetarian choices.

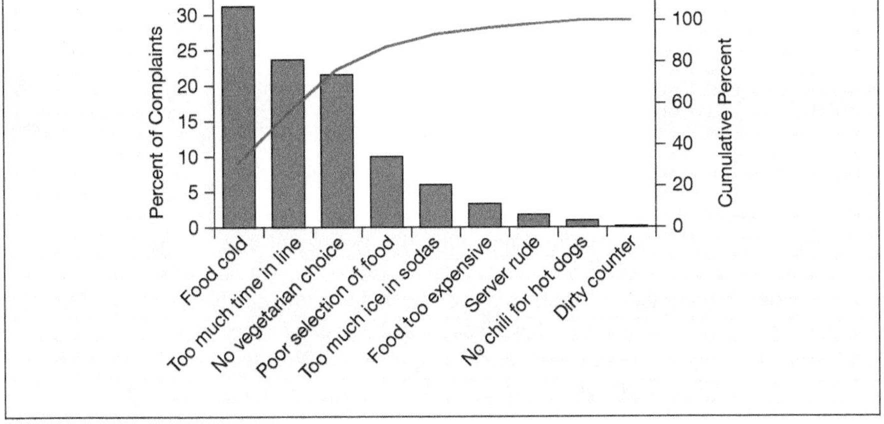

FIGURE 3.17

Pareto Chart

Concessions

Note: The cumulative percentage was added as a second data series on a secondary axis.

Stacked Column Chart

In a **stacked column chart** like Figure 3.18, the bar height is the sum of several subtotals. Areas may be compared by color to show patterns in the subgroups, as well as showing the total. Stacked column charts can be effective for any number of groups but work best when you have only a few. Use numerical labels if exact data values are of importance.

FIGURE 3.18

Stacked Column Chart
MedSchool

Source: www.aamc.org.

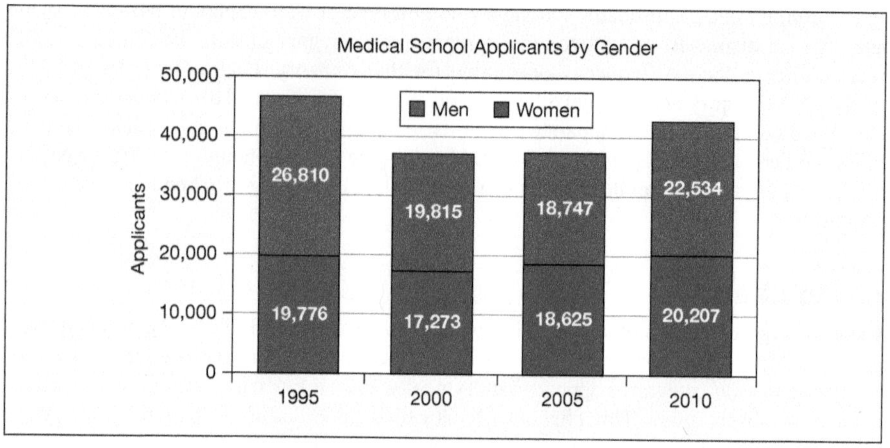

Tips for Effective Bar and Column Charts

The following guidelines will help you to create the most effective bar charts:

1. The numerical variable of interest usually is shown with vertical bars on the *Y*-axis, while the category labels go on the *X*-axis.
2. If the quantity displayed is a time series, the category labels (e.g., years) are displayed on the horizontal *X*-axis with time increasing from left to right.
3. The height or length of each bar should be proportional to the quantity displayed. This is easy, since most software packages default to a zero origin on a bar graph. The zero-origin rule is essential for a corporate annual report or investor stock prospectus (e.g., to avoid overstating earnings). However, nonzero origins may be justified to reveal sufficient detail.
4. Put numerical values at the top of each bar, except when labels would impair legibility (e.g., lots of bars) or when visual simplicity is needed (e.g., for a general audience).

Mini Case 3.3

Vail Resorts Epic Pass

When Vail Resorts was conducting market research for their new season ski pass, the Epic Pass, they surveyed their guests to determine which features of a season pass were most important. Features of a season pass include the number of days of skiing allowed (limited vs. unlimited), the number of resorts included on the pass, the number of blackout dates (all holidays, some holidays, or no blackouts), and the price of the pass.

A market survey was sent to a random sample of Vail Resort guests. They received 1,930 responses. The respondents were sorted into groups based on the number of ski vacations they typically take each year. A summary of the responses is displayed in the clustered column chart below. The chart clearly shows that the feature considered most important to all three groups was the price of the pass. Determining the right price of the pass was critical in order to create a valuable product that a skier would purchase. Subsequent surveys provided more data that was used to price the Epic Pass at $579. Charts can be effective communication tools by allowing the analyst to compare and summarize information from many different groups and across different variables. Decision makers can then see in a snapshot the areas on which to focus.

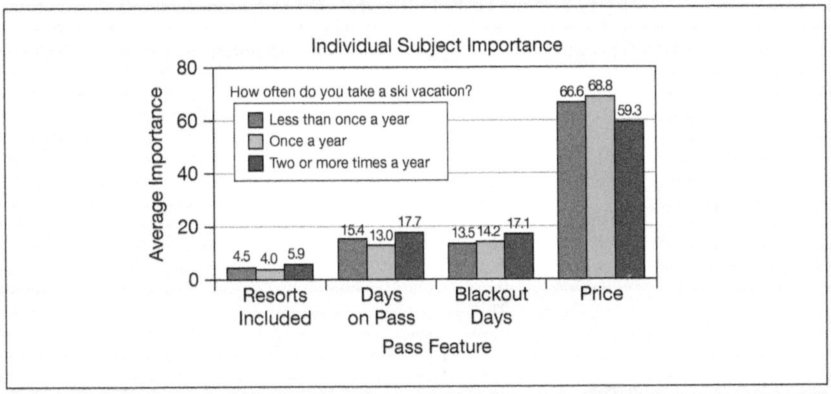

SECTION EXERCISES

connect

3.15 (a) Use Excel to prepare a line chart to display the following gasoline price data. Modify the default colors, fonts, etc., to make the display effective. (b) Change it to a *2-D column chart.* Modify the display if necessary to make the display attractive. (c) Do you prefer the line chart or bar chart? Why? *Hint:* Do *not* include the years when you make the chart. After the chart is completed, you can right-click the chart, choose Select Data, select Horizontal Axis Labels, and then click Edit to insert the range for the years as *X*-axis labels.

Average U.S. Retail Price of Gasoline (dollars per gallon) GasPrice

Year	*Price*	*Year*	*Price*
1960	0.31	1990	1.16
1965	0.31	1995	1.15
1970	0.36	2000	1.51
1975	0.57	2005	2.30
1980	1.25	2010	3.02
1985	1.20		

Sources: www.fueleconomy.gov and eia.doe.gov. Pre-1980 prices are for unleaded gas.

3.16 (a) Use Excel to prepare a *2-D stacked column chart* for television sales by year. Modify the colors, fonts, etc., to make the display effective. (b) Change your graph to a *3-D stacked column chart.* Modify the chart if necessary to make it attractive. (c) Is 3-D better than 2-D? Why? (d) Right-click the data series, choose Add Data Labels, and add labels to the data. Do the labels help?

U.S. Television Sales, 2002–2005 ($ thousands) TVSales

Year	*Projection TV*	*LCD TV*	*Plasma TV*
2002	3,574	246	515
2003	4,351	664	1,590
2004	6,271	1,579	2,347
2005	5,320	3,295	4,012

Source: *Statistical Abstract of the United States, 2007,* p. 643.

3.17 (a) Use Excel to prepare a Pareto chart of the following data. (b) Which three complaint categories account for approximately 80 percent of all complaints? (c) Which category should the telephone company focus on first? **Complaints**

Telephone Company Service Complaints, $n = 791$		
Customer Complaints	***Frequency***	***Percent***
Wait too long	350	44.2%
Service person rude	187	23.6%
Difficult to reach a real person	90	11.4%
Service person not helpful	85	10.7%
Automated instructions confusing	45	5.7%
Customer service phone number hard to find	21	2.7%
Automated voice annoying	13	1.6%

3.6 PIE CHARTS

LO 3-7

Make an effective pie chart.

Many statisticians feel that a table or bar chart is often a better choice than a **pie chart**. But, because of their visual appeal, pie charts appear daily in company annual reports and the popular press (e.g., *USA Today, The Wall Street Journal, Scientific American*), so you must understand their uses and misuses. A pie chart can only convey a *general idea of the data* because it is hard to assess areas precisely. It should have only a few slices (typically two to five) and the slices should be labeled with data values or percents. The only correct use of a pie chart is to *portray data that sum to a total* (e.g., percent market shares). A pie chart is never used to display time series data.

A simple *2-D pie chart* is best, as in Figure 3.19. The *3-D pie chart* (Figure 3.20) adds visual interest, but the sizes of pie slices are harder to assess. Nonetheless, you will see 3-D charts in business publications because of their strong visual impact. A simple bar chart (Figure 3.21) can be used to display the same data, and would be preferred by

FIGURE 3.19

2-D Pie with Labels

Textbook

Source: Web survey of 269 students at two large public universities.

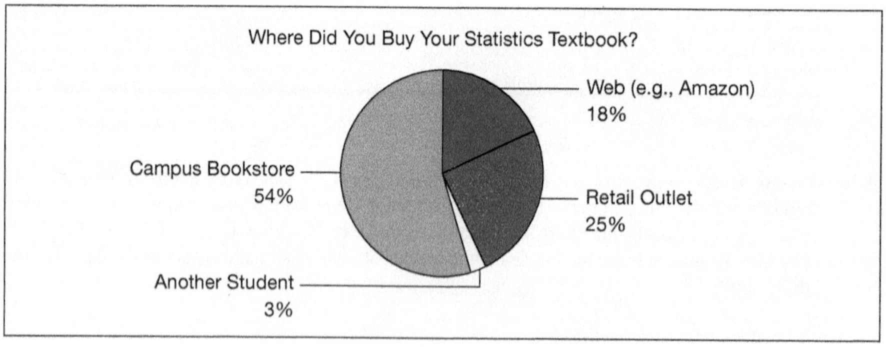

FIGURE 3.20

3-D Exploded Pie Chart

PieCharts

Source: Based on data from www.tiaa-cref.org.

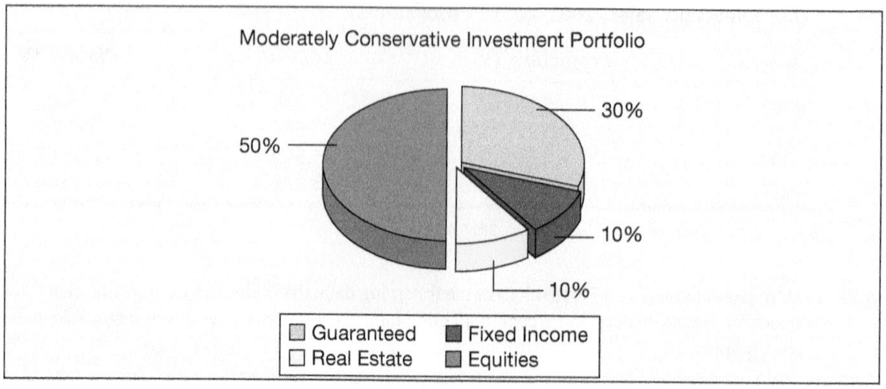

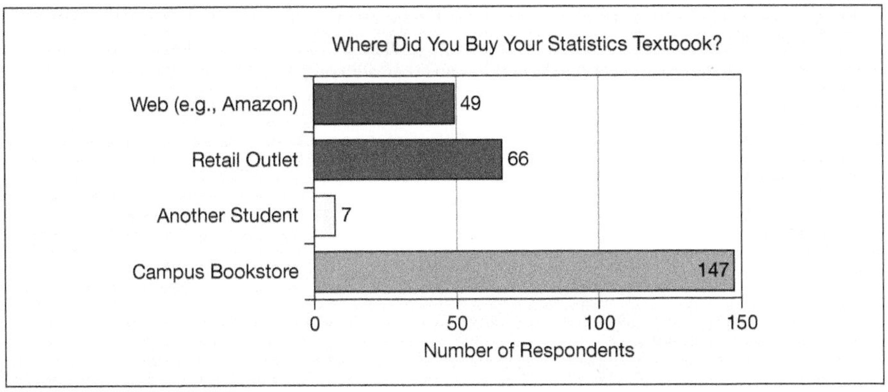

FIGURE 3.21

Bar Chart Alternative

Textbook

Source: Web survey of 269 students at two large public universities.

many statisticians. Black-and-white charts may be used internally in business, but color is typically preferred for customers, stockholders, or investors. *Caution*: If you use Excel to make pie charts with data labels on the slices, the chart can shrink so much that it is difficult to read.

Common Pie Chart Errors

- Pie charts can only convey a general idea of the data values.
- Pie charts are ineffective when they have too many slices.
- Pie chart data must represent *parts of a whole* (e.g., percent market share).

SECTION EXERCISES

connect

3.18 (a) Use Excel to prepare a *2-D pie chart* for these web-surfing data. Modify the default colors, fonts, etc., as you judge appropriate to make the display effective. (b) Right-click the chart area, select Chart Type, and change to an *exploded 2-D pie chart*. (c) Right-click the chart area, select Chart Type, and change to a *bar chart*. Which do you prefer? Why? *Hint:* Include data labels with the percent *values*.

Are You Concerned About Being Tracked While Web Surfing? WebSurf

Level of Concern	*Percent*
Very concerned	68
Somewhat concerned	23
Not very concerned	9
Total	100

3.19 (a) Use Excel to prepare a *2-D pie chart* for the following data. Modify the default colors, fonts, etc., as you judge appropriate to make the display effective. (b) Right-click the chart area, select Chart Type, and change to a *3-D pie chart*. (c) Right-click the chart area, select Chart Type, and change to a *bar chart*. Which do you prefer? Why? *Hint:* Include data labels with the percent *values*.

Dolon Corporation Medical Claims in 2014 Dolon

Spent On	*Percent of Total*
Hospital services	47.5
Physicians	27.0
Pharmaceuticals	19.5
Mental health	5.0
Other	1.0
Total	100.0

3.20 (a) Use Excel to prepare a *2-D pie chart* for these LCD (liquid crystal display) shipments data. Modify the default colors, fonts, etc., as you judge appropriate to make the display effective. (b) Do you feel that the chart has become too cluttered (i.e., are you displaying too many slices)? Would a bar chart be better? Explain. *Hint:* Include data labels with the percent *values*.

World Market Share of LCD Shipments in 2010 LCDMarket

Company	*Percent*
Samsung	18.0
Vizio	16.7
Sony	11.3
Sanyo	8.0
LG Electronics	7.8
Others	38.1
Total	100.0

Source: http://news.cnet.com/. Data are for first quarter of 2010. Percents may not add to 100 due to rounding.

3.7 SCATTER PLOTS

LO 3-8

Make and interpret a scatter plot.

A **scatter plot** shows n pairs of observations $(x_1, y_1), (x_2, y_2), \ldots, (x_n, y_n)$ as dots (or some other symbol) on an X-Y graph. This type of display is so important in statistics that it deserves careful attention. A scatter plot is a starting point for bivariate data analysis. We create scatter plots to investigate the relationship between two variables. Typically, we would like to know if there is an *association* between two variables and, if so, what kind of association exists. As we did with univariate data analysis, let's look at a scatter plot to see what we can observe.

EXAMPLE 3.3

Birth Rates and Life Expectancy

Source: The CIA World Factbook 2003, www.cia.gov.

Figure 3.22 shows a scatter plot with life expectancy on the X-axis and birth rates on the Y-axis. In this illustration, there seems to be an association between X and Y. That is, nations with higher birth rates tend to have lower life expectancy (and vice versa). No cause-and-effect relationship is implied, since in this example both variables could be influenced by a third variable that is not mentioned (e.g., GDP per capita).

FIGURE 3.22 **Scatter Plot of Birth Rates and Life Expectancy (n = 153 nations)** BirthLife

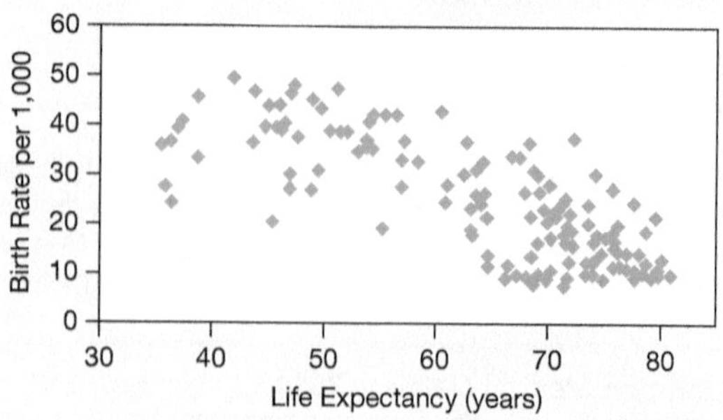

Figure 3.23 shows some scatter plot patterns similar to those that that you might observe when you have a sample of (X, Y) data pairs. A scatter plot can convey patterns in data pairs that would not be apparent from a table. Compare the scatter plots in Figure 3.24 with the prototypes and use your own words to describe the patterns that you see.

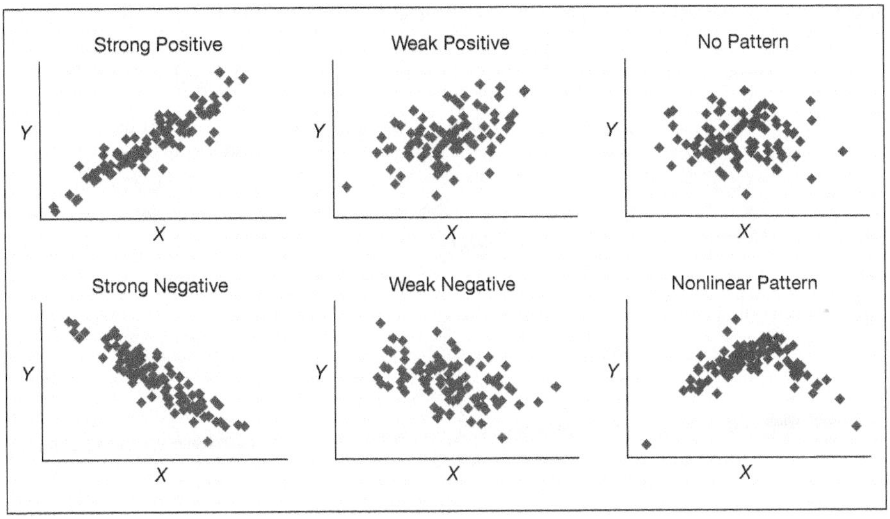

FIGURE 3.23

Prototype Scatter Plot Patterns

FIGURE 3.24

Four Scatter Plots

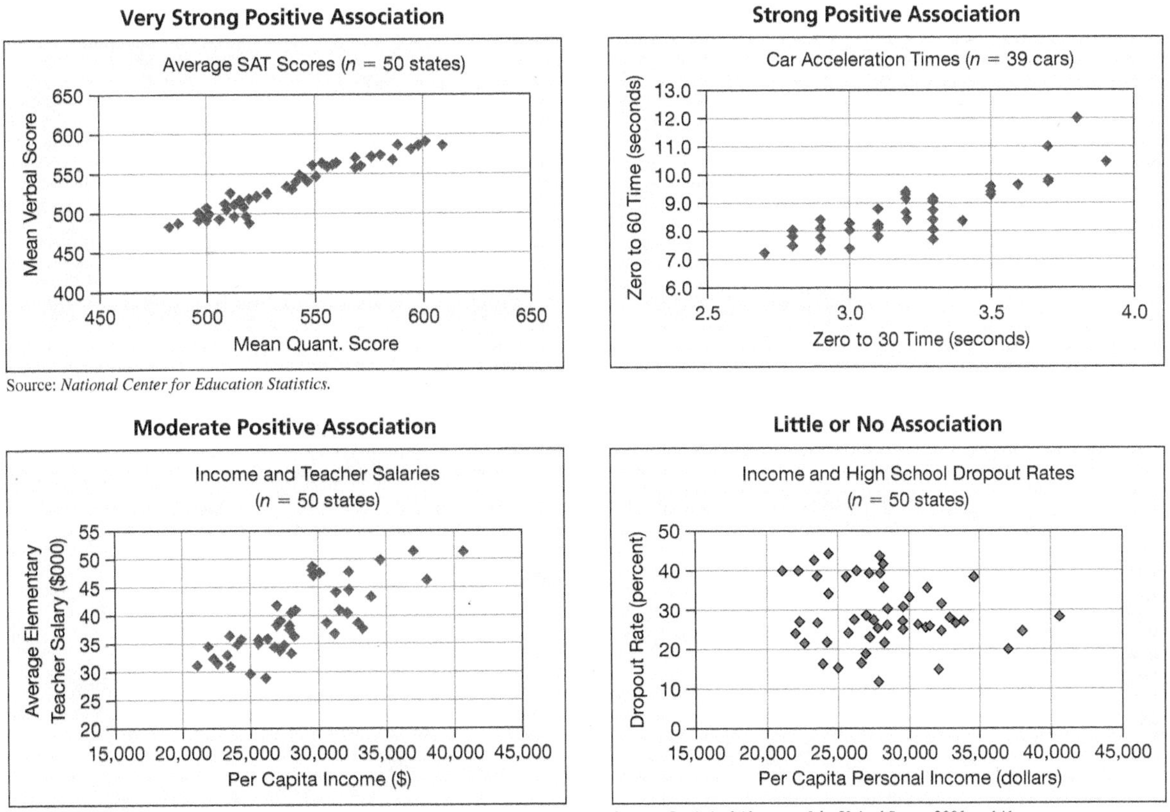

Source: *National Center for Education Statistics.*

Source: *Statistical Abstract of the United States, 2001*, p. 151.

Source: *Statistical Abstract of the United States, 2001*, p. 141.

Making an Excel Scatter Plot

Making a scatter plot is easy using Excel. However, you will probably want to improve the graph after making it, as explained in the following steps. Note that Excel assumes that the first column is *X* and the second column is *Y*.

Step 1: Highlight the (x, y) data pairs that you want to display in the scatter plot, click on the Insert ribbon, click on the Scatter icon, and choose a scatter plot style. The default scatter plot is quite basic, so you may wish to customize it.

Step 2: To customize your graph, click on it. Its border will change to show that it has been selected, and the *Chart Elements* menu will appear. Select a specific feature to edit (e.g., *Chart Title, Axis Titles, Gridlines*). Alternatively, you can just right-click on any feature of your graph (e.g., chart area, plot area, X-axis, Y-axis, gridlines) and explore the options until you are satisfied with the graph's appearance. Here is an example of a customized scatter plot.

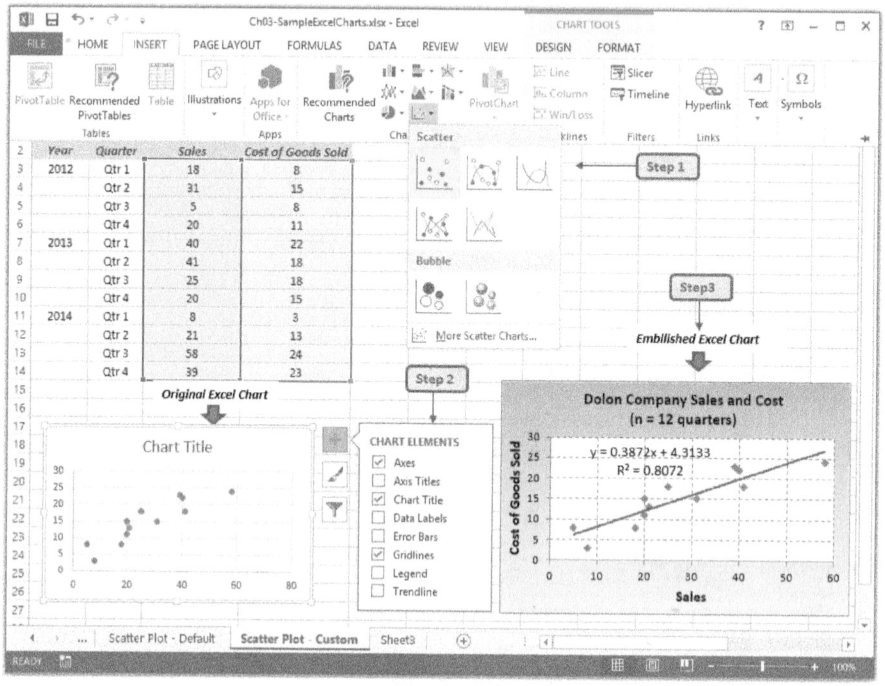

Step 3: If you wish to add a fitted trend, right-click on the data series on the scatter plot and choose Add Trendline. By default, the fitted trend will be linear. There is an option to display the trend equation and its R^2 statistic (a measure of "fit" of the line).

Linear Trend Example Figure 3.25 shows Excel's fitted linear trend for X = total gross leasable area and Y = total retail sales for a sample of 28 states. The slope of the line (0.2594)

FIGURE 3.25

Excel Scatter Plot with Fitted Trend Line (n = 28 states)

RetailSales

Source: *Statistical Abstract of the United States, 2007*, p. 660.

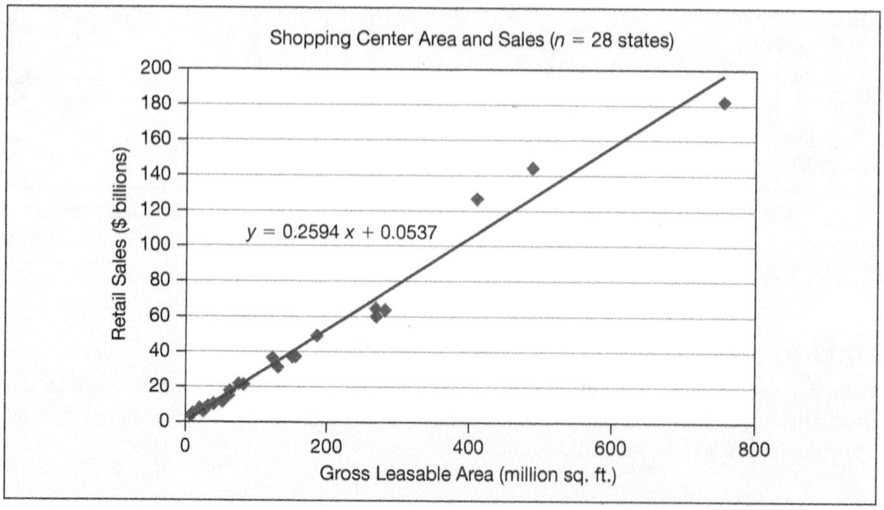

suggests that a unit change in *X* (each "unit" is one million square feet) is associated with an extra $0.2594 billion in retail sales, on average. The intercept is near zero, suggesting that a shopping center with no leasable area would have no sales. Later (in Chapter 12) you will learn how Excel fits a **trend line,** how to interpret it, and when such a line is meaningful. But since almost every student discovers this option the first time he or she makes a scatter plot, we must mention Excel's fitted trend line here purely as a *descriptive tool* that may help you find patterns in (*X*, *Y*) data.

SECTION EXERCISES

connect

3.21 (a) Use Excel to make a scatter plot of the data for bottled water sales for 10 weeks, placing Price on the *X*-axis and Units Sold on the *Y*-axis. Add titles and modify the default colors, fonts, etc., as you judge appropriate to make the scatter plot effective. (b) Describe the relationship (if any) between *X* and *Y*. Weak? Strong? Negative? Positive? Linear? Nonlinear? **WaterSold**

Unit Price	*Units Sold*
1.15	186
0.94	216
1.04	173
1.05	182
1.08	183
1.33	150
0.99	190
1.25	165
1.16	190
1.11	201

3.22 (a) Use Excel to make a scatter plot of these vehicle data, placing Weight on the *X*-axis and City MPG on the *Y*-axis. Add titles and modify the default colors, fonts, etc., as you judge appropriate to make the scatter plot effective. (b) Describe the relationship (if any) between *X* and *Y*. Weak? Strong? Negative? Positive? Linear? Nonlinear?

Weight and MPG for 20 Randomly Selected Vehicles CityMPG

Vehicle	*City MPG*	*Weight (lbs.)*
Acura TSX	23	3,320
BMW 3-Series	19	3,390
Chevrolet Corvette	19	3,255
Chevrolet Silverado 1500	14	4,935
Chrysler Pacifica	17	4,660
Dodge Caravan	18	4,210
Ford Focus	26	2,760
Infiniti FX	16	4,295
Jaguar XJ8	18	3,805
Lexus IS300	18	3,390
Lincoln Aviator	13	5,000
Mazda 6	19	3,355
Land Rover Freelander	17	3,640
Mercedes-Benz S-Class	17	4,195
Nissan 350Z	20	3,345
Nissan Xterra	16	4,315
Pontiac Vibe	28	2,805
Pontiac Grand Am	25	3,095
Toyota Sienna	19	4,120
Volvo C70	20	3,690

Random sample of 2003 vehicles.

3.23 (a) Use Excel to make a scatter plot of the following exam score data, placing Midterm on the *X*-axis and Final on the *Y*-axis. Add titles and modify the default colors, fonts, etc., as you judge appropriate to make the scatter plot effective. (b) Describe the relationship (if any) between *X* and *Y*. Weak? Strong? Negative? Positive? Linear? Nonlinear?

Exam Scores for 18 Statistics Students ExamScores

Name	Midterm Score	Final Score	Name	Midterm Score	Final Score
Aaron	50	30	Joe	68	83
Angela	95	83	Lisa	75	58
Brandon	75	90	Liz	70	83
Buck	60	83	Michele	60	73
Carole	60	75	Nancy	88	78
Cecilia	63	45	Ryan	93	100
Charles	90	100	Tania	73	83
Dmitri	88	90	Ursula	33	53
Ellie	75	68	Xiaodong	60	70

3.24 (a) Use Excel to make a scatter plot of the data, placing Floor Space on the *X*-axis and Weekly Sales on the *Y*-axis. Add titles and modify the default colors, fonts, etc., as you judge appropriate to make the scatter plot effective. (b) Describe the relationship (if any) between *X* and *Y*. Weak? Strong? Negative? Positive? Linear? Nonlinear? FloorSpace

Floor Space (sq. ft.)	Weekly Sales (dollars)
6,060	16,380
5,230	14,400
4,280	13,820
5,580	18,230
5,670	14,200
5,020	12,800
5,410	15,840
4,990	16,610
4,220	13,610
4,160	10,050
4,870	15,320
5,470	13,270

3.8 TABLES

LO 3-9

Make simple tables and pivot tables.

Tables are the simplest form of data display, yet creating effective tables is an acquired skill. By arranging numbers in rows and columns, their meaning can be enhanced so it can be understood at a glance.

EXAMPLE 3.4

School Expenditures

Table 3.7 is a *compound table* that contains time series data (going down the columns) on seven variables (going across the rows). The data can be viewed in several ways. We can focus on the time pattern (going down the columns) or on comparing public and private spending (between columns) for a given school level (elementary/secondary or college/university). Or we can compare spending by school level (elementary/secondary or college/university) for a given type of control (public or private). Figures are rounded to three or four significant digits to make it easier for the reader. Units of measurement are stated in the footnote to keep the column headings simple. Columns are grouped using merged heading cells (blank columns could be inserted to add vertical separation). Presentation tables can be linked dynamically to spreadsheets so that slides can be updated quickly, but take care that data changes do not adversely affect the table layout.

TABLE 3.7 School Expenditures by Control and Level, 1980–2010 Schools

		Elementary and Secondary			*Colleges and Universities*		
Year	*All Schools*	*Public*	*Private*	*Total*	*Public*	*Private*	*Total*
1980	442.6	265.3	19.9	285.2	104.4	52.9	157.4
1985	485.8	278.0	25.2	303.2	118.4	64.2	182.6
1990	618.4	359.7	31.1	390.8	145.0	82.6	227.6
1995	692.4	398.2	33.1	431.3	164.8	96.3	261.1
2000	823.3	484.2	38.9	523.1	193.1	107.1	300.2
2005	980.9	559.4	46.4	605.8	241.6	133.5	375.1
2010	1,111.0	602.0	48.0	650.0	289.0	172.0	461.0

Source: U.S. Census Bureau, *Statistical Abstract of the United States, 2012*, p. 145. All figures are in constant 2008–2009 dollars.

Tips for Effective Tables

Here are some tips for creating effective tables:

1. Keep the table simple, consistent with its purpose. Put summary tables in the *main body* of the written report and detailed tables in an *appendix*. In a slide presentation, the main point of the table should be clear to the reader within *10 seconds*. If not, break the table into parts or aggregate the data.
2. Display the data to be compared in columns rather than rows. Research shows that people find it easier to compare across rather than down.
3. For presentation purposes, round off to three or four significant digits (e.g., 142 rather than 142.213). People mentally round numbers anyway. Exceptions: when accounting requirements supersede the desire for rounding or when the numbers are used in subsequent calculations.
4. Physical table layout should guide the eye toward the comparison you wish to emphasize. Spaces or shading may be used to separate rows or columns. Use lines sparingly.
5. Row and column headings should be simple yet descriptive.
6. Within a column, use a consistent number of decimal digits. Right-justify or decimal-align the data unless all field widths are the same within the column.

Pivot Tables PivotTable

One of Excel's most popular and powerful features is the **pivot table**, which provides interactive analysis of a data matrix. The simplest kind of pivot table has rows and columns. Each of its cells shows a statistic for a row and column combination. The row and column variables must be either *categorical* or *discrete numerical* and the variable for the table cells must be *numerical* (review Chapter 2 if you do not remember these terms). After the table is created, you can change the table by dragging variable names from the list specified in your data matrix. You can change the displayed statistic in the cells (sum, count, average, maximum, minimum, product) by right-clicking the display and selecting from the *field settings* menu. We show here the steps needed to create a pivot table for a small data matrix (25 homes, 3 variables). The first table shows the *sum* of square feet for all the homes in each category. The second table was created by copying the first table and then changing the cells to display the *average* square feet of homes in that cell.

Step 1: Select the Insert tab and specify the data range.

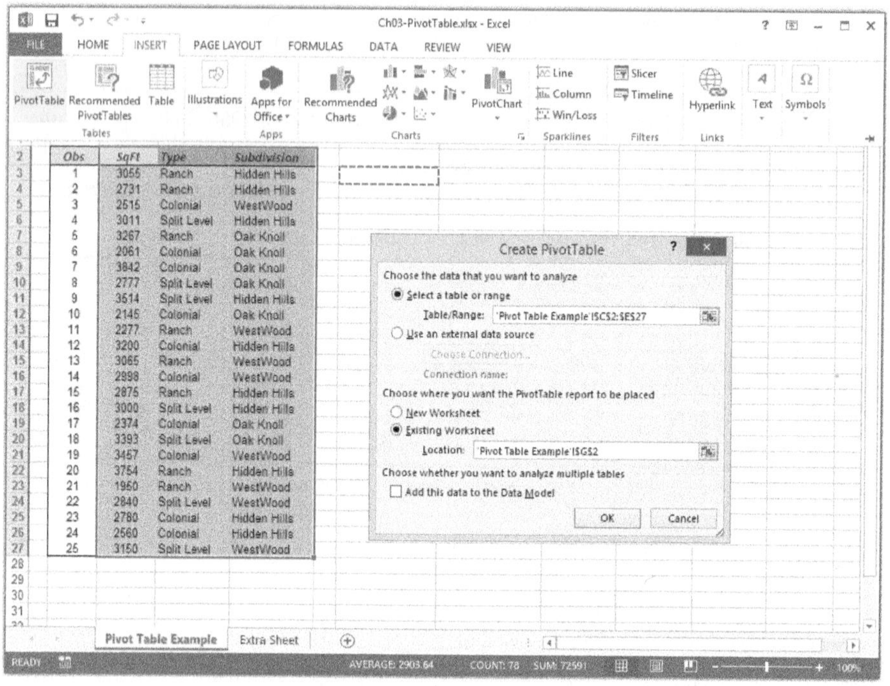

Step 2: Drag and drop desired fields for rows, columns, and the table body.

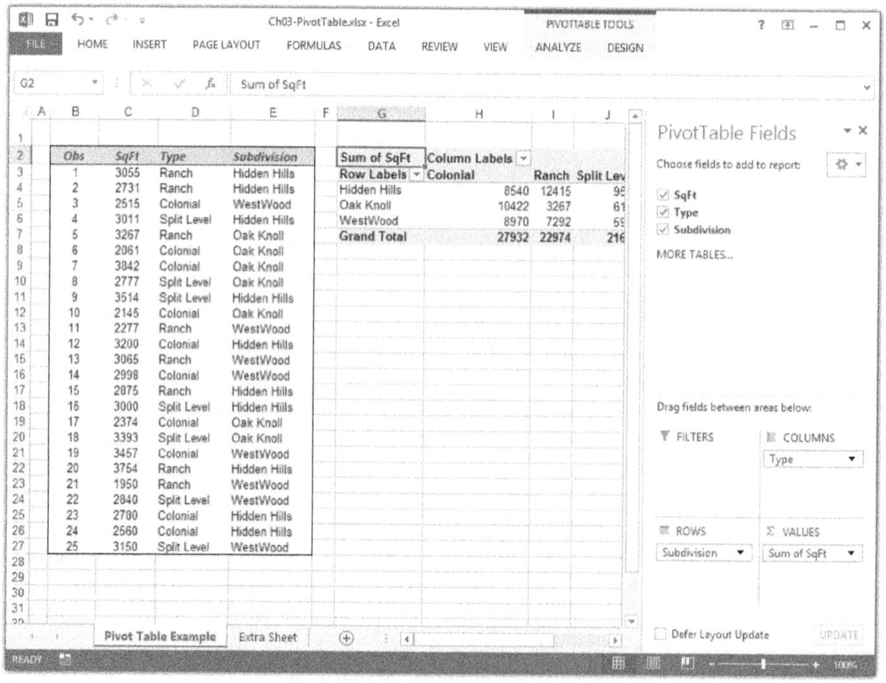

Step 3: Now you can format the table or right-click to choose desired field setting.

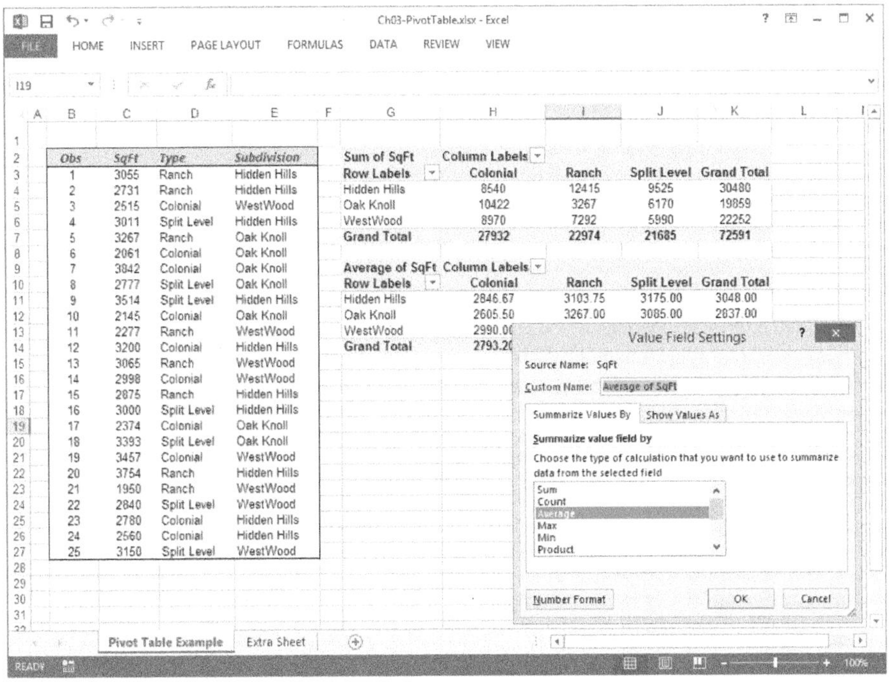

The McGraw-Hill Connect® website has a more detailed step-by-step guide to creating a pivot table (see the end of this chapter list of *LearningStats* demonstrations). A pivot table is especially useful when you have a large data matrix with several variables. For example, Figure 3.26 shows two pivot tables based on tax return data for $n = 4{,}801$ U.S. taxpayers. The first pivot table shows the number of taxpayers by filing type (single, married joint,

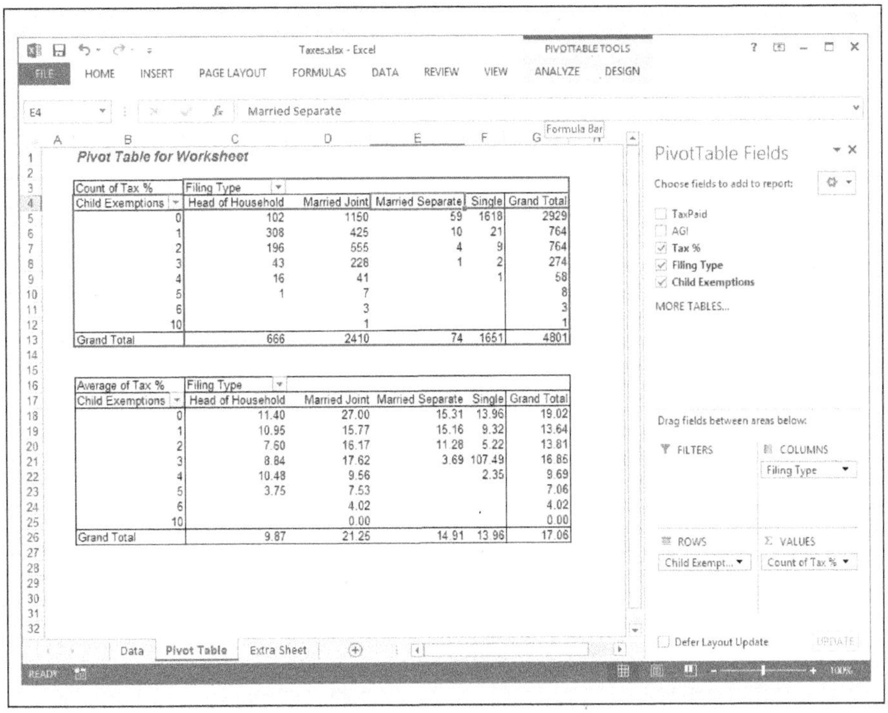

FIGURE 3.26

Two Pivot Tables for U.S. Income Tax Returns ($n = 4{,}801$) Taxes married separate, head of household) cross-tabulated against the number of child exemptions (0, 1, 2, . . . , 10). The second pivot table shows average tax rate (percent) for each cell in the cross-tabulation. Note that some of the averages are based on small cell counts.

3.9 DECEPTIVE GRAPHS

LO 3-10

Recognize deceptive graphing techniques.

We have explained how to create *good* graphs. Now, let's turn things around. As an impartial consumer of information, you need a checklist of errors to beware. Those who want to slant the facts may do these things deliberately, although most errors occur through ignorance. Use this list to protect yourself against ignorant or unscrupulous practitioners of the graphical arts.

Error 1: Nonzero Origin A nonzero origin will exaggerate the trend. Measured distances do not match the stated values or axis demarcations. The accounting profession is particularly aggressive in enforcing this rule. Although zero origins are preferred, sometimes a nonzero origin is needed to show sufficient detail. Here are two charts of the same data. The first chart (nonzero origin) exaggerates the trend.

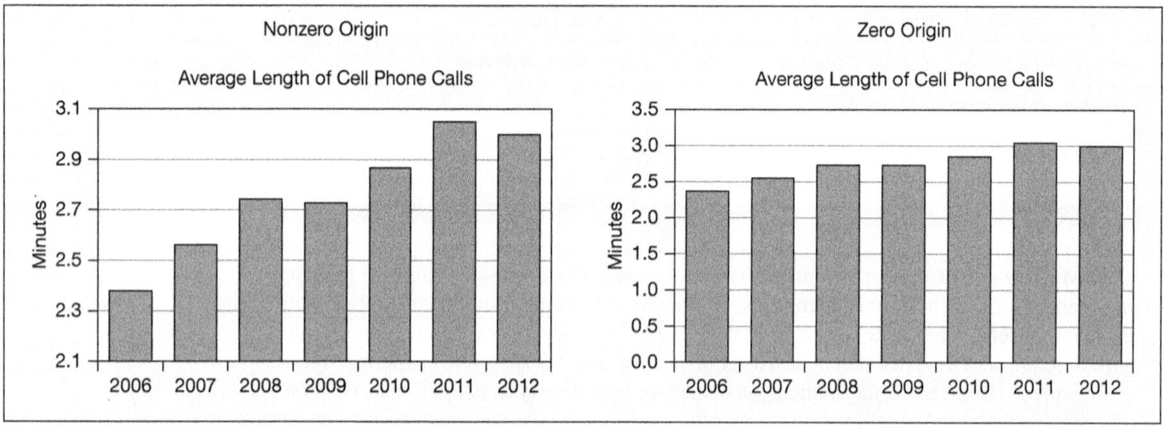

Error 2: Elastic Graph Proportions By shortening the X-axis in relation to the Y-axis, vertical change is exaggerated. For a time series (X-axis representing time), this can make a sluggish sales or profit curve appear steep. Conversely, a wide X-axis and short Y-axis can downplay alarming changes (e.g., hacker attacks, industrial accidents). Keep the *aspect ratio* (width/ height) below 2.00. Excel graphs use a default aspect ratio of about 1.68. The Golden Ratio you learned in art history suggests that 1.62 is ideal. Older TV screens use a 1.33 ratio, as do older PCs (640 × 480 pixels). Movies use a wide-screen format (up to 2.55) but DVDs may crop them to fit on a television screen. HDTV and multimedia computers use a 16:9 aspect ratio (about 1.78). Newer ultrawide monitors offer ratios of 21:9 (about 2.33). Charts whose height exceeds their width don't fit well on pages or computer screens. These two charts show the same data. Which *seems* to be growing faster?

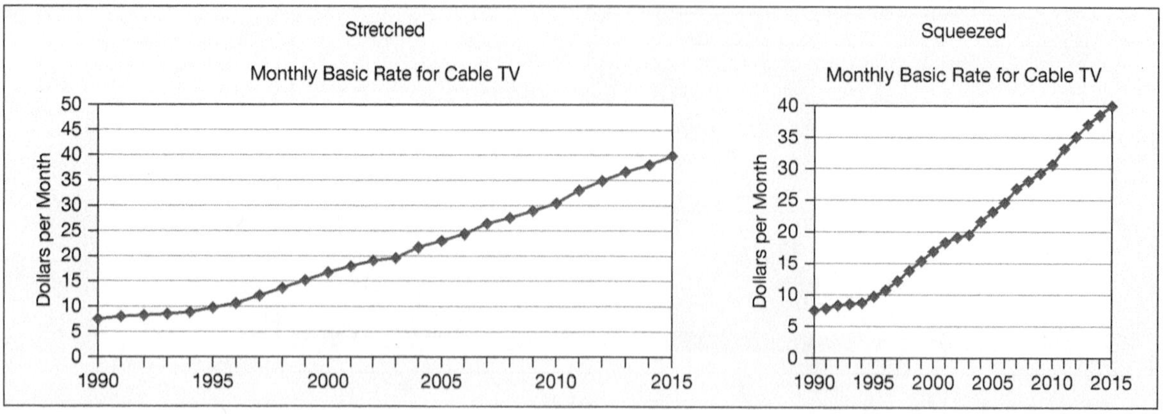

Error 3: Dramatic Titles and Distracting Pictures The title often is designed more to grab the reader's attention than to convey the chart's content (Criminals on a Spree, Deficit Swamps Economy). Sometimes the title attempts to draw your conclusion for you (Inflation Wipes Out Savings, Imports Dwarf Exports). A title should be short but adequate for the purpose.

To add visual pizzazz, artists may superimpose the chart on a photograph (e.g., a gasoline price chart atop a photo of an oil-drilling platform) or add colorful cartoon figures, banners, or drawings. This is mostly harmless but can distract the reader or impart an emotional slant. Advertisements sometimes feature mature, attractive, conservatively attired actors portraying scientists, doctors, or business leaders examining scientific-looking charts. Because the public respects science's reputation, such displays impart credibility to self-serving commercial claims. The medical school applications graph illustrates these deceptive elements.

Error 4: 3-D and Novelty Graphs Depth may enhance the visual impact of a bar chart, but it introduces ambiguity in bar height. Do we measure from the back of the bar or from the front? *3-D bar charts* are common in publications intended for a general readership (e.g., *USAToday*) but are seen less often in business. Novelty charts such as the *pyramid chart* should be avoided because they distort the bar volume and make it hard to measure bar height.

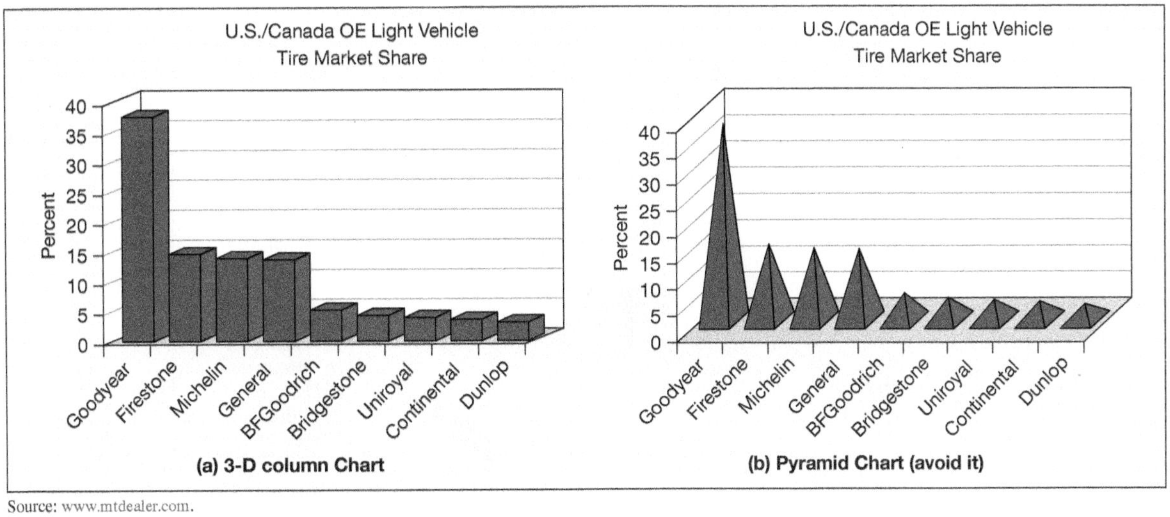

Source: www.mtdealer.com.

Error 5: Rotated Graphs By making a graph 3-dimensional and rotating it through space, the author can make trends appear to dwindle into the distance or loom alarmingly toward you. This example (medical school applications) combines several errors (nonzero origin, leading title, distracting picture, vague source, rotated 3-D look). Resist the temptation to use rotated graphs.

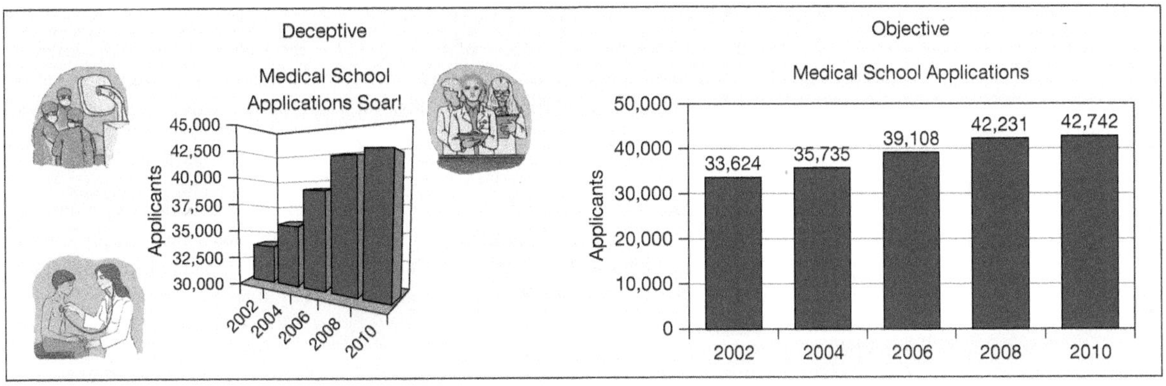

Source: www.aamc.org.

Error 6: Unclear Definitions or Scales Missing or unclear units of measurement (dollars? percent?) can render a chart useless. Even if the vertical scale is in dollars, we must know whether the variable being plotted is sales, profits, assets, or whatever. If percent, indicate clearly *percentage of what.* Without "tick" marks on the axis, the reader cannot identify individual data values. Gridlines help the viewer compare magnitudes but are often omitted to avoid graph clutter. For maximum clarity in a bar graph, label each bar with its numerical value.

Error 7: Vague Sources Large federal agencies or corporations employ thousands of people and issue hundreds of reports per year. Vague sources like "Department of Commerce" may indicate that the author lost the citation, didn't know the data source, or mixed data from several sources. Scientific publications insist on complete source citations. Rules are less rigorous for publications aimed at a general audience.

Error 8: Complex Graphs Complicated visual displays make the reader work harder. Keep your main objective in mind. Omit "bonus" detail or put it in the appendix. Apply the *10-second rule* to graphs. If the message really is complex, can it be broken into smaller parts? This example (surgery volume) combines several errors (silly subtitle, distracting pictures, no data labels, no definitions, vague source, too much information).

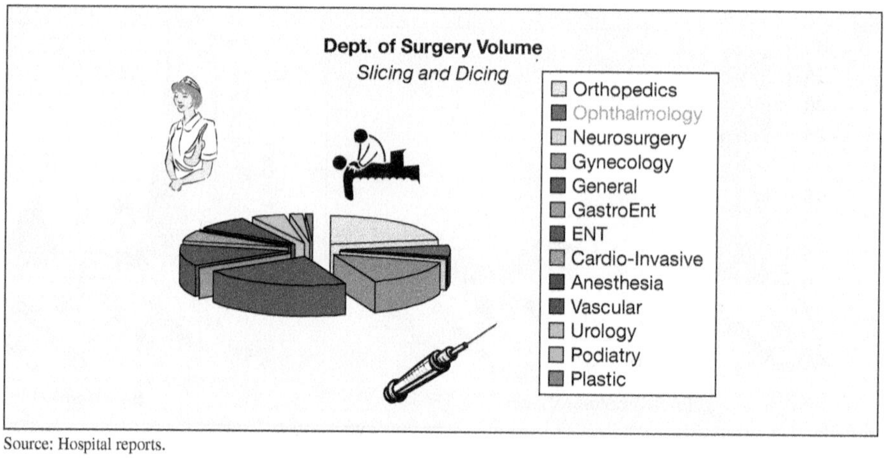

Source: Hospital reports.

Error 9: Gratuitous Effects Slide shows often use color and special effects (sound, interesting slide transitions, spinning text, etc.) to attract attention. But once the novelty wears off, audiences may find special effects annoying.

Error 10: Estimated Data In a spirit of zeal to include the "latest" figures, the last few data points in a time series are often estimated. Or perhaps a couple of years were missing or incompatible, so the author had to "fill in the blanks." At a minimum, estimated points should be noted.

Error 11: Area Trick One of the most pernicious visual tricks is simultaneously enlarging the width of the bars as their height increases, so the bar area misstates the true proportion (e.g., by replacing graph bars with figures like human beings, coins, or gas pumps). As figure height increases, so does width, distorting the area. This example (physician salaries) illustrates this distortion.

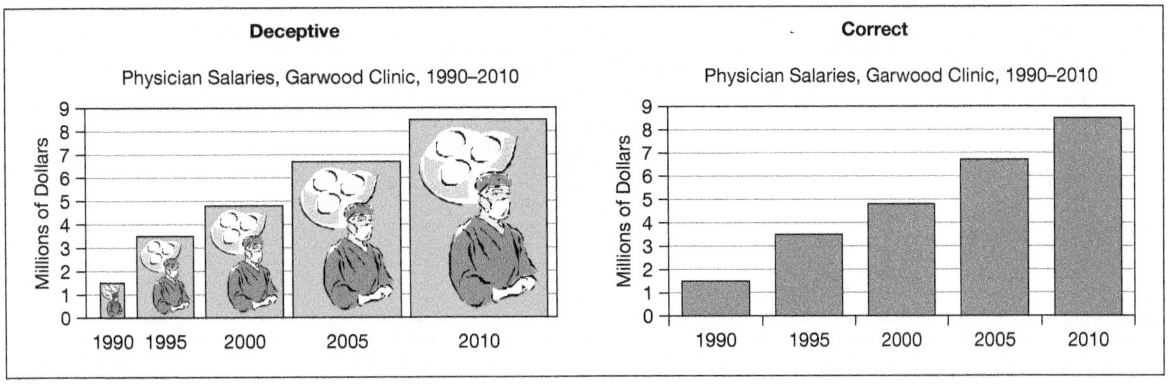

Final Advice

Can you trust any visual display (unless you created it yourself)? Be a skeptic, and be pleasantly surprised if the graph lives up to the best standards. Print media compete with TV and the web, so newspapers and magazines must use colorful charts to attract reader interest. People enjoy visual displays, so we accept some artistic liberties. Mass-readership publications like *U.S. News & World Report, Time, USA Today,* or even specialized business-oriented publications like *Forbes, Fortune, Bloomberg Businessweek,* and *The Wall Street Journal* should not be judged by the same standards you would apply to an academic journal. But businesses do want charts that follow the rules, because a deceptive chart may have serious consequences. Decisions may be made about products or services that affect lives, market share, and jobs (including yours). So know the rules, try to follow them, and expect your peers and subordinates to do the same. Catchy graphics have a place in selling your ideas but shouldn't dominate the data.

Further Challenges

If you enjoy playing with computers, try to learn these skills on your own:

- Copy and paste Excel charts into Word or PowerPoint.
- Copy and paste charts from other software (MINITAB, MegaStat, JMP, SPSS).
- Use screen captures and edit the results in Paint if necessary.
- Use presentation software (e.g., PowerPoint) with transition effects.
- Know how (and when) to link PowerPoint charts to spreadsheets.
- Use clip art and create your own graphics.

CHAPTER SUMMARY

For a set of observations on a single numerical variable, a **stem-and-leaf plot** or a **dot plot** displays the individual data values, while a **frequency distribution** classifies the data into classes called **bins** for a **histogram** of **frequencies** for each bin. The number of bins and their limits are matters left to your judgment, though **Sturges' Rule** offers advice on the number of bins. The **line chart** shows values of one or more **time series** variables plotted against time. A **log scale** is sometimes used in time series charts when data vary by orders of magnitude. The **bar chart** or **column chart** shows a **numerical** data value for each category of an **attribute.** However, a bar chart can also be used for a time series. A **scatter plot** can reveal the association (or lack of association) between two variables *X* and *Y*. The **pie chart** (showing a **numerical** data value for each category of an **attribute** if the data values are parts of a whole) is common but should be used with caution. Sometimes a **simple table** is the best visual display. Creating effective visual displays is an acquired skill. Excel offers a wide range of charts from which to choose. Deceptive graphs are found frequently in both media and business presentations, and the consumer should be aware of common errors.

KEY TERMS

arithmetic scale
bar chart
center
column chart
dot plot
frequency distribution
frequency polygon
histogram
left-skewed
line chart
logarithmic scale
modal class
ogive
outlier
Pareto chart
pie chart
pivot table
right-skewed
scatter plot
shape
stacked column chart
stacked dot plot
stem-and-leaf plot
Sturges' Rule
symmetric
trend line
variability

CHAPTER REVIEW

1. Name two attractive features and two limitations of the (a) stem-and-leaf plot and (b) dot plot.
2. (a) What is a frequency distribution? (b) What are the steps in creating one?
3. (a) What is a histogram? (b) What does it show?
4. (a) What is a bimodal histogram? (b) Explain the difference between left-skewed, symmetric, and right-skewed histograms. (c) What is an outlier?
5. (a) What is a scatter plot? (b) What do scatter plots reveal? (c) Sketch a scatter plot with a moderate positive correlation. (d) Sketch a scatter plot with a strong negative correlation.
6. For what kind of data would we use a bar chart? List three tips for creating effective bar charts.
7. For what kind of data would we use a line chart? List three tips for creating effective line charts.
8. (a) List the three most common types of charts in business, and sketch each type (no real data, just a sketch). (b) List three specialized charts that can be created in Excel, and sketch each type (no real data, just a sketch).
9. (a) For what kind of data would we use a pie chart? (b) Name two common pie chart errors. (c) Why are pie charts regarded with skepticism by some statisticians?
10. Which types of charts can be used for time series data?
11. (a) When might we need a log scale? (b) What do equal distances on a log scale represent? (c) State one drawback of a log scale graph.
12. When might we use a stacked column chart? An area chart? A Pareto chart?
13. List five deceptive graphical techniques.
14. What is a pivot table? Why is it useful?

CHAPTER EXERCISES

Note: In these exercises, you may use a software package if your instructor agrees. For example, use MegaStat's Descriptive Statistics for dot plots or Frequency Distributions for histograms. Use MINITAB's Graphs or a similar software package to create the dot plot or histogram.

3.25 The durations (minutes) of 26 electric power outages in the community of Sonando Heights over the past five years are shown below. (a) Make a stem-and-leaf diagram. (b) Make a histogram. (c) Describe the shape of the distribution. **Duration**

32	44	25	66	27	12	62	9	51	4	17	50	35
99	30	21	12	53	25	2	18	24	84	30	17	17

3.26 The U.S. Postal Service will ship a Priority Mail® Large Flat Rate Box (12" × 12" × 5½") anywhere in the United States for a fixed price, regardless of weight. The weights (ounces) of 20 randomly chosen boxes are shown below. (a) Make a stem-and-leaf diagram. (b) Make a histogram. (c) Describe the shape of the distribution. **Weights**

72	86	28	67	64	65	45	86	31	32
39	92	90	91	84	62	80	74	63	86

3.27 A study of 40 U.S. cardiac care centers showed the following ratios of nurses to beds. (a) Prepare a dot plot. (b) Prepare a frequency distribution and histogram (you may either specify the bins yourself or use automatic bins). (c) Describe the distribution, based on these displays. **Nurses**

1.48	1.16	1.24	1.52	1.30	1.28	1.68	1.40	1.12	0.98	0.93	2.76
1.34	1.58	1.72	1.38	1.44	1.41	1.34	1.96	1.29	1.21	2.00	1.50
1.68	1.39	1.62	1.17	1.07	2.11	2.40	1.35	1.48	1.59	1.81	1.15
1.35	1.42	1.33	1.41								

3.28 The first Rose Bowl (football) was played in 1902. The next was not played until 1916, but a Rose Bowl has been played every year since then. The margin of victory in each of the 95 Rose Bowls from 1902 through 2011 is shown below (0 indicates a tie). (a) Prepare a stem-and-leaf plot. (b) Prepare a frequency distribution and histogram (you may either specify the bins yourself or use automatic bins). (c) Describe the distribution, based on these displays. (Data are from http://en.wikipedia.org) **RoseBowl**

0	7	7	7	7	7	7	7	8	9	10	10	13	13
14	14	14	14	14	14	14	14	14	14	17	17	17	17
17	17	17	17	18	20	20	20	20	20	20	20	21	21
21	21	21	21	21	22	22	23	23	24	24	25	26	27
27	27	27	28	28	28	28	29	29	32	34	34	34	34
34	35	35	37	38	38	38	38	38	38	40	41	41	42
42	42	44	45	45	45	46	47	49	49	49			

3.29 An executive's telephone log showed the following data for the length of 65 calls initiated during the last week of July. (a) Prepare a dot plot. (b) Prepare a frequency distribution and histogram (you may either specify the bins yourself or use automatic bins). (c) Describe the distribution, based on these displays. **CallLength**

1	2	10	5	3	3	2	20	1	1
6	3	13	2	2	1	26	3	1	3
1	2	1	7	1	2	3	1	2	12
1	4	2	2	29	1	1	1	8	5
1	4	2	1	1	1	1	6	1	2
3	3	6	1	3	1	1	5	1	18
2	13	13	1	6					

3.30 Below are batting averages of the New York Yankees players who were at bat five times or more in 2006. (a) Construct a frequency distribution. Explain how you chose the number of bins and the bin limits. (b) Make a histogram and describe its appearance. (c) Repeat, using a different number of bins and different bin limits. (d) Did your visual impression of the data change when you changed the number of bins? Explain. **Yankees**

Batting Averages for the 2006 New York Yankees

Player	*Avg*	*Player*	*Avg*	*Player*	*Avg*
Derek Jeter	0.343	Miguel Cairo	0.239	Sal Fasano	0.143
Johnny Damon	0.285	Bobby Abreu	0.330	Terrence Long	0.167
Alex Rodriguez	0.290	Hideki Matsui	0.302	Kevin Thompson	0.300
Robinson Cano	0.342	Gary Sheffield	0.298	Kevin Reese	0.417
Jorge Posada	0.277	Craig Wilson	0.212	Andy Cannizaro	0.250
Melky Cabrera	0.280	Bubba Crosby	0.207	Randy Johnson	0.167
Jason Giambi	0.253	Aaron Guiel	0.256	Wil Nieves	0.000
Bernie Williams	0.281	Kelly Stinnett	0.228		
Andy Phillips	0.240	Nick Green	0.240		

Source: www.thebaseballcube.com.

3.31 Download the full data set of measurements of cockpit noise level for a commercial jet airliner from the McGraw-Hill Connect® website (only six data values are shown). (a) Use Excel to make a scatter plot, placing Airspeed on the X-axis and Noise Level on the Y-axis. Add titles and modify the default colors, fonts, etc., as you judge appropriate to make the scatter plot effective. (b) Describe the relationship (if any) between X and Y. Weak? Strong? Negative? Positive? Linear? Nonlinear? *Hint:* You may need to rescale the X and Y axes to see more detail.

Airspeed and Cockpit Noise (n = 61 measurements) CockpitNoise

Obs	*Airspeed (knots)*	*Noise Level (dB)*
1	250	83
2	340	89
3	320	88
.	.	.
.	.	.
.	.	.
59	370	91
60	405	93
61	250	82

Note: The decibel (dB) is a logarithmic unit that indicates the ratio of measured sound pressure to a benchmark. Some familiar examples for comparison: Vuvuzela horn at 1 m (120 dB), jack hammer at 1 m (100 dB), handheld electric mixer (65 dB).

3.32 Download the full data set from the McGraw-Hill Connect® website (only six data values are shown). (a) Use Excel to make a scatter plot, placing Revenue on the X-axis and Net Income on the Y-axis. Add titles and modify the default colors, fonts, etc., as you judge appropriate to make the scatter plot effective. (b) Describe the relationship (if any) between X and Y. Weak? Strong? Negative? Positive? Linear? Nonlinear?

Revenue and Net Income (millions) for 27 Randomly Chosen Fortune 1000 Companies RevenueIncome

Company	*Revenue*	*Net Income*
1	1,494.9	30.8
2	1,523.2	328.9
3	1,565.8	90.5
.	.	.
.	.	.
.	.	.
25	11,066.8	168.2
26	11,164.2	253.6
27	19,468.0	496.5

Source: money.cnn.com/magazines/fortune/fortune500/2006/full_list/301_400.html. Data are from the April 17, 2006, issue.

3.33 Download the full data set from the McGraw-Hill Connect® website (only six data values are shown). (a) Use Excel to make a scatter plot, placing GDP per Capita on the X-axis and Birth Rate on the Y-axis. Add titles and modify the default colors, fonts, etc., as you judge appropriate to make the scatter plot effective. (b) Describe the relationship (if any) between X and Y. Weak? Strong? Negative? Positive? Linear? Nonlinear?

GDP per Capita and Birth Rate (n = 153 nations) GDPBirthRate

Nation	*GDP per Capita*	*Birth Rate*
Afghanistan	800	41.03
Albania	3,800	18.59
Algeria	5,600	22.34
.	.	.
.	.	.
.	.	.
Yemen	820	43.30
Zambia	870	41.01
Zimbabwe	2,450	24.59

Source: Central Intelligence Agency, *The World Factbook*, 2003.

3.34 (a) What kind of display is this? (b) Identify its strengths and weaknesses, using the tips and checklists shown in this chapter. (c) Can you suggest any improvements? Would a different type of display be better? WomenPilots

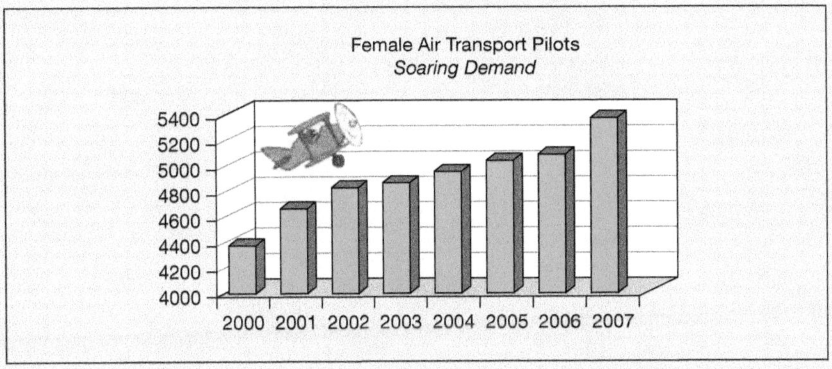

Source: www.faa.gov.

3.35 (a) What kind of display is this? (b) Identify its strengths and weaknesses, using the tips and checklists shown in this chapter. (c) Can you suggest any improvements? Would a different type of display be better? MedError

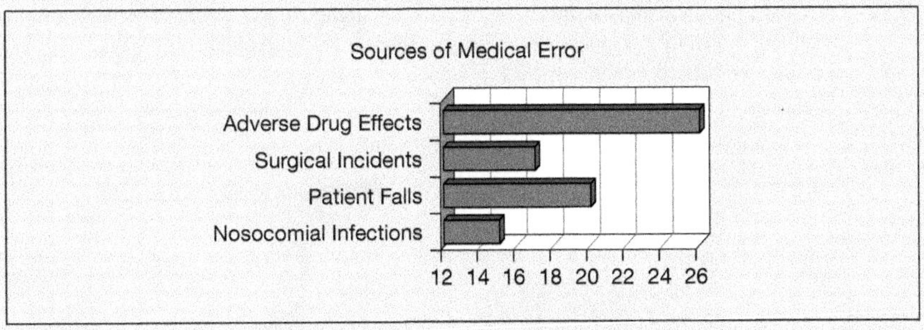

3.36 (a) What kind of display is this? (b) Identify its strengths and weaknesses, using the tips and checklists shown in this chapter. (c) Can you suggest any improvements? Would a different type of display be better? Oxnard

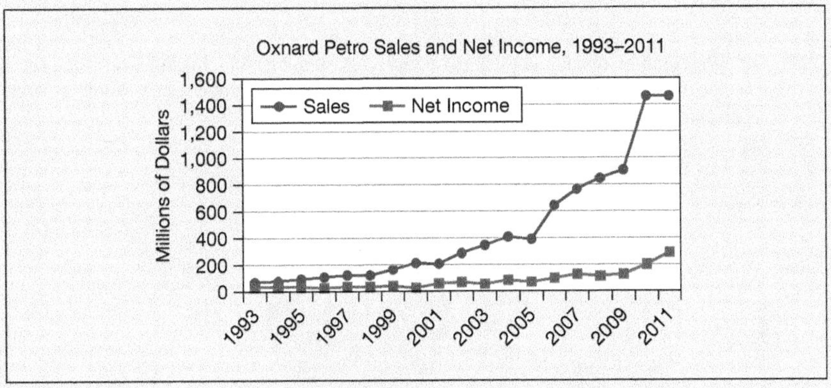

3.37 (a) What kind of display is this? (b) Identify its strengths and weaknesses, using the tips and checklists shown in this chapter. (c) Can you suggest any improvements? Would a different type of display be better?

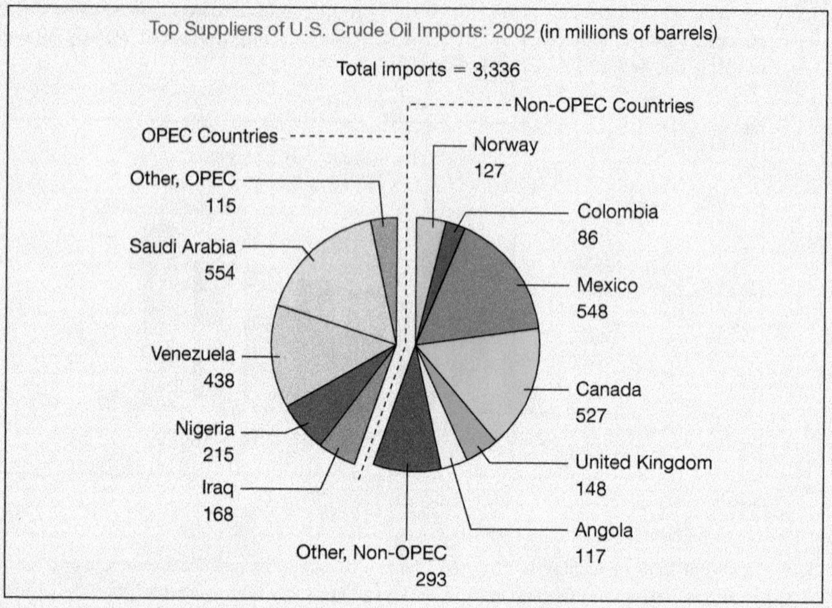

Source: *Statistical Abstract of the United States, 2003.*

3.38 (a) What kind of display is this? (b) Identify its strengths and weaknesses, using the tips and checklists shown in this chapter. (c) Can you suggest any improvements? Would a different type of display be better? **BirthRate**

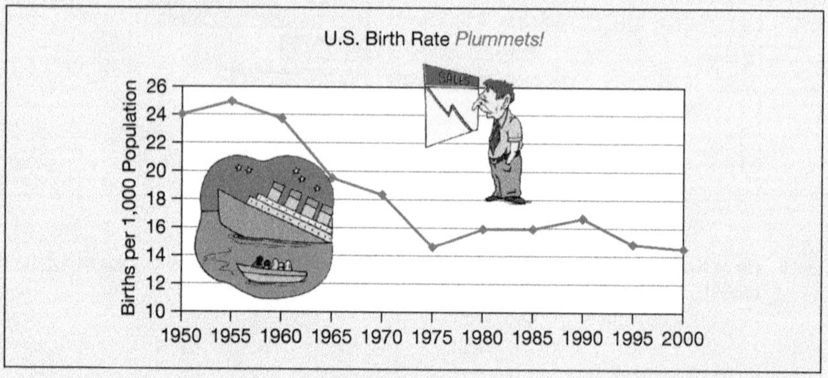

3.39 (a) What kind of display is this? (b) Identify its strengths and weaknesses, using the tips and checklists shown in this chapter. (c) Can you suggest any improvements? Would a different type of display be better? **Advertising**

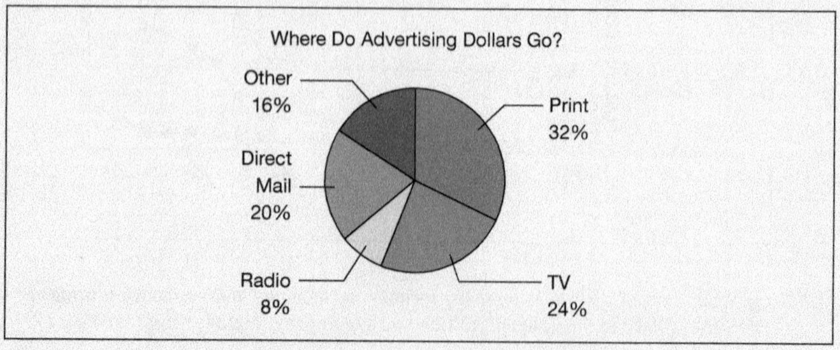

Source: *Statistical Abstract of the United States, 2002,* p. 772.

3.40 (a) What kind of display is this? (b) Identify its strengths and weaknesses, using the tips and checklists shown in this chapter. (c) Can you suggest any improvements? Would a different type of display be better?

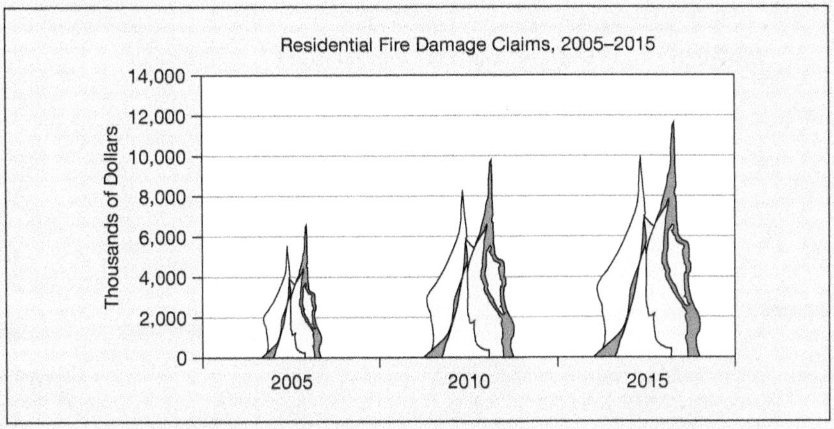

Source: Insurance company records.

3.41 (a) What kind of display is this? (b) Identify its strengths and weaknesses, using the tips and checklists shown in this chapter. (c) Can you suggest any improvements? Would a different type of display be better? **Bankruptcies**

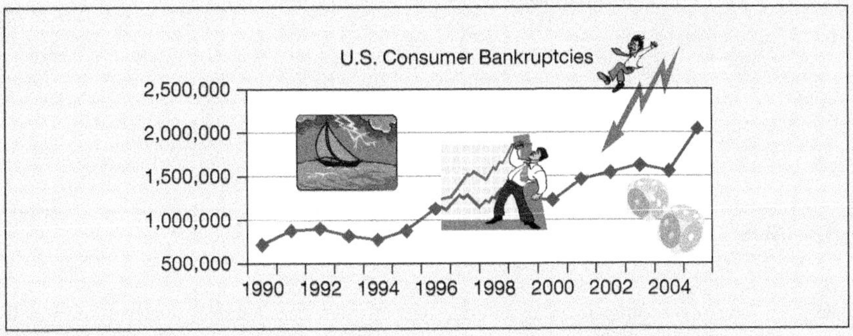

Source: *American Bankruptcy Institute*, www.abiworld.org.

3.42 (a) What kind of display is this? (b) Identify its strengths and weaknesses, using the tips and checklists shown in this chapter. (c) Can you suggest any improvements? Would a different type of display be better?

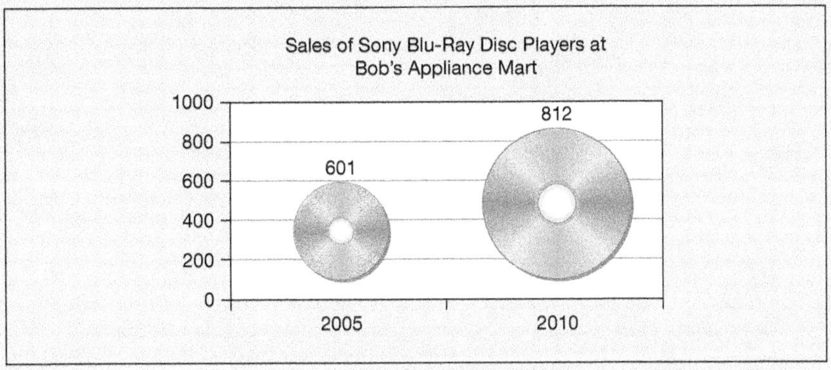

3.43 (a) Use Excel to prepare an appropriate type of chart (bar, line, pie, scatter) to display the following data. Modify the default colors, fonts, etc., as you judge appropriate to make the display effective. (b) Would more than one kind of display be acceptable? Why or why not?

Where Did You Purchase Your Statistics Textbook? Textbook

Response	*Count*
Campus Bookstore	147
Retail Outlet	66
Web (e.g., Amazon)	49
Another Student	7
Total	269

Source: Survey of statistics students at two large public universities.

3.44 (a) Use Excel to prepare an appropriate type of chart (bar, line, pie, scatter) to display the following data. Modify the default colors, fonts, etc., as you judge appropriate to make the display effective. (b) Would more than one kind of display be acceptable? Why or why not?

New Car Color Preferences for U.S. Buyers CarColor

Color	*Percent*
Blue	12
Green	7
Natural	12
Red	13
Silver/Grey	24
White	16
Black	13
Other	3
Total	100

Source: *Detroit Auto Scene* 24, no. 1 (2006), p. 1.

3.45 (a) Use Excel to prepare an appropriate type of chart (bar, line, pie, scatter) to display the following data. Modify the default colors, fonts, etc., as you judge appropriate to make the display effective. (b) Would more than one kind of display be acceptable? Why or why not?

Domestic Market Share, Ten Largest U.S. Airlines AirlineMkt

Airline	*Percent*
AirTran	3.3
Alaska	2.9
American	14.3
Continental	7.6
Delta	10.8
JetBlue	4.3
Northwest	6.4
Southwest	13.0
United	11.0
US Airways	8.3
Other	18.1
Total	100.0

Source: www.transtats.bts.gov. Data are for February 2008 to January 2009. Based on revenue passenger miles.

3.46 (a) Use Excel to prepare an appropriate type of chart (bar, line, pie, scatter) to display the following data. Modify the default colors, fonts, etc., as you judge appropriate to make the display effective. (b) Would more than one kind of display be acceptable? Why or why not?

U.S. and World Petroleum Usage (millions of barrels per day) Petroleum

Used by	*1996*	*1998*	*2000*	*2002*	*2004*	*2006*	*2007*	*2008*	*2009*	*2010*
U.S.	18.3	18.9	19.7	19.8	20.7	20.7	20.7	19.5	18.8	19.3
Non-U.S.	53.2	55.1	57.0	58.4	61.9	64.6	65.6	66.3	65.6	67.7

Source: www.eia.doe.gov.

3.47 (a) Use Excel to prepare an appropriate type of chart (bar, line, pie, scatter) to display the following data. Modify the default colors, fonts, etc., as you judge appropriate to make the display effective. (b) Would more than one kind of display be acceptable? Why or why not?

U.S. Market Share for Search Engines WebSearch

Search Engine	*Percent*
Google	45.4
Yahoo	28.2
Microsoft	11.7
Ask	5.8
AOL/Time Warner	5.4
All Others	3.5
Total	100.0

Source: *The New York Times*, December 4, 2006, p. C1.

3.48 (a) Use Excel to prepare an appropriate type of chart (bar, line, pie, scatter) to display the following data. Modify the default colors, fonts, etc., as you judge appropriate to make the display effective. (b) Would more than one kind of display be acceptable? Why or why not?

U.S. Energy Consumption by Source Energy

Source	*Quad BTU*	*Percent*
Petroleum	37.06	38.4%
Natural Gas	23.15	24.0%
Coal	20.49	21.2%
Nuclear	8.52	8.8%
Renewables	7.17	7.4%
Other	0.21	0.2%
Total	96.60	100.0%

Source: *Statistical Abstract of the United States, 2011*, p. 583.

3.49 (a) Use Excel to prepare a Pareto chart of the following data. (b) Which three service providers account for approximately 80 percent of all responses?

Cell Phone Service Provider n **= 158** CellPhone

Service Provider	*Percent*	*Cumulative Percent*
Verizon	37.3	37.3
Cingular	29.7	67.1
T-Mobile	13.3	80.4
Sprint	8.9	89.2
Other	4.4	93.7
Nextel	3.2	96.8
Alltel	2.5	99.4
Virgin	0.6	100.0

Source: Web survey of 158 statistics students, 2007.

DO-IT-YOURSELF

3.50 (a) Clip an example of a deceptive visual data presentation from a recent magazine or newspaper. (If it is from a library, make a photocopy instead.) Try to choose an outrageous example that violates many principles of ideal graphs. (b) Cite the exact source where you found the display. (c) What do you think is its presumed purpose? (d) Write a short, critical evaluation of its strengths and weaknesses. Be sure to attach the original clipping (or a good photocopy) to your analysis.

RELATED READING

Visual Displays

Cleveland, William S. *Visualizing Data*. Hobart Press, 1993.

Huff, Darrell; and Irving Geiss. *How to Lie with Statistics*. W. W. Norton, 1954.

Jones, Gerald E. *How to Lie with Charts*. 2nd ed. La Puerta, 2007.

Monmonier, Mark. *How to Lie with Maps*. University of Chicago Press, 1996.

Tufte, Edward R. *The Visual Display of Quantitative Information*. 2nd ed. Graphics Press, 2004.

Wilkinson, Leland. *The Grammar of Graphics*. Springer, 2005.

Wong, Dona M. *The Wall Street Journal Guide to Information Graphics: The Dos and Don'ts of Presenting Data, Facts, and Figures*. W. W. Norton, 2010.

Zelazny, Gene. *Say It with Charts: The Executive's Guide to Visual Communication*. 4th ed. McGraw-Hill Professional, 2001.

CHAPTER 3 More Learning Resources

You can access these *LearningStats* demonstrations through McGraw-Hill's Connect® to help you understand visual data displays.

connect™

Topic	*LearningStats Demonstrations*
Effective visual displays	Presenting Data—I Presenting Data—II EDA Graphics
How to make an Excel chart	Excel Charts: Step-by-Step Pivot Tables: Step-by-Step Using MegaStat Excel Charts: Histograms Using MINITAB
Applications	Bimodal Data Sturges' Rule Stem-and-Leaf Plots
Screen Cam Tutorials	Excel Basics Making Excel Histograms Making Scatter Plots

Key: = PowerPoint = Excel = PDF = Screen Cam Tutorials

Megastat Software

MegaStat by J. B. Orris of Butler University is a simple Excel add-in that can be downloaded from http://www.mhhe.com/megastat and installed on your own PC or Mac. MegaStat goes beyond Excel's built-in statistical functions to offer a full range of statistical tools to help you analyze data, create graphs, and perform calculations. MegaStat examples are shown throughout this textbook.

Chapter 4. Descriptve Statistics

CHAPTER 4 Descriptive Statistics

CHAPTER CONTENTS

CHAPTER LEARNING OBJECTIVES

LO

When you finish this chapter you should be able to

LO 4-1 Explain the concepts of center, variability, and shape.

LO 4-2 Calculate and interpret common measures of center.

LO 4-3 Calculate and interpret common measures of variability.

LO 4-4 Apply Chebyshev's theorem.

LO 4-5 Apply the Empirical Rule and recognize outliers.

LO 4-6 Transform a data set into standardized values.

LO 4-7 Calculate quartiles and other percentiles.

LO 4-8 Make and interpret box plots.

LO 4-9 Calculate and interpret a correlation coefficient and covariance.

LO 4-10 Calculate the mean and standard deviation from grouped data.

LO 4-11 Assess skewness and kurtosis in a sample.

4.1 NUMERICAL DESCRIPTION

LO 4-1

Explain the concepts of center, variability, and shape.

The last chapter explained *visual* descriptions of data (e.g., histograms, dot plots, scatter plots). This chapter explains *numerical* descriptions of data. Descriptive measures derived from a sample (n items) are *statistics,* while for a population (N items or infinite) they are *parameters*. For a sample of numerical data, we are interested in three key characteristics: center, variability, and shape. Table 4.1 summarizes the questions that we will be asking about the data.

TABLE 4.1 Characteristics of Numerical Data

Characteristic	*Interpretation*
Center	Where are the data values concentrated? What seem to be typical or middle data values? Is there central tendency?
Variability	How much dispersion is there in the data? How spread out are the data values? Are there unusual values?
Shape	Are the data values distributed symmetrically? Skewed? Sharply peaked? Flat? Bimodal?

EXAMPLE 4.1

Vehicle Quality

Every year, J.D. Power and Associates issues its initial vehicle quality ratings. These ratings are of interest to consumers, dealers, and manufacturers. Table 4.2 shows defect rates for 33 vehicle brands. We will demonstrate how numerical statistics can be used to summarize a data set like this. The reported defect rates are based on a random sample of vehicles within each brand.

TABLE 4.2 Defects per 100 Vehicles JDPower

Brand	*Defects*	*Brand*	*Defects*	*Brand*	*Defects*
Acura	86	Hyundai	102	MINI	133
Audi	111	Infiniti	107	Mitsubishi	146
BMW	113	Jaguar	130	Nissan	111
Buick	114	Jeep	129	Porsche	83
Cadillac	111	Kia	126	Ram	110
Chevrolet	111	Land Rover	170	Scion	114
Chrysler	122	Lexus	88	Suburu	121
Dodge	130	Lincoln	106	Suzuki	122
Ford	93	Mazda	114	Toyota	117
GMC	126	Mercedes-Benz	87	Volkswagen	135
Honda	95	Mercury	113	Volvo	109

Source: J.D. Power and Associates 2010 Initial Quality Study™. Ratings are intended for educational purposes only, and should not be used as a guide to consumer decisions.

Preliminary Analysis

Before calculating any statistics, we consider how the data were collected. A web search reveals that J.D. Power and Associates is a well-established independent company whose methods are widely considered to be objective. Data on defects are obtained by inspecting randomly chosen vehicles for each brand, counting the defects, and dividing the number of defects by the number of vehicles inspected. J.D. Power multiplies the result by 100 to obtain defects per 100 vehicles, rounded to the nearest integer. The underlying measurement scale is continuous (e.g., if 4 defects were found in 3 vehicles, the defect rate would be 1.333333, or 133 defects per 100 vehicles). Defect rates would vary from year to year, and perhaps even within a given model year, so the timing of the study could affect the results. Since the analysis is based on sampling of vehicles within each brand, we must allow for the possibility of sampling error. With these cautions in mind, we look at the data. A good first step is to sort the data, as shown in Table 4.3.

TABLE 4.3

Defects per 100 Vehicles Ranked Lowest to Highest JDPower

Brand	*Defects*	*Brand*	*Defects*	*Brand*	*Defects*
Porsche	83	Audi	111	Chrysler	122
Acura	86	Cadillac	111	Suzuki	122
Mercedes-Benz	87	Chevrolet	111	GMC	126
Lexus	88	Nissan	111	Kia	126
Ford	93	BMW	113	Jeep	129
Honda	95	Mercury	113	Dodge	130
Hyundai	102	Buick	114	Jaguar	130
Lincoln	106	Mazda	114	MINI	133
Infiniti	107	Scion	114	Volkswagen	135
Volvo	109	Toyota	117	Mitsubishi	146
Ram	110	Suburu	121	Land Rover	170

The sorted data in Table 4.3 provide insight into both *center* and *variability*. The values range from 83 (Porsche) to 170 (Land Rover), while the middle values seem mostly to lie between 110 and 120. The dot plot in Figure 4.1 reveals additional detail, including one unusual value.

FIGURE 4.1

Dot Plot of J.D. Power Data (n = 33) JDPower

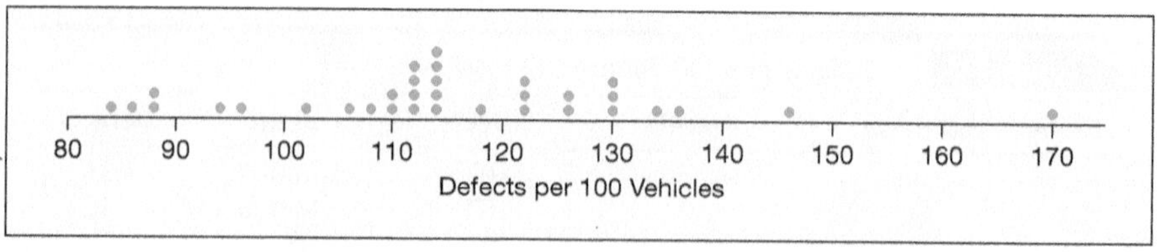

Except for tiny samples, sorting would be done in Excel. As illustrated in Figure 4.2, highlight the data array (including the headings), click on the Data tab, choose the Sort icon, select the column to sort on, and click OK.

The next visual step is a histogram, shown in Figure 4.3. The modal class (largest frequency) between 100 and 120 reveals the *center*. The *shape* of the histogram is right-skewed.

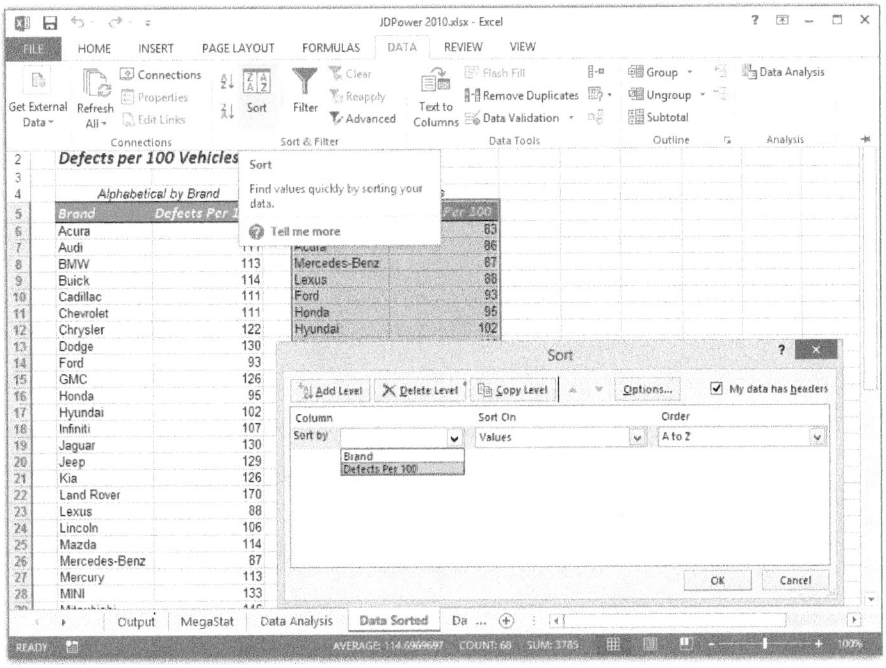

FIGURE 4.2

Sorting Data in Excel

JDPower

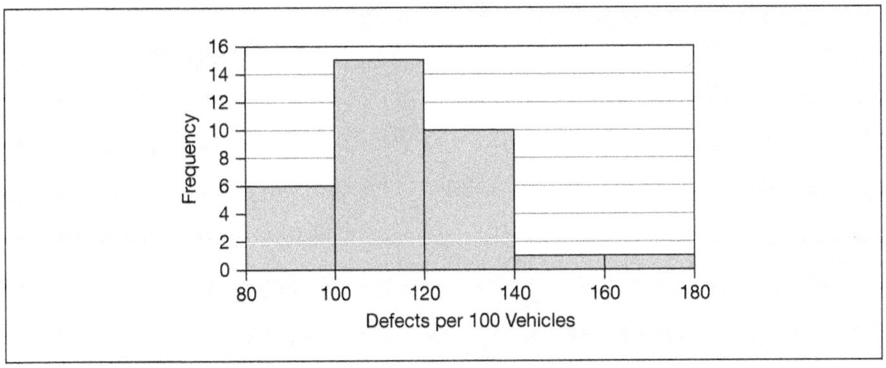

FIGURE 4.3

Histogram of J.D. Power Data (n = 33)

JDPower

4.2 MEASURES OF CENTER

LO 4-2

Calculate and interpret common measures of center.

When we speak of *center*, we are trying to describe the middle or typical values of a distribution. You can assess central tendency in a general way from a dot plot or histogram, but numerical statistics allow more precise statements. Table 4.4 lists six common measures of center. Each has strengths and weaknesses. We need to look at several of them to obtain a clear picture of central tendency.

Mean

The most familiar statistical measure of center is the **mean**. It is the sum of the data values divided by the number of data items. For a population we denote it μ, while for a sample we call it $\bar{x}$. We use equation 4.1 to calculate the mean of a population:

$$\mu = \frac{\sum_{i=1}^{N} x_i}{N} \quad \text{(population definition)} \qquad \textbf{(4.1)}$$

TABLE 4.4 Six Measures of Center

Statistic	*Formula*	*Excel Formula*	*Pro*	*Con*
Mean	$\frac{1}{n}\sum_{i=1}^{n} x_i$	=AVERAGE(Data)	Familiar and uses all the sample information.	Influenced by extreme values.
Median	Middle value in sorted array	=MEDIAN(Data)	Robust when extreme data values exist.	Ignores extremes and can be affected by gaps in data values.
Mode*	Most frequently occurring data value	=MODE.SNGL(Data)	Useful for attribute data or discrete data with a small range.	May not be unique, and is not helpful for continuous data.
Midrange	$\frac{x_{min} + x_{max}}{2}$	=0.5*(MIN(Data) +MAX(Data))	Easy to understand and calculate.	Influenced by extreme values and ignores most data values.
Geometric mean (G)	$\sqrt[n]{x_1 x_2 \cdots x_n}$	=GEOMEAN(Data)	Useful for growth rates and mitigates high extremes.	Less familiar and requires positive data.
Trimmed mean	Same as the mean except omit highest and lowest k% of data values (e.g., 5%)	=TRIMMEAN(Data, Percent)	Mitigates effects of extreme values.	Excludes some data values that could be relevant.

*Equivalent to =MODE(Data) in earlier versions of Excel (see Appendix J for further discussion).

Since we rarely deal with populations, the sample notation of equation 4.2 is more commonly seen:

$$\bar{x} = \frac{\sum_{i=1}^{n} x_i}{n} \quad \text{(sample definition)} \tag{4.2}$$

We calculate the mean by using Excel's function =AVERAGE(Data) where Data is an array containing the data. So for the sample of $n = 33$ car brands:

$$\bar{x} = \frac{\sum_{i=1}^{n} x_i}{n} = \frac{83 + 86 + 87 + \cdots + 135 + 146 + 170}{33} = \frac{3785}{33} = 114.697$$

Characteristics of the Mean

The arithmetic mean is the "average" with which most of us are familiar. The mean is affected by every sample item. It is the balancing point or fulcrum in a distribution if we view the X-axis as a lever arm and represent each data item as a physical weight, as illustrated in Figure 4.4 for the J.D. Power data.

FIGURE 4.4

Mean as Fulcrum (n = 33 vehicles)

JDPower

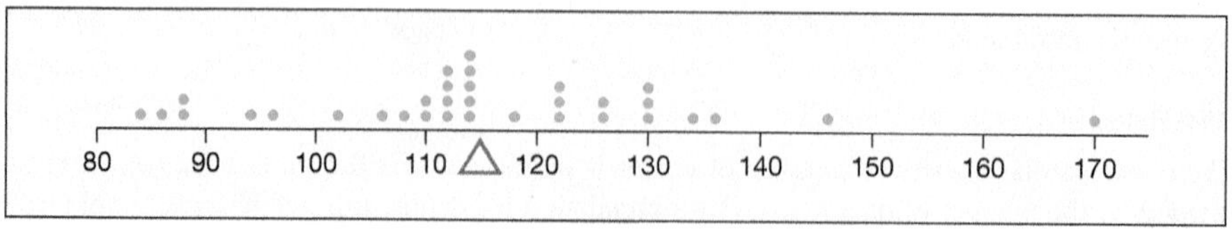

The mean is the balancing point because it has the property that distances from the mean to the data points *always* sum to zero:

$$\sum_{i=1}^{n} (x_i - \bar{x}) = 0 \tag{4.3}$$

This statement is true for *any* sample or population, regardless of its shape (skewed, symmetric, bimodal, etc.). Even when there are extreme values, the distances below the mean are *exactly* counterbalanced by the distances above the mean.

For example, Bob's scores on five quizzes were 42, 60, 70, 75, 78. His mean is pulled down to 65, mainly because of his poor showing on one quiz, as illustrated in Figure 4.5. Although the data are asymmetric, the three scores above the mean exactly counterbalance the two scores below the mean:

$$\sum_{i=1}^{n}(x_i - \bar{x}) = (42 - 65) + (60 - 65) + (70 - 65) + (75 - 65) + (78 - 65)$$
$$= (-23) + (-5) + (5) + (10) + (13) = -28 + 28 = 0$$

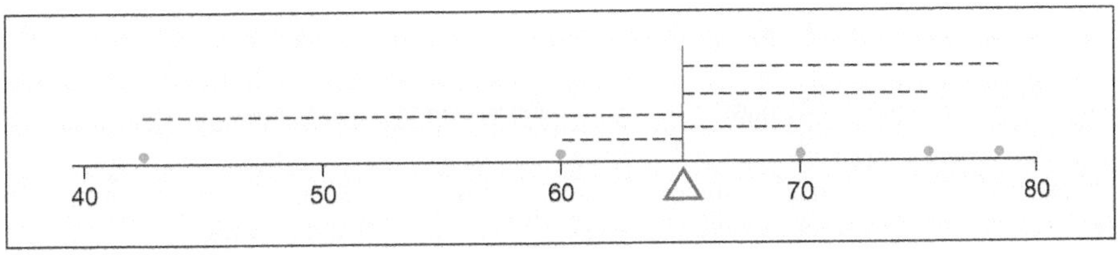

FIGURE 4.5

Bob's Quiz Scores (n = 5 quizzes).

Median

The **median** (denoted M) is the 50th percentile or midpoint of the *sorted* sample data set $x_1, x_2, \ldots, x_n$. It separates the upper and lower halves of the sorted observations:

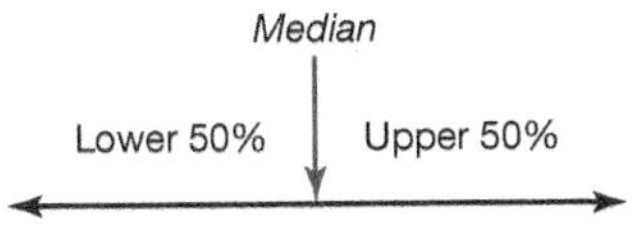

The median is the middle observation in the sorted array if n is odd, but the average of the middle two observations if n is even, as illustrated in Figure 4.6.

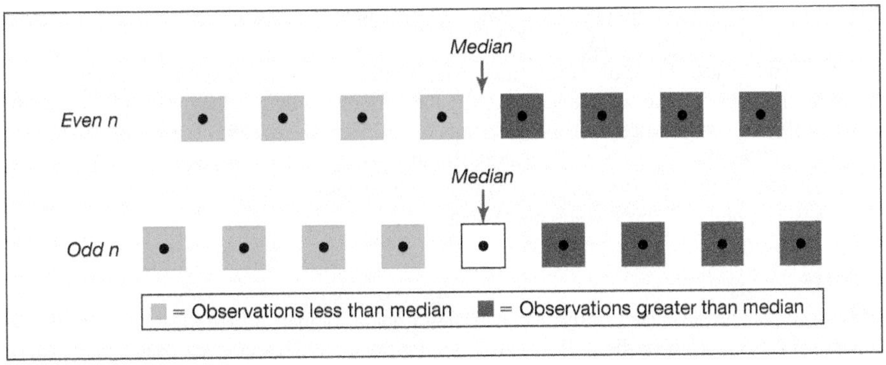

FIGURE 4.6

Illustration of the Median

For example, if we have an even n, say $n = 6$, then the median is halfway *between* the third and fourth observation in the sorted array: $M = (x_3 + x_4)/2 = (15 + 17)/2 = 16$.

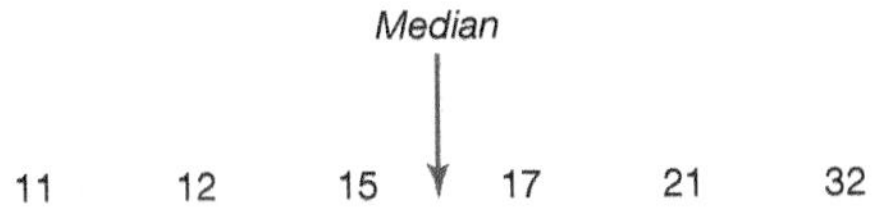

But for an odd n, say $n = 7$, the median is the fourth observation in the sorted array: $M = x_4 = 25$.

Median

12 23 23 (25) 27 34 41

It is tempting to imagine that half the observations are less than the median, but this is not necessarily the case. For example, here are 11 exam scores in ascending order:

Median

51 66 71 78 78 (78) 81 82 82 91 99

Their median is 78. But only three data values are *below* 78, while five data values are *above* 78. This median did not provide a clean "50-50 split" in the data because there were several identical exam scores clustered at the middle of the distribution. This situation is not so unusual. In fact, we might expect it when there is strong central tendency in a data set.

Excel's function for the median is =MEDIAN(Data) where Data is the data array. For the 33 vehicle quality ratings (odd n) the median is the 17th observation (16 below, 16 above), which is $x_{17} = 113$. However, you can verify that 113 occurs twice, so this does not provide a clean "50-50 split" in the data.

The median is especially useful when there are extreme values. For example, government statistics use the median income because a few very high incomes will render the mean atypical. The median's insensitivity to extremes may seem advantageous or not, depending on your point of view. Consider three students' scores on five quizzes:

Tom's scores: 20, 40, 70, 75, 80	Mean = 57, Median = 70
Jake's scores: 60, 65, 70, 90, 95	Mean = 76, Median = 70
Mary's scores: 50, 65, 70, 75, 90	Mean = 70, Median = 70

Each student has the same median quiz score (70). Tom, whose mean is pulled down by a few low scores, would rather have his grade based on the median. Jake, whose mean is pulled up by a few high scores, would prefer the mean. Mary is indifferent, since her measures of center agree (she has symmetric scores).

The median lacks some of the mean's useful mathematical properties. For example, if we multiply the mean by the sample size, we get the sum of the data values. But this is not true for the median. For instance, Tom's total points on all five quizzes (285) are the product of the sample size times his mean ($5 \times 57 = 285$). But this is not true for his median ($5 \times 70 = 350$). That is one reason why instructors tend to base their semester grades on the mean. Otherwise, the lowest and highest scores would not "count."

Mode

The **mode** is the most frequently occurring data value. It may be similar to the mean and median if data values near the center of the sorted array tend to occur often. But it may also be quite different from the mean and median. A data set may have multiple modes or no mode at all. For example, consider these four students' scores on five quizzes:

Lee's scores: 60, 70, 70, 70, 80	Mean = 70,	Median = 70,	Mode = 70
Pat's scores: 45, 45, 70, 90, 100	Mean = 70,	Median = 70,	Mode = 45
Sam's scores: 50, 60, 70, 80, 90	Mean = 70,	Median = 70,	Mode = none
Xiao's scores: 50, 50, 70, 90, 90	Mean = 70,	Median = 70,	Modes = 50, 90

Each student has the same mean (70) and median (70). Lee's mode (70) is the same as his mean and median, but Pat's mode (45) is nowhere near the "middle." Sam has no mode, while Xiao has two modes (50, 90). These examples illustrate some quirks of the mode.

The mode is easy to define, but *not* easy to calculate (except in very small samples), because it requires tabulating the frequency of occurrence of every distinct data value. For example, the sample of $n = 33$ brands has a unique mode at 111 (occurs four times), although several other data values have multiple occurrences.

83	86	87	88	93	95	102	106	107	109	110
111	111	111	111	113	113	114	114	114	117	121
122	122	126	126	129	130	130	133	135	146	170

Excel's function =MODE.SNGL(Data) will return #N/A if there is no mode. If there are multiple modes, =MODE.SNGL(Data) will return the first one it finds. Sometimes the mode is far from the "middle" of the distribution and may not be at all "typical." For *continuous* data, the mode generally isn't useful because continuous data values rarely repeat. To assess central tendency in continuous data, we would rely on the mean or median. But the mode is good for describing central tendency in *categorical data* such as gender (male, female) or college major (accounting, finance, etc.). Indeed, the mode is the *only* useful measure of central tendency for categorical data. The mode is also useful to describe a *discrete* variable with a *small range* (e.g., responses to a five-point Likert scale).

Tip

The mode is most useful for discrete or categorical data with only a few distinct data values. For continuous data or data with a wide range, the mode is rarely useful.

Two Illustrations of the Mode Figure 4.7 shows a dot plot of P/E ratios (current stock price divided by the last 12 months' earnings) for a random sample of 44 Standard & Poor's 500 stocks (see Chapter 3, Table 3.2). Although P/E ratios are continuous, the data are rounded to the nearest integer.

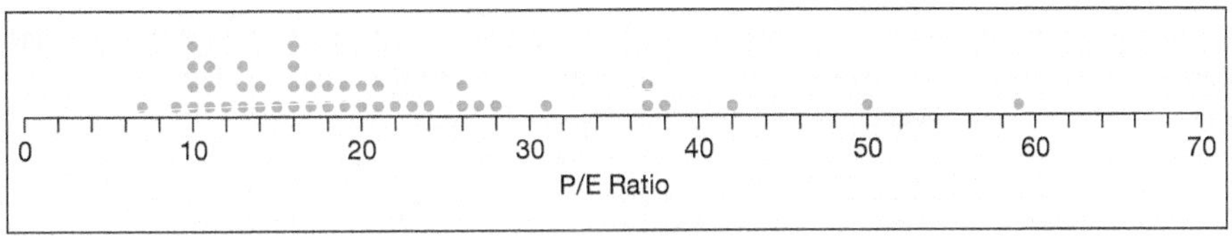

FIGURE 4.7

Dot Plot for P/E Ratios (n = 44 stocks)

PERatios

For these 44 observations, there are modes at 10 and 16 (each occurs four times), suggesting that these are somewhat "typical" P/E ratios. However, 11 and 13 occur three times, suggesting that the mode is not a robust measure of center for this data set. That is, we suspect that these modes would be unlikely to recur if we were to take a different sample of 44 stocks.

There may be a logical reason for the existence of modes. For example, points scored by winning college football teams on a given Saturday will tend to have modes at multiples of 7 (e.g., 7, 14, 21, etc.) because each touchdown yields 7 points (counting the extra point). Other mini-modes in football scores reflect commonly occurring combinations of scoring events. Figure 4.8 shows a dot plot of the points scored by the winning team in the first 95 Rose Bowl games (one game was a scoreless tie). The mode is 14 (occurs 10 times), but there are several other local modes. If you are a football fan, you can figure out, for example, why 20 points occur so often.

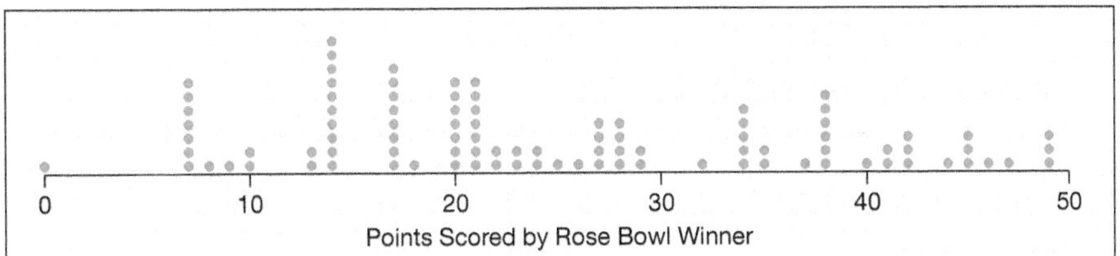

FIGURE 4.8

Dot Plot of Rose Bowl Winners' Points (n = 95 games)

RoseBowl

A **bimodal distribution** or a **multimodal distribution** occurs when dissimilar populations are combined into one sample. For example, if heights of 500 adult men and 500 adult women are combined into a single sample of 1,000 adults, we would get something like the second polygon in Figure 4.9.

FIGURE 4.9

Frequency Polygons of Heights of 1,000 Men and Women Heights

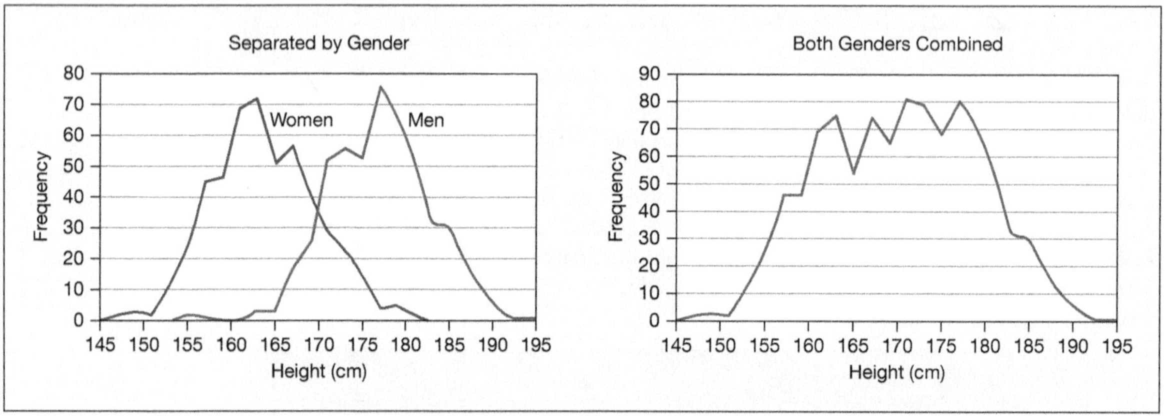

In such a case, the mean of all 1,000 adults would not represent central tendency for either gender. When heterogeneity is known to exist, it would be better to create separate histograms or frequency polygons and carry out the analysis on each group separately. Unfortunately, we don't always know when heterogeneous populations have been combined into one sample.

Shape

The shape of a distribution may be judged by looking at the histogram or by comparing the mean and median. In **symmetric data**, the mean and median are about the same. When the data are **skewed right** (or **positively skewed**), the mean exceeds the median. When the data are **skewed left** (or **negatively skewed**), the mean is below the median. Figure 4.10 shows prototype population shapes showing varying degrees of **skewness**.

FIGURE 4.10

Skewness Prototype Populations

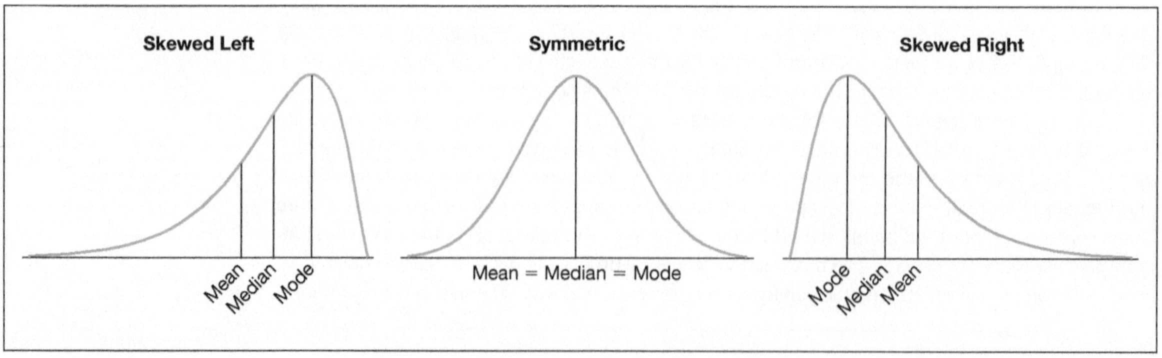

Table 4.5 summarizes the symptoms of skewness in a sample. Since few data sets are exactly symmetric, skewness is a matter of degree. Due to the nature of random sampling, the mean and median may differ, even when a symmetric population is being sampled. Small differences between the mean and median do not indicate significant skewness and may lack practical importance.

TABLE 4.5

Symptoms of Skewness

Distribution's Shape	***Histogram Appearance***	***Statistics***
Skewed left (negative skewness)	Long tail of histogram points left (a few low values but most data on right)	Mean < Median
Symmetric	Tails of histogram are balanced (low/high values offset)	Mean ≈ Median
Skewed right (positive skewness)	Long tail of histogram points right (most data on left but a few high values)	Mean > Median

For example, in Figure 4.11 the average spending per customer at 74 Noodles & Company restaurants appears somewhat right-skewed, so we would expect the mean to exceed the median. Actually, the difference is slight (using the spreadsheet raw data, the mean is $7.04 and the median is $7.00). The student GPA histogram in Figure 4.11 appears left-skewed, so we would expect the mean to be lower than the median. But again, the difference is slight (using the spreadsheet raw data, the mean is 3.17 and the median is 3.20). Since a histogram's appearance is affected by the way its bins are set up, its shape offers only a rough guide to skewness.

FIGURE 4.11

Histograms to Illustrate Skewness

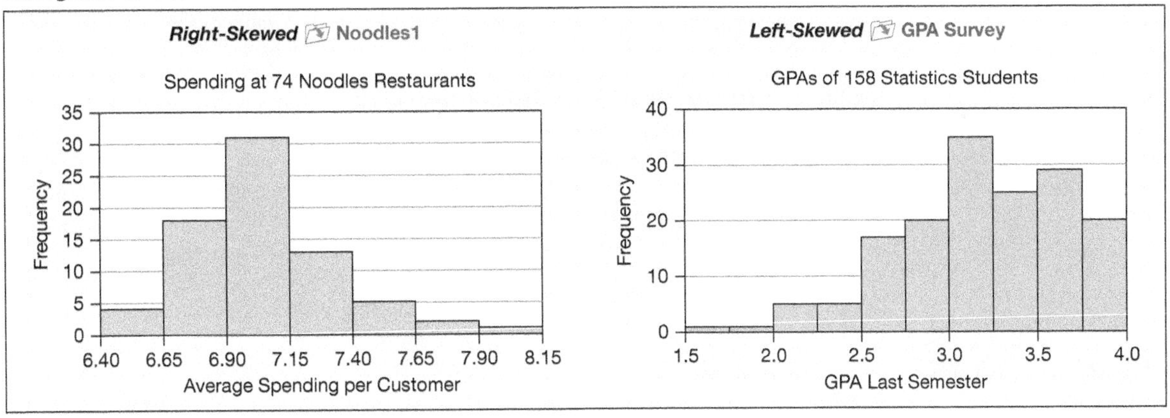

For the sample of J.D. Power quality ratings, the mean (114.17) exceeds the median (113), which suggests right-skewness. However, this small difference between the mean and median may lack practical importance. The histograms in Figure 4.3 suggest that the skewness is minimal. In Section 4.8, we will introduce more precise tests for skewness.

Business data tend to be right-skewed because financial variables often are unlimited at the top but are bounded from below by zero (e.g., salaries, employees, inventory). This is also true for engineering data (e.g., time to failure, defect rates) and sports (e.g., scores in soccer). Even in a Likert scale (1, 2, 3, 4, 5) a few responses in the opposite tail can skew the mean if most replies are clustered toward the top or bottom of the scale.

Descriptive Statistics in Excel

As shown in Figure 4.12, select the Data tab and click the Data Analysis icon (on the far right side of the top menu). When the Data Analysis menu appears, select Descriptive Statistics. On the Descriptive Statistics menu form, click anywhere inside the Input Range field, then highlight the data block (in this case C4:C37). Specify a destination cell for the upper left corner of the output range (cell K1 in this example). Notice that we checked the Labels in first row box, since cell C4 is actually a column heading that will be used to label the output in cell K1. Check the Summary Statistics box and then click OK. The resulting statistics are shown in Figure 4.12. You probably recognize some of them (e.g., mean, median, mode) and the others will be covered later in this chapter.

FIGURE 4.12

Excel's Data Analysis and Descriptive Statistics JDPower

Note: If Data Analysis does not appear on the upper right of the Data tab, click File in the extreme upper left corner, select Add-Ins, and then check the box for Analysis ToolPak.

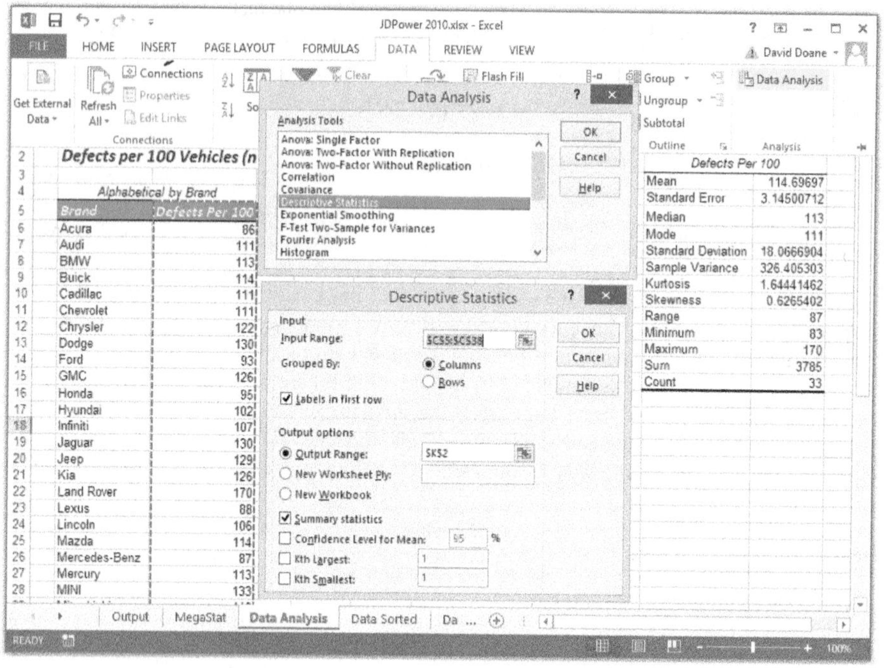

Descriptive Statistics Using MegaStat

You can get similar statistics (and more) from MegaStat as illustrated in Figure 4.13. Click the Add-Ins tab on the top menu, and then click on the MegaStat icon (left side of the top menu in this example). On the list of MegaStat procedures, click Descriptive Statistics. On the new menu, enter the data range (in this case C4:C37) in the Input range field (or highlight the data block on the worksheet. You can see that MegaStat offers you many statistics, plus some visual displays such as a dot plot, stem-and-leaf, and other graphs. We have only chosen a few of them for this illustration. MegaStat output normally appears on a separate worksheet, but the results have been

FIGURE 4.13

MegaStat's Descriptive Statistics JDPower

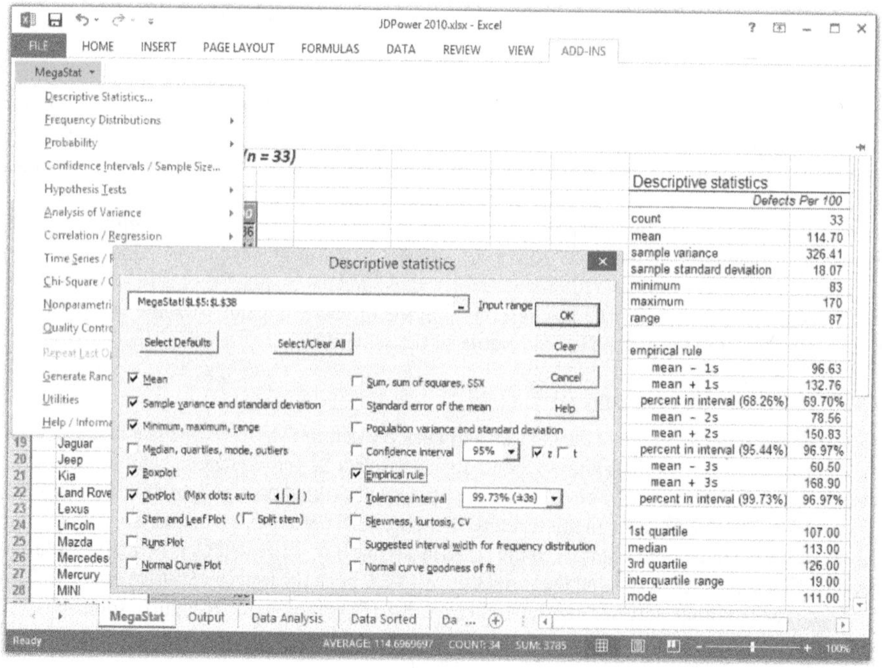

copied to the data worksheet so that everything can be seen in one picture. Try using both Excel and MegaStat to see the similarities and differences in their interfaces and results.

Descriptive Statistics Using MINITAB

MINITAB is a comprehensive software system for statistical analysis. It has nothing to do with Excel, although you can copy data from Excel to MINITAB's worksheet (and vice versa). You can get a wide range of statistics and attractive graphs from MINITAB, which is widely available at colleges and universities. This textbook emphasizes Excel and MegaStat, but it is wise to learn about other software that may give you just the result you want (or in a more attractive form), so we will show MINITAB results when they are appropriate. Figure 4.14 shows MINITAB's menus and a graphical summary of descriptive statistics for the J.D. Power data.

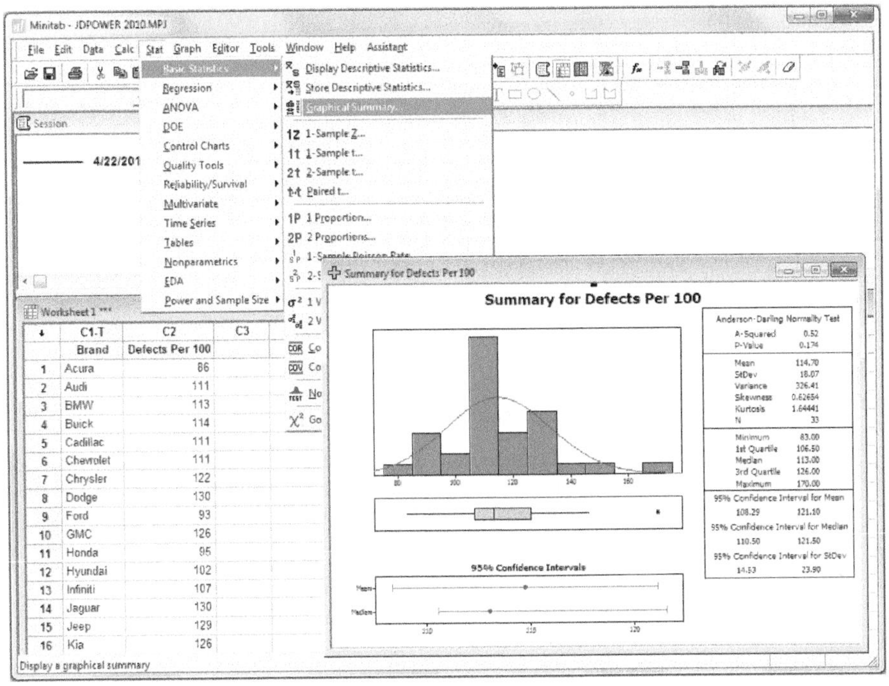

FIGURE 4.14

MINITAB's Basic Statistics > Graphical Summary

SECTION EXERCISES

connect

4.1 (a) For each data set, find the mean, median, and mode. (b) Discuss anything about the data that affects the usefulness of each statistic as a measure of center.

a. Class absences (12 students): 0, 0, 0, 0, 0, 1, 2, 3, 3, 5, 5, 15
b. Exam scores (9 students): 40, 40, 65, 71, 72, 75, 76, 78, 98
c. GPAs (8 students): 2.25, 2.55, 2.95, 3.02, 3.04, 3.37, 3.51, 3.66

4.2 For each data set, is the mode a good measure of center? Explain.

a. Genders of 12 CEOs: M, M, F, M, F, M, M, M, F, M, M, M
b. Ages of 10 college freshmen: 17, 17, 18, 18, 18, 18, 18, 18, 19, 20
c. Ages of 8 MBA students: 24, 26, 27, 28, 30, 31, 33, 37

4.3 For each data set, is the mode a good measure of center? Explain.

a. GMAT scores (8 MBA applicants): 490, 495, 542, 587, 599, 622, 630, 641
b. Exam grades (12 students): F, D, C, C, C, C, C, C, B, B, A, A
c. Body Mass Index (7 Army recruits): 18.6, 20.2, 22.4, 23.7, 24.2, 28.8, 28.8

4.4 For each data set, which best indicates a "typical" data value (mean, median, either)?

a. Days on campus by 11 students: 1, 1, 2, 2, 3, 3, 3, 4, 4, 5, 5
b. P/E ratios of 6 stocks: 1.5, 6.5, 6.6, 7.3, 8.2, 9.1
c. Textbooks in 9 backpacks: 0, 0, 0, 0, 0, 1, 2, 3, 4

4.5 For each data set, which best indicates a "typical" data value (mean, median, either)?

a. MPG for 7 Honda Civics: 21.8, 24.1, 24.6, 26.2, 28.4, 35.2, 36.3
b. Number of riders in 8 cars: 1, 1, 1, 1, 1, 1, 4, 6
c. Diners at 10 restaurant tables: 1, 2, 2, 2, 3, 3, 4, 4, 4, 5

4.6 Days on the market are shown for the 36 most recent home sales in the city of Sonando Hills. (a) Calculate the mean, median, and mode. (b) Is the distribution skewed? Explain. (c) Is the mode a useful measure of center for this data set? **Homes**

18	70	52	17	86	121	86	3	66
96	41	50	176	26	28	6	55	21
43	20	56	71	57	16	20	30	31
44	44	92	179	80	98	44	66	15

4.7 Scores are shown for the most recent state civil service exam taken by 24 applicants for positions in law enforcement. (a) Calculate the mean, median, and mode. (b) Is the distribution skewed? Explain. (c) Is the mode a useful measure of center for this data set? **Civil**

83	93	74	98	85	82	79	78
82	68	67	82	78	83	70	99
18	96	93	62	64	93	27	58

4.8 Prof. Hardtack gave four Friday quizzes last semester in his 10-student senior tax accounting class. (a) Find the mean, median, and mode for each quiz. (b) Do these measures of center agree? Explain. (c) For each data set, note strengths or weaknesses of each statistic of center. (d) Are the data symmetric or skewed? If skewed, which direction? (e) Briefly describe and compare student performance on each quiz. **Quizzes**

Quiz 1: 60, 60, 60, 60, 71, 73, 74, 75, 88, 99

Quiz 2: 65, 65, 65, 65, 70, 74, 79, 79, 79, 79

Quiz 3: 66, 67, 70, 71, 72, 72, 74, 74, 95, 99

Quiz 4: 10, 49, 70, 80, 85, 88, 90, 93, 97, 98

4.9 CitiBank recorded the number of customers to use a downtown ATM during the noon hour on 32 consecutive workdays. (a) Find the mean, median, and mode. (b) Do these measures of center agree? Explain. (c) Make a histogram or dot plot. (d) Are the data symmetric or skewed? If skewed, which direction? **CitiBank**

25	37	23	26	30	40	25	26
39	32	21	26	19	27	32	25
18	26	34	18	31	35	21	33
33	9	16	32	35	42	15	24

4.10 On Friday night, the owner of Chez Pierre in downtown Chicago noted the amount spent for dinner for 28 four-person tables. (a) Find the mean, median, and mode. (b) Do these measures of center agree? Explain. (c) Make a histogram or dot plot. (d) Are the data symmetric or skewed? If skewed, which direction? **Dinner**

95	103	109	170	114	113	107
124	105	80	104	84	176	115
69	95	134	108	61	160	128
68	95	61	150	52	87	136

4.11 An executive's telephone log showed the lengths of 65 calls initiated during the last week of July. (a) Sort the data. (b) Find the mean, median, and mode. (c) Do the measures of center agree? Explain. (d) Are the data symmetric or skewed? If skewed, which direction? **CallLength**

1	2	10	5	3	3	2	20	1	1
6	3	13	2	2	1	26	3	1	3
1	2	1	7	1	2	3	1	2	12
1	4	2	2	29	1	1	1	8	5
1	4	2	1	1	1	1	6	1	2
3	3	6	1	3	1	1	5	1	18
2	13	13	1	6					

Mini Case 4.1

ATM Deposits

Table 4.6 shows a sorted random sample of 100 deposits at an ATM located in the student union on a college campus. The sample was selected at random from 1,459 deposits in one 30-day month. Deposits range from $3 to $1,341. The dot plot shown in Figure 4.15 indicates a right-skewed distribution with a few large values in the right tail and a strong clustering on the left (i.e., most ATM deposits are small). Excel's **Descriptive Statistics** indicate a very skewed distribution, since the mean (233.89) greatly exceeds the median (135). The mode (100) is somewhat "typical," occurring five times. However, 40 and 50 each occurs four times (mini-modes).

TABLE 4.6 **100 ATM Deposits (dollars)** ATMDeposits

3	10	15	15	20	20	20	22	23	25	26	26
30	30	35	35	36	39	40	40	40	40	47	50
50	50	50	53	55	60	60	60	67	75	78	86
90	96	100	100	100	100	100	103	105	118	125	125
130	131	139	140	145	150	150	153	153	156	160	163
170	176	185	198	200	200	200	220	232	237	252	259
260	268	270	279	295	309	345	350	366	375	431	433
450	450	474	484	495	553	600	720	777	855	960	987
1,020	1,050	1,200	1,341								

Source: Michigan State University Federal Credit Union.

FIGURE 4.15 **Dot Plot for ATM Deposits (n = 100)**

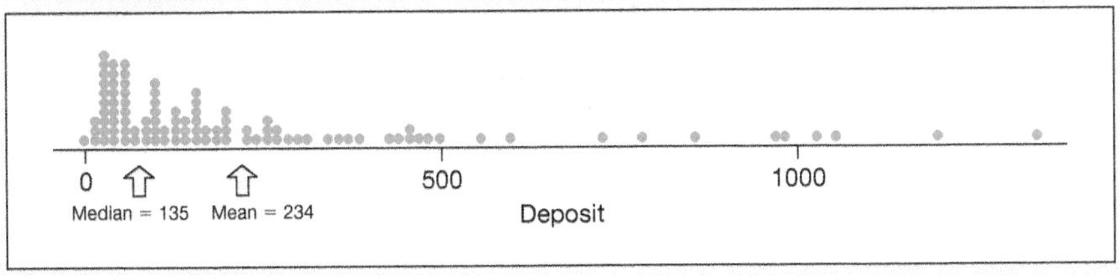

Geometric Mean

The **geometric mean** (denoted G) is a multiplicative average, obtained by multiplying the data values and then taking the nth root of the product. This is a measure of central tendency used when all the data values are positive (greater than zero).

$$G = \sqrt[n]{x_1 x_2 \cdots x_n} \quad \text{for the geometric mean} \tag{4.4}$$

For example, the geometric mean for X = 2, 3, 7, 9, 10, 12 is:

$$G = \sqrt[6]{(2)(3)(7)(9)(10)(12)} = \sqrt[6]{45{,}360} = 5.972$$

The product of n numbers can be quite large. For the J.D. Power quality data:

$$G = \sqrt[33]{(83)(86)(87)\cdots(135)(146)(170)} = \sqrt[33]{6.25105 \times 10^{67}} = 113.35$$

The calculation is easy using Excel's function =**GEOMEAN(Data)**. Scientific calculators have a y^x key whose inverse permits taking the nth root needed to calculate G. However, if the data values are large, the product can exceed the calculator's capacity. The geometric mean tends to mitigate the effects of high outliers.

Growth Rates

We can use a variation on the geometric mean to find the *average growth rate* for a time series (e.g., sales in a growing company):

(4.5) $$GR = \sqrt[n-1]{\frac{x_n}{x_1}} - 1 \quad \text{(average growth rate of a time series)}$$

For example, from 2006 to 2010, JetBlue Airlines' revenues grew as shown in Table 4.7.

TABLE 4.7

JetBlue Airlines Revenue (millions of dollars)

JetBlue

Year	Revenue
2006	2,361
2007	2,843
2008	3,392
2009	3,292
2010	3,779

Source: http://money.msn.com. Data are for December 31 of each year.

The *average growth rate* is given by taking the geometric mean of the ratios of each year's revenue to the preceding year. However, due to cancellations, only the first and last years are relevant:

$$GR = \sqrt[4]{\left(\frac{2843}{2361}\right)\left(\frac{3392}{2843}\right)\left(\frac{3292}{3392}\right)\left(\frac{3779}{3292}\right)} - 1 = \sqrt[4]{\frac{3779}{2361}} - 1 = 1.125 - 1 = 0.125$$

or 12.5 percent per year. In Excel, we could use the formula =(3779/2361)^(1/4)-1 to get the same result.

Midrange

The **midrange** is the point halfway between the lowest and highest values of X. It is easy to calculate but is not a robust measure of central tendency because it is sensitive to extreme data values. It is useful when you only have x_{min} and x_{max}.

(4.6) $$\text{Midrange} = \frac{x_{min} + x_{max}}{2}$$

For the J.D. Power data:

$$\text{Midrange} = \frac{x_1 + x_{33}}{2} = \frac{83 + 170}{2} = 126.5$$

For the J.D. Power data, the midrange is higher than the mean (114.70) or median (113), and is a dubious measure of center because it is "pulled up" by one high data value $x_{max} = 170$.

Trimmed Mean

The **trimmed mean** is calculated like any other mean, except that the highest and lowest k percent of the observations in the sorted data array are removed. The trimmed mean mitigates the effects of extreme high values on either end. For a 5 percent trimmed mean, the Excel function is =TRIMMEAN(Data, 0.10) because $.05 + .05 = .10$. For the J.D. Power data ($n = 33$), we would remove only one observation from each end because $.05 \times 33 = 1.65 = 1$ (truncated to the next *lower* integer) and then take the average of the middle 31 observations.

Excel's measures of center for the J.D. Power data:

Mean:	=AVERAGE(Data)	= 114.70
Median:	=MEDIAN(Data)	= 113
Mode:	=MODE.SNGL(Data)	= 111
Geo Mean:	=GEOMEAN(Data)	= 113.35
Midrange:	=(MIN(Data)+MAX(Data))/2	= 126.5
5% Trim Mean:	=TRIMMEAN(Data,0.1)	= 113.94

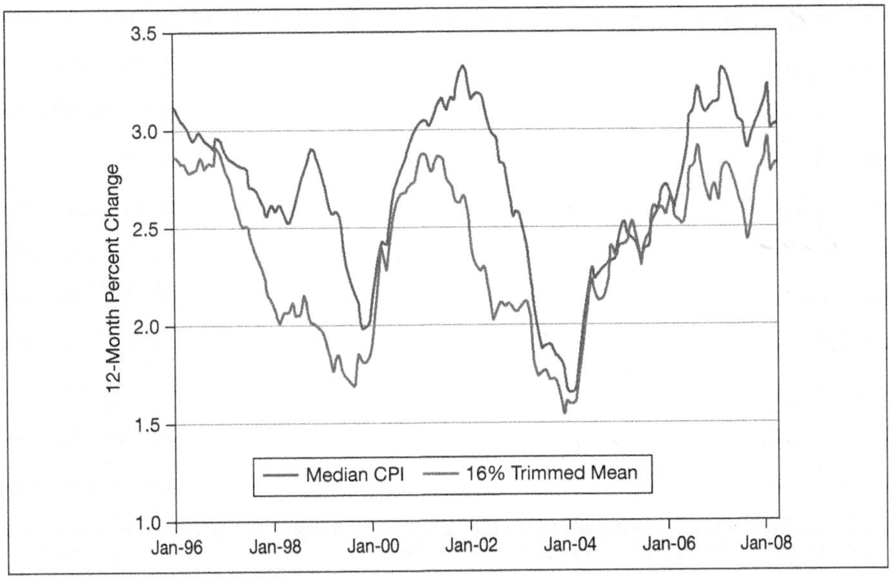

FIGURE 4.16

16 Percent Trimmed Mean for CPI

Source: Federal Reserve Bank of Cleveland, www.clevelandfed.org

The Federal Reserve uses a 16 percent trimmed mean to mitigate the effect of extremes in its analysis of trends in the Consumer Price Index, as illustrated in Figure 4.16.

Mini Case 4.2

Prices of Lipitor®

Prescription drug prices vary across the United States and even among pharmacies in the same city. A consumer research group examined prices for a 30-day supply of Lipitor® (a cholesterol-lowering prescription drug) in three U.S. cities at various pharmacies. Attention has recently been focused on prices of such drugs because recent medical research has suggested more aggressive treatment of high cholesterol levels in patients at risk for heart disease. This poses an economic issue for government because Medicare is expected to pay some of the cost of prescription drugs. It is also an issue for Pfizer, the maker of Lipitor®, who expects a fair return on its investments in research and patents. Finally, it is an issue for consumers who seek to shop wisely.

From the dot plots in Figure 4.17, we gain an impression of the *variability* of the data (the *range* of prices for each drug) as well as the *center* of the data (the middle or typical data values). Lipitor® prices vary from about \$60 to about \$91 and typically are in the \$70s. The dot plots suggest that Providence tends to have higher prices, and New Orleans lower prices, though there is considerable variation among pharmacies.

FIGURE 4.17 **Dot Plots for Lipitor® Prices**

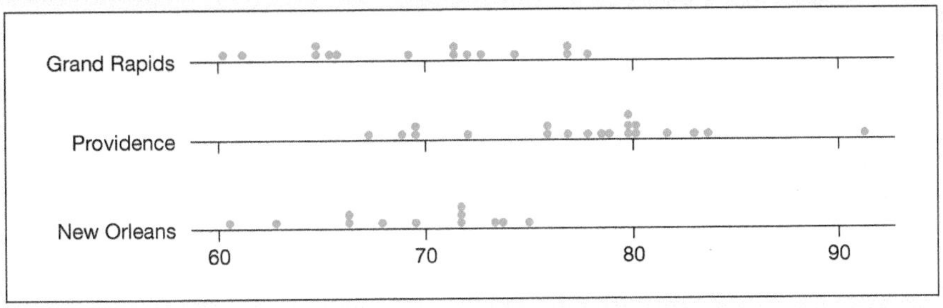

In Table 4.8, the measures of center unanimously say that Providence has higher prices. New Orleans and Grand Rapids are similar, although Grand Rapids has slightly higher prices. The means and medians for each city are similar, suggesting no significant skewness. Because these are decimal data values, the mode is not appropriate, and is therefore omitted.

TABLE 4.8 Measures of Center for Lipitor® Prices Lipitor

Statistic	*New Orleans*	*Providence*	*Grand Rapids*
Sample size	12	20	15
Mean	69.27	77.54	69.73
Median	70.70	78.75	71.56
Geometric mean	69.14	77.33	69.51
Midrange	67.77	79.18	69.19
5% Trim mean	69.57	77.36	69.81

Source: Survey by the Public Interest Research Group (www.pirg.org) in March/April 2003. Prices were studied for 10 drugs in 555 pharmacies in 48 cities in 19 states. Public Interest Research Groups are an alliance of state-based, citizen-funded advocacy organizations that seek to protect the environment, encourage a fair marketplace for consumers, and foster responsive, democratic government. Mode is omitted (decimal data).

SECTION EXERCISES

connect

4.12 (a) For each data set, find the median, midrange, and geometric mean. (b) Are they reasonable measures of central tendency? Explain.

a. Exam scores (9 students) 42, 55, 65, 67, 68, 75, 76, 78, 94
b. GPAs (8 students) 2.25, 2.55, 2.95, 3.02, 3.04, 3.37, 3.51, 3.66
c. Class absences (12 students) 0, 0, 0, 0, 0, 1, 2, 3, 3, 5, 5, 15

4.13 (a) Write the Excel function for the 10 percent trimmed mean of a data set in cells A1:A50. (b) How many observations would be trimmed in each tail? (c) How many would be trimmed overall?

4.14 In the Excel function =TRIMMEAN(Data,.10), how many observations would be trimmed from each end of the sorted data array named **Data** if (a) $n = 41$, (b) $n = 66$, and (c) $n = 83$?

4.15 The city of Sonando Hills has 8 police officers. In January, the work-related medical expenses for each officer were 0, 0, 0, 0, 0, 0, 150, 650. (a) Calculate the mean, median, mode, midrange, and geometric mean. (b) Which measure of center would you use to budget the expected medical expenses for the whole year by all officers?

4.16 Spirit Airlines kept track of the number of empty seats on flight 308 (DEN–DTW) for 10 consecutive trips on each weekday except Friday. (a) Sort the data for each day. (b) Find the mean, median, mode, midrange, geometric mean, and 10 percent trimmed mean (i.e., dropping the first and last sorted observations) for each day. (c) Do the measures of center agree? Explain. (d) Note strengths or weaknesses of each statistic of center for the data. EmptySeats

Monday: 6, 1, 5, 9, 1, 1, 6, 5, 5, 1
Tuesday: 1, 3, 3, 1, 4, 6, 9, 7, 7, 6
Wednesday: 6, 0, 6, 0, 6, 10, 0, 0, 4, 6
Thursday: 1, 1, 10, 1, 1, 1, 1, 1, 1, 1

4.17 CitiBank recorded the number of customers to use a downtown ATM during the noon hour on 32 consecutive workdays. (a) Find the mean, midrange, geometric mean, and 10 percent trimmed mean. (b) Do these measures of center agree? Explain. CitiBank

25	37	23	26	30	40	25	26
39	32	21	26	19	27	32	25
18	26	34	18	31	35	21	33
33	9	16	32	35	42	15	24

4.18 On Friday night, the owner of Chez Pierre in downtown Chicago noted the amount spent for dinner at 28 four-person tables. (a) Find the mean, midrange, geometric mean, and 10 percent trimmed mean. (b) Do these measures of center agree? Explain. **Dinner**

95	103	109	170	114	113	107
124	105	80	104	84	176	115
69	95	134	108	61	160	128
68	95	61	150	52	87	136

4.19 An executive's telephone log showed the lengths of 65 calls initiated during the last week of July. (a) Find the mean, median, mode, midrange, geometric mean, and 10 percent trimmed mean. (b) Are the data symmetric or skewed? If skewed, which direction? **CallLength**

1	2	10	5	3	3	2	20	1	1
6	3	13	2	2	1	26	3	1	3
1	2	1	7	1	2	3	1	2	12
1	4	2	2	29	1	1	1	8	5
1	4	2	1	1	1	1	6	1	2
3	3	6	1	3	1	1	5	1	18
2	13	13	1	6					

4.20 The number of Internet users in Latin America grew from 78.5 million in 2000 to 156.6 million in 2010. Use the geometric mean to find the annual growth rate.

4.3 MEASURES OF VARIABILITY

LO 4-3

Calculate and interpret common measures of variability.

We can use a statistic such as the mean to describe the *center* of a distribution. But it is just as important to describe *variation* around the center. Consider possible sample distributions of study time spent by several college students taking an economics class:

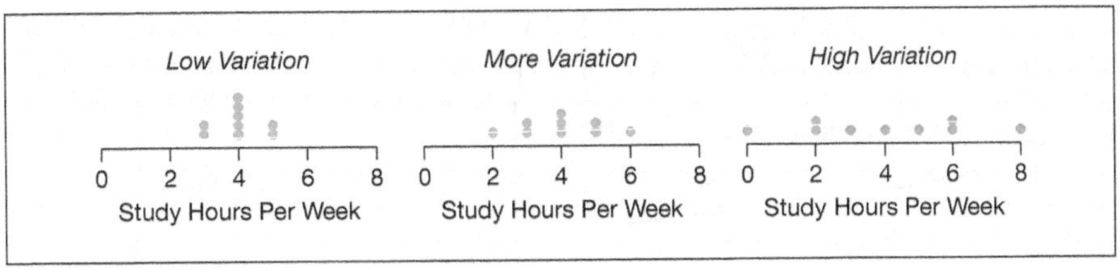

Each diagram has the same mean, but they differ in dispersion around the mean. The problem is: how do we *describe* variability in a sample? Histograms and dot plots tell us something about variation in a data set (the "spread" of data points about the center), but precise measures of dispersion are needed. Because different variables have different means and different units of measurement (dollars, pounds, yen), we want measures of variability that can be applied to many situations.

Table 4.9 lists several common measures of variability. All formulas shown are for sample data sets.

Range

The **range** is the difference between the largest and smallest observations:

$$\text{Range} = x_{max} - x_{min} \tag{4.7}$$

For the J.D. Power data, the range is:

$$\text{Range} = 170 - 83 = 87$$

Although it is easy to calculate, a drawback of the range is that it only considers the two extreme data values. It seems desirable to seek a broad-based measure of variability that is based on *all* the data values $x_1, x_2, \ldots, x_n$.

TABLE 4.9 Five Measures of Variability for a Sample

Statistic	*Formula*	*Excel**	*Pro*	*Con*
Range (R)	$x_{max} - x_{min}$	=MAX(Data)-MIN(Data)	Easy to calculate and easy to interpret.	Sensitive to extreme data values.
Sample variance (s^2)	$\frac{\sum_{i=1}^{n}(x_i - \bar{x})^2}{n-1}$	=VAR.S(Data)	Plays a key role in mathematical statistics.	Less intuitive meaning.
Sample standard deviation (s)	$\sqrt{\frac{\sum_{i=1}^{n}(x_i - \bar{x})^2}{n-1}}$	=STDEV.S(Data)	Most common measure. Same units as the raw data ($, £, ¥, grams, etc.).	Less intuitive meaning.
Coefficient of variation (CV)	$100 \times \frac{s}{\bar{x}}$	None	Expresses relative variation in *percent* so can compare data sets with different units of measurement.	Requires nonnegative data.
Mean absolute deviation (MAD)	$\frac{\sum_{i=1}^{n}\lvert x_i - \bar{x}\rvert}{n}$	=AVEDEV(Data)	Easy to understand.	Lacks "nice" theoretical properties.

*Excel sample functions =VAR.S(Data) and =STDEV.S(Data) give the same results as the older (pre-2010) functions =VAR(Data) and =STDEV(Data). These newer functions will not work in older versions of Excel, but the old functions work in newer versions of Excel.

Variance and Standard Deviation

If we calculate the differences between each data value x_i and the mean, we would have both positive and negative differences. The mean is the balancing point of the distribution, so if we just sum these differences and take the average, we will always get zero, which obviously doesn't give us a useful measure of variability. One way to avoid this is to *square* the differences before we find the average. Following this logic, the **population variance** (denoted σ^2, where σ is the lowercase Greek letter "sigma") is defined as the sum of squared deviations from the mean divided by the population size:

(4.8)
$$\sigma^2 = \frac{\sum_{i=1}^{N}(x_i - \mu)^2}{N}$$

If we have a sample (i.e., most of the time), we replace μ with $\bar{x}$ to get the **sample variance** (denoted s^2):

(4.9)
$$s^2 = \frac{\sum_{i=1}^{n}(x_i - \bar{x})^2}{n-1}$$

A variance is basically a mean squared deviation. But why then do we divide by $n - 1$ instead of n when using sample data? This question perplexes many students. A sample contains n pieces of information, each of which can have any value, independently from the others. But once you have calculated the sample mean (as you must in order to find the variance), there are only $n - 1$ pieces of independent information left (since the sample values must add to a fixed total that gives the mean). We divide the sum of squared deviations by $n - 1$ instead of n because we have "lost" one piece of information. Otherwise, s^2 would tend to underestimate the unknown population variance σ^2.

In describing variability, we most often use the **standard deviation** (the square root of the variance). The standard deviation is a single number that helps us understand how individual values in a data set vary from the mean. Because the square root has been taken, its units of measurement are the same as X (e.g., dollars, kilograms, miles). To find the standard deviation of a population we use:

$$\sigma = \sqrt{\frac{\sum_{i=1}^{N}(x_i - \mu)^2}{N}} \tag{4.10}$$

and for the standard deviation of a sample:

$$s = \sqrt{\frac{\sum_{i=1}^{n}(x_i - \bar{x})^2}{n-1}} \tag{4.11}$$

Many inexpensive calculators have built-in formulas for the standard deviation. To distinguish between the population and sample formulas, some calculators have one function key labeled σ_x and another labeled s_x. Others have one key labeled σ_n and another labeled σ_{n-1}. The only question is whether to divide the numerator by the number of data items or the number of data items minus one. Computers and calculators don't know whether your data are a sample or a population. They will use whichever formula you request. It is up to you to know which is appropriate for your data. Excel has built-in functions for these calculations:

	Excel 2010		*Pre-2010 Excel*	
	Sample	***Population***	***Sample***	***Population***
Variance	=VAR.S(Data)	=VAR.P(Data)	=VAR(Data)	=VARP(Data)
Std deviation	=STDEV.S(Data)	=STDEV.P(Data)	=STDEV(Data)	=STDEVP(Data)

Calculating a Standard Deviation

Table 4.10 illustrates the calculation of a standard deviation using Stephanie's scores on five quizzes (40, 55, 75, 95, 95). Her mean is 72.

TABLE 4.10

Worksheet for Standard Deviation Stephanie

i	x_i	$x_i - \bar{x}$	$(x_i - \bar{x})^2$	x_i^2
1	40	40 − 72 = −32	$(-32)^2$ = 1,024	40^2 = 1,600
2	55	55 − 72 = −17	$(-17)^2$ = 289	55^2 = 3,025
3	75	75 − 72 = +3	$(3)^2$ = 9	75^2 = 5,625
4	95	95 − 72 = +23	$(23)^2$ = 529	95^2 = 9,025
5	95	95 − 72 = +23	$(23)^2$ = 529	95^2 = 9,025
Sum	360	0	2,380	28,300
Mean	72			

Notice that the deviations around the mean (column three) sum to zero, an important property of the mean. Because the mean is rarely a "nice" number, such calculations typically require a spreadsheet or a calculator. Stephanie's sample standard deviation is:

$$s = \sqrt{\frac{\sum_{i=1}^{n}(x_i - \bar{x})^2}{n-1}} = \sqrt{\frac{2,380}{5-1}} = \sqrt{595} = 24.39$$

Alternatively, the **two-sum formula** can also be used to calculate the standard deviation:

$$s = \sqrt{\frac{\sum_{i=1}^{n}x_i^2 - \frac{\left(\sum_{i=1}^{n}x_i\right)^2}{n}}{n-1}} \tag{4.12}$$

This formula avoids calculating the mean and subtracting it from each observation. Scientific calculators use this formula and also give the sums $\sum_{i=1}^{n} x_i$ and $\sum_{i=1}^{n} x_i^2$. For Stephanie's five quiz scores, using the sums shown in Table 4.10, we get the same result as from the definitional formula:

$$s = \sqrt{\frac{\sum_{i=1}^{n} x_i^2 - \frac{\left(\sum_{i=1}^{n} x_i\right)^2}{n}}{n-1}} = \sqrt{\frac{28{,}300 - \frac{(360)^2}{5}}{5-1}} = \sqrt{\frac{28{,}300 - 25{,}920}{5-1}} = \sqrt{595} = 24.39$$

Because it is less intuitive (and because we usually rely on spreadsheets, calculators, or statistical software), some textbooks omit the two-sum formula. For business data, either formula should be OK.

Characteristics of the Standard Deviation

The standard deviation is nonnegative because the deviations around the mean are squared. When every observation is exactly equal to the mean, then the standard deviation is zero (i.e., there is no variation). For example, if every student received the same score on an exam, the numerators of formulas 4.8 through 4.12 would be zero because every student would be at the mean. At the other extreme, the greatest dispersion would be if the data were concentrated at $x_{\min}$ and $x_{\max}$ (e.g., if half the class scored 0 and the other half scored 100).

But the standard deviation can have any nonnegative value, depending on the unit of measurement. For example, yields on n randomly chosen investment bond funds (e.g., Westcore Plus at 7.2 percent in 2010) would have a small standard deviation compared to annual revenues of n randomly chosen Fortune 500 corporations (e.g., Walmart at $429 billion in 2010).

Standard deviations can be compared *only* for data sets measured in the same units. For example, prices of hotel rooms in Tokyo (yen) cannot be compared with prices of hotel rooms in Paris (euros). Also, standard deviations should not be compared if the means differ substantially, even when the units of measurement are the same. For instance, weights of apples (ounces) have a smaller mean than weights of watermelons (ounces).

Standard Deviation Used to Compare Risks

"Generally speaking, standard deviation is how much an investment's returns have varied historically from its average. The statistical measure is usually computed using monthly returns for the most recent three-year period . . . Standard deviation can be useful when comparing the investment risk of various mutual funds. If two funds have similar average returns but different standard deviations, the fund with the higher standard deviation is the more volatile of the two."

From *T. Rowe Price Investor,* September 2009, p. 8.

Coefficient of Variation

To compare dispersion in data sets with dissimilar units of measurement (e.g., kilograms and ounces) or dissimilar means (e.g., home prices in two different cities), we define the **coefficient of variation** (CV), which is a unit-free measure of dispersion:

(4.13) $$CV = 100 \times \frac{s}{\bar{x}}$$

The *CV* is the standard deviation expressed as a percent of the mean. In some data sets, the standard deviation can actually exceed the mean, so the *CV* can exceed 100 percent. This can happen in skewed data sets, especially if there are outliers. The *CV* is useful for comparing variables measured in different units. For example:

Defect rates: $s = 24.94, \bar{x} = 134.51$	$CV = 100 \times (24.94)/(134.51) = 19\%$
ATM deposits: $s = 280.80, \bar{x} = 233.89$	$CV = 100 \times (280.80)/(233.89) = 120\%$
P/E ratios: $s = 14.08, \bar{x} = 22.72$	$CV = 100 \times (14.08)/(22.72) = 62\%$

Despite the different units of measurement, we can say that ATM deposits have much greater relative dispersion (120 percent) than either defect rates (18 percent) or P/E ratios (62 percent). The chief weakness of the *CV* is that it is undefined if the mean is zero or negative, so it is appropriate only for positive data.

Mean Absolute Deviation

An additional measure of dispersion is the **mean absolute deviation** (*MAD*). This statistic reveals the average distance from the center. Absolute values must be used since otherwise the deviations around the mean would sum to zero.

$$MAD = \frac{\sum_{i=1}^{n} |x_i - \bar{x}|}{n} \qquad \textbf{(4.14)}$$

The *MAD* is appealing because of its simple, concrete interpretation. Using the lever analogy, the *MAD* tells us what the average distance is from an individual data point to the fulcrum. Excel's function =AVEDEV(Data) will calculate the *MAD*.

Mini Case 4.3

Bear Markets

Investors know that stock prices have extended cycles of downturns ("bear markets") or upturns ("bull markets"). But how long must an investor be prepared to wait for the cycle to end? Table 4.11 shows the duration of 15 bear markets since 1929 and the decline in the S&P 500 stock index.

TABLE 4.11 Duration of 15 Bear Markets BearMarkets

Peak	*Trough*	*Duration (months)*	*S&P Loss (%)*
Sep 1929	Jun 1932	34	83.4
Jun 1946	Apr 1947	11	21.0
Aug 1956	Feb 1957	7	10.2
Aug 1957	Dec 1957	5	15.0
Jan 1962	Jun 1962	6	22.3
Feb 1966	Sep 1966	8	15.6
Dec 1968	Jun 1970	19	29.3
Jan 1973	Sep 1974	21	42.6
Jan 1977	Feb 1978	14	14.1
Dec 1980	Jul 1982	20	16.9
Sep 1987	Nov 1987	3	29.5
Jun 1990	Oct 1990	5	14.7
Jul 1998	Aug 1998	2	15.4
Sep 2000	Mar 2003	31	42.0
Oct 2007	Mar 2009	17	50.6

Note: Downturns are defined as a loss in value of 10 percent or more. Standard & Poor's 500 stock index and S&P 500 are registered trademarks. Calculations for the bear market that began in 2007 are based on a 30-day trailing moving average of the S&P 500 index.

Figure 4.18 shows that bear markets typically are short-lived (under 1 year) but may last nearly 3 years. S&P losses generally are in the 10–40 percent range, with one notable exception (the 1929 crash).

FIGURE 4.18 **Dot Plots of Bear Market Measurements**

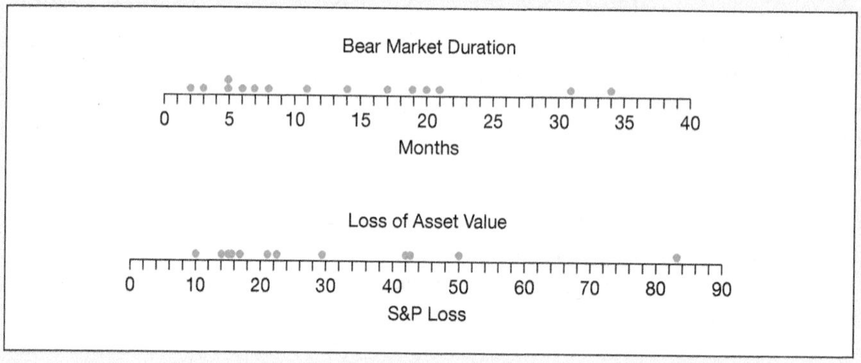

Table 4.12 shows that both duration (months) and S&P loss (percent) are right-skewed (mean substantially exceeding median) and have similar coefficients of variation. The other measures of center and variability cannot be compared because the units of measurement differ.

TABLE 4.12 **Statistical Summary of 15 Bear Markets**

Statistic	*Duration (months)*	*S&P Loss (%)*
Count	15	15
Mean	13.53	28.173
Median	11.00	21.000
Sample variance	99.27	383.266
Sample standard deviation	9.96	19.577
Minimum	2	10.2
Maximum	34	83.4
Range	32	73.2
Coefficient of variation	73.6%	69.5%
Mean absolute deviation (MAD)	8.17	14.45

SECTION EXERCISES

connect

4.21 (a) Find the mean and standard deviation for each sample. (b) What does this exercise show about the standard deviation?

Sample A: 6, 7, 8

Sample B: 61, 62, 63

Sample C: 1,000, 1,001, 1,002

4.22 For each data set: (a) Find the mean. (b) Find the standard deviation, treating the data as a sample. (c) Find the standard deviation, treating the data as a population. (d) What does this exercise show about the two formulas?

Data Set A: 6, 7, 8

Data Set B: 4, 5, 6, 7, 8, 9, 10

Data Set C: 1, 2, 3, 4, 5, 6, 7, 8, 9, 10, 11, 12, 13

4.23 In fuel economy tests in city driving conditions, a hybrid vehicle's mean was 43.2 mpg with a standard deviation of 2.2 mpg. A comparably sized gasoline vehicle's mean was 27.2 mpg with a standard deviation of 1.9 mpg. Which vehicle's mpg was more consistent in relative terms?

4.24 Over the past month, Bob's bowling score mean was 182 with a standard deviation of 9.1. His bowling partner Cedric's mean was 152 with a standard deviation of 7.6. Which bowler is more consistent in relative terms?

4.25 Use Excel's AVEDEV function to find the mean absolute deviation (MAD) of the integers 1 through 10.

4.26 Use Excel's AVEDEV function to find the mean absolute deviation (*MAD*) of these five numbers: 12, 18, 21, 22, 27.

4.27 (a) Find the coefficient of variation for prices of these three stocks. (b) Which stock has the greatest relative variation? (c) To measure variability, why not just compare the standard deviations?

Stock A: $\bar{x} = \$24.50, s = 5.25$

Stock B: $\bar{x} = \$147.25, s = 12.25$

Stock C: $\bar{x} = \$5.75, s = 2.08$

4.28 Prof. Hardtack gave four Friday quizzes last semester in his senior tax accounting class. A random sample of 10 student scores is shown for each quiz. (a) Find the sample mean, standard deviation, and coefficient of variation for each quiz. (b) How do these data sets differ in terms of center and variability? (c) Briefly describe and compare student performance on each quiz. **Quizzes**

Quiz 1: 60, 60, 60, 60, 71, 73, 74, 75, 88, 99

Quiz 2: 65, 65, 65, 65, 70, 74, 79, 79, 79, 79

Quiz 3: 66, 67, 70, 71, 72, 72, 74, 74, 95, 99

Quiz 4: 10, 49, 70, 80, 85, 88, 90, 93, 97, 98

4.29 Noodles and Company tested consumer reaction to two spaghetti sauces. Each of 70 raters assessed both sauces on a scale of 1 (worst) to 10 (best) using several taste criteria. To correct for possible bias in tasting order, half the raters tasted *Sauce A* first, while the other half tasted *Sauce B* first. Actual results are shown below for "overall liking." (a) Calculate the mean and standard deviation for each sample. (b) Calculate the coefficient of variation for each sample. (c) What is your conclusion about consumer preferences for the two sauces? (Source: Noodles and Company) **Spaghetti**

Sauce A:

6, 7, 7, 8, 8, 6, 8, 6, 8, 7, 8, 8, 6, 8, 7, 7, 7, 8, 8, 8, 7, 7, 6, 7, 7,
8, 3, 8, 8, 7, 8, 6, 7, 8, 7, 7, 3, 6, 8, 7, 1, 8, 8, 7, 6, 7, 7, 4, 8, 8,
3, 8, 7, 7, 7, 5, 7, 7, 7, 9, 5, 7, 6, 8, 8, 8, 4, 5, 9, 8

Sauce B:

7, 7, 7, 8, 8, 7, 8, 6, 8, 7, 7, 6, 7, 7, 8, 7, 8, 7, 8, 8, 7, 8, 5, 7, 7,
9, 4, 8, 8, 7, 8, 8, 8, 8, 7, 7, 3, 7, 9, 8, 9, 7, 8, 8, 6, 7, 7, 7, 8, 8,
7, 7, 8, 6, 6, 7, 7, 9, 7, 9, 8, 8, 6, 7, 7, 9, 4, 4, 9, 8

Mini Case 4.4

What Is the DJIA? DJIA

The Dow Jones Industrial Average (commonly called the DJIA) is the oldest U.S. stock market price index, based on the prices of 30 large, widely held, and actively traded "blue chip" public companies in the United States (e.g., Coca-Cola, Microsoft, Walmart, Walt Disney). Actually, only a few of its 30 component companies are "industrial." The DJIA is measured in "points" rather than dollars. Originally, a simple mean of stock prices, the DJIA now is the sum of the 30 stock prices divided by a "divisor" to compensate for stock splits and other changes over time. The divisor is revised as often as necessary (see www.djindexes.com/mdsidx or www.cbot.com for the latest value). Since high-priced stocks comprise a larger proportion of the sum, the DJIA is more strongly affected by changes in high-priced stocks. That is, a 10 percent price increase in a $10 stock would have less effect than a 10 percent price increase in a $50 stock, even if both companies have the same total market capitalization (the total number of shares times the price per share; often referred to as "market cap"). Broad-based market price indexes (e.g., NSDQ, AMEX, NYSE, S&P 500, Russ 2K) are widely used by fund managers, but the venerable "Dow" is still the one you see first on CNN or MSNBC.

Center versus Variability

Figure 4.19 shows histograms of hole diameters drilled in a steel plate during a manufacturing process. The desired distribution is shown in red. The samples from Machine *A* have the desired *mean* diameter (5 mm) but too much *variation* around the mean. It might be an older machine whose moving parts have become loose through normal wear, so there is greater variation in the holes drilled. Samples from Machine *B* have acceptable *variation* in hole diameter, but the *mean* is incorrectly adjusted (less than the desired 5 mm). To monitor quality, we would take frequent samples from the output of each machine, so that the process can be stopped and adjusted if the sample statistics indicate a problem.

FIGURE 4.19

Center versus Variability

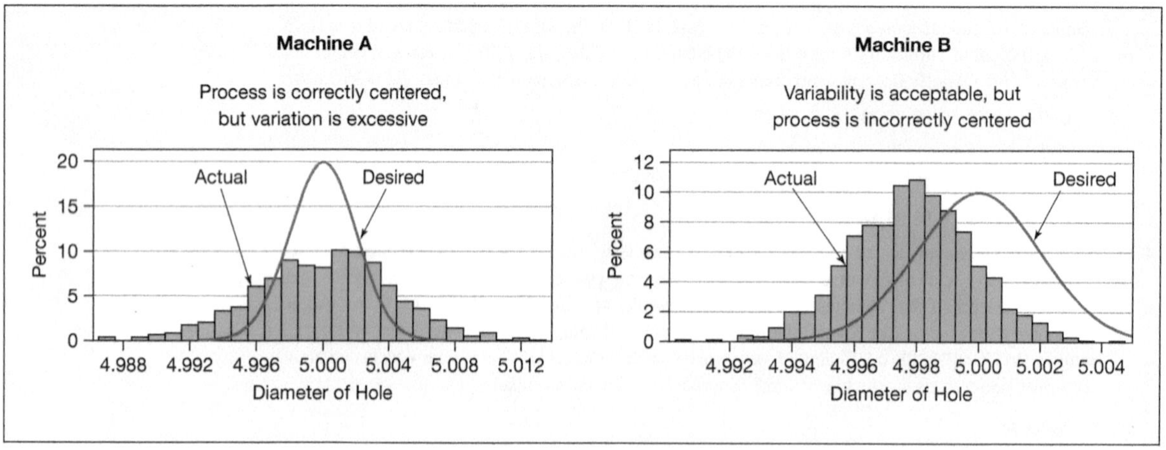

4.4 STANDARDIZED DATA

LO 4-4

Apply Chebyshev's theorem.

LO 4-5

Apply the Empirical Rule and recognize outliers.

LO 4-6

Transform a data set into standardized values.

The standard deviation is an important measure of variability because of its many roles in statistics. One of its main uses is to gauge the position of items within a data array.

Chebyshev's Theorem

The French mathematician Jules Bienaymé (1796–1878) and the Russian mathematician Pafnuty Chebyshev (1821–1894) proved that, for any data set, no matter how it is distributed, the percentage of observations that lie within *k* standard deviations of the mean (i.e., within $\mu \pm k\sigma$) must be at least $100\,[1 - 1/k^2]$. Commonly called **Chebyshev's Theorem**, it says that for *any population* with mean μ and standard deviation σ:

$k = 2$ at least 75.0% will lie within $\mu \pm 2\sigma$.

$k = 3$ at least 88.9% will lie within $\mu \pm 3\sigma$.

$k = 4$ at least 93.8% will lie within $\mu \pm 4\sigma$.

For example, for an exam with $\mu = 72$ and $\sigma = 8$, at least 75 percent of the scores will be within the interval $72 \pm 2(8)$ or [56, 88] regardless how the scores are distributed. Although applicable to any data set, these limits tend to be rather wide.

The Empirical Rule

More precise statements can be made about data from a normal or Gaussian distribution, named for its discoverer Karl Gauss (1777–1855). The Gaussian distribution is the well-known bell-shaped curve. Commonly called the **Empirical Rule**, it says that for data from a *normal distribution,* we expect the interval $\mu \pm k\sigma$ to contain a known percentage of the data:

$k = 1$ 68.26% will lie within $\mu \pm 1\sigma$.

$k = 2$ 95.44% will lie within $\mu \pm 2\sigma$.

$k = 3$ 99.73% will lie within $\mu \pm 3\sigma$.

The Empirical Rule is illustrated in Figure 4.20. The Empirical Rule does *not* give an upper bound, but merely describes what is *expected.* Rounding off a bit, we say that in samples from a normal distribution we expect 68 percent of the data within 1 standard deviation, 95 percent within 2 standard deviations, and virtually all of the data within 3 standard deviations. Data values outside $\mu \pm 3\sigma$ are rare (less than 1%) in a normal distribution and are called **outliers.**

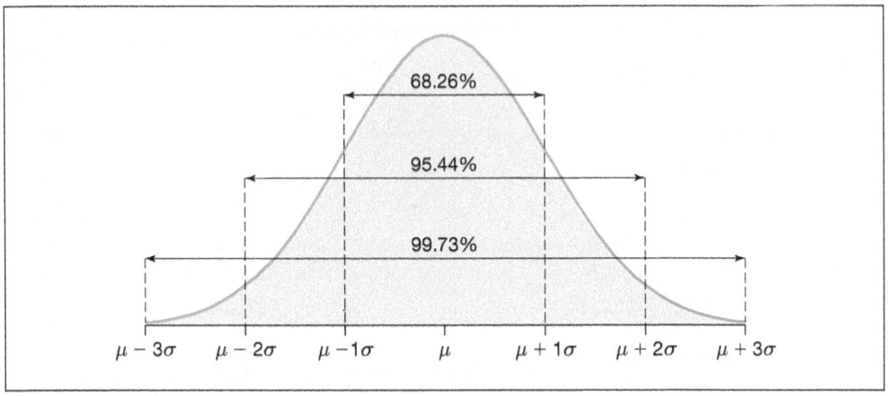

FIGURE 4.20

The Empirical Rule for a Normal Population

EXAMPLE 4.2

Exam Scores

Suppose 80 students take an exam. How many students will score within 2 standard deviations of the mean? Assuming that exam scores follow a normal or bell-shaped curve, we might be willing to rely on the Empirical Rule, which predicts that 95.44% × 80 or approximately 76 students will score within 2 standard deviations from the mean. Since a normal distribution is symmetric about the mean, we expect that about 2 students will score more than 2 standard deviations above the mean, and 2 below the mean. Using the Empirical Rule, we can further say that it is unlikely that any student will score more than 3 standard deviations from the mean ($99.73\% \times 80 = 79.78 \approx 80$).

Standardized Data

A general approach to identifying unusual observations is to redefine each observation in terms of its distance from the mean in standard deviations to obtain **standardized data.** We get the standardized value (called a **z-score**) by transforming each value of the observed data:

$$z_i = \frac{x_i - \mu}{\sigma} \quad \textit{for a population} \qquad \textbf{(4.15)}$$

$$z_i = \frac{x_i - \bar{x}}{s} \quad \textit{for a sample} \qquad \textbf{(4.16)}$$

By looking at the standardized z-score (z_i), we can tell at a glance how far away from the mean an observation lies. Excel's function =STANDARDIZE(XValue, Mean, StDev) makes it easy to calculate standardized values from a column of data. For the J.D. Power data, we set Mean = 114.697 and StDev = 18.067 and then use Excel to produce Table 4.13.

TABLE 4.13

Standardized z-Scores for Vehicle Brands ($n = 33$)
JDPower

Brand	Defects per 100	z-Score	Brand	Defects per 100	z-Score
Porsche	83	−1.754	Buick	114	−0.039
Acura	86	−1.588	Mazda	114	−0.039
Mercedes-Benz	87	−1.533	Scion	114	−0.039
Lexus	88	−1.478	Toyota	117	0.127
Ford	93	−1.201	Suburu	121	0.349
Honda	95	−1.090	Chrysler	122	0.404
Hyundai	102	−0.703	Suzuki	122	0.404
Lincoln	106	−0.481	GMC	126	0.626
Infiniti	107	−0.426	Kia	126	0.626
Volvo	109	−0.315	Jeep	129	0.792
Ram	110	−0.260	Dodge	130	0.847
Audi	111	−0.205	Jaguar	130	0.847
Cadillac	111	−0.205	MINI	133	1.013
Chevrolet	111	−0.205	Volkswagen	135	1.124
Nissan	111	−0.205	Mitsubishi	146	1.733
BMW	113	−0.094	Land Rover	170	3.061
Mercury	113	−0.094			

There is one *outlier* (beyond three standard deviations from the mean). No other data values are *unusual* (beyond two standard deviations from the mean). The standardized z-score for Land Rover is:

$$z_i = \frac{x_i - \bar{x}}{s} = \frac{170 - 114.697}{18.067} = 3.061 \quad \text{Outlier (more than 3 standard deviations from } \bar{x}\text{)}$$

By tabulating the standardized z-scores, we can compare our sample with the Empirical Rule. For the J.D. Power data, you can verify from Table 4.13 that 23 of 33 observations (69.70 percent) lie within the range $\bar{x} \pm 1s$ (i.e., standardized z-score within the range -1 to $+1$). This compares favorably with the Empirical Rule (68.26 percent if the distribution is normal). Further, 32 of 33 observations (96.97 percent) lie within the range $\bar{x} \pm 2s$ (i.e., standardized z-score within the range -2 to $+2$). This compares favorably with the Empirical Rule (95.44 percent if the distribution is normal). However, the existence of an outlier casts doubt on the idea of a normal distribution.

In its Descriptive Statistics menu, MegaStat has an option to tabulate sample frequencies within each interval ($\bar{x} \pm 1s, \bar{x} \pm 2s, \bar{x} \pm 3s$) based on z-scores. Figure 4.21 shows the Empirical Rule for the J.D. Power data.

FIGURE 4.21

Empirical Rule Using MegaStat ($n = 33$)
JDPower

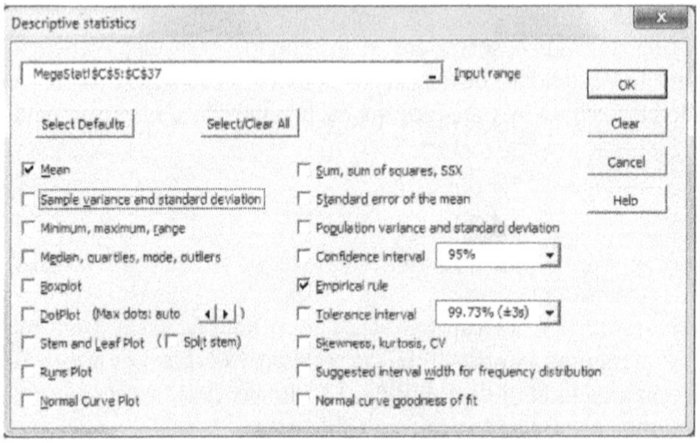

Descriptive statistics	Defects Per 100
count	33
mean	114.70
sample variance	326.41
sample standard deviation	18.07
minimum	83
maximum	170
range	87
empirical rule	
mean − 1s	96.63
mean + 1s	132.76
percent in interval (68.26%)	69.70%
mean − 2s	78.56
mean + 2s	150.83
percent in interval (95.44%)	96.97%
mean − 3s	60.50
mean + 3s	168.90
percent in interval (99.73%)	96.97%

For a large sample (e.g., $n = 1{,}000$), it would *not* be surprising to see a few data values outside the three standard deviation range (e.g., 99.73 percent of 1,000 is 997, so we would expect three outliers). For a small sample (say, fewer than 30 observations), comparing the sample frequencies with a normal distribution may be risky because we really don't have much information about *shape*.

What to Do about Outliers?

Extreme values of a variable are vexing, but what do we do about them? It is tempting to discard unusual data points. Discarding an outlier would be reasonable only if we had reason to suppose it is erroneous data. For example, a blood pressure reading of 1200/80 seems impossible (probably was supposed to be 120/80). Perhaps the lab technician was distracted by a conversation while marking down the reading. An outrageous observation may be invalid. But how do we guard against self-deception? More than one scientist has been convinced to disregard data that didn't fit the pattern, when in fact the weird observation was trying to say something important. For example, in the 1980s, instruments monitoring the ozone layer over Antarctica automatically disregarded readings two standard deviations from the long-term mean as likely due to measurement error (*New Scientist,* December 6, 2008, p. 32). Fortunately, the raw data were retrievable, and scientists were able to spot an increase in the number of discarded readings as the "ozone hole" grew. Strict new regulations on the release of chlorofluorocarbons have been successful in restoring the ozone in the atmosphere. At this stage of your statistical training, it suffices to *recognize* unusual data points and outliers and their potential impact, and to know that there are entire books that cover the topic of outliers (see Related Reading).

Unusual Observations

Based on its standardized z-score, a data value is classified as:

Unusual if $|z_i| > 2$ (beyond $\mu \pm 2\sigma$)

Outlier if $|z_i| > 3$ (beyond $\mu \pm 3\sigma$)

Estimating Sigma

For a normal distribution, essentially all the observations lie within $\mu \pm 3\sigma$, so the range is approximately 6σ (from $\mu - 3\sigma$ to $\mu + 3\sigma$). Therefore, if you know the range $x_{max} - x_{min}$, you can estimate the standard deviation as $\sigma = (x_{max} - x_{min})/6$. This rule can come in handy for approximating the standard deviation when all you know is the range. For example, the caffeine content of a cup of tea depends on the type of tea and length of time the tea steeps, with a range of 20 to 90 mg. Knowing the range, we could estimate the standard deviation as $s = (90 - 20)/6$, or about 12 mg. This estimate assumes that the caffeine content of a cup of tea is normally distributed.

Mini Case 4.5

Presidential Ages

At 47, President Barack Obama was perceived to be unusually young when he became president. But how unusual was he? Table 4.14 shows the sorted ages at inauguration of the first 44 U.S. Presidents. President Obama is tied as the fourth youngest president. For these 44 presidents, the mean is 54.68 years with a standard deviation of 6.227 years. In terms of his standardized z-score, President Obama ($x = 47$, $z = -1.23$) is not unusual.

Only our youngest president, Theodore Roosevelt ($x = 42$, $z = -2.04$) was unusual, as were our two oldest presidents, William Henry Harrison ($x = 68$, $z = 2.14$) and Ronald Reagan ($x = 69$, $z = 2.30$).

TABLE 4.14 **Ages at Inauguration of 44 U.S. Presidents (sorted)** **Presidents**

President	*Age*	*President*	*Age*	*President*	*Age*
T. Roosevelt	42	Lincoln	52	Washington	57
Kennedy	43	Carter	52	Jefferson	57
Grant	46	Van Buren	*54*	Madison	57
Cleveland	47	Hayes	*54*	J. Q. Adams	57
Clinton	47	McKinley	*54*	Monroe	58
Obama	47	Hoover	*54*	Truman	60
Pierce	48	G. W. Bush	*54*	J. Adams	61
Polk	49	B. Harrison	55	Jackson	61
Garfield	49	Cleveland	55	Ford	61
Fillmore	50	Harding	55	Eisenhower	62
Tyler	*51*	L. Johnson	55	Taylor	64
Arthur	*51*	A. Johnson	56	G. H. W. Bush	64
Taft	*51*	Wilson	56	Buchanan	65
Coolidge	*51*	Nixon	56	W. H. Harrison	68
F. Roosevelt	*51*			Reagan	69

The dot plot in Figure 4.22 shows modes at 51 and 54 (five times each).

FIGURE 4.22 **Dot Plot of Presidents' Ages at Inauguration**

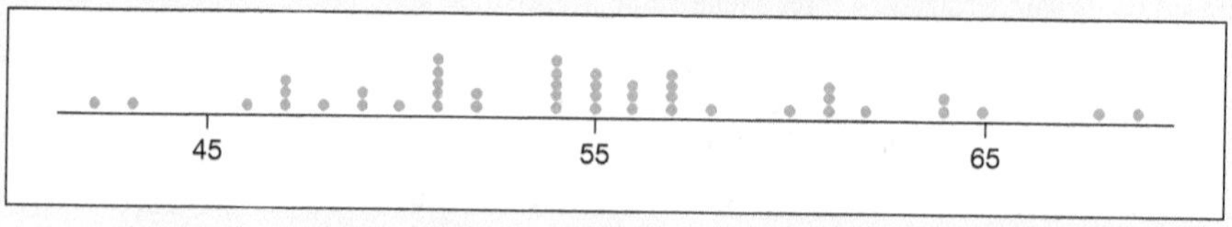

Using six classes, based on Sturges' Rule, Figure 4.23 shows that the modal class is 50 to 55 (13 presidents are in that class). However, since the next higher class has almost as many observations, it might be more helpful to say that presidents tend to be between 50 and 59 years of age upon inauguration (25 presidents are within this range). By that criterion, President Obama was relatively young.

FIGURE 4.23 **Histogram of Presidents' Ages at Inauguration**

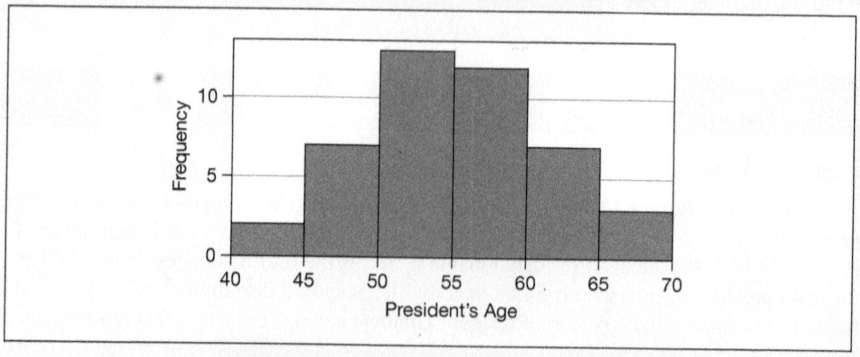

SECTION EXERCISES

connect

4.30 (a) By Chebyshev's Theorem, at least how many students in a class of 200 would score within the range $\mu \pm 2\sigma$? (b) By the Empirical Rule, how many students in a class of 200 would score within the range $\mu \pm 2\sigma$? (c) What assumption is required in order to apply the Empirical Rule?

4.31 An exam has a mean of 70 with a standard deviation of 10. Use Chebyshev's Theorem to find a lower bound for the number of students in a class of 400 who scored between 50 and 90.

4.32 The mean monthly rent of students at Oxnard University is \$875 with a standard deviation of \$219. (a) John's rent is \$1,325. What is his standardized z-score? (b) Is John's rent an outlier? (c) How high would the rent have to be to qualify as an outlier?

4.33 The mean collection period for accounts receivable at Ephemeral Products is 18.5 days with a standard deviation of 4.8 days. (a) What is the standardized z-score for an account that is paid in 30 days? (b) Is that account an outlier? (c) How many days (to the nearest integer) would qualify an account as an outlier?

4.34 Convert each individual data value to a standardized z-score. Is it an outlier?

a. Ages of airline passengers: $x = 92, \mu = 46, \sigma = 13$
b. Accounting exam scores: $x = 70, \mu = 81, \sigma = 6$
c. Condo rental vacancy days: $x = 28, \mu = 22, \sigma = 7$

4.35 Convert each individual X data value to a standardized Z value and interpret it.

a. Class exam:	John's score is 91, $\mu = 79, \sigma = 5$
b. Student GPA:	Mary's GPA is 3.18, $\mu = 2.87, \sigma = 0.31$
c. Weekly study hours:	Jaime studies 18 hours, $\mu = 15.0, \sigma = 5.0$

4.36 In a regional high school swim meet, women's times (in seconds) in the 200-yard freestyle ranged from 109.7 to 126.2. Estimate the standard deviation, using the Empirical Rule.

4.37 Find the original data value corresponding to each standardized z-score.

a. Student GPAs: Bob's z-score	$z = +1.71, \mu = 2.98, \sigma = 0.36$
b. Weekly work hours: Sarah's z-score	$z = +1.18, \mu = 21.6, \sigma = 7.1$
c. Bowling scores: Dave's z-score	$z = -1.35, \mu = 150, \sigma = 40$

4.38 CitiBank recorded the number of customers to use a downtown ATM during the noon hour on 32 consecutive workdays. (a) Use Excel or MegaStat to sort and standardize the data. (b) Based on the Empirical Rule, are there outliers? Unusual data values? (c) Compare the percent of observations that lie within 1 and 2 standard deviations of the mean with a normal distribution. What is your conclusion? CitiBank

25	37	23	26	30	40	25	26
39	32	21	26	19	27	32	25
18	26	34	18	31	35	21	33
33	9	16	32	35	42	15	24

4.39 An executive's telephone log showed the lengths of 65 calls initiated during the last week of July. (a) Use Excel or MegaStat to sort and standardize the data. (b) Based on the standardized z-scores, are there outliers? Unusual data values? (c) Compare the percent of observations that lie within 1 and 2 standard deviations of the mean with a normal distribution. What is your conclusion? CallLength

1	2	10	5	3	3	2	20	1	1
6	3	13	2	2	1	26	3	1	3
1	2	1	7	1	2	3	1	2	12
1	4	2	2	29	1	1	1	8	5
1	4	2	1	1	1	1	6	1	2
3	3	6	1	3	1	1	5	1	18
2	13	13	1	6					

LO 4-7

Calculate quartiles and other percentiles.

4.5 PERCENTILES, QUARTILES, AND BOX PLOTS

LO 4-8

Make and interpret box plots.

Percentiles

You are familiar with percentile scores of national educational tests such as ACT, SAT, and GMAT, which tell you where you stand in comparison with others. For example, if you are in the 83rd percentile, then 83 percent of the test-takers scored below you, and you are in the top 17 percent of all test-takers. However, only when the sample is large can we meaningfully divide the data into 100 groups (*percentiles*). Alternatively, we can divide the data into 10 groups (*deciles*), 5 groups (*quintiles*), or 4 groups (*quartiles*).

Percentiles in Excel

The *P*th percentile of a sorted data array $x_1, x_2, \ldots, x_n$ is the value of x that defines the lowest P percent of the data values. Excel's formula for the *P*th percentile is =PERCENTILE.EXC(Data, Proportion), where Proportion is the *proportion* below the *P*th percentile. For example, =PERCENTILE.EXC(Data, .95) returns the 95th percentile. In older versions of Excel, the function =PERCENTILE(Data, Proportion) will give somewhat different results (see Appendix J).

Percentiles generally have to be interpolated *between* two data values. For example, suppose you want the 95th percentile for a sample of $n = 73$ items. Since $.95 \times 73 = 69.35$, you would have to interpolate between the 69th and 70th observations (i.e., between x_{69} and x_{70}) to obtain the 95th percentile. The Excel formula =PERCENTILE.EXC(Data, .95) handles this interpolation automatically.

In health care, manufacturing, and banking, selected percentiles (e.g., 5, 25, 50, 75, and 95 percent) are calculated to establish *benchmarks* so that any firm can compare itself with similar firms (i.e., other firms in the same industry) in terms of profit margin, debt ratio, defect rate, or any other relevant performance measure. In finance, quartiles (25, 50, and 75 percent) are commonly used to assess financial performance of companies and stock portfolio performances. In human resources, percentiles are used in employee salary benchmarking. Occupational Employment Statistics (OES) published by the U.S. Bureau of Labor Statistics (www.bls.gov) show the 25th, 50th, and 75th percentiles for over 800 occupations in different metropolitan areas. An individual could use these benchmarks to assess his/her potential earnings in different locations, or an employer could use them to estimate the cost of hiring its employees. The number of groups depends on the task at hand and the sample size, but quartiles deserve special attention because they are meaningful even for fairly small samples.

Quartiles

The **quartiles** (denoted Q_1, Q_2, Q_3) are scale points that divide the sorted data into four groups of approximately equal size, that is, the 25th, 50th, and 75th percentiles, respectively.

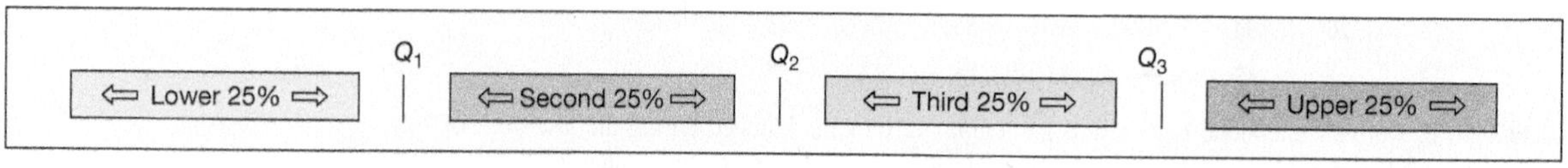

The second quartile Q_2 is the *median*. Since equal numbers of data values lie below and above the median, it is an important indicator of *center*.

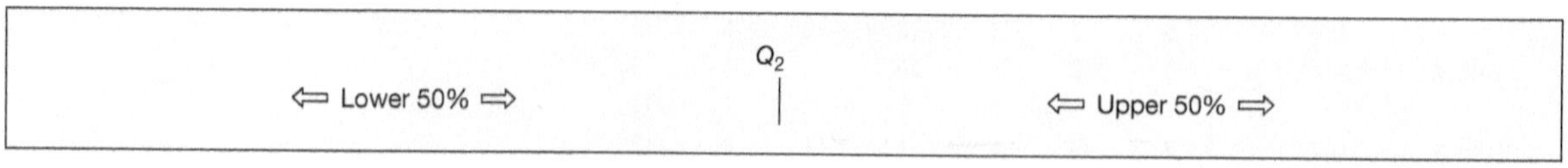

The first and third quartiles Q_1 and Q_3 indicate *center* because they define the boundaries for the middle 50 percent of the data. But Q_1 and Q_3 also indicate *variability* because the **interquartile range** $Q_3 - Q_1$ (denoted *IQR*) measures the degree of spread in the data (the middle 50 percent).

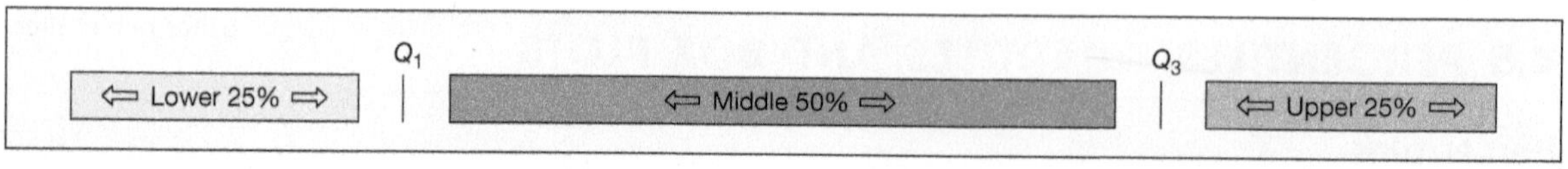

Conceptually, the first quartile Q_1 is the median of the data values below Q_2, and the third quartile Q_3 is the median of the data values above Q_2. Depending on n, the quartiles Q_1, Q_2, Q_3

FIGURE 4.24

Possible Quartile Positions

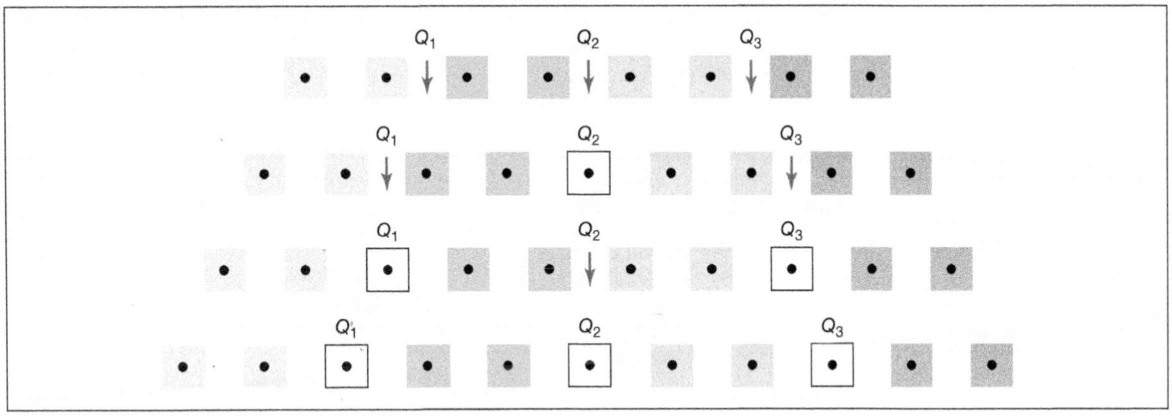

may be members of the data set or may lie *between* two of the sorted data values. Figure 4.24 shows four possible situations.

Method of Medians

For small data sets, you can find the quartiles using the **method of medians**, as illustrated in Figure 4.25.

- Step 1: Sort the observations.
- Step 2: Find the median Q_2.
- Step 3: Find the median of the data values that lie below Q_2.
- Step 4: Find the median of the data values that lie above Q_2.

When interpolation is necessary, we simply go halfway between the two data values. This method is attractive because it is quick and logical (see Freund 1987 in Related Reading). However, Excel uses a different method.

EXAMPLE 4.3

Method of Medians

A financial analyst has a portfolio of 12 energy equipment stocks. She has data on their recent price/earnings (P/E) ratios. To find the quartiles, she sorts the data, finds Q_2 (the median) halfway between the middle two data values, and then finds Q_1 and Q_3 (medians of the lower and upper halves, respectively) as illustrated in Figure 4.25.

FIGURE 4.25 **Method of Medians**

Company	*Sorted P/E*
Maverick Tube	7
BJ Services	22
FMC Technologies	25
Nabors Industries	29
Baker Hughes	31
Varco International	35
National-Oilwell	36
Smith International	36
Cooper Cameron	39
Schlumberger	42
Halliburton	46
Transocean	49

Q_1 is between x_3 and x_4 so
$Q_1 = (x_3 + x_4)/2 = (25 + 29)/2 = 27.0$

Q_2 is between x_6 and x_7 so
$Q_2 = (x_6 + x_7)/2 = (35 + 36)/2 = 35.5$

Q_3 is between x_9 and x_{10} so
$Q_3 = (x_9 + x_{10})/2 = (39 + 42)/2 = 40.5$

Source: Data are from *BusinessWeek*, November 22, 2004, pp. 95–98.

Excel Quartiles

Excel does not use the method of medians, but instead uses a formula[1] to interpolate its quartiles. Excel has a function =QUARTILE.EXC(Data, k) to return the kth quartile in a data array $x_1, x_2, \ldots, x_n$. For example =QUARTILE.EXC(Data, 1) will return Q_1 and =QUARTILE.EXC (Data, 3) will return Q_3. You could get the same results by using =PERCENTILE.EXC(Data, .25) and =PERCENTILE.EXC(Data, .75). Table 4.15 summarizes Excel's quartile methods.

TABLE 4.15

Calculating Quartiles Using Excel

Note: The older Excel functions =QUARTILE and =PERCENTILE will give different results from the functions shown in this table. The functions ending in .EXC will match MINITAB and other statistical packages.

Quartile	*Percent Below*	*Excel Quartile Function*	*Excel Percentile Function*	*Interpolated Position in Data Array*
Q_1	25%	=QUARTILE.EXC(Data,1)	=PERCENTILE.EXC(Data,.25)	$.25n + .25$
Q_2	50%	=QUARTILE.EXC(Data,2)	=PERCENTILE.EXC(Data,.50)	$.50n + .50$
Q_3	75%	=QUARTILE.EXC(Data,3)	=PERCENTILE.EXC(Data,.75)	$.75n + .75$

Excel's Q_2 (the median) will be the same as with the method of medians. Although Excel's Q_1 and Q_3 may differ from the method of medians, the differences are usually unimportant. Figure 4.26 illustrates calculations for Excel's interpolation methods for a small sample of 12 P/E ratios.

EXAMPLE 4.4

Excel Formula Method

Figure 4.26 illustrates Excel's quartile calculations using =QUARTILE.EXC for the same sample of P/E ratios. The resulting quartiles are similar to those using the method of medians.

FIGURE 4.26 **Excel's Quartile Interpolation Method**

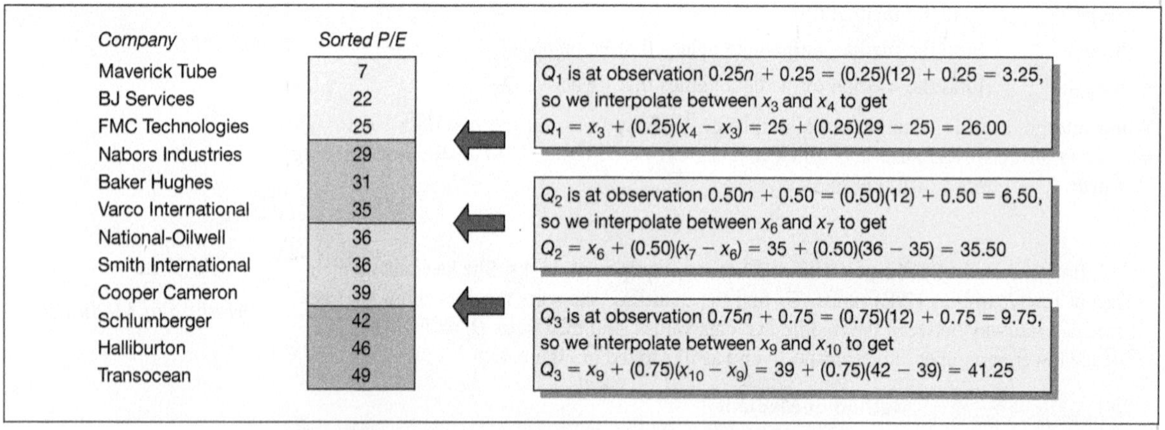

Source: Data are from *BusinessWeek*, November 22, 2004, pp. 95–98.

Tip

Whether you use the method of medians or Excel, your quartiles will be about the same. Small differences in calculation techniques typically do not lead to different conclusions in business applications.

[1]There are several acceptable ways to define the quartile position within a data array. Excel's QUARTILE.EXC and PERCENTILE.EXC functions define the Pth percentile position as $pn + p$ where $p = P/100$. See Eric Langford, "Quartiles in Elementary Statistics," *Journal of Statistics Education* 14, no. 3, November 2006. Different interpolation formulas generally give similar results.

Quartiles are robust statistics that generally resist outliers. However, quartiles do not always provide clean cutpoints in the sorted data, particularly in small samples or when there are repeating data values. For example:

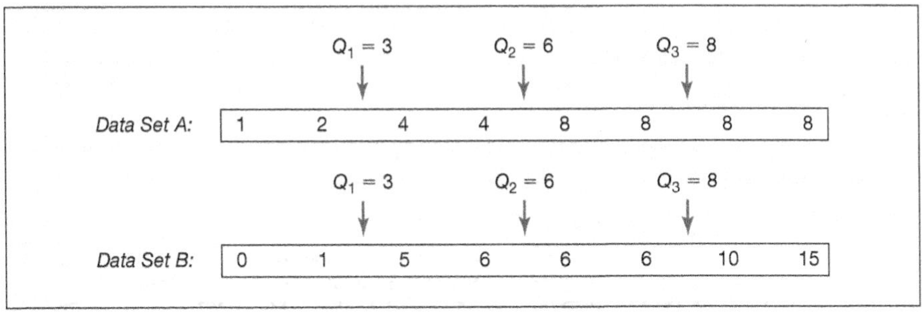

These two data sets have identical quartiles, but are not really similar. Because of the small sample size and "gaps" in the data, the quartiles do not represent either data set well.

Box Plots

A useful tool of *exploratory data analysis* (EDA) is the **box plot** (also called a *box-and-whisker plot*) based on the **five-number summary**:

$x_{min}, Q_1, Q_2, Q_3, x_{max}$

The box plot is displayed visually, like this.

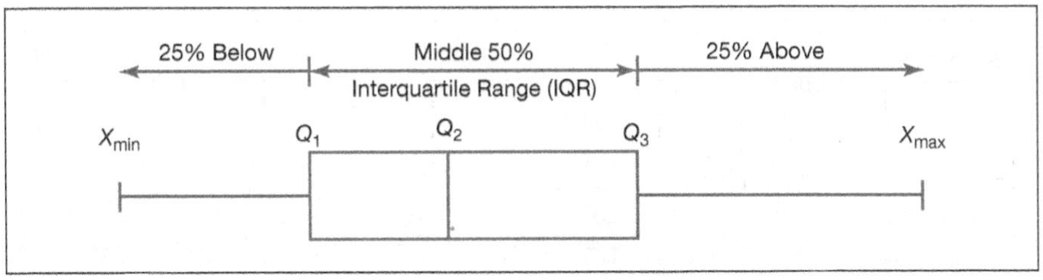

A box plot shows *center* (position of the median Q_2). A box plot shows *variability* (width of the "box" defined by Q_1 and Q_3 and the range between x_{min} and x_{max}). A box plot shows *shape* (skewness if the whiskers are of unequal length and/or if the median is not in the center of the box). Figure 4.27 shows simple boxplots and histograms for samples drawn from different types of populations. Despite sampling variation, the shape of each boxplot reveals the shape of its parent population. A boxplot gives a simple visual complement to

FIGURE 4.27

Sample Boxplots from Four Populations (n = 1000)

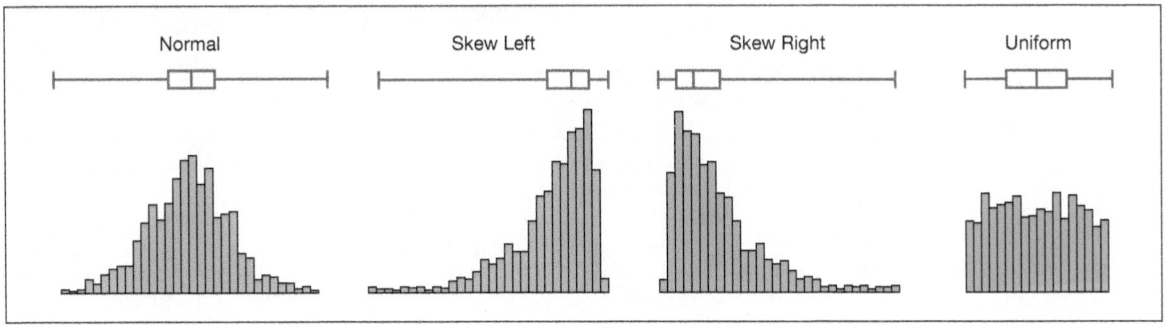

the histogram and/or numerical statistics that we use to describe data. For example, the five-number summary for the J.D. Power data ($n = 33$ vehicle brands) is:

$$x_{min} = 83,\ Q_1 = 107,\ Q_2 = 113,\ Q_3 = 126,\ x_{max} = 170$$

Figure 4.28 shows a box plot of the J.D. Power data. Below the box plot there is a well-labeled scale showing the values of X. The vertical lines that define the ends of the box are located at Q_1 and Q_3 on the X-axis. The vertical line within the box is the median (Q_2). The "whiskers" are the horizontal lines that connect each side of the box to x_{min} and x_{max} and their length suggests the length of each tail of the distribution. The long right whisker suggests right-skewness, a conclusion also suggested by the fact that the median is to the left of the center of the box.

FIGURE 4.28

Simple Box Plot of J.D. Power Data ($n = 33$ brands) JDPower

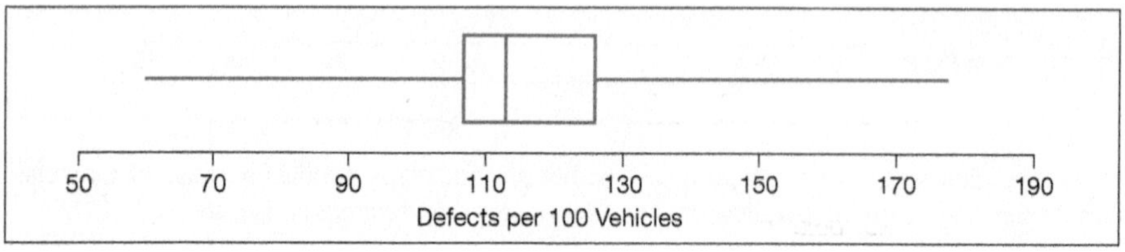

Fences and Unusual Data Values

We can use the quartiles to identify unusual data points. The idea is to detect data values that are far below Q_1 or far above Q_3. The *fences* are based on the *interquartile range* $Q_3 - Q_1$:

		Inner fences	*Outer fences*
(4.17)	Lower fence:	$Q_1 - 1.5(Q_3 - Q_1)$	$Q_1 - 3.0(Q_3 - Q_1)$
(4.18)	Upper fence:	$Q_3 + 1.5(Q_3 - Q_1)$	$Q_3 + 3.0(Q_3 - Q_1)$

On a boxplot, MegaStat and other software packages define observations outside the inner fences as *outliers* while those outside the outer fences are *extreme outliers*. For the J.D. Power data ($Q_1 = 107$ and $Q_3 = 126$), the fences are:

	Inner fences	*Outer fences*
Lower fence:	$107 - 1.5(126 - 107) = 78.5$	$107 - 3.0(126 - 107) = 50$
Upper fence:	$126 + 1.5(126 - 107) = 154.5$	$126 + 3.0(126 - 107) = 183$

In this example, there is one outlier (170) that lies above the *inner* fence. There are no extreme outliers that exceed the *outer* fence. Outliers are shown on a box plot by truncating the whisker at the fences and displaying the unusual data points as dots or asterisks, as in Figure 4.29. MegaStat shows fences *only if there are outliers*. Note that this "fences" criterion for "outliers" is not the same as the Empirical Rule.

FIGURE 4.29

Box Plot with Fences JDPower

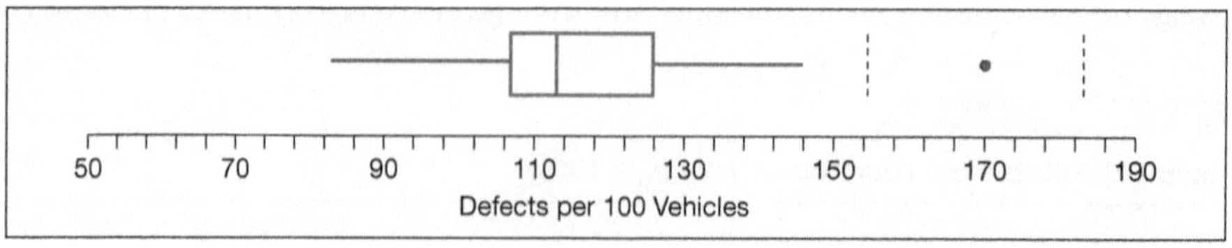

A diagram helps to visualize the fence calculations. To get the fences, we merely add or subtract a multiple of the *IQR* from Q_1 and Q_3.

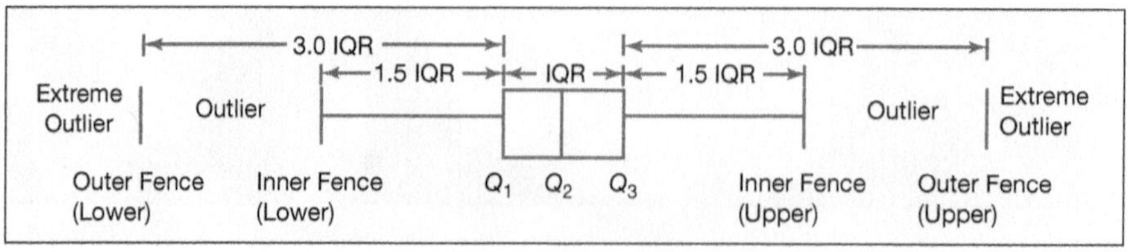

Midhinge

Quartiles can be used to define an additional measure of center that has the advantage of not being influenced by outliers. The **midhinge** is the average of the first and third quartiles:

$$\text{Midhinge} = \frac{Q_1 + Q_3}{2} \qquad \textbf{(4.19)}$$

The name "midhinge" derives from the idea that, if the "box" were folded at its halfway point, it would resemble a hinge:

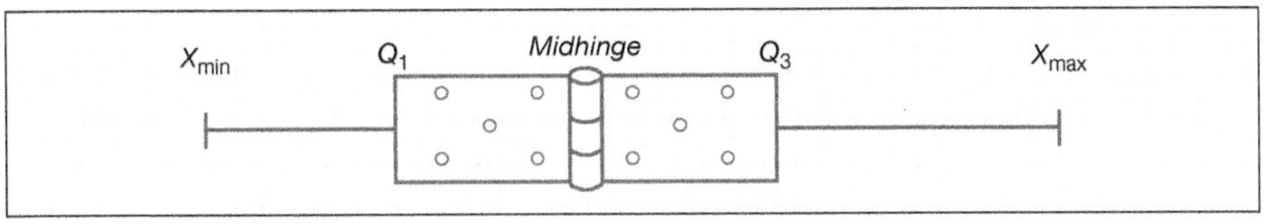

Since the midhinge is always exactly *halfway* between Q_1 and Q_3 while the median Q_2 can be *anywhere* within the "box," we have a new way to describe skewness:

Median < Midhinge	⇒ Skewed right (longer right tail)
Median ≅ Midhinge	⇒ Symmetric (tails roughly equal)
Median > Midhinge	⇒ Skewed left (longer left tail)

EXAMPLE 4.5

Hospital Bed Occupancy

The 24 boxplots in Figure 4.30 show occupied beds in a hospital emergency room hour by hour. Each boxplot is based on $n = 52$ Saturdays in one year. There are 24 hourly readings, so the total sample is $24 \times 52 = 1{,}248$ data points. Boxplots are shown vertically to facilitate comparisons over time. The median (50th percentile) and quartiles (25th and 75th percentiles) change slowly and predictably over the course of the day. In several boxplots there are unusual values (very high occupancy) marked with an asterisk. Since the upper whiskers are longer than the lower whiskers, the occupancy rates are positively skewed. On several occasions (e.g., between midnight and 8 a.m.) there were Saturdays with zero bed occupancy. Similar charts can be prepared for each day of the week, aiding the hospital in planning its emergency room staffing and bed capacity.

FIGURE 4.30 **Boxplots of Hospital Emergency Room Bed Occupancy**

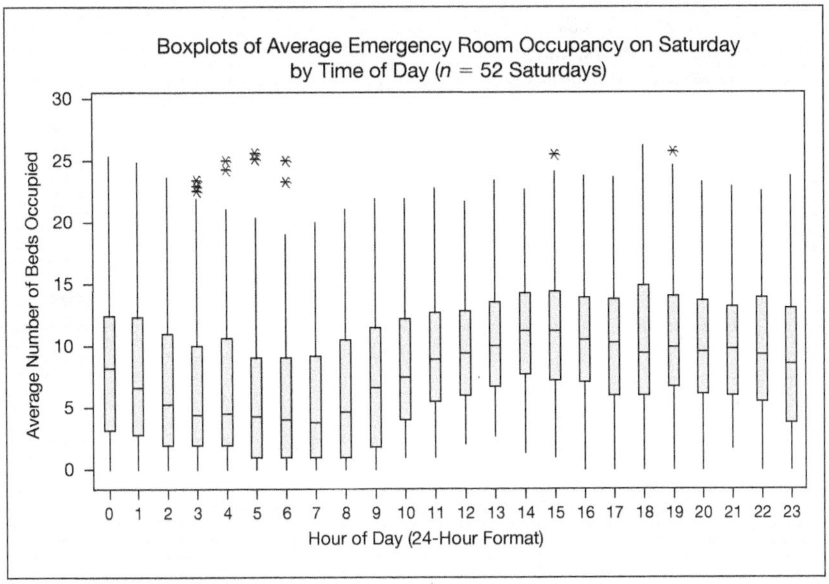

SECTION EXERCISES

connect

4.40 Scores on an accounting exam ranged from 42 to 96, with quartiles $Q_1 = 61$, $Q_2 = 77$, and $Q_3 = 85$. (a) Sketch a simple boxplot (5-number summary without fences) using a nicely scaled X-axis. (b) Describe its shape (skewed left, symmetric, skewed right).

4.41 In 2007, total compensation (in thousands of dollars) for 40 randomly chosen CEOs ranged from 790 to 192,920, with quartiles $Q_1 = 3{,}825$, $Q_2 = 8{,}890$, and $Q_3 = 17{,}948$. (a) Sketch a simple boxplot (5-number summary without fences) using a nicely scaled X-axis. (b) Describe its shape (skewed left, symmetric, skewed right).

4.42 Waiting times (minutes) for a table at Joey's BBQ on Friday at 5:30 p.m. have quartiles $Q_1 = 21$, $Q_2 = 27$ and $Q_3 = 33$. Using the inner fences as a criterion, would a wait time of 45 minutes be considered an outlier?

4.43 Coffee temperatures (degrees Fahrenheit) at a certain restaurant have quartiles $Q_1 = 160$, $Q_2 = 165$, and $Q_3 = 170$. Using the inner fences as a criterion, would a temperature of 149 be considered an outlier?

4.44 The Comer-Correr Taco Wagon is only open from 11:00 a.m. to 2:00 p.m. on Saturday. The owner kept track of the number of customers served on Saturday for 60 weeks. (a) Visually estimate the quartiles Q_1, Q_2, Q_3. (b) Approximately how many customers were served on the busiest day? The slowest day? (c) Is the distribution symmetric? **Customers**

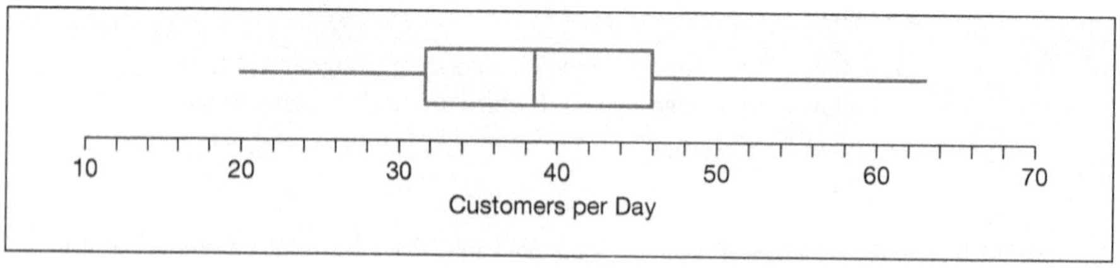

4.45 On San Martin Boulevard, embedded sensors kept track of the vehicle traffic count each hour for five weekdays, Monday through Friday between 6 a.m. and 8 p.m. (5 weeks × 14 hours = 70 observations). (a) Visually estimate the quartiles Q_1, Q_2, Q_3. (b) Estimate x_{min} and x_{max}. (c) Is the distribution symmetric? **Traffic**

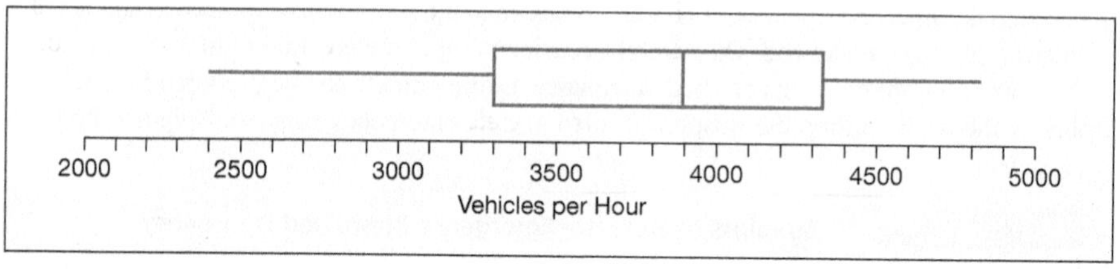

4.46 CitiBank recorded the number of customers to use a downtown ATM during the noon hour on 32 consecutive workdays. (a) Use Excel to find the quartiles. What do they tell you? (b) Find the midhinge. What does it tell you? (c) Make a box plot and interpret it. **CitiBank**

25	37	23	26	30	40	25	26
39	32	21	26	19	27	32	25
18	26	34	18	31	35	21	33
33	9	16	32	35	42	15	24

4.47 An executive's telephone log showed the lengths of 65 calls initiated during the last week of July. (a) Use Excel to find the quartiles. What do they tell you? (b) Find the midhinge. What does it tell you? (c) Make a box plot and interpret it. **CallLength**

1	2	10	5	3	3	2	20	1	1
6	3	13	2	2	1	26	3	1	3
1	2	1	7	1	2	3	1	2	12
1	4	2	2	29	1	1	1	8	5
1	4	2	1	1	1	1	6	1	2
3	3	6	1	3	1	1	5	1	18
2	13	13	1	6					

Mini Case 4.6

Airline Delays UnitedAir

In 2005, United Airlines announced that it would award 500 frequent flier miles to every traveler on flights that arrived more than 30 minutes late on all flights departing from Chicago O'Hare to seven other hub airports (see *The Wall Street Journal,* June 14, 2005). What is the likelihood of such a delay? On a randomly chosen day (Tuesday, April 26, 2005), the Bureau of Transportation Statistics website (www.bts.gov) showed 278 United Airlines departures from O'Hare. The mean arrival delay was −7.45 minutes (i.e., flights arrived early, on average). The quartiles were $Q_1 = -19$ minutes, $Q_2 = -10$ minutes, and $Q_3 = -3$ minutes. While these statistics show that most of the flights arrive early, we must look further to estimate the probability of a frequent flier bonus.

In the box plot with fences (Figure 4.31), the "box" is entirely below zero. In the right tail, one flight was slightly above the inner fence (unusual) and eight flights were above the outer fence (outliers). An empirical estimate of the probability of a frequent flier award is 8/278 or about a 3 percent chance. A longer period of study might alter this estimate (e.g., if there were days of bad winter weather or traffic congestion).

FIGURE 4.31 **Box Plot of Flight Arrival Delays**

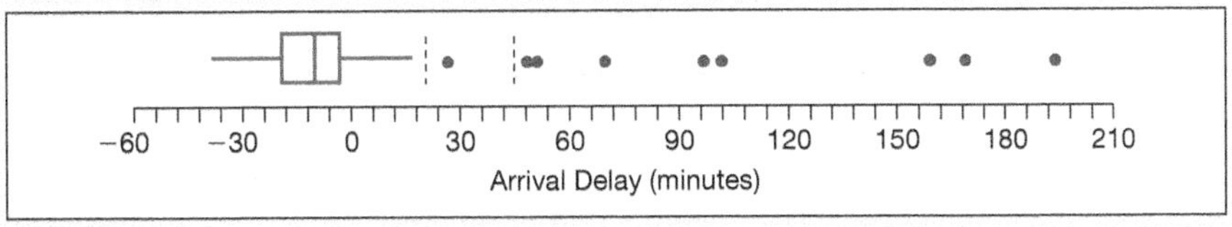

The dot plot (Figure 4.32) shows that the distribution of arrival delays is rather bell-shaped, except for the unusual values in the right tail. This is consistent with the view that "normal" flight operations are predictable, with only random variation around the mean. While it is difficult for flights to arrive earlier than planned, unusual factors could delay them by a lot.

FIGURE 4.32 **Dot Plot of Flight Arrival Delays**

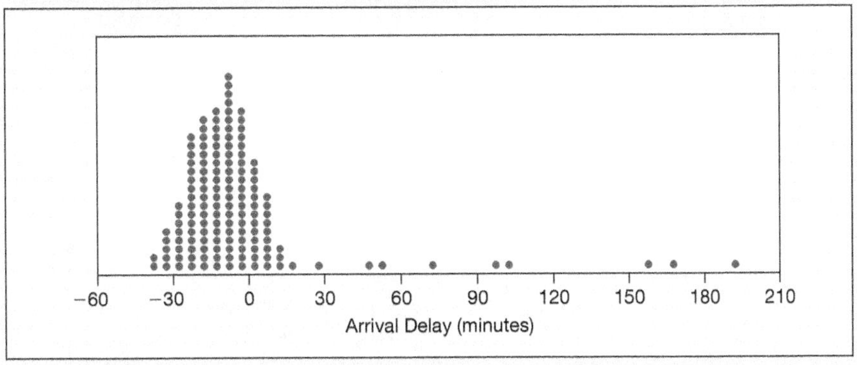

4.6 CORRELATION AND COVARIANCE

LO 4-9

Calculate and interpret a correlation coefficient and covariance.

You often hear the term "significant correlation" in casual use, often imprecisely or incorrectly. Actually, the **sample correlation coefficient** is a well-known statistic that describes the degree of linearity between *paired* observations on two quantitative variables X and Y. The data set consists of n pairs (x_i, y_i) that are usually displayed on a *scatter plot* (review

Chapter 3 if you need to refresh your memory about making scatter plots). The formula for the sample correlation coefficient is:

$$r = \frac{\sum_{i=1}^{n}(x_i - \bar{x})(y_i - \bar{y})}{\sqrt{\sum_{i=1}^{n}(x_i - \bar{x})^2}\sqrt{\sum_{i=1}^{n}(y_i - \bar{y})^2}} \tag{4.20}$$

Its range is $-1 \le r \le +1$. When r is near 0 there is little or no linear relationship between X and Y. An r value near $+1$ indicates a strong positive relationship, while an r value near -1 indicates a strong negative relationship. In Chapter 12, you will learn how to determine when a correlation is "significant" in a statistical sense (i.e., significantly different than zero), but for now it is enough to recognize the correlation coefficient as a *descriptive statistic*.

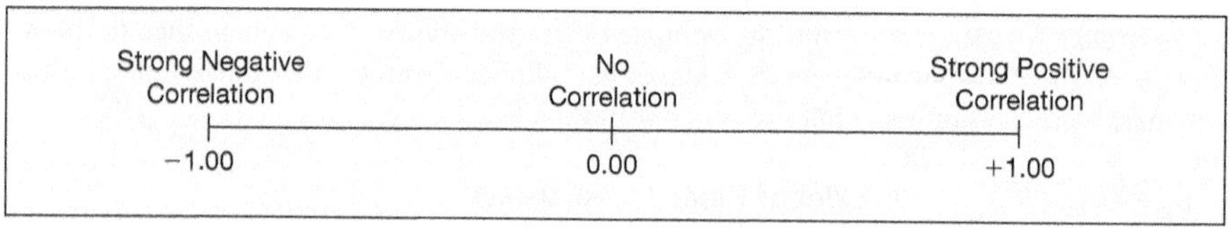

Excel's formula =CORREL(XData,YData) will return the sample correlation coefficient for two columns (or rows) of paired data. In fact, many scientific pocket calculators will calculate r. The diagrams in Figure 4.33 will give you some idea of what various correlations look like. The correlation coefficient is a measure of the *linear relationship*—so take special note of the last scatter plot, which shows a relationship but not a *linear* one.

FIGURE 4.33

Illustration of Correlation Coefficients

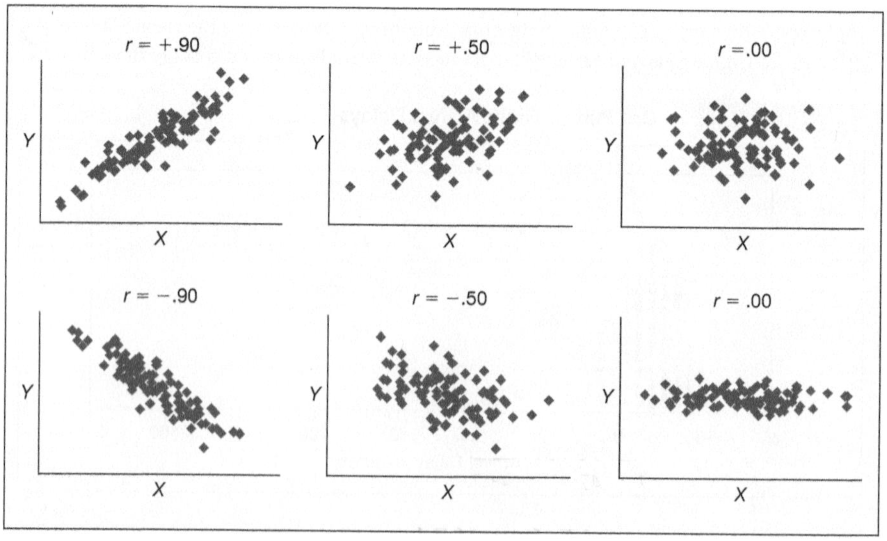

Covariance

The **covariance** of two random variables X and Y is denoted Cov(X,Y) or simply σ_{XY}. The covariance measures the degree to which the values of X and Y change together. This concept is particularly important in financial portfolio analysis. For example, if the prices of two stocks X and Y tend to move in the same direction, their covariance is positive ($\sigma_{XY} > 0$), and conversely if their prices tend to move in opposite directions ($\sigma_{XY} < 0$). If the prices of X and Y are unrelated, their covariance is zero ($\sigma_{XY} = 0$). A portfolio manager can apply this concept to reduce volatility in the overall portfolio, by combining stocks in a way that reduces variation. To estimate the covariance, we would generally use the sample formula.

For a population:
$$\sigma_{XY} = \frac{\sum_{i=1}^{N}(x_i - \mu_X)(y_i - \mu_Y)}{N} \qquad \textbf{(4.21)}$$

For a sample:
$$s_{XY} = \frac{\sum_{i=1}^{n}(x_i - \bar{x})(y_i - \bar{y})}{n - 1} \qquad \textbf{(4.22)}$$

The units of measurement for the covariance are unpredictable because the means and/or units of measurement of X and Y may differ. For this reason, analysts generally work with the correlation coefficient, which is a standardized value of the covariance. As you have already learned, the correlation coefficient always lies between -1 and $+1$. Conceptually, a correlation coefficient is the covariance divided by the product of the standard deviations of X and Y. For a population, the correlation coefficient is indicated by the lowercase Greek letter ρ (rho), while for a sample we use the lowercase Roman letter r (as you saw in formula 4.20 in the previous section).

Population correlation coefficient:
$$\rho = \frac{\sigma_{XY}}{\sigma_X \sigma_Y} \qquad \textbf{(4.23)}$$

where

σ_X = population standard deviation of X

σ_Y = population standard deviation of Y

Sample correlation coefficient:
$$r = \frac{s_{XY}}{s_X s_Y} \qquad \textbf{(4.24)}$$

where

s_X = sample standard deviation of X

s_Y = sample standard deviation of Y

Application: Stock Prices TwoStocks The prices of two stocks are recorded at the close of trading each Friday for 12 weeks, as displayed in Figure 4.34.

Closing Price for Week (n = 8 weeks)								
Company	***1***	***2***	***3***	***4***	***5***	***6***	***7***	***8***
X (AardCo)	41.87	47.87	43.26	37.76	45.86	45.22	46.83	46.49
Y (Zymurgy)	9.11	8.07	11.02	13.24	9.14	12.04	6.96	9.27

We can see that these two stock prices tend to move in opposite directions, so we anticipate a negative covariance (and a negative correlation). We can do the calculations using Excel functions with named data ranges. Because Excel's =COVAR function uses the population formula, we must make an adjustment to get a *sample* covariance (since here we have only a sample of stock prices). To avoid this extra step, Excel 2010 introduced =COVARIANCE.S for a sample or =COVARIANCE.P for a population (but these two functions are not available in earlier versions of Excel).

FIGURE 4.34

Scatter Plot of Two Stock Prices ($n = 8$)
TwoStocks

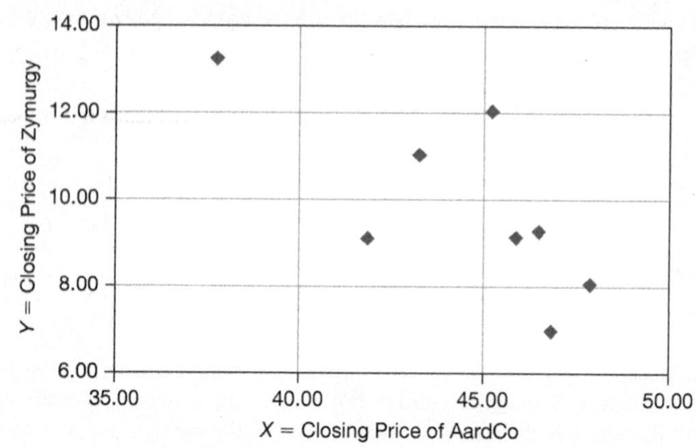

Statistic	*Result*	*Excel 2010 Formula*	*Excel 2007 Formula*
Sample covariance:	$s_{XY} = -5.0890$	=COVARIANCE.S (XData, YData)	=COVAR(XData, YData)*(n/(n-1)
Std. dev. of X:	$s_X = 3.3146$	=STDEV.S(Xdata)	=STDEV(XData)
Std. dev. of Y:	$s_Y = 2.0896$	=STDEV.S(Ydata)	=STDEV(YData)
Sample correlation:	$r = -0.7347$	=CORREL(Xdata,YData)	=CORREL(Xdata,YData)
Sample size:	$n = 8$ weeks	=COUNT(XData)	=COUNT(XData)

Applying the formula for a sample correlation coefficient:

$$r = \frac{s_{XY}}{s_X s_Y} = \frac{-5.0890}{(3.3146)(2.0896)} = -0.7347$$

This is the same value for the correlation coefficient that we would get from formula 4.20. Using this type of information, a financial analyst can construct a portfolio whose total value is more stable, knowing that these stock prices tend to move in opposite directions.

Correlations Help Portfolio Design

"A good way to decrease the standard deviation of your portfolio is through diversification. By investing in different types of funds, you can minimize the impact that any one sub-asset class may have on your total holding."

From T. Rowe Price Investor, *September 2009, p. 8.*

Mini Case 4.7

Vail Resorts Customer Satisfaction

Figure 4.35 is a matrix showing correlations between several satisfaction variables from a sample of respondents to a Vail Resorts' satisfaction survey. The correlations are all positive, suggesting that greater satisfaction with any one of these criteria tends to be associated with greater satisfaction with the others (positive covariance). The highest correlation

($r = 0.488$) is between *SkiSafe* (attention to skier safety) and *SkiPatV* (Ski Patrol visibility). This makes intuitive sense. When a skier sees a ski patroller, you would expect increased perception that the organization is concerned with skier safety. While many of the correlations seem small, they are all *statistically significant* (as you will learn in Chapter 12).

FIGURE 4.35 **Correlation Matrix of Skier Satisfaction Variables ($n = 502$)**
VailGuestSat

	LiftOps	*LiftWait*	*TrailVar*	*SnoAmt*	*GroomT*	*SkiSafe*	*SkiPatV*
LiftOps	1.000						
LiftWait	0.180	1.000					
TrailVar	0.206	0.128	1.000				
SnoAmt	0.242	0.227	0.373	1.000			
GroomT	0.271	0.251	0.221	0.299	1.000		
SkiSafe	0.306	0.196	0.172	0.200	0.274	1.000	
SkiPatV	0.190	0.207	0.172	0.184	0.149	0.488	1.000

where

LiftOps = helpfulness/friendliness of lift operators
LiftWait = lift line wait
TrailVar = trail variety
SnoAmt = amount of snow
GroomTr = amount of groomed trails
SkiSafe = attention to skier safety
SkiPatV = Ski Patrol visibility

SECTION EXERCISES

connect

4.48 For each *X-Y* data set ($n = 12$): (a) Make a scatter plot. (b) Find the sample correlation coefficient. (c) Is there a linear relationship between *X* and *Y*? If so, describe it. *Note:* Use Excel or MegaStat or MINITAB if your instructor permits. **XYDataSets**

Data Set (a)

X	64.7	25.9	65.6	49.6	50.3	26.7	39.5	56.0	90.8	35.9	39.9	64.1
Y	5.8	18.1	10.6	11.9	11.4	14.6	15.7	4.4	2.2	15.4	14.7	9.9

Data Set (b)

X	55.1	59.8	72.3	86.4	31.1	41.8	40.7	36.8	42.7	28.9	24.8	16.2
Y	15.7	17.5	15.2	20.6	7.3	8.2	9.8	8.2	13.7	11.2	7.5	4.5

Data Set (c)

X	53.3	18.1	49.8	43.8	68.3	30.4	18.6	45.8	34.0	56.7	60.3	29.3
Y	10.2	6.9	14.8	13.4	16.8	9.5	16.3	16.4	1.5	11.4	10.9	19.7

4.49 Your laptop gets warm (even hot) when you place it on your lap because it is dissipating heat from its microprocessor and related components. (a) Use the information in the following table to make a scatter plot. (b) Describe the relationship between *Microprocessor Speed* and *Power Dissipation*. (c) Calculate the correlation coefficient. **MicroSpeed**

Chip	Microprocessor Speed (MHz)	Power Dissipation (watts)
1989 Intel 80486	20	3
1993 pentium	100	10
1997 Pentium II	233	35
1998 Intel Celeron	300	20
1999 Pentium III	600	42
1999 AMD Athlon	600	50
2000 Pentium 4	1300	51
2004 Celeron D	2100	73
2004 Pentium 4	3800	115
2005 Pentium D	3200	130
2007 AMD Phenom	2300	95
2008 Intel Core 2	3200	136
2009 Intel Core i7	2900	95
2009 AMD Phenom II	3200	125

Sources: http://en.wikipedia.org and *New Scientist,* 208, no. 2780 (October 2, 2010), p. 41.

4.50 For a sample of (X, Y) data values, the covariance is 48.724, the standard deviation of X is 11.724, and the standard deviation of Y is 8.244. (a) Find the sample correlation coefficient. (b) What does the sample correlation coefficient suggest about the relationship between X and Y? (c) Why is the sample correlation easier to interpret than the sample covariance?

4.51 (a) Make a scatter plot of the following data on X = home size and Y = selling price (thousands of dollars) for new homes (n = 20) in a suburb of an eastern city. (b) Find the sample correlation coefficient. (c) Is there a linear relationship between X and Y? If so, describe it. *Note:* Use Excel or MegaStat or MINITAB if your instructor permits. **HomePrice**

Square Feet	Selling Price (thousands)	Square Feet	Selling Price (thousands)
3,570	861	3,460	737
3,410	740	3,340	806
2,690	563	3,240	809
3,260	698	2,660	639
3,130	624	3,160	778
3,460	737	3,310	760
3,340	806	2,930	729
3,240	809	3,020	720
2,660	639	2,320	575
3,160	778	3,130	785

4.7 GROUPED DATA

Weighted Mean

LO 4-10

Calculate the mean and standard deviation from grouped data.

The **weighted mean** is a sum that assigns each data value a weight w_j that represents a fraction of the total (i.e., the k weights must sum to 1).

(4.25)
$$\bar{x} = \sum_{j=1}^{k} w_j x_j \quad \text{where} \quad \sum_{j=1}^{k} w_j = 1.00$$

For example, your instructor might give a weight of 30 percent to homework, 20 percent to the midterm exam, 40 percent to the final exam, and 10 percent to a term project (so that .30 + .20 + .40 + .10 = 1.00). Suppose your scores on these were 85, 68, 78, and 90. Your weighted average for the course would be

$$\bar{x} = \sum_{j=1}^{k} w_j x_j = .30 \times 85 + .20 \times 68 + .40 \times 78 + .10 \times 90 = 79.3$$

Despite a low score on the midterm exam, you are right at the borderline for an 80 (if your instructor rounds up). The weighted mean is widely used in cost accounting (weights for cost categories), finance (asset weights in investment portfolios), and other business applications.

Grouped Data

We can apply the idea of a weighted mean when we must work with observations that have been grouped. When a data set is tabulated into bins, we lose information about the location of the x values within bins but gain clarity of presentation because grouped data can be displayed more compactly than raw data. As long as the bin limits are given, we can estimate the mean and standard deviation using weights based on the bin frequencies. The accuracy of the grouped estimates will depend on the number of bins, distribution of data within bins, and bin frequencies.

Grouped Mean and Standard Deviation

Table 4.16 shows a frequency distribution for prices of Lipitor®, a cholesterol-lowering prescription drug, for three cities (see **Mini Case 4.2**). The observations are classified into bins of equal width 5. When calculating a mean or standard deviation from grouped data, we treat all observations within a bin *as if they were located at the midpoint*. For example, in the third class (70 but less than 75), we pretend that all 11 prices were equal to \$72.50 (the interval midpoint). In reality, observations may be scattered within each interval, but we assume that *on average* they are located at the class midpoint.

TABLE 4.16 Worksheet for Grouped Lipitor® Data (n = 47) LipitorGrp

From	*To*	f_j	m_j	$f_j m_j$	$m_j - \bar{x}$	$(m_j - \bar{x})^2$	$f(m - \bar{x})^2$
60	65	6	62.5	375.0	−10.42553	108.69172	652.15029
65	70	11	67.5	742.5	−5.42553	29.43640	323.80036
70	75	11	72.5	797.5	−0.42553	0.18108	1.99185
75	80	13	77.5	1,007.5	4.57447	20.92576	272.03486
80	85	5	82.5	412.5	9.57447	91.67044	458.35220
85	90	0	87.5	0.0	14.57447	212.41512	0.00000
90	95	1	92.5	92.5	19.57447	383.15980	383.15980
	Sum	47	Sum	3,427.5		Sum	2,091.48936
			Mean ($\bar{x}$)	72.925532		Std Dev (s)	6.74293408

Each interval j has a midpoint m_j and a frequency f_j. We calculate the estimated mean by multiplying the midpoint of each class by its class frequency, taking the sum over all k classes, and dividing by sample size n.

$$\bar{x} = \frac{\sum_{j=1}^{k} f_j m_j}{n} = \frac{3{,}427.5}{47} = 72.9255 \qquad \textbf{(4.26)}$$

We then estimate the standard deviation by subtracting the estimated mean from each class midpoint, squaring the difference, multiplying by the class frequency, taking the sum over all classes to obtain the sum of squared deviations about the mean, dividing by $n - 1$, and taking the square root. *Avoid the common mistake of "rounding off" the mean before subtracting it from each midpoint.*

(4.27)
$$s = \sqrt{\sum_{j=1}^{k} \frac{f_j(m_j - \bar{x})^2}{n-1}} = \sqrt{\frac{2{,}091.48936}{47-1}} = 6.74293$$

Once we have the mean and standard deviation, we can estimate the coefficient of variation in the usual way:

$$CV = 100(s/\bar{x}) = 100\,(6.74293/72.925532) = 9.2\%$$

Accuracy Issues

How accurate are grouped estimates of $\bar{x}$ and s? To the extent that observations are *not* evenly spaced within the bins, accuracy would be lost. But, unless there is systematic skewness (say, clustering at the low end of each class), the effects of uneven distributions within bins will tend to average out.

Accuracy tends to improve as the number of bins increases. If the first or last class is open-ended, there will be no class midpoint, and therefore no way to estimate the mean. For nonnegative data (e.g., GPA), we can assume a lower limit of zero when the first class is open-ended, although this assumption may make the first class too wide. Such an assumption may occasionally be possible for an open-ended top class (e.g., the upper limit of people's ages could be assumed to be 100), but many variables have no obvious upper limit (e.g., income). It is usually possible to estimate the median and quartiles from grouped data even with open-ended classes (the end of chapter *LearningStats* demonstrations give the formulas and illustrate grouped quartile calculations).

SECTION EXERCISES

connect

4.52 Estimate the mean from this table of grouped data and frequencies:

From		*To*	*f*
0	<	20	5
20	<	40	12
40	<	60	18
60	<	80	9
		Total	44

4.53 Estimate the mean from the following table of grouped data and frequencies.

From		*To*	*f*
2	<	6	7
6	<	10	12
10	<	14	3
14	<	18	2
18	<	22	1
		Total	25

4.8 SKEWNESS AND KURTOSIS

Skewness

LO 4-11

Assess skewness and kurtosis in a sample.

In a general way, *skewness* (as shown in Figure 4.36) may be judged by looking at the sample histogram, or by comparing the mean and median. However, this comparison is imprecise and does not take account of sample size. When more precision is needed, we look at the sample's **skewness coefficient** provided by Excel and MINITAB:

$$\text{Skewness} = \frac{n}{(n-1)(n-2)} \sum_{i=1}^{n} \left(\frac{x_i - \bar{x}}{s} \right)^3 \tag{4.28}$$

This unit-free statistic can be used to compare two samples measured in different units (say, dollars and yen) or to compare one sample with a known reference distribution such as the symmetric normal (bell-shaped) distribution. The skewness coefficient is obtained from Excel's Tools > Data Analysis > Descriptive Statistics or by the function =SKEW(Data).

FIGURE 4.36

Skewness Prototype Populations

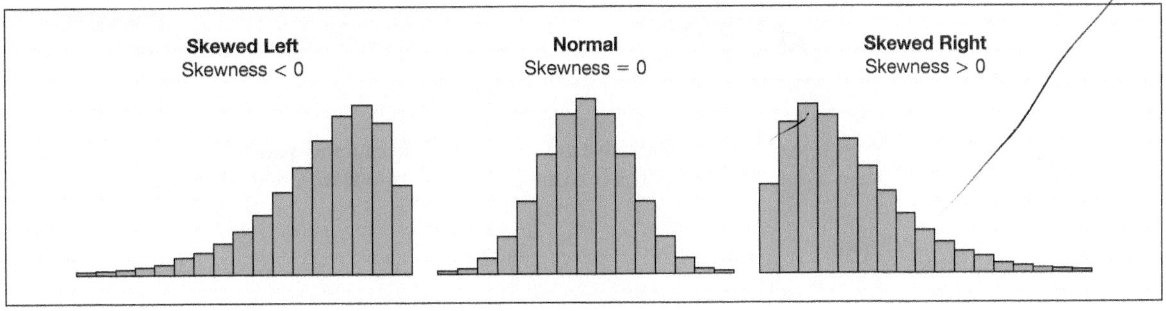

Table 4.17 shows the expected range within which the sample skewness coefficient would be expected to fall 90 percent of the time if the population being sampled were normal. A sample skewness statistic within the 90 percent range may be attributed to random variation, while coefficients outside the range would suggest that the sample came from a nonnormal population. As n increases, the range of chance variation narrows.

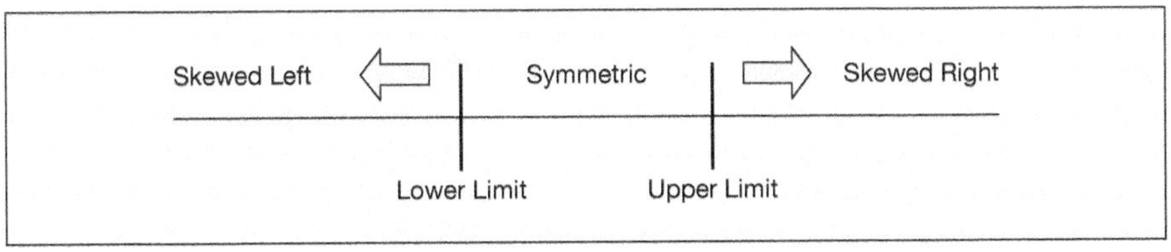

TABLE 4.17

90 Percent Range for Excel's Sample Skewness Coefficient

n	*Lower 5%*	*Upper 5%*	*n*	*Lower 5%*	*Upper 5%*
20	−0.84	+0.84	90	−0.41	+0.41
30	−0.69	+0.69	100	−0.40	+0.40
40	−0.61	+0.61	150	−0.33	+0.33
50	−0.55	+0.55	200	−0.28	+0.28
60	−0.51	+0.51	300	−0.23	+0.23
70	−0.47	+0.47	400	−0.20	+0.20
80	−0.44	+0.44	500	−0.18	+0.18

Source: Simulation of 100,000 samples using R with CRAN e1071 library.

Kurtosis

Kurtosis refers to the relative length of the tails and the degree of concentration in the center. A normal bell-shaped population is called **mesokurtic** and serves as a benchmark (see Figure 4.37). A population that is flatter than a normal (i.e., has heavier tails) is called **platykurtic** while one that is more sharply peaked than a normal (i.e., has thinner tails) is **leptokurtic**. Kurtosis is *not* the same thing as variability, although the two are easily confused.

FIGURE 4.37

Kurtosis Prototype Shapes

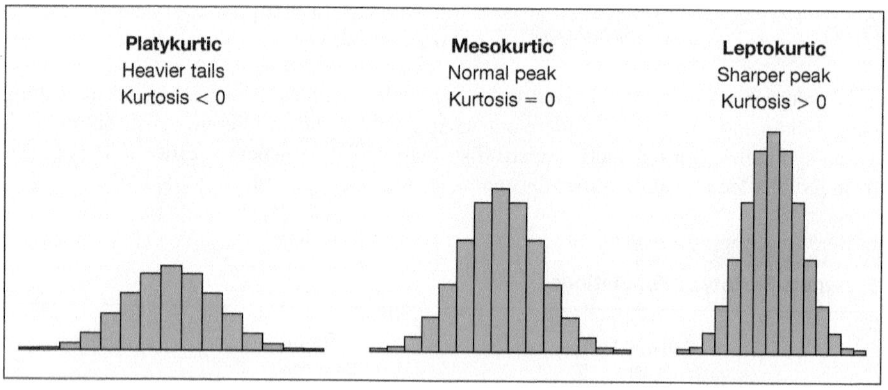

A histogram is an unreliable guide to kurtosis because its scale and axis proportions may vary, so a numerical statistic is needed. Excel and MINITAB use this statistic:

$$\text{Kurtosis} = \frac{n(n+1)}{(n-1)(n-2)(n-3)} \sum_{i=1}^{n} \left(\frac{x_i - \bar{x}}{s}\right)^4 - \frac{3(n-1)^2}{(n-2)(n-3)} \quad (4.29)$$

The sample kurtosis coefficient is obtained from Excel's function =KURT(Data). Table 4.18 shows the expected range within which sample kurtosis coefficients would be expected to fall 90 percent of the time if the population is normal. A sample coefficient within the ranges shown may be attributed to chance variation, while a coefficient outside this range would suggest that the sample differs from a normal population. As sample size increases, the chance range narrows. Unless you have at least 50 observations, inferences about kurtosis are risky.

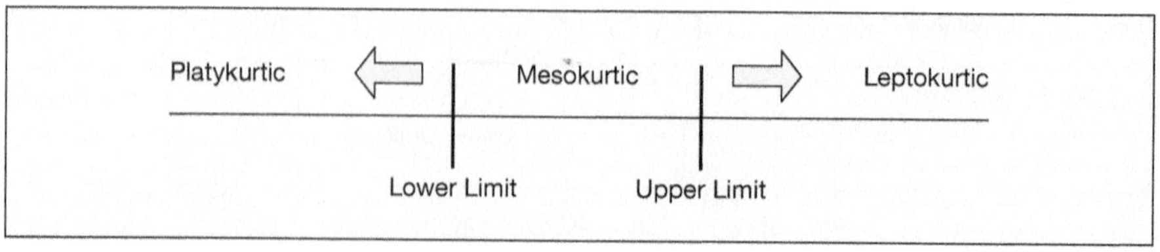

TABLE 4.18

90 Percent Range for Excel's Sample Kurtosis Coefficient

n	*Lower 5%*	*Upper 5%*	*n*	*Lower 5%*	*Upper 5%*
40	−0.89	1.35	100	−0.62	0.88
50	−0.82	1.23	150	−0.53	0.71
60	−0.76	1.13	200	−0.47	0.62
70	−0.72	1.04	300	−0.40	0.50
80	−0.68	0.98	400	−0.35	0.44
90	−0.65	0.92	500	−0.32	0.39

Source: Simulation of 100,000 samples using R with CRAN e1071 library. Note that lower and upper table limits are *not* symmetric.

Mini Case 4.8

Stock Prices StockPrices

An investor is tracking four stocks, two in the computer data services sector (IBM and EDS) and two in the consumer appliance sector (Maytag and Whirlpool). The analyst chose a two-month period of observation and recorded the closing price of each stock (42 trading days). Figure 4.38 shows MINITAB box plots for the stock prices (note that each has a different price scale).

Looking at the numerical statistics (Table 4.19), EDS's skewness coefficient (1.04) suggests a right-skewed distribution (for $n = 40$, the normal skewness range is $-.594$ to $+.594$). This conclusion is supported by the EDS box plot, with its long right whisker and an outlier in the right tail. Maytag's kurtosis coefficient (-1.40) suggests a flatter-than-normal distribution (for $n = 50$, the kurtosis coefficient range is -0.81 to $+1.23$), although the sample size is too small to assess kurtosis reliably. Maytag's coefficient of variation (*CV*) is also high. The Maytag box plot supports the view of high relative variation. In addition to patterns in price variation, an investor would consider many other factors (e.g., prospects for growth, dividends, stability, etc.) in evaluating a portfolio.

FIGURE 4.38 **Box Plots for Prices of Four Stocks**

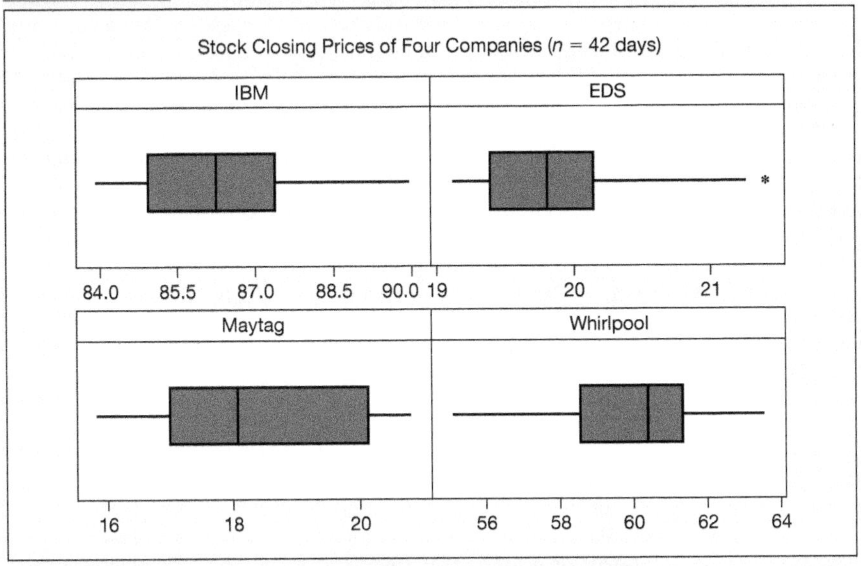

TABLE 4.19 **Four Companies' Stock Prices**

Statistic	*IBM*	*EDS*	*Maytag*	*Whirlpool*
Mean	86.40	19.86	18.39	59.80
Standard deviation	1.70	0.59	1.59	1.94
Skewness	0.51	1.04	0.23	−0.48
Kurtosis	−0.62	0.72	−1.40	−0.16
CV (%)	2.0%	3.0%	8.6%	3.2%
Quartile 1	84.97	19.40	17.07	58.53
Quartile 2	86.25	19.80	18.10	60.20
Quartile 3	87.37	20.13	20.11	61.28

Source: Data are from the Center for Research in Security Prices (CRSP®), a financial research center at the University of Chicago Graduate School of Business. Example is for statistical education only, and not as a guide to investment decisions. Maytag was acquired by Whirlpool in 2006.

Excel Hints

Hint 1: Formats When You Copy Data from Excel
Excel's dollar format (e.g., $214.07) or comma format (e.g., 12,417) will cause many statistical packages (e.g., MINITAB) to interpret the pasted data as text (because "$" and "," are not numbers). For example, in MINITAB a column heading C1-T indicates that the data column is text. Text cannot be analyzed numerically, so you can't get means, medians, etc. Check the format before you copy and paste.

Hint 2: Decimals When You Copy Data from Excel
Suppose you have adjusted Excel's decimal cell format to display 2.4 instead of 2.35477. When you copy this cell and paste it into MINITAB, the pasted cell contains 2.4 (not 2.35477). Thus, Excel's statistical calculations (based on 2.35477) will not agree with MINITAB. If you copy several columns of data (e.g., for a regression model), the differences can be serious.

CHAPTER SUMMARY

The **mean** and **median** describe a sample's **center** and also indicate **skewness.** The **mode** is useful for discrete data with a small range. The **trimmed mean** eliminates extreme values. The **geometric mean** mitigates high extremes but cannot be used when zeros or negative values are present. The **midrange** is easy to calculate but is sensitive to extremes. Variability is typically measured by the **standard deviation** while relative dispersion is given by the **coefficient of variation** for nonnegative data. **Standardized data** reveal **outliers** or unusual data values, and the **Empirical Rule** offers a comparison with a normal distribution. In measuring dispersion, the **mean absolute deviation** or **MAD** is easy to understand but lacks nice mathematical properties. **Quartiles** are meaningful even for fairly small data sets, while **percentiles** are used only for large data sets. **Box plots** show the quartiles and data range. The **correlation coefficient** measures the degree of linearity between two variables. The **covariance** measures the degree to which two variables move together. We can estimate many common descriptive statistics from **grouped data**. Sample coefficients of **skewness** and **kurtosis** allow more precise inferences about the **shape** of the population being sampled instead of relying on histograms.

KEY TERMS

Center
geometric mean
mean
median
midhinge
midrange
mode
trimmed mean
weighted mean

Variability
Chebyshev's Theorem
coefficient of variation
Empirical Rule
mean absolute deviation
outliers
population variance
range
sample variance
standard deviation
standardized data
two-sum formula
z-score

Shape
bimodal distribution
kurtosis
leptokurtic
mesokurtic
multimodal distribution
negatively skewed
platykurtic
positively skewed
skewed left
skewed right
skewness
skewness coefficient
symmetric data

Other
box plot
covariance
five-number summary
interquartile range
method of medians
quartiles
sample correlation coefficient

Choosing the Appropriate Statistic or Visual Display

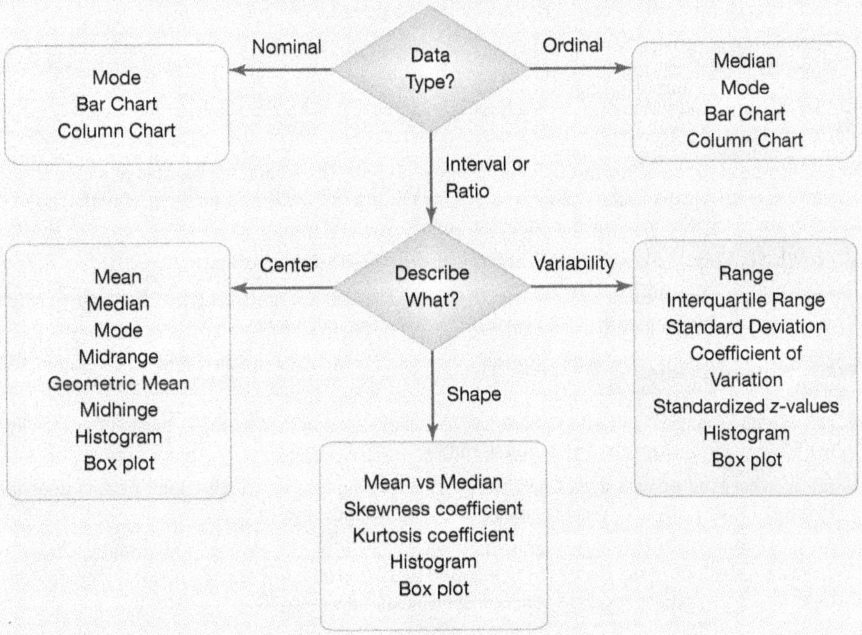

Commonly Used Formulas in Descriptive Statistics

Sample mean: $\bar{x} = \frac{1}{n}\sum_{i=1}^{n} x_i$

Geometric mean: $G = \sqrt[n]{x_1 x_2 \ldots x_n}$

Growth rate: $GR = \sqrt[n-1]{\frac{x_n}{x_1}} - 1$

Range: $\text{Range} = x_{\text{max}} - x_{\text{min}}$

Midrange: $\text{Midrange} = \frac{x_{\text{max}} + x_{\text{min}}}{2}$

Sample standard deviation: $s = \sqrt{\frac{\sum_{i=1}^{n}(x_i - \bar{x})^2}{n-1}}$

Coefficient of variation: Population $CV = 100 \times \frac{\sigma}{\mu}$ Sample $CV = 100 \times \frac{s}{\bar{x}}$

Standardized variable: Population $z_i = \frac{x_i - \mu}{\sigma}$ Sample $z_i = \frac{x_i - \bar{x}}{s}$

Midhinge: $\text{Midhinge} = \frac{Q_1 + Q_3}{2}$

Sample correlation coefficient: $r = \frac{\sum_{i=1}^{n}(x_i - \bar{x})(y_i - \bar{y})}{\sqrt{\sum_{i=1}^{n}(x_i - \bar{x})^2}\sqrt{\sum_{i=1}^{n}(y_i - \bar{y})^2}}$ or $r = \frac{s_{XY}}{s_X s_Y}$

Weighted mean: $\bar{x} = \sum_{j=1}^{k} w_j x_j$ where $\sum_{j=1}^{k} w_j = 1.00$

Grouped mean: $\bar{x} = \sum_{j=1}^{k} \frac{f_j m_j}{n}$

CHAPTER REVIEW

connect

1. What are descriptive statistics? How do they differ from visual displays of data?
2. Explain each concept: (a) center, (b) variability, and (c) shape.
3. (a) Why is sorting usually the first step in data analysis? (b) Why is it useful to begin a data analysis by thinking about how the data were collected?
4. List strengths and weaknesses of each measure of center and write its Excel function: (a) mean, (b) median, and (c) mode.
5. (a) Why must the deviations around the mean sum to zero? (b) What is the position of the median in the data array when n is even? When n is odd? (c) Why is the mode of little use in continuous data? (d) For what type of data is the mode most useful?
6. (a) What is a bimodal distribution? (b) Explain two ways to detect skewness.
7. List strengths and weaknesses of each measure of center and give its Excel function (if any): (a) midrange, (b) geometric mean, and (c) 10 percent trimmed mean.
8. (a) What is variability? (b) Name five measures of variability. List the main characteristics (strengths, weaknesses) of each measure.
9. (a) Which standard deviation formula (population, sample) is used most often? Why? (b) When is the coefficient of variation useful?
10. (a) To what kind of data does Chebyshev's Theorem apply? (b) To what kind of data does the Empirical Rule apply? (c) What is an outlier? An unusual data value?
11. (a) In a normal distribution, approximately what percent of observations are within 1, 2, and 3 standard deviations of the mean? (b) In a sample of 10,000 observations, about how many observations would you expect beyond 3 standard deviations of the mean?
12. (a) Write the mathematical formula for a standardized variable. (b) Write the Excel formula for standardizing a data value in cell F17 from an array with mean Mu and standard deviation Sigma.
13. (a) Why is it dangerous to delete an outlier? (b) When might it be acceptable to delete an outlier?
14. (a) Explain how quartiles can measure both center and variability. (b) Why don't we calculate percentiles for small samples?
15. (a) Explain the method of medians for calculating quartiles. (b) Write the Excel formula for the first quartile of an array named XData.
16. (a) What is a box plot? What does it tell us? (b) What is the role of fences in a box plot? (c) Define the midhinge and interquartile range.
17. What does a correlation coefficient measure? What is its range? Why is a correlation coefficient easier to interpret than a covariance?
18. (a) Why is some accuracy lost when we estimate the mean or standard deviation from grouped data? (b) Why do open-ended classes in a frequency distribution make it impossible to estimate the mean and standard deviation? (c) When would grouped data be presented instead of the entire sample of raw data?
19. (a) What is the skewness coefficient of a normal distribution? A uniform distribution? (b) Why do we need a table for sample skewness coefficients that is based on sample size?
20. (a) What is kurtosis? (b) Sketch a platykurtic population, a leptokurtic population, and a mesokurtic population. (c) Why can't we rely on a histogram to assess kurtosis?

CHAPTER EXERCISES

connect

4.54 (a) For each data set, calculate the mean, median, and mode. (b) Which, if any, of these three measures is the weakest indicator of a "typical" data value? Why?

a. Number of e-mail accounts (12 students): 1, 1, 1, 1, 2, 2, 2, 3, 3, 3, 3, 3
b. Number of siblings (5 students): 0, 1, 2, 2, 10
c. Asset turnover ratio (8 retail firms): 1.85, 1.87, 2.02, 2.05, 2.11, 2.18, 2.29, 3.01

4.55 If the mean asset turnover for retail firms is 2.02 with a standard deviation of 0.22, without assuming a normal distribution, within what range will at least 75% of retail firms' asset turnover fall?

4.56 For each data set: (a) Find the mean, median, and mode. (b) Which, if any, of these three measures is the weakest indicator of a "typical" data value? Why?

a. 100 m dash times ($n = 6$ top runners): 9.87, 9.98, 10.02, 10.15, 10.36, 10.36

b. Number of children ($n = 13$ families): 0, 1, 1, 2, 2, 2, 2, 2, 2, 2, 2, 2, 6

c. Number of cars in driveway ($n = 8$ homes): 0, 0, 1, 1, 2, 2, 3, 5

4.57 During a rock concert, the noise level (in decibels) in front row seats has a mean of 95 dB with a standard deviation of 8 dB. Without assuming a normal distribution, find the minimum percentage of noise level readings within 3 standard deviations of the mean.

4.58 Bags of jelly beans have a mean weight of 396 gm with a standard deviation of 5 gm. Use Chebyshev's Theorem to find a lower bound for the number of bags in a sample of 200 that weigh between 386 and 406 gm.

4.59 Based on experience, the Ball Corporation's aluminum can manufacturing facility in Ft. Atkinson, Wisconsin, knows that the metal thickness of incoming shipments has a mean of 0.2731 mm with a standard deviation of 0.000959 mm. (a) A certain shipment has a diameter of 0.2761. Find the standardized z-score for this shipment. (b) Is this an outlier?

4.60 SAT scores for the entering class of 2010 at Oxnard University were normally distributed with a mean of 1340 and a standard deviation of 90. Bob's SAT score was 1430. (a) Find Bob's standardized z-score. (b) By the Empirical Rule, is Bob's SAT score unusual?

4.61 Find the data value that corresponds to each of the following z-scores.

a. Final exam scores: Allison's z-score $= 2.30$, $\mu = 74$, $\sigma = 7$

b. Weekly grocery bill: James' z-score $= -1.45$, $\mu = \$53$, $\sigma = \$12$

c. Daily video game play time: Eric's z-score $= -0.79$, $\mu = 4.00$ hours, $\sigma = 1.15$ hours

4.62 The average time a Boulder High varsity lacrosse player plays in a game is 30 minutes with a standard deviation of 7 minutes. Nolan's playing time in last week's game against Fairview was 48 minutes. (a) Calculate the z-score for Nolan's playing time against Fairview. (b) By the Empirical Rule, was Nolan's playing time *unusual* when compared to the typical playing time?

4.63 The number of blueberries in a blueberry muffin baked by EarthHarvest Bakeries can range from 18 to 30 blueberries. (a) Use the Empirical Rule to estimate the standard deviation of the number of blueberries in a muffin. (b) What assumption did you make about the distribution of the number of blueberries?

Note: Unless otherwise instructed, you may use any desired statistical software for calculations and graphs in the following problems.

DESCRIBING DATA

4.64 Below are monthly rents paid by 30 students who live off campus. (a) Find the mean, median, and mode. (b) Do the measures of central tendency agree? Explain. (c) Calculate the standard deviation. (d) Sort and standardize the data. (e) Are there outliers or unusual data values? (f) Using the Empirical Rule, do you think the data could be from a normal population? **Rents**

730	730	730	930	700	570
690	1,030	740	620	720	670
560	740	650	660	850	930
600	620	760	690	710	500
730	800	820	840	720	700

4.65 How many days in advance do travelers purchase their airline tickets? Below are data showing the advance days for a sample of 28 passengers on United Airlines Flight 815 from Chicago to Los Angeles. (a) Calculate the mean, median, mode, and midrange. (b) Calculate the quartiles and midhinge. (c) Why can't you use the geometric mean for this data set? **Days**

11	7	11	4	15	14	71	29	8	7	16	28	17	249
0	20	77	18	14	3	15	52	20	0	9	9	21	3

4.66 The durations (minutes) of 26 electric power outages in the community of Sonando Heights over the past five years are shown below. (a) Find the mean, median, and mode. (b) Are the mean and median about the same? (c) Is the mode a good measure of center for this data set? Explain. (d) Is the distribution skewed? Explain. **Duration**

32	44	25	66	27	12	62	9	51	4	17	50	35
99	30	21	12	53	25	2	18	24	84	30	17	17

4.67 The U.S. Postal Service will ship a Priority Mail® Large Flat Rate Box (12″ × 12″ × 5½″) anywhere in the United States for a fixed price, regardless of weight. The weights (ounces) of 20 randomly chosen boxes are shown below. (a) Find the mean, median, and mode. (b) Are the mean and median about the same? If not, why not? (c) Is the mode a "typical" data value? Explain. (d) Is the distribution skewed? Explain. **Weights**

72	86	28	67	64	65	45	86	31	32
39	92	90	91	84	62	80	74	63	86

4.68 A sample of size $n = 70$ showed a skewness coefficient of 0.773 and a kurtosis coefficient of 1.277. What is the distribution's shape?

4.69 The "expense ratio" is a measure of the cost of managing the portfolio. Investors prefer a low expense ratio, all else equal. Below are expense ratios for 23 randomly chosen stock funds and 21 randomly chosen bond funds. (a) Calculate the mean and median for each sample. (b) Calculate the standard deviation and coefficient of variation for each sample. (c) Which type of fund has more variability? Explain. **Funds**

23 Stock Funds

1.12	1.44	1.27	1.75	0.99	1.45	1.19	1.22	0.99	3.18	1.21	1.89
0.60	2.10	0.73	0.90	1.79	1.35	1.08	1.28	1.20	1.68	0.15	

21 Bond Funds

1.96	0.51	1.12	0.64	0.69	0.20	1.44	0.68	0.40	0.94	0.75	1.77
0.93	1.25	0.85	0.99	0.95	0.35	0.64	0.41	0.90			

4.70 This year, Dolon Company's website averaged 12,104 daily views with a standard deviation of 3,026. Last year, the mean number of daily page views was 6,804 with a standard deviation of 1,701. Describe the *relative* variation in page views in these two years.

4.71 At Chipotle Mexican Grill, the number of calories in an order of chips and salsa is normally distributed with a mean of 620 and a standard deviation of 12. Bob's order had only 580 calories. Was this an outlier? Explain.

4.72 A plumbing supplier's mean monthly demand for vinyl washers is 24,212 with a standard deviation of 6,053. The mean monthly demand for steam boilers is 6.8 with a standard deviation of 1.7. Which demand pattern has more relative variation? Explain.

4.73 The table below shows average daily sales of Rice Krispies in the month of June in 74 Noodles & Company restaurants. (a) Make a histogram for the data. (b) Would you say the distribution is skewed? (c) Calculate the mean and standard deviation. (d) Are there any outliers? **RiceKrispies**

32	8	14	20	28	19	37	31	16	16
16	29	11	34	31	18	22	17	27	16
24	49	25	18	25	21	15	16	20	11
21	29	14	25	10	15	8	12	12	19
21	28	27	26	12	24	18	19	24	16
17	20	23	13	17	17	19	36	16	34
25	15	16	13	20	13	13	23	17	22
11	17	17	9						

4.74 Analysis of portfolio returns over a 20-year period showed the statistics below. (a) Calculate and compare the coefficients of variation. (b) Why would we use a coefficient of variation? Why not just compare the standard deviations? (c) What do the data tell you about risk and return? **Returns**

Comparative Returns on Four Types of Investments

Investment	*Mean Return*	*Standard Deviation*	*Coefficient of Variation*
Venture funds	19.2	14.0	
Common stocks	15.6	14.0	
Real estate	11.5	16.8	
Federal short-term paper	6.7	1.9	

4.75 Analysis of annualized returns over a 10-year period showed that prepaid tuition plans had a mean return of 6.3 percent with a standard deviation of 2.7 percent, while the Standard & Poor's 500 stock index had a mean return of 12.9 percent with a standard deviation of 15.8 percent. (a) Calculate and compare the coefficients of variation. (b) Why would we use a coefficient of variation? Why not just compare the standard deviations?

4.76 Caffeine content in a 5-ounce cup of brewed coffee ranges from 60 to 180 mg, depending on brew time, coffee bean type, and grind. (a) Use the midrange as a measure of center. (b) Use the Empirical Rule to estimate the standard deviation. (c) Why is the assumption of a normal, bell-shaped distribution important in making these estimates? (d) Why might caffeine content of coffee *not* be normal?

4.77 Chlorine is added to city water to kill bacteria. In a certain year, chlorine content in water from the Lake Huron Water Treatment plant ranged from 0.79 ppm (parts per million) to 0.92 ppm. (a) Use the midrange as a measure of center. (b) Use the Empirical Rule to estimate the standard deviation.

THINKING ABOUT DISTRIBUTIONS

4.78 At the Midlothian Independent Bank, a study shows that the mean ATM transaction takes 74 seconds, the median 63 seconds, and the mode 51 seconds. (a) Sketch the distribution, based on these statistics. (b) What factors might cause the distribution to be like this?

4.79 At the Eureka library, the mean time a book is checked out is 13 days, the median is 10 days, and the mode is 7 days. (a) Sketch the distribution, based on these statistics. (b) What factors might cause the distribution to be like this?

4.80 On Professor Hardtack's last cost accounting exam, the mean score was 71, the median was 77, and the mode was 81. (a) Sketch the distribution, based on these statistics. (b) What factors might cause the distribution to be like this?

4.81 The median life span of a mouse is 118 weeks. (a) Would you expect the mean to be higher or lower than 118? (b) Would you expect the life spans of mice to be normally distributed? Explain.

4.82 The median waiting time for a liver transplant in the United States is 321 days. Would you expect the mean to be higher or lower than 321 days? Explain. (See http://www.livermd.org/.)

4.83 A small suburban community agreed to purchase police services from the county sheriff's department. The newspaper said, "In the past, the charge for police protection from the Sheriff's Department has been based on the median cost of the salary, fringe benefits, etc. That is, the cost per deputy was set halfway between the most expensive deputy and the least expensive." (a) Is this the median? If not, what is it? (b) Which would probably cost the city more, the midrange or the median? Why?

4.84 A company's contractual "trigger" point for a union absenteeism penalty is a certain distance above the *mean* days missed by all workers. Now the company wants to switch the trigger to a certain number of days above the *median* days missed for all workers. (a) Visualize the distribution of missed days for all workers (symmetric, skewed left, skewed right). (b) Discuss the probable effect on the trigger point of switching from the mean to the median. (c) What position would the union be likely to take on the company's proposed switch?

EXCEL PROJECTS

4.85 (a) Use Excel functions to calculate the mean and standard deviation for weekend occupancy rates (percent) in nine resort hotels during the off-season. (b) What conclusion would a casual observer draw about center and variability, based on your statistics? (c) Now calculate the median for each sample. (d) Make a dot plot for each sample. (e) What did you learn from the medians and dot plots that was not apparent from the means and standard deviations? Occupancy

Observation	Week 1	Week 2	Week 3	Week 4
1	32	33	38	37
2	41	35	39	42
3	44	45	39	45
4	47	50	40	46
5	50	52	56	47
6	53	54	57	48
7	56	58	58	50
8	59	59	61	67
9	68	64	62	68

4.86 (a) Enter the Excel function =ROUND(NORMINV(RAND(),70,10),0) in cells B1:B100. This will create 100 random data points from a normal distribution using parameters $\mu = 70$ and $\sigma = 10$. Think of these numbers as exam scores for 100 students. (b) Use the Excel functions =AVERAGE(B1:B100) and =STDEV.S(B1:B100) to calculate the sample mean and standard deviation for your data array. (c) Write down the sample mean and standard deviation. (d) Compare the sample statistics with the desired parameters $\mu = 70$ and $\sigma = 10$. Do Excel's random samples have approximately the desired characteristics?

GROUPED DATA

Note: In each of the following tables, the upper bin limit is excluded from that bin but is included as the lower limit of the next bin.

4.87 A random sample of individuals who filed their own income taxes were asked how much time (hours) they spent preparing last year's federal income tax forms. (a) Estimate the mean. (b) Estimate the standard deviation. (c) Do you think the observations would be distributed uniformly within each interval? Why would that matter? (d) Why do you imagine that unequal bin sizes (interval widths) were used? Taxes

From	To (not incl)	f
0	2	7
2	4	42
4	8	33
8	16	21
16	32	11
32	64	6

4.88 This table shows the distribution of winning times in the Kentucky Derby (a horse race) over 84 years. (a) From the grouped data, calculate the mean. Show your calculations clearly in a worksheet. (b) What additional information would you have gained by having the raw data? (c) Do you think it likely that the distribution of times within each interval might not be uniform? Why would that matter?

Kentucky Derby Winning Times, 1930–2013 (seconds) Derby

From	*To*	*f*
119	120	1
120	121	5
121	122	19
122	123	27
123	124	12
124	125	10
125	126	5
126	127	3
127	128	2
	Total	84

Source: See en.wikipedia.org.

4.89 The self-reported number of hours worked per week by 204 top executives is given below. (a) Estimate the mean, standard deviation, and coefficient of variation using an Excel worksheet to organize your calculations. (b) Do the unequal class sizes hamper your calculations? Why do you suppose that was done?

Weekly Hours of Work by Top Executives Work

From	*To*	*f*
40	50	12
50	60	116
60	80	74
80	100	2
	Total	204

4.90 How long does it take to fly from Denver to Atlanta on Delta Airlines? The table below shows 56 observations on flight times (in minutes) for the first week of March 2005. (a) Use the grouped data formula to estimate the mean and standard deviation. (b) Using the ungrouped data (not shown), the *ungrouped* sample mean is 161.63 minutes and the ungrouped standard deviation is 8.07 minutes. How close did your *grouped* estimates come? (c) Why might flight times *not* be uniformly distributed within the second and third class intervals? (*Source:* www.bts.gov.)

Flight Times DEN to ATL (minutes) DeltaAir

From		*To*	*frequency*
140	<	150	1
150	<	160	25
160	<	170	24
170	<	180	4
180	<	190	2
	Total		56

DO-IT-YOURSELF SAMPLING PROJECTS

4.91 (a) Record the points scored by the winning team in 30 college football games played last weekend (if it is not football season, do the same for basketball or another sport of your choice). If you can't find 30 scores, do the best you can. (b) Make a frequency distribution and histogram. Describe the histogram. (c) Calculate the mean, median, and mode. Which is the best measure of center? Why? (d) Calculate the standard deviation and coefficient of variation. (e) Standardize the data. Are there any outliers? (f) Make a box plot. What does it tell you?

4.92 (a) Record the length (in minutes) of 30 movies chosen at random from your cable TV guide (or a similar source). Include the name of each movie. (b) Make a frequency distribution and histogram. Describe the histogram. (c) Calculate the mean, median, and mode. Which is the best measure of center? Why? (d) Standardize the data. Are there any outliers?

SCATTER PLOTS AND CORRELATION

4.93 (a) Make an Excel scatter plot of $X = 1990$ assault rate per 100,000 population and $Y = 2004$ assault rate per 100,000 population for the 50 U.S. states. (b) Use Excel's =CORREL function to find the correlation coefficient. (c) What do the graph and correlation coefficient say about assault rates by state for these two years? (d) Use MegaStat or Excel to find the mean, median, and standard deviation of assault rates in these two years. What does this comparison tell you? **Assault**

4.94 (a) Make an Excel scatter plot of X = airspeed (nautical miles per hour) and Y = cockpit noise level (decibels) for 61 aircraft flights. (b) Use Excel's =CORREL function to find the correlation coefficient. (c) What do the graph and correlation coefficient say about the relationship between airspeed and cockpit noise? Why might such a relationship exist? *Optional:* Fit an Excel trend line to the scatter plot and interpret it. **CockpitNoise**

MINI-PROJECTS

Note that in the following data sets, only the first three and last three observations are shown. You may download the complete data files from the problems in McGraw-Hill's Connect® or through your instructor. Choose a data set and prepare a brief, descriptive report. Refer to Appendix I for tips on report writing. You may use any computer software you wish (e.g., Excel, JMP, MegaStat, MINITAB, Stata, SPSS). Include relevant worksheets or graphs in your report. If some questions do not apply to your data set, explain why not.

4.95 (a) Sort the data and find X_{min} and X_{max}. (b) Make a histogram. Describe its shape. (c) Calculate the mean and median. Are the data skewed? (d) Calculate the standard deviation. (e) Standardize the data. Are there outliers? If so, list them along with their z-scores. (f) Calculate the quartiles and make a box plot. Describe its appearance.

DATA SET A Advertising Dollars as Percent of Sales in Selected Industries ($n = 30$) Ads

Industry	*Percent*
Accident and health insurance	0.9
Apparel and other finished products	5.5
Beverages	7.4
⋮	⋮
Steel works and blast furnaces	1.9
Tires and inner tubes	1.8
Wine, brandy, and spirits	11.3

Source: George E. Belch and Michael A. Belch, *Advertising and Promotion*, pp. 219–220. Copyright © 2004 Richard D. Irwin.

DATA SET B Maximum Rate of Climb for Selected Piston Aircraft ($n = 54$) ClimbRate

Manufacturer/Model	*Year*	*Climb (ft./min.)*
AMD CH 2000	2000	820
Beech Baron 58	1984	1,750
Beech Baron 58P	1984	1,475
⋮	⋮	⋮
Sky Arrow 650 TC	1998	750
Socata TB20 Trinidad	1999	1,200
Tiger AG-5B	2002	850

Source: *Flying Magazine* (various issues from 1997 to 2002).

DATA SET C **December Heating Degree-Days for Selected U.S. Cities ($n = 35$) Heating**

City	*Degree-Days*
Albuquerque	911
Baltimore	884
Bismarck	1,538
⋮	⋮
St. Louis	955
Washington, D.C.	809
Wichita	949

Source: U.S. Bureau of the Census, *Statistical Abstract of the United States*.

Note: A degree-day is the sum over all days in the month of the difference between 65 degrees Fahrenheit and the daily mean temperature of each city.

DATA SET D **Commercial Bank Profit as Percent of Revenue ($n = 39$) Banks**

Bank	*Percent*
AmSouth Bancorp	21
Bank of America Corp.	22
Bank of New York Co.	18
⋮	⋮
Wachovia Corp.	19
Wells Fargo	20
Zions Bancorp	18

Source: *Fortune* 149, no. 7 (April 5, 2004).

Note: These banks are in the Fortune 1000 companies.

DATA SET E **Caffeine Content of Randomly Selected Beverages ($n = 32$) Caffeine**

Company/Brand	*mg/oz.*
Barq's Root Beer	1.83
Coca-Cola Classic	2.83
Cool from Nestea	1.33
⋮	⋮
Snapple Sweet Tea	1.00
Sunkist Orange Soda	3.42
Vanilla Coke	2.83

Source: National Soft Drink Association (www.nsda.org).

DATA SET F **Super Bowl Scores 1967–2014 ($n = 48$ games) SuperBowl**

Year	*Teams and Scores*
1967	Green Bay 35, Kansas City 10
1968	Green Bay 33, Oakland 14
1969	NY Jets 16, Baltimore 7
⋮	⋮
2012	NY Giants 21, New England 17
2013	Baltimore 34, San Francisco 31
2014	Seattle 43, Denver 8

Source: *Sports Illustrated 2004 Sports Almanac, Detroit Free Press,* www.cbs.sportsline.com, www.nfl.com, and en.wikipedia.org.

DATA SET G Property Crimes per 100,000 Residents (n = 68 cities) Crime

City and State	Crime
Albuquerque, NM	8,515
Anaheim, CA	2,827
Anchorage, AK	4,370
⋮	⋮
Virginia Beach, VA	3,438
Washington, DC	6,434
Wichita, KS	5,733

Source: *Statistical Abstract of the United States, 2002.*

DATA SET H Size of Whole Foods Stores (n = 171) WholeFoods

Location (Store Name)	Sq. Ft.
Albuquerque, NM (Academy)	33,000
Alexandria, VA (Annandale)	29,811
Ann Arbor, MI (Washtenaw)	51,300
⋮	⋮
Winter Park, FL	20,909
Woodland Hills, CA	28,180
Wynnewood, PA	14,000

Source: www.wholefoodsmarket.com/stores/.

RELATED READING

Freund, John E.; and Benjamin M. Perles. "A New Look at Quartiles of Ungrouped Data." *The American Statistician* 41, no. 3 (August 1987), pp. 200–203.

Pukelsheim, Friedrich. "The Three Sigma Rule." *The American Statistician* 48, no. 2 (May 1994), pp. 88–91.

CHAPTER 4 More Learning Resources

You can access these *LearningStats* demonstrations through McGraw-Hill's Connect® to help you understand descriptive statistics.

connect™

Topic	*LearningStats Demonstrations*
Overview	Describing Data Using MegaStat Using MINITAB
Descriptive statistics	Basic Statistic Quartiles Box Plots Grouped Data Significant Digits
ScreenCam Tutorials	Using MegaStat Excel Descriptive Statistics Excel Scatter Plots

Key: = PowerPoint = Excel = PDF = ScreenCam Tutorials

EXAM REVIEW QUESTIONS FOR CHAPTERS 1–4

1. Which type of statistic (descriptive, inferential) is each of the following?
   a. Estimating the default rate on all U.S. mortgages from a random sample of 500 loans.
   b. Reporting the percent of students in your statistics class who use Verizon.
   c. Using a sample of 50 iPhones to predict the average battery life in typical usage.
2. Which is *not* an ethical obligation of a statistician? Explain.
   a. To know and follow accepted procedures.
   b. To ensure data integrity and accurate calculations.
   c. To support client wishes in drawing conclusions from the data.
3. "Driving without a seat belt is not risky. I've done it for 25 years without an accident." This *best* illustrates which fallacy?
   a. Unconscious bias.
   b. Conclusion from a small sample.
   c. *Post hoc* reasoning.
4. Which data type (categorical, numerical) is each of the following?
   a. Your current credit card balance.
   b. Your college major.
   c. Your car's odometer mileage reading today.
5. Give the type of measurement (nominal, ordinal, interval, ratio) for each variable.
   a. Length of time required for a randomly chosen vehicle to cross a toll bridge.
   b. Student's ranking of five cell phone service providers.
   c. The type of charge card used by a customer (Visa, MasterCard, AmEx, Other).
6. Tell if each variable is continuous or discrete.
   a. Tonnage carried by an oil tanker at sea.
   b. Wind velocity at 7 o'clock this morning.
   c. Number of text messages you received yesterday.
7. To choose a sample of 12 students from a statistics class of 36 students, which type of sample (simple random, systematic, cluster, convenience) is each of these?
   a. Picking every student who was wearing blue that day.
   b. Using Excel's =RANDBETWEEN(1,36) to choose students from the class list.
   c. Selecting every 3rd student starting from a randomly chosen position.
8. Which of the following is *not* a reason for sampling? Explain.
   a. The destructive nature of some tests.
   b. High cost of studying the entire population.
   c. The expense of obtaining random numbers.
9. Which statement is *correct*? Why not the others?
   a. Likert scales are interval if scale distances are meaningful.
   b. Cross-sectional data are measured over time.
   c. A census is always preferable to a sample.
10. Which statement is *false*? Explain.
    a. Sampling error can be reduced by using appropriate data coding.
    b. Selection bias means that respondents are not typical of the target population.
    c. Simple random sampling requires a list of the population.
11. The management of a theme park obtained a random sample of the ages of 36 riders of its Space Adventure Simulator. (a) Make a nice histogram. (b) Did your histogram follow Sturges' Rule? If not, why not? (c) Describe the distribution of sample data. (d) Make a dot plot of the data. (e) What can be learned from each display (dot plot and histogram)?

39	46	15	38	39	47	50	61	17
40	54	36	16	18	34	42	10	16
16	13	38	14	16	56	17	18	53
24	17	12	21	8	18	13	13	10

12. Which one of the following is *true*? Why not the others?
    a. Histograms are useful for visualizing correlations.
    b. Pyramid charts are generally preferred to bar charts.
    c. A correlation coefficient can be negative.
13. Which data would be most suitable for a pie chart? Why not the others?
    a. Presidential vote in the last election by party (Democratic, Republican, Other).
    b. Retail prices of six major brands of color laser printers.
    c. Labor cost per vehicle for 10 major world automakers.
14. Find the mean, standard deviation, and coefficient of variation for $X = 5, 10, 20, 10, 15$.
15. Here are the ages of a random sample of 20 CEOs (chief executive officers) of Fortune 500 U.S. corporations. (a) Find the mean, median, and mode. (b) Discuss advantages and disadvantages of each of these measures of center for this data set. (c) Find the quartiles and interpret them. (d) Sketch a box plot and describe it.

57	56	58	46	70	62	55	60	59	64
62	67	61	55	53	58	63	51	52	77

16. A consulting firm used a random sample of 12 CIOs (chief information officers) of large businesses to examine the relationship (if any) between salary (in thousands) and years of service in the firm. (a) Make a scatter plot and describe it. (b) Calculate a correlation coefficient and interpret it.

Years (X)	4	15	15	8	11	5	5	8	10	1	6	17
Salary (Y)	133	129	143	132	144	61	128	79	140	116	88	170

17. Which statement is *true*? Why not the others?
    a. We expect the median to exceed the mean in positively skewed data.
    b. The geometric mean is not possible when there are negative data values.
    c. The midrange is resistant to outliers.
18. Which statement is *false*? Explain.
    a. If $\mu = 52$ and $\sigma = 15$, then $X = 81$ would be an outlier.
    b. If the data are from a normal population, about 68 percent of the values will be within $\mu \pm \sigma$.
    c. If $\mu = 640$ and $\sigma = 128$ then the coefficient of variation is 20 percent.
19. Which is *not* a characteristic of using a log scale to display time series data? Explain.
    a. A log scale helps if we are comparing changes in two time series of dissimilar magnitude.
    b. General business audiences find it easier to interpret a log scale.
    c. If you display data on a log scale, equal distances represent equal ratios.

Chapter 5. Probaility

CHAPTER 5 Probability

CHAPTER CONTENTS

CHAPTER LEARNING OBJECTIVES

LO

When you finish this chapter you should be able to

LO 5-1 Describe the sample space of a random experiment.

LO 5-2 Distinguish among the three views of probability.

LO 5-3 Apply the definitions and rules of probability.

LO 5-4 Calculate odds from given probabilities.

LO 5-5 Determine when events are independent.

LO 5-6 Apply the concepts of probability to contingency tables.

LO 5-7 Interpret a tree diagram.

LO 5-8 Use Bayes' Theorem to calculate revised probabilities.

LO 5-9 Apply counting rules to calculate possible event arrangements.

You've learned that a statistic is a measurement that describes a sample data set of observations. Descriptive statistics allow us to describe a business process that we have already observed. But how will that process behave in the future? Nothing makes a business person more nervous than not being able to anticipate customer demand, supplier delivery dates, or their employees' output. Businesses want to be able to quantify the *uncertainty* of future events. What are the chances that revenue next month will exceed last year's average? How likely is it that our new production system will help us decrease our product defect rate? Businesses also want to understand how they can increase the chance of positive future events (increasing market share) and decrease the chance of negative future events (failing to meet forecasted sales.) The field of study called *probability* allows us to understand and quantify the uncertainty about the future. We use the rules of probability to bridge the gap between what we know now and what is unknown about the future.

5.1 RANDOM EXPERIMENTS

Sample Space

LO 5-1

Describe the sample space of a random experiment.

A **random experiment** is an observational process whose results cannot be known in advance. For example, when a customer enters a Lexus dealership, will the customer buy a car or not? How much will the customer spend? The set of all possible *outcomes* (denoted S) is the **sample space** for the experiment. Some sample spaces can be enumerated easily, while others may be immense or impossible to enumerate. For example, when CitiBank makes a consumer loan, we might define a sample space with only two outcomes:

$$S = \{\text{default, no default}\}$$

The sample space describing a Walmart customer's payment method might have four outcomes:

$$S = \{\text{cash, debit card, credit card, check}\}$$

The sample space to describe rolling a die has six outcomes:

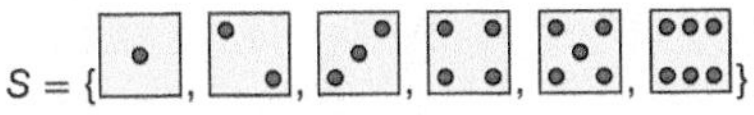

When two dice are rolled, the sample space consists of 36 outcomes, each of which is a pair:

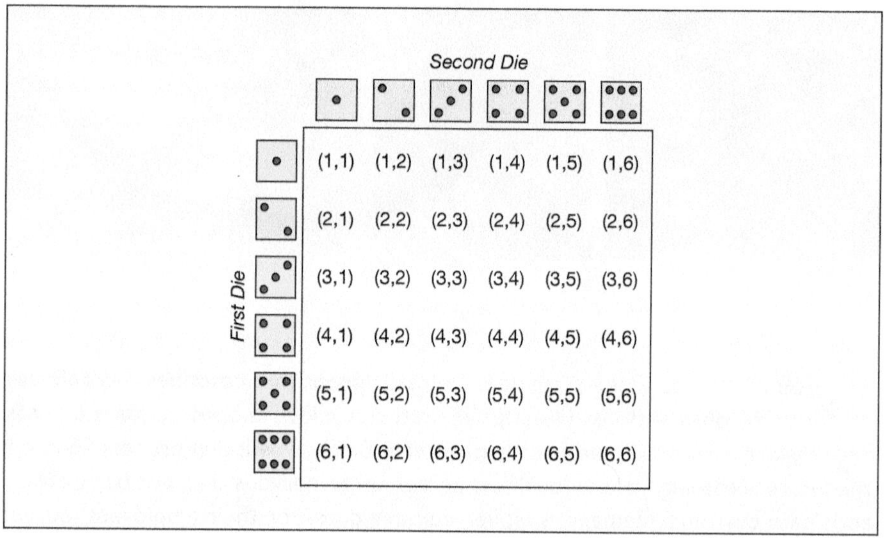

A sample space could be so large that it is impractical to enumerate the possibilities (e.g., the 12-digit UPC bar code on a product in your local Walmart could have 1 trillion values). If the outcome of the experiment is a *continuous* measurement, the sample space cannot be listed, but it can be described by a rule. For example, the sample space for the length of a randomly chosen cell phone call would be

$$S = \{\text{all } X \text{ such that } X \geq 0\}$$

and the sample space to describe a randomly chosen student's GPA would be

$$S = \{\text{all } X \text{ such that } 0.00 \leq X \leq 4.00\}$$

Similarly, some *discrete* measurements are best described by a rule. For example, the sample space for the number of hits on a YouTube website on a given day is:

$$S = \{\text{all } X \text{ such that } X = 0, 1, 2, \ldots\}$$

Event

An **event** is any subset of outcomes in the sample space. A **simple event**, or *elementary event,* is a single outcome. A discrete sample space S consists of all the simple events, denoted $E_1, E_2, \ldots, E_n$.

(5.1) $$S = \{E_1, E_2, \ldots, E_n\}$$

Consider the random experiment of tossing a balanced coin. The sample space for this experiment would be $S = \{\text{heads, tails}\}$. The chance of observing a head is the same as the chance of observing a tail. We say that these two elementary events are *equally likely*. When you buy a lottery ticket, the sample space $S = \{\text{win, lose}\}$ also has two elementary events; however, these events are not equally likely.

Simple events are the building blocks from which we can define a **compound event** consisting of two or more simple events. For example, Amazon's website for "Books & Music" has seven categories that a shopper might choose: $S = \{$Books, DVD, VHS, Magazines, Newspapers, Music, Textbooks$\}$. Within this sample space, we could define compound events "electronic media" as $A = \{$Music, DVD, VHS$\}$ and "print periodicals" as $B =$ (Newspapers, Magazines$\}$.

SECTION EXERCISES

connect

5.1 A credit card customer at Barnes and Noble can use Visa (V), MasterCard (M), or American Express (A). The merchandise may be books (B), electronic media (E), or other (O). (a) Enumerate the elementary events in the sample space describing a customer's purchase. (b) Would each elementary event be equally likely? Explain.

5.2 A survey asked tax accounting firms their business form (S = sole proprietorship, P = partnership, C = corporation) and type of risk insurance they carry (L = liability only, T = property loss only, B = both liability and property). (a) Enumerate the elementary events in the sample space. (b) Would each elementary event be equally likely? Explain.

5.3 A baseball player bats either left-handed (L) or right-handed (R). The player either gets on base (B) or does not get on base (B'). (a) Enumerate the elementary events in the sample space. (b) Would these elementary events be equally likely? Explain.

5.4 A die is thrown (1, 2, 3, 4, 5, 6) and a coin is tossed (H, T). (a) Enumerate the elementary events in the sample space for the die/coin combination. (b) Are the elementary events equally likely? Explain.

5.2 PROBABILITY

LO 5-2

Distinguish among the three views of probability.

The concept of probability is so familiar to most people that it can easily be misused. Therefore, we begin with some precise definitions and a few rules.

Definitions

The **probability** of an event is a number that measures the relative likelihood that the event will occur. The probability of an event A, denoted $P(A)$, must lie within the interval from 0 to 1:

$$0 \leq P(A) \leq 1 \tag{5.2}$$

$P(A) = 0$ means the event cannot occur (e.g., a naturalized citizen becoming president of the United States) while $P(A) = 1$ means the event is certain to occur (e.g., rain occurring in Hilo, Hawaii, sometime this year). In a discrete sample space, the probabilities of all simple events must sum to 1, since it is certain that one of them will occur:

$$P(S) = P(E_1) + P(E_2) + \cdots + P(E_n) = 1 \tag{5.3}$$

For example, if 32 percent of purchases are made by credit card, 15 percent by debit card, 35 percent by cash, and 18 percent by check, then:

$$P(\text{credit card}) + P(\text{debit card}) + P(\text{cash}) + P(\text{check}) = .32 + .15 + .35 + .18 = 1$$

What Is "Probability"?

There are three distinct ways of assigning probability, listed in Table 5.1. Many people mix them up or use them interchangeably; however, each approach must be considered separately.

TABLE 5.1 Three Views of Probability

Approach	*How Assigned?*	*Example*
Empirical	Estimated from observed outcome frequency	There is a 2 percent chance of twins in a randomly chosen birth.
Classical	Known *a priori* by the nature of the experiment	There is a 50 percent chance of heads on a coin flip.
Subjective	Based on informed opinion or judgment	There is a 60 percent chance that Toronto will bid for the 2024 Winter Olympics.

Empirical Approach

Sometimes we can collect empirical data through observations or experiments. We can use the **empirical** or **relative frequency approach** to assign probabilities by counting the frequency of observed outcomes (f) defined in our experimental sample space and dividing by the number of observations (n). The estimated probability is f/n. For example, we could estimate the reliability of a bar code scanner:

$$P(\text{a missed scan}) = \frac{\text{number of missed scans}}{\text{number of items scanned}}$$

or the default rate on student loans:

$$P(\text{a student defaults}) = \frac{\text{number of defaults}}{\text{number of loans}}$$

As we increase the number of observations (n) or the number of times we perform the experiment, our estimate will become more and more accurate. We use the ratio f/n to represent the probability. Here are some examples of empirical probabilities:

- An industrial components manufacturer interviewed 280 production workers before hiring 70 of them.

  H = event that a randomly chosen interviewee is hired

  $$P(H) = f/n = \frac{70}{280} = .25$$

- Over 20 years, a medical malpractice insurer saw only one claim for "wrong-site" surgery (e.g., amputating the wrong limb) in 112,994 malpractice claims.

  M = event that malpractice claim is for wrong-site surgery

  $$P(M) = f/n = \frac{1}{112{,}994} = .00000885$$

- On average, 2,118 out of 100,000 Americans live to age 100 or older.

  C = event that a randomly chosen American lives to 100 or older

  $$P(C) = f/n = \frac{2{,}118}{100{,}000} = .02118$$

Law of Large Numbers An important probability theorem is the **law of large numbers**, which says that as the number of trials increases, any empirical probability approaches its theoretical limit. Imagine flipping a coin 50 times. You know that the proportion of heads should be near .50. But in any finite sample it will probably not be .50, but something like 7 out of 13 (.5385) or 28 out of 60 (.4667). Coin flip experiments show that a large n may be needed before the proportion gets really close to .50, as illustrated in Figure 5.1.

A common variation on the law of large numbers says that, as the sample size increases, there is an increased probability that any event (even an unlikely one) will occur. For example, the same five winning numbers [4, 21, 23, 34, 39] came up twice in a three-day period in the North Carolina Cash-5 game.[1] Was something wrong with the lottery? The odds on this event are indeed small (191,919 to 1), but in a large number of drawings, an event like this becomes less surprising. Similarly, the odds that one ticket will win the lottery are low; yet the probability is high that *someone* will win the lottery because so many people buy lottery tickets. Gamblers tend to misconstrue this principle as implying that a streak of bad luck is "bound to change" if they just keep betting. Unfortunately, the necessary number of tries is likely to exhaust the gambler's bankroll.

Practical Issues for Actuaries You may know that **actuarial science** is a high-paying career that involves estimating empirical probabilities. Actuaries help companies calculate payout rates on life insurance, pension plans, and health care plans. Actuaries created the

[1]See Leonard A. Stefanski, "The North Carolina Lottery Coincidence," *The American Statistician* 62, no. 2 (May 2008), pp. 130–134.

FIGURE 5.1

Results of 10, 20, 50, and 200 Coin Flips CoinFlips

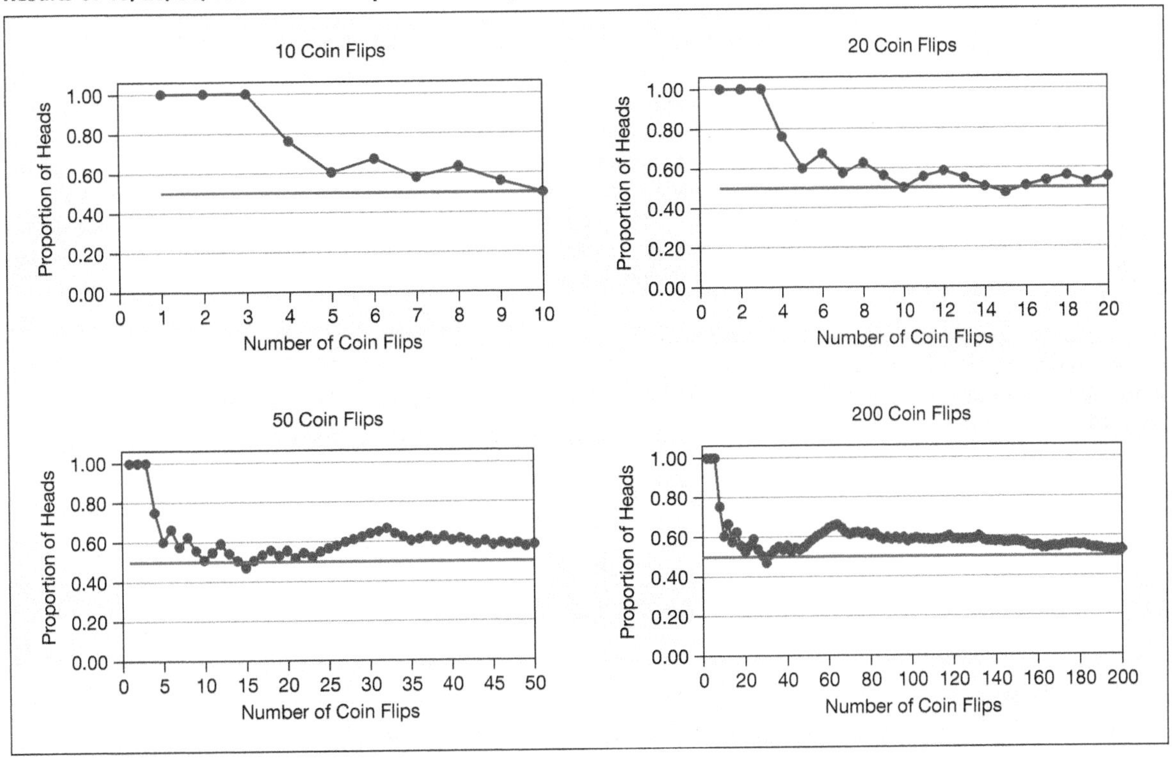

tables that guide IRA withdrawal rates for individuals from age 70 to 99. Here are a few challenges that actuaries face:

- Is n "large enough" to say that f/n has become a good approximation to the probability of the event of interest? Data collection costs money, and decisions must be made. The sample should be large enough but not larger than necessary for a given level of precision.
- Was the experiment repeated identically? Subtle variations may exist in the experimental conditions and data collection procedures.
- Is the underlying process stable over time? For example, default rates on 2007 student loans may not apply in 2017, due to changes in attitudes and interest rates.
- Do nonstatistical factors override data collection? Drug companies want clinical trials of a promising AIDS treatment to last long enough to ascertain its adverse side effects, yet ethical considerations forbid withholding a drug that could be beneficial.
- What if repeated trials are impossible? A good example occurred when Lloyd's of London was asked to insure a traveling exhibition of Monet paintings that was sent on a tour of the United States. Such an event only occurs once, so we have no f/n to help us.

Classical Approach

Statisticians use the term *a priori* to refer to the process of assigning probabilities before we actually observe the event or try an experiment. When flipping a coin or rolling a pair of dice, we do not actually have to perform an experiment because the nature of the process allows us to envision the entire sample space. Instead, we can use deduction to determine $P(A)$. This is the **classical approach** to probability. For example, in the sample space for the two-dice experiment shown in Figure 5.2, there are 36 possible outcomes, so the probability of rolling a seven is known to be:

$$P(\text{rolling a seven}) = \frac{\text{number of possible outcomes with 7 dots}}{\text{number of outcomes in sample space}} = \frac{6}{36} = .1667$$

The probability is obtained *a priori* without actually doing an experiment. We can apply pure reason to cards, lottery numbers, and roulette. Also, in some physical situations we can assume that the probability of an event such as a defect (leak, blemish) occurring in a particular unit of area, volume, or length is proportional to the ratio of that unit's size to the total area, volume, or length. Examples would be pits on rolled steel, stress fractures in concrete, or leaks in pipelines. These are *a priori* or *classical* probabilities if they are based on logic or theory, not on experience. Such calculations are rarely possible in business situations.

FIGURE 5.2

Sample Space for Rolling Two Dice DiceRolls

(1,1)	(1,2)	(1,3)	(1,4)	(1,5)	**(1,6)**
(2,1)	(2,2)	(2,3)	(2,4)	**(2,5)**	(2,6)
(3,1)	(3,2)	(3,3)	**(3,4)**	(3,5)	(3,6)
(4,1)	(4,2)	**(4,3)**	(4,4)	(4,5)	(4,6)
(5,1)	**(5,2)**	(5,3)	(5,4)	(5,5)	(5,6)
(6,1)	(6,2)	(6,3)	(6,4)	(6,5)	(6,6)

Subjective Approach

A *subjective* probability reflects someone's informed judgment about the likelihood of an event. The **subjective approach** to probability is needed when there is no repeatable random experiment. For example:

- What is the probability that Ford's new supplier of plastic fasteners will be able to meet the September 23 shipment deadline?
- What is the probability that a new truck product program will show a return on investment of at least 10 percent?
- What is the probability that the price of Ford's stock will rise within the next 30 days?

In such cases, we rely on personal judgment or expert opinion. However, such a judgment is not random because it is typically based on experience with similar events and knowledge of the underlying causal processes. Assessing the New York Knicks's chances of an NBA title next year would be an example. Thus, subjective probabilities have something in common with empirical probabilities, although their empirical basis is informal and not quantified.

SECTION EXERCISES

connect

Instructions for Exercises 5.5–5.12: Which kind of probability is it (empirical, classical, subjective)?

5.5 "There is a 20% chance that a new stock offered in an initial public offering (IPO) will reach or exceed its target price on the first day."

5.6 "There is a 25% chance that AT&T Wireless and Verizon will merge."

5.7 "Commercial rocket launches have a 95% success rate."

5.8 "The probability of rolling three sevens in a row with dice is .0046."

5.9 The probability that a randomly selected student in your class is celebrating a birthday today is 1/365.

5.10 More than 30 percent of the results from major search engines for the keyword phrase "ring tone" are fake pages created by spammers.

5.11 Based on the reported experience of climbers from a given year, a climber who attempts Everest has a 31 percent chance of success.

5.12 An entrepreneur who plans to open a Cuban restaurant in Nashville has a 20 percent chance of success.

5.3 RULES OF PROBABILITY

LO 5-3

Apply the definitions and rules of probability.

LO 5-4

Calculate odds from given probabilities.

The field of probability has a distinct vocabulary that is important to understand. This section reviews the definitions of probability terms and illustrates how to use them.

Complement of an Event

The **complement** of an event A is denoted A' and consists of everything in the sample space S except event A, as illustrated in the **Venn diagram** in Figure 5.3.

Since A and A' together comprise the sample space, their probabilities sum to 1:

$$P(A) + P(A') = 1 \tag{5.4}$$

The probability of the complement of A is found by subtracting the probability of A from 1:

$$P(A') = 1 - P(A) \tag{5.5}$$

For example, it has been reported that about 33 percent of all new small businesses fail within the first 2 years. From this we can determine that the probability that a new small business will survive at least 2 years is:

$$P(\text{survival}) = 1 - P(\text{failure}) = 1 - .33 = .67, \text{ or } 67\%$$

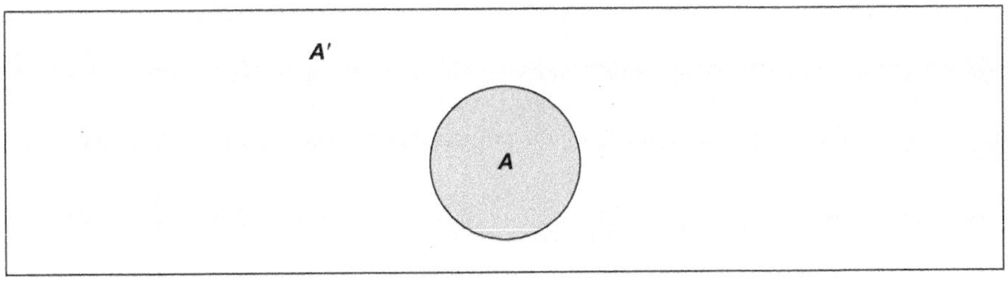

FIGURE 5.3
Complement of Event A

Union of Two Events

The **union** of two events consists of all outcomes in the sample space S that are contained either in event A or in event B or in both. The union of A and B is sometimes denoted $A \cup B$ or "A or B" as illustrated in the Venn diagram in Figure 5.4. The symbol $\cup$ may be read "or" since it means that either or both events occur. For example, when we choose a card at random from a deck of playing cards, if Q is the event that we draw a queen and R is the event that we draw a red card, $Q \cup R$ consists of getting *either* a queen (4 possibilities in 52) *or* a red card (26 possibilities in 52) or *both* a queen and a red card (2 possibilities in 52).

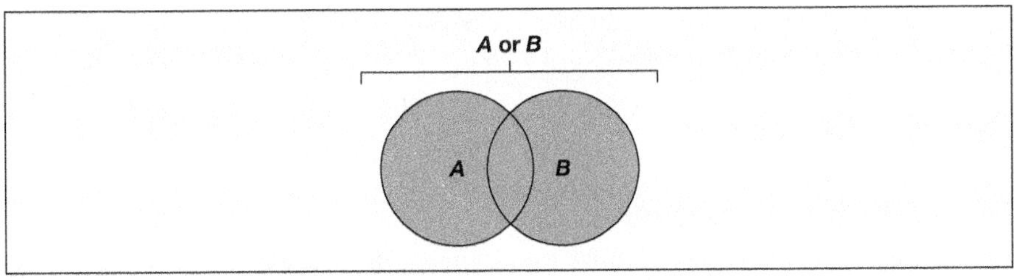

FIGURE 5.4
Union of Two Events

Intersection of Two Events

The **intersection** of two events A and B is the event consisting of all outcomes in the sample space S that are contained in both event A and event B. The intersection of A and B is denoted

$A \cap B$ or "A and B" as illustrated in the Venn diagram in Figure 5.5. The probability of $A \cap B$ is called the **joint probability** and is denoted $P(A \cap B)$.

FIGURE 5.5

Intersection of Two Events

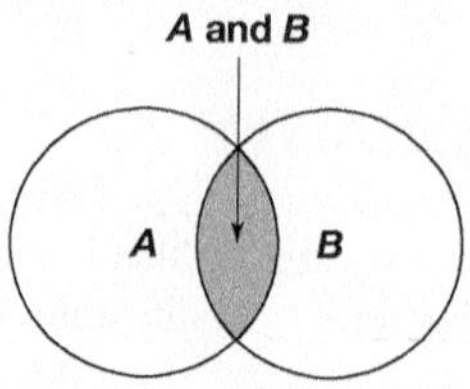

The symbol $\cap$ may be read "and" since the intersection means that both events occur. For example, if Q is the event that we draw a queen and R is the event that we draw a red card, then, $Q \cap R$ is the event that we get a card that is both a queen and red. That is, the intersection of sets Q and R consists of two cards (Q♥ and Q♦).

General Law of Addition

The **general law of addition** says that the probability of the union of two events A and B is the sum of their probabilities less the probability of their intersection.

General Law of Addition

(5.6) $$P(A \cup B) = P(A) + P(B) - P(A \cap B)$$

The rationale for this formula is apparent from an examination of Figure 5.5. If we just add the probabilities of A and B, we would count the intersection twice, so we must subtract the probability of $A \cap B$ to avoid overstating the probability of $A \cup B$. For the card example:

Queen:	$P(Q) = 4/52$	(there are 4 queens in a deck)
Red:	$P(R) = 26/52$	(there are 26 red cards in a deck)
Queen and Red:	$P(Q \cap R) = 2/52$	(there are 2 red queens in a deck)

Therefore,

Queen or Red: $$P(Q \cup R) = P(Q) + P(R) - P(Q \cap R)$$
$$= 4/52 + 26/52 - 2/52$$
$$= 28/52 = .5385, \text{ or a } 53.85\% \text{ chance}$$

This result, while simple to calculate, is not obvious.

EXAMPLE 5.1

Cell Phones and Credit Cards WebSurvey

A survey of introductory statistics students showed that 29.7 percent have AT&T wireless service (event A), 73.4 percent have a Visa card (event B), and 20.3 percent have both (event $A \cap B$). The probability that a student uses AT&T *or* has a Visa card is:

$$P(A \cup B) = P(A) + P(B) - P(A \cap B) = .297 + .734 - .203 = .828$$

Mutually Exclusive Events

Events A and B are **mutually exclusive** (or **disjoint**) if their intersection is the **empty set** (a set that contains no elements). In other words, one event precludes the other from occurring. The null set is denoted ϕ.

(5.7) $$\text{If } A \cap B = \phi, \text{ then } P(A \cap B) = 0$$

As illustrated in Figure 5.6, the probability of $A \cap B$ is zero when the events do not overlap. For example, if A is the event that an Applebee's customer finishes her lunch in less than 30 minutes and B is the event that she takes 30 minutes or more, then $P(A \cap B) = P(\phi) = 0$. Here are examples of events that are mutually exclusive (cannot be in both categories):

- *Customer age:* A = under 21, B = over 65
- *Purebred dog breed:* A = border collie, B = golden retriever
- *Business form:* A = corporation, B = sole proprietorship

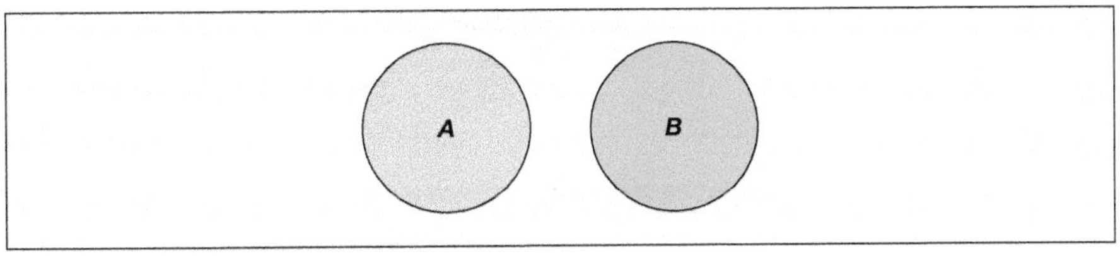

FIGURE 5.6

Mutually Exclusive Events

These events may not cover all of the possibilities (e.g., a business could also be a partnership or S-corporation). The only issue is whether the categories overlap. Here are examples of events that are *not* mutually exclusive (can be in both categories):

- *Student's major:* A = marketing major, B = economics major
- *Bank account:* A = Bank of America, B = J.P. Morgan Chase Bank
- *Credit card held:* A = Visa, B = MasterCard, C = American Express

Special Law of Addition

If A and B are mutually exclusive events, then $P(A \cap B) = 0$ and the general addition law can be simplified to the sum of the individual probabilities for A and B, the **special law of addition.**

Special Law of Addition

$$P(A \cup B) = P(A) + P(B) \quad \text{(addition law for mutually exclusive events)} \quad \textbf{(5.8)}$$

For example, if we look at a person's age, then $P(\text{under } 21) = .28$ and $P(\text{over } 65) = .12$, so $P(\text{under 21 } or \text{ over 65}) = .28 + .12 = .40$ since these events do not overlap.

Collectively Exhaustive Events

Events are **collectively exhaustive** if their union is the entire sample space S (i.e., all the events that can possibly occur). Two mutually exclusive, collectively exhaustive events are **binary** (or *dichotomous*) **events**. For example, a car repair is either covered by the warranty (A) or is not covered by the warranty (A'). There can be more than two mutually exclusive, collectively exhaustive events. For example, a Walmart customer can pay by credit card (A), debit card (B), cash (C), or check (D).

Conditional Probability

The probability of event A *given* that event B has occurred is a **conditional probability**, denoted $P(A \mid B)$ which is read "the probability of A given B." The vertical line is read as "given." The conditional probability is the joint probability of A and B divided by the probability of B.

$$P(A \mid B) = \frac{P(A \cap B)}{P(B)} \quad \text{for } P(B) > 0 \quad \textbf{(5.9)}$$

The logic of formula 5.9 is apparent by looking at the Venn diagram in Figure 5.7. The sample space is restricted to B, an event that we know has occurred (the green shaded circle). The intersection, $(A \cap B)$, is the part of B that is also in A (the blue shaded area). The ratio of the relative size of set $(A \cap B)$ to set B is the conditional probability $P(A \mid B)$.

FIGURE 5.7
Conditional Probability

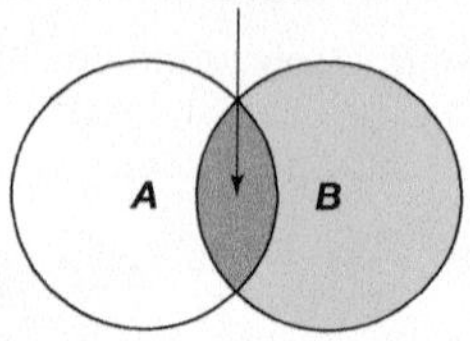

EXAMPLE 5.2
High School Dropouts

Of the population age 16–21 and not in college, 13.50 percent are unemployed, 29.05 percent are high school dropouts, and 5.32 percent are unemployed high school dropouts. What is the conditional probability that a member of this population is unemployed, given that the person is a high school dropout? To answer this question, define:

U = the event that the person is unemployed
D = the event that the person is a high school dropout

This "story problem" contains three facts:

$$P(U) = .1350 \qquad P(D) = .2905 \qquad P(U \cap D) = .0532$$

So by formula 5.9 the conditional probability of an unemployed youth given that the person dropped out of high school is:

$$P(U \mid D) = \frac{P(U \cap D)}{P(D)} = \frac{.0532}{.2905} = .1831, \text{ or } 18.31\%$$

The *conditional* probability of being unemployed is $P(U \mid D) = .1831$ (18.31 percent), which is greater than the *unconditional probability* of being unemployed $P(U) = .1350$ (13.50 percent). In other words, knowing that someone is a high school dropout alters the probability that the person is unemployed.

Using algebra we can rewrite formula 5.9, resulting in a **general law of multiplication** for the joint probability of two events.

General Law of Multiplication

(5.10) $$P(A \cap B) = P(A \mid B)P(B)$$

EXAMPLE 5.3
Video Game Purchases

Suppose 30 percent of video games are purchased as digital content. Of those games purchased as digital content, 47 percent are acquired from a gaming website. What is the joint probability that a video game was purchased as digital content through a gaming website? To answer this question, define:

D = the event that a video game was purchased as digital content
G = the event that a video game was purchased through a gaming website

This "story problem" contains two facts:

$$P(D) = .30 \qquad P(G \mid D) = .47$$

So by formula 5.10 the joint probability that a video game was purchased as digital and through a gaming website is:

$$P(D \cap G) = .30 \times .47 = .141.$$

Therefore, 14.1 percent of video games are purchased as digital content through a gaming website.

Odds of an Event

Statisticians usually speak of probabilities rather than odds, but in sports and games of chance, we often hear **odds** quoted. We define the *odds in favor* of an event *A* as the ratio of the probability that event *A* will occur to the probability that event *A* will not occur. Its reciprocal is the *odds against* event *A*.

Odds *in favor* of *A*:

$$\frac{P(A)}{P(A')} = \frac{P(A)}{1 - P(A)}$$

Odds *against* *A*:

$$\frac{P(A')}{P(A)} = \frac{1 - P(A)}{P(A)}$$

If a probability is expressed as a percentage, you can easily convert it to odds. For example, suppose the IRS tax audit rate is 1.41 percent among taxpayers earning between \$100,000 and \$199,999. Let A = the event that the taxpayer is audited and set $P(A) = .0141$. The odds against an audit are:

$$\frac{P(\text{no audit})}{P(\text{audit})} = \frac{1 - P(A)}{P(A)} = \frac{1 - .0141}{.0141} = 70 \text{ to } 1 \textit{ against} \text{ being audited}$$

In horse racing and other sports, odds usually are quoted *against* winning. If the odds against event *A* are quoted as *b* to *a*, then the implied probability of event *A* is:

$$P(A) = \frac{a}{a + b}$$

For example, if a race horse has 4 to 1 odds *against* winning, this is equivalent to saying that the odds-makers assign the horse a 20 percent chance of winning:

$$P(\text{win}) = \frac{a}{a + b} = \frac{1}{1 + 4} = \frac{1}{5} = .20, \text{ or } 20\%$$

SECTION EXERCISES

connect

5.13 Are these characteristics of a student at your university mutually exclusive or not? Explain.

a. A = works 20 hours or more, B = majoring in accounting
b. A = born in the United States, B = born in Canada
c. A = owns a Toyota, B = owns a Honda

5.14 Are these events collectively exhaustive or not? Explain.

a. A = college grad, B = some college, C = no college
b. A = born in the United States, B = born in Canada, C = born in Mexico
c. A = full-time student, B = part-time student, C = not enrolled as a student

5.15 Given $P(A) = .40$, $P(B) = .50$, and $P(A \cap B) = .05$, find (a) $P(A \cup B)$, (b) $P(A \mid B)$, and (c) $P(B \mid A)$.

5.16 Given $P(A) = .70$, $P(B) = .30$, and $P(A \cap B) = .00$, find (a) $P(A \cup B)$, (b) $P(A \mid B)$, and (c) $P(B \mid A)$.

5.17 Suppose Samsung ships 21.7 percent of the liquid crystal displays (LCDs) in the world. Let S be the event that a randomly selected LCD was made by Samsung. Find (a) $P(S)$, (b) $P(S')$, (c) the odds *in favor* of event S, and (d) the odds *against* event S.

5.18 Suppose the probability of an IRS audit is 1.7 percent for U.S. taxpayers who file form 1040 and who earned $100,000 or more. (a) What are the odds that such a taxpayer will be audited? (b) What are the odds *against* such a taxpayer being audited?

5.19 List *two* mutually exclusive events that describe the possible outcomes of each situation.

a. A pharmaceutical firm seeks FDA approval for a new drug.
b. A baseball batter goes to bat.
c. A woman has a mammogram test.

5.20 List *more than two* events (i.e., categorical events) that might describe the outcome of each situation.

a. A student applies for admission to Oxnard University.
b. A football quarterback throws a pass.
c. A bank customer makes an ATM transaction.

5.21 Let S be the event that a randomly chosen female aged 18–24 is a smoker. Let C be the event that a randomly chosen female aged 18–24 is a Caucasian. Given $P(S) = .246$, $P(C) = .830$, and $P(S \cap C) = .232$, find each probability.

a. $P(S')$.
b. $P(S \cup C)$.
c. $P(S \mid C)$.
d. $P(S \mid C')$.

5.22 Let C be the event that a randomly chosen adult has some college education. Let M be the event that a randomly chosen adult is married. Given $P(C) = .4$, $P(M) = .5$ and $P(C \cap M) = .24$, find each probability.

a. $P(C')$.
b. $P(C \cup M)$.
c. $P(M \mid C)$.
d. $P(C \mid M)$.

5.4 INDEPENDENT EVENTS

LO 5-5

Determine when events are independent.

When $P(A)$ differs from $P(A \mid B)$, the events are **dependent**. You can easily think of examples of dependence. For example, cell phone text messaging is more common among young people, while arteriosclerosis is more common among older people. Therefore, knowing a person's age would affect the *probability* that the individual uses text messaging or has arteriosclerosis. Dependent events may be causally related, but statistical dependence does *not* prove cause and effect. It only means that knowing that event B has occurred will affect the *probability* that event A will occur.

When knowing that event B has occurred does *not* affect the probability that event A will occur, then events A and B are **independent**. In other words, event A is independent of event B if the conditional probability $P(A \mid B)$ is the same as the unconditional probability $P(A)$; that is, if the probability of event A is the same whether event B occurs or not. For example, if text messaging among high school students is *independent* of gender, this means that knowing whether a student is a male or female does not *change* the probability that the student uses text messaging.

Independent Events

(5.11) Event A is independent of event B if and only if $P(A \mid B) = P(A)$.

If A and B are independent events, we can simplify the general law of multiplication (formula 5.10) to show that the joint probability of events A and B is the product of their individual probabilities. Recall the general law of multiplication:

$$P(A \cap B) = P(A \mid B)P(B)$$

If A and B are independent, then we can substitute $P(A)$ for $P(A \mid B)$. The result is shown in formula 5.12, the **special law of multiplication**.

Special Law of Multiplication

If events A and B are independent, then

$$P(A \cap B) = P(A)P(B) \qquad \textbf{(5.12)}$$

EXAMPLE 5.4

Restaurant Orders

Based on past data, the probability that a customer at a certain Noodles & Company restaurant will order a dessert (event D) with the meal is .08. The probability that a customer will order a bottled beverage (event B) is .14. The joint probability that a customer will order both a dessert *and* a bottled beverage is .0112. Is ordering a dessert independent of ordering a bottled beverage?

$$P(D) = .08 \qquad P(B) = .14 \qquad P(D \cap B) = .0112$$

$$P(D) \times P(B) = .08 \times .14 = .0112 = P(D \cap B)$$

We see that $P(D \cap B) = P(D) \times P(B)$, so D and B are independent of each other. If we know that a customer has ordered a bottled beverage, does this information change the probability that he or she will also order a dessert? No, because the events are independent.

EXAMPLE 5.5

Television Ads

The target audience is 2,000,000 viewers. Ad A reaches 500,000 viewers, ad B reaches 300,000 viewers, and both ads reach 100,000 viewers. That is:

$$P(A) = \frac{500{,}000}{2{,}000{,}000} = .25 \quad P(B) = \frac{300{,}000}{2{,}000{,}000} = .15 \quad P(A \cap B) = \frac{100{,}000}{2{,}000{,}000} = .05$$

Applying the definition of conditional probability from formula 5.9, the conditional probability that ad A reaches a viewer *given* that ad B reaches the viewer is:

$$P(A \mid B) = \frac{P(A \cap B)}{P(B)} = \frac{.05}{.15} = .3333 \text{ or } 33.3\%$$

We see that A and B are not independent because $P(A) = .25$ is not equal to $P(A \mid B) = .3333$. That is, knowing that ad B reached the viewer raises the probability that ad A reached the viewer from $P(A) = .25$ to $P(A \mid B) = .3333$. Alternatively, since $P(A)\,P(B) = (.25)\,(.15) = .0375$ is not equal to $P(A \cap B) = .05$, we know that events A and B are not independent.

Applications of the Multiplication Law

The probability of more than two independent events occurring simultaneously is the product of their separate probabilities, as shown in formula 5.13 for n independent events $A_1, A_2, \ldots, A_n$.

$$P(A_1 \cap A_2 \cap \cdots \cap A_n) = P(A_1)\,P(A_2) \cdots P(A_n) \quad \text{if the events are independent} \qquad \textbf{(5.13)}$$

The special multiplication law for independent events can be applied to system reliability. To illustrate, suppose a website has two independent file servers (i.e., no shared power or other components). Each server has 99 percent reliability (i.e., is "up" 99 percent of the time). What is the total system reliability? Let F_1 be the event that server 1 fails, and F_2 be the event that server 2 fails. Then

$$P(F_1) = 1 - 0.99 = .01$$
$$P(F_2) = 1 - 0.99 = .01$$

Applying the rule of independence:

$$P(F_1 \cap F_2) = P(F_1)\, P(F_2) = (.01)(.01) = .0001$$

The probability that at least one server is up is 1 minus the probability that both servers are down, or 1 − .0001 = .9999. Dual file servers dramatically improve reliability to 99.99 percent.

When individual components have a low reliability, high reliability can still be achieved with massive redundancy. For example, a Teramac supercomputer has over 7 million components. About 3 percent are defective (nanodevices are extremely difficult to manufacture). Yet programs can run reliably because there is significant redundancy in the interconnect circuitry, so that a valid path can almost always be found (see *Scientific American* 293, no. 5 [November 2005], p. 75).

EXAMPLE 5.6

Space Shuttle

Redundancy can increase system reliability even when individual component reliability is low. For example, the NASA space shuttle has three flight computers. Suppose that they function independently but that each has an unacceptable .03 chance of failure (3 failures in 100 missions). Let F_j = event that computer j fails. Then

$$\begin{aligned} P(\text{all 3 fail}) &= P(F_1 \cap F_2 \cap F_3) \\ &= P(F_1)\, P(F_2)\, P(F_3) \qquad \text{(presuming that failures are independent)} \\ &= (.03)\,(.03)\,(.03) \\ &= .000027, \text{ or 27 in 1,000,000 missions.} \end{aligned}$$

Triple redundancy can reduce the probability of computer failure to .000027 (27 failures in 1,000,000 missions). Of course, in practice, it is very difficult to have truly independent computers, since they may share electrical buses or cables. On one shuttle mission, two of the three computers actually did fail, which proved the value of redundancy. Another example of space shuttle redundancy is the four independent fuel gauges that prevent the shuttle's main engines from shutting down too soon. Initial launch rules allowed the shuttle to fly as long as two of them were functional, but after the *Challenger* launch explosion, the rules were modified to require that 3 of 4 be functional, and were modified again after the *Columbia* accident to require that all 4 be functional (see http://aolsvc.news.aol.com).

The Five Nines Rule

How high must reliability be? Prime business customers expect public carrier-class telecommunications data links to be available 99.999 percent of the time. This so-called five nines rule implies only 5 minutes of downtime per year. Such high reliability is needed not only in telecommunications but also for mission-critical systems such as airline reservation systems or banking funds transfers. Table 5.2 shows some expected system reliabilities in contemporary applications.

Suppose a certain network web server is up only 94 percent of the time (i.e., its probability of being down is .06). How many independent servers are needed to ensure that the system is

TABLE 5.2

Typical System Reliabilities in Various Applications

Type of System	*Typical Reliability (%)*
Commercial fiber-optic cable systems	99.999
Cellular-radio base stations with mobile switches connected to public-switched telephone networks	99.99
Private-enterprise networking (e.g., connecting two company offices)	99.9
Airline luggage systems	99

up at least 99.99 percent of the time? This is equivalent to requiring that the probability of all the servers being down is .0001 (i.e., 1 − .9999). Four servers will accomplish the goal*:

2 servers: $P(F_1 \cap F_2) = (.06)(.06) = .0036$

3 servers: $P(F_1 \cap F_2 \cap F_3) = (.06)(.06)(.06) = .000216$

4 servers: $P(F_1 \cap F_2 \cap F_3 \cap F_4) = (.06)(.06)(.06)(.06) = .00001296$

Applications of Redundancy

The principle of redundancy is found in many places. Basketball teams have more than five players, even though only five can play at once. You set two alarm clocks in case the first doesn't wake you up. The Embraer Legacy 13-passenger jet ($21.2 million) has two identical generators on each of its two engines to allow the plane to be used as a commercial regional jet (requiring 99.5 percent dispatch reliability) as well as for private corporate travel. With four generators, plus an auxiliary power unit that can be started and run in flight, the Legacy can fly even after the failure of a generator or two (*Flying* 131, no. 9 [September 2004], p. 50).

Older airliners (e.g., Boeing 747) had four engines, not only because older engine designs were less powerful but also because they were less reliable. Particularly for transoceanic flights, four-engine planes could fly even if one engine failed (or maybe even two). Modern airliners (e.g., Boeing 777) have only two engines because newer engines are more powerful and more reliable.

It is not just a matter of individual component reliability but also of cost and consequence. Cars have only one battery because the consequence of battery failure (walking home or calling AAA) does not justify the expense of having a backup battery. But spare tires are cheap enough that most cars carry one (maybe two, if you are driving in Alaska).

Redundancy is not required when components are highly reliable, cost per component is high, and consequences of system failure are tolerable (e.g., cell phone, alarm clock). Unfortunately, true component independence is difficult to achieve. The same catastrophe (fire, flood, etc.) that damages one component may well damage the backup system. On August 24, 2001, a twin-engine Air Transat Airbus A330 transiting the Atlantic Ocean did have a double engine shutdown with 293 passengers aboard. Fortunately, the pilot was able to glide 85 miles to a landing in the Azores, resulting in only minor injuries (*Aviation Week and Space Technology*, September 3, 2001, p. 34).

Dependent Events in Business

Banks and credit unions know that the probability that a customer will default on a car loan is dependent on his/her past record of unpaid credit obligations. That is why lenders consult credit bureaus (e.g., Equifax, Experian, and TransUnion) before they make a loan. Your credit score is based on factors such as the ratio of your credit card balance to your credit limit, length of your credit history, number of accounts with balances, and frequency of requests for credit. Your score can be compared with actuarial data and national averages to see what percentile you are in. The lender can then decide whether your loan is worth the risk.

*In general, if p is the probability of failure, we can set $p^k = .0001$, plug in $p = .06$, take the log of both sides, and solve for k. In this case, $k = 3.27$, so we can then round up to the next higher integer.

Automobile insurance companies (e.g., AAA, Allstate, State Farm) know that the probability that a driver will be involved in an accident depends on the driver's age, past traffic convictions, and similar factors. This actuarial information is used in deciding whether to accept you as a new customer and in setting your insurance premium. The situation is similar for life insurance. Can you think of factors that might affect a person's life insurance premium?

In each of these loan and insurance examples, knowing B will affect our estimate of the likelihood of A. Obviously, bankers and insurance companies need to quantify these conditional probabilities precisely. An *actuary* studies conditional probabilities empirically, using accident statistics, mortality tables, and insurance claims records. Although few people undergo the extensive training to become actuaries, many businesses rely on actuarial services, so a business student needs to understand the concepts of conditional probability and statistical independence.

SECTION EXERCISES

connect

5.23 Given $P(J) = .26$, $P(K) = .48$. If A and B are independent, find $P(J \cup K)$.

5.24 Given $P(A) = .40$, $P(B) = .50$. If A and B are independent, find $P(A \cap B)$.

5.25 Given $P(A) = .40$, $P(B) = .50$, and $P(A \cap B) = .05$. (a) Find $P(A \mid B)$. (b) In this problem, are A and B independent?

5.26 Which pairs of events are independent?

a. $P(A) = .60$, $P(B) = .40$, $P(A \cap B) = .24$.
b. $P(A) = .90$, $P(B) = .20$, $P(A \cap B) = .18$.
c. $P(A) = .50$, $P(B) = .70$, $P(A \cap B) = .25$.

5.27 Given $P(J) = .2$, $P(K) = .4$ and $P(J \cap K) = .15$. (a) Find $P(J \mid K)$. (b) In this problem, are J and K independent?

5.28 Which pairs of events are independent?

a. $P(J) = .50$, $P(K) = .40$, $P(J \cap K) = .3$.
b. $P(J) = .60$, $P(K) = .20$, $P(J \cap K) = .12$.
c. $P(J) = .15$, $P(K) = .5$, $P(J \cap K) = .1$.

5.29 The probability that a student has a Visa card (event V) is .73. The probability that a student has a MasterCard (event M) is .18. The probability that a student has both cards is .03. (a) Find the probability that a student has either a Visa card or a MasterCard. (b) In this problem, are V and M independent? Explain.

5.30 Bob sets two alarm clocks (battery-powered) to be sure he arises for his Monday 8:00 a.m. accounting exam. There is a 75 percent chance that either clock will wake Bob. (a) What is the probability that Bob will oversleep? (b) If Bob had three clocks, would he have a 99 percent chance of waking up?

5.31 A hospital's backup power system has three independent emergency electrical generators, each with uptime averaging 95 percent (some downtime is necessary for maintenance). Any of the generators can handle the hospital's power needs. Does the overall reliability of the backup power system meet the five nines test?

5.32 Over 1,000 people try to climb Mt. Everest every year. Of those who try to climb Everest, 31 percent succeed. The probability that a climber is at least 60 years old is .04. The probability that a climber is at least 60 years old and succeeds in climbing Everest is .005. (a) Find the probability of success, given that a climber is at least 60 years old. (b) Is success in climbing Everest independent of age?

5.33 Suppose 50 percent of the customers at Pizza Palooza order a square pizza, 80 percent order a soft drink, and 40 percent order both a square pizza and a soft drink. Is ordering a soft drink independent of ordering a square pizza? Explain.

5.5 CONTINGENCY TABLES

LO 5-6

Apply the concepts of probability to contingency tables.

In Chapter 3, you saw how Excel's pivot tables can be used to display the frequency of co-occurrence of data values (e.g., how many taxpayers in a sample are filing as "single" and also have at least one child?). Since a probability usually is estimated as a *relative frequency*, we can use tables of relative frequencies to learn about relationships (e.g., dependent events or conditional probabilities) that are extremely useful in business planning. Data for the table may be from a survey or from actuarial records.

What Is a Contingency Table?

To better understand dependent events and conditional probability, let's look at some real data. A **contingency table** is a cross-tabulation of frequencies into rows and columns. The intersection of each row and column is a *cell* that shows a frequency. A contingency table is like a frequency distribution for a single variable, except it has *two* variables (rows and columns). A contingency table with r rows and c columns has rc cells and is called an $r \times c$ table. Contingency tables often are used to report the results of a survey.

Table 5.3 shows a cross-tabulation of tuition cost versus five-year net salary gains for MBA degree recipients at 67 top-tier graduate schools of business. Here, salary gain is compensation after graduation, minus the sum of tuition and forgone compensation. Are large salary gains more likely for graduates of high-tuition MBA programs?

TABLE 5.3

Contingency Table of Frequencies (n = 67 MBA programs)

MBASalary

	Salary Gain			
Tuition	*Small (S_1) Under \$50K*	*Medium (S_2) \$50K–\$100K*	*Large (S_3) \$100K+*	*Row Total*
Low (T_1) Under \$40K	5	10	1	16
Medium (T_2) \$40K–\$50K	7	11	1	19
High (T_3) \$50K+	5	12	15	32
Column Total	17	33	17	67

Source: Data are from *Forbes* 172, no. 8 (October 13, 2003), p. 78. Copyright © 2005 Forbes, Inc.

Inspection of this table reveals that MBA graduates of the high-tuition schools do tend to have large salary gains (15 of the 67 schools) and that about half of the top-tier schools charge high tuition (32 of 67 schools). We can make more precise interpretations of these data by applying the concepts of probability.

Marginal Probabilities

The **marginal probability** of an event is a relative frequency that is found by dividing a row or column total by the total sample size. For example, using the column totals, 33 out of 67 schools had medium salary gains, so the marginal probability of a medium salary gain is $P(S_2) = 33/67 = .4925$. In other words, salary gains at about 49 percent of the top-tier schools were between \$50,000 and \$100,000. This calculation is shown in Table 5.4.

TABLE 5.4

Marginal Probability of Event S_2

	Salary Gain			
Tuition	*Small (S_1)*	*Medium (S_2)*	*Large (S_3)*	*Row Total*
Low (T_1)	5	10	1	16
Medium (T_2)	7	11	1	19
High (T_3)	5	12	15	32
Column Total	17	33	17	67

Using the row totals, for example, we see that 16 of the 67 schools had low tuition so the marginal probability of low tuition is $P(T_1) = 16/67 = .2388$. In other words, there is a 24 percent chance that a top-tier school's MBA tuition is under \$40,000. This calculation is illustrated in Table 5.5.

TABLE 5.5

Marginal Probability of Event T_1

	Salary Gain			
Tuition	*Small (S_1)*	*Medium (S_2)*	*Large (S_3)*	*Row Total*
Low (T_1)	5	10	1	16
Medium (T_2)	7	11	1	19
High (T_3)	5	12	15	32
Column Total	17	33	17	67

Joint Probabilities

Each of the nine main cells is used to calculate a *joint probability* representing the intersection of *two* events. For example, the upper right-hand cell is the joint event that the school has low tuition (T_1) *and* has large salary gains (S_3). We can write this probability either as $P(T_1 \text{ and } S_3)$ or as $P(T_1 \cap S_3)$. Since only 1 out of 67 schools is in this category, the joint probability is $P(T_1 \text{ and } S_3) = 1/67 = .0149$. In other words, there is less than a 2 percent chance that a top-tier school has *both* low tuition *and* high salary gains. This calculation is illustrated in Table 5.6.

TABLE 5.6

Joint Probability of Event $T_1 \cap S_3$

	Salary Gain			
Tuition	*Small (S_1)*	*Medium (S_2)*	*Large (S_3)*	*Row Total*
Low (T_1)	5	10	1	16
Medium (T_2)	7	11	1	19
High (T_3)	5	12	15	32
Column Total	17	33	17	67

Conditional Probabilities

Conditional probabilities may be found by *restricting* ourselves to a single row or column (the *condition*). For example, suppose we know that a school's MBA tuition is high (T_3). When we restrict ourselves to the 32 schools in the third row (those with high tuition) the conditional probabilities of any event may be calculated. For example, Table 5.7 illustrates the calculation of the conditional probability that salary gains are small (S_1) *given* that the MBA tuition is large (T_3). This conditional probability may be written $P(S_1 \mid T_3)$. We see that $P(S_1 \mid T_3) = 5/32 = .1563$, so there is about a 16 percent chance that a top-tier school's salary gains will be small despite its high tuition because there were 5 small-gain schools out of the 32 high-tuition schools.

TABLE 5.7

Conditional Probability $P(S_1 \mid T_3)$

	Salary Gain			
Tuition	*Small (S_1)*	*Medium (S_2)*	*Large (S_3)*	*Row Total*
Low (T_1)	5	10	1	16
Medium (T_2)	7	11	1	19
High (T_3)	5	12	15	32
Column Total	17	33	17	67

Here are some other conditional probabilities and their interpretations:

Low Tuition MBA Program

$P(S_1 \mid T_1) = 5/16 = .3125$ There is a 31 percent probability that schools whose tuition is low will have small MBA salary gains.

$P(S_2 \mid T_1) = 10/16 = .6250$ There is a 63 percent probability that schools whose tuition is low will have medium MBA salary gains.

$P(S_3 \mid T_1) = 1/16 = .0625$ There is a 6 percent probability that schools whose tuition is low will have large MBA salary gains.

High Tuition MBA Program

$P(S_1 \mid T_3) = 5/32 = .1563$ There is a 16 percent probability that schools whose tuition is high will have small MBA salary gains.

$P(S_2 \mid T_3) = 12/32 = .3750$ There is a 38 percent probability that schools whose tuition is high will have medium MBA salary gains.

$P(S_3 \mid T_3) = 15/32 = .4688$ There is a 47 percent probability that schools whose tuition is high will have large MBA salary gains.

Caveat Conditional probabilities show, as we would expect, that higher tuition is associated with higher MBA salary gains (and conversely). But these results pertain only to a set of elite universities at a particular point in time, and few MBA students actually have access to such schools. Data from different universities or at a different point in time might show a different pattern.

Independence

To check whether events in a contingency table are independent, we can look at *conditional probabilities*. For example, if large salary gains (S_3) were independent of low tuition (T_1), then the conditional probability $P(S_3 \mid T_1)$ would be the same as the marginal probability $P(S_3)$. But this is not the case:

Conditional	*Marginal*
$P(S_3 \mid T_1) = 1/16 = .0625$	$P(S_3) = 17/67 = .2537$

Thus, large salary gains (S_3) are *not* independent of low tuition (T_1). Alternatively, we could ask whether $P(S_3 \text{ and } T_1) = P(S_3)P(T_1)$ is a necessary condition for independence. But

$$P(S_3)P(T_1) = (17/67)(16/67) = .0606$$

which is *not* equal to the observed joint probability

$$P(S_3 \text{ and } T_1) = 1/67 = .0149$$

Therefore, large salary gains (S_3) are *not* independent of low tuition (T_1).

Relative Frequencies

To facilitate probability calculations, we can divide each cell frequency f_{ij} by the total sample size ($n = 67$) to get the *relative frequencies* f_{ij}/n shown in Table 5.8. For example, the upper left-hand cell becomes $5/67 = .0746$.

TABLE 5.8

Relative Frequency Table Each Cell Is f_{ij}/n

	Salary Gains			
Tuition	*Small (S_1)*	*Medium (S_2)*	*Large (S_3)*	*Row Total*
Low (T_1)	.0746	.1493	.0149	.2388
Medium (T_2)	.1045	.1642	.0149	.2836
High (T_3)	.0746	.1791	.2239	.4776
Column Total	.2537	.4926	.2537	1.0000

The nine joint probabilities sum to 1.0000 since these are all the possible intersections. Except for rounding, summing the joint probabilities across a row or down a column gives *marginal* (or *unconditional*) probabilities for the respective row or column. The marginal row and column probabilities sum to 1.0000 (except for rounding):

$$\textit{Columns (Salary): } P(S_1) + P(S_2) + P(S_3) = .2537 + .4926 + .2537 = 1.0000$$

$$\textit{Rows (Tuition): } P(T_1) + P(T_2) + P(T_3) = .2388 + .2836 + .4776 = 1.0000$$

Table 5.8 may be written in symbolic form as shown in Table 5.9.

TABLE 5.9

Symbolic Notation for Relative Frequencies

	Salary Gains			
Tuition	*Small* (S_1)	*Medium* (S_2)	*Large* (S_3)	*Row Total*
Low (T_1)	$P(T_1 \text{ and } S_1)$	$P(T_1 \text{ and } S_2)$	$P(T_1 \text{ and } S_3)$	$P(T_1)$
Medium (T_2)	$P(T_2 \text{ and } S_1)$	$P(T_2 \text{ and } S_2)$	$P(T_2 \text{ and } S_3)$	$P(T_2)$
High (T_3)	$P(T_3 \text{ and } S_1)$	$P(T_3 \text{ and } S_2)$	$P(T_3 \text{ and } S_3)$	$P(T_3)$
Column Total	$P(S_1)$	$P(S_2)$	$P(S_3)$	1.0000

EXAMPLE 5.7

Payment Method and Purchase Quantity

Payment

A small grocery store would like to know if the number of items purchased by a customer is independent of the type of payment method the customer chooses to use. Having this information can help the store manager determine how to set up his/her various checkout lanes. The manager collected a random sample of 368 customer transactions. The results are shown in Table 5.10.

TABLE 5.10 **Contingency Table for Payment Method by Number of Items Purchased**

	Payment Method			
Number of Items Purchased	*Cash*	*Check*	*Credit/ Debit Card*	*Row Total*
5 or fewer	30	15	43	88
6 to 9	46	23	66	135
10 to 19	31	15	43	89
20 or more	19	10	27	56
Column Total	126	63	179	368

Looking at the frequency data presented in the table we can calculate the marginal probability that a customer will use cash to make the payment. Let C be the event that the customer chose cash as the payment method.

$$P(C) = \frac{126}{368} = .3424$$

Is $P(C)$ the same if we condition on number of items purchased?

$$P(C \mid 5 \text{ or fewer}) = \frac{30}{88} = .3409 \qquad P(C \mid 6 \text{ to } 9) = \frac{46}{135} = .3407$$

$$P(C \mid 10 \text{ to } 19) = \frac{31}{89} = .3483 \qquad P(C \mid 20 \text{ or more}) = \frac{19}{56} = .3393$$

Notice that there is little difference in these probabilities. If we perform the same type of analysis for the next two payment methods, we find that *payment method* and *number of items purchased* are essentially independent. Based on this study, the manager might decide to offer a cash-only checkout lane that is *not* restricted to the number of items purchased.

How Do We Get a Contingency Table?

Contingency tables do not just "happen" but require careful data organization and forethought. They are constructed from raw data. In this example, numerical values were mapped into discrete codes, as shown in Table 5.11. If the data were already categorical (e.g., a survey with discrete responses), this step would have been unnecessary. Once the data are coded, we tabulate the frequency in each cell of the contingency table. The tabulation would be done using Excel's pivot table or another software package (e.g., MINITAB's Stat > Tables > Cross Tabulation).

TABLE 5.11

Data Coding for MBA Data MBASalary

Note: S_1 is salary gain under \$50K, S_2 = salary gain \$50K–\$100K, and S_3 is salary gain \$100K+. T_1 is tuition under \$40K, T_2 is tuition from \$40K–\$50K, and T_3 is tuition of \$50K+. Data are provided for educational purposes and not as a guide to financial gains.

Source: *Forbes* 172, no. 8 (October 13, 2003), p. 78. Copyright © 2005 Forbes, Inc.

	Original Data (\$000)		Coded Data	
School	***Tuition***	***Gain***	***Tuition***	***Gain***
Alabama (Manderson)	67	21	T_3	S_1
Arizona (Eller)	69	42	T_3	S_1
Arizona State (Carey)	70	41	T_3	S_1
Auburn	46	18	T_2	S_1
Babson (Olin)	22	53	T_1	S_2
⋮	⋮	⋮	⋮	⋮
Wake Forest (Babcock)	91	50	T_3	S_2
Washington U.—St. Louis (Olin)	120	61	T_3	S_2
William & Mary	94	45	T_3	S_1
Wisconsin—Madison	81	48	T_3	S_1
Yale	137	65	T_3	S_2

Mini Case 5.1

Business Ownership: Gender and Company Size

Table 5.12 is a contingency table showing the number of employer businesses in the United States based on ownership gender and number of employees. A business is considered female-owned if 51 percent or more of the ownership is female. An employer based business is one in which the business has a payroll.

TABLE 5.12 **Business Ownership by Gender and Number of Employees** Ownership

	Number of Employees			
Ownership	*1–4*	*5–99*	*100+*	*Total*
Female-Owned (F)	507,400	294,700	7,700	809,800
Male- or Equally Owned (M)	3,110,364	1,908,813	101,155	5,120,332
Total	3,617,764	2,203,513	108,855	5,930,132

Source: www.census.gov/econ.

Marginal probabilities can be found by calculating the ratio of the column or row totals to the grand total. We see that the $P(F)$ = 809800/5930132 = .1366. In other words, 13.66 percent of employer businesses are female-owned. Likewise, P(1–4 employees) = 3617764/5930132 = .6101, so 61.01 percent of employer businesses have only 1–4 employees on their payroll.

Conditional probabilities can be found from Table 5.12 by restricting ourselves to a single row or column (the *condition*). For example, for businesses with 100 or more employees:

$P(F \mid 100+) = 7700/108855 = .0707$ There is a 7.07 percent chance that a business is female-owned *given* that the business has 100 or more employees.

$P(M \mid 100+) = 101155/108855 = .9293$ There is a 92.93 percent chance that a business is male- or equally owned *given* that the business has 100 or more employees.

These conditional probabilities show that large businesses are much less likely to be female-owned than male- or equally-owned (.0707 < .9293). We can also conclude that the chance of a large business being female-owned is about half that when considering employer businesses of all sizes (.0707 < .1366).

Table 5.13 shows the *relative frequency* obtained by dividing each table frequency by the grand total (n = 5,930,132).

TABLE 5.13 **Business Ownership by Gender and Number of Employees**

	Number of Employees			
Ownership	*1–4*	*5–99*	*100+*	*Total*
Female-Owned (F)	.0856	.0497	.0013	0.1366
Male- or Equally Owned (M)	.5245	.3219	.0171	0.8634
Total	.6101	.3716	.0184	1.0000

For example, the joint probability $P(F \cap 1\text{–}4 \text{ employees}) = .0856$ (i.e., about 8.56 percent of employer businesses are female-owned with fewer than 5 employees). The six joint probabilities sum to 1.0000, as they should (except for rounding).

SECTION EXERCISES

connect

5.34 The contingency table below shows the results of a survey of online video viewing by age. Find the following probabilities or percentages:

a. Probability that a viewer is aged 18–34.
b. Probability that a viewer prefers watching TV videos.
c. Percentage of viewers who are 18–34 and prefer watching user-created videos.
d. Percentage of viewers aged 18–34 who prefer watching user-created videos.
e. Percentage of viewers who are 35–54 or prefer user created-videos.

	Type of Videos Preferred		
Viewer Age	*User Created*	*TV*	*Row Total*
18–34	39	30	69
35–54	10	10	20
55+	3	8	11
Column Total	52	48	100

5.35 The contingency table below summarizes a survey of 1,000 bottled beverage consumers. Find the following probabilities or percentages: **BondFunds**

a. Probability that a consumer recycles beverage bottles.
b. Probability that a consumer who lives in a state with a deposit law does not recycle.
c. Percentage of consumers who recycle and live in a state with a deposit law.
d. Percentage of consumers in states with a deposit law who recycle.

	Lives in a state with a deposit law	Lives in a state with no deposit law	Row Total
Recycles beverage bottles	154	186	340
Does not recycle beverage bottles	66	594	660
Column Total	220	780	1000

5.36 A survey of 158 introductory statistics students showed the following contingency table. Find each event probability. **WebSurvey**

a. $P(V)$ b. $P(A)$ c. $P(A \cap V)$
d. $P(A \cup V)$ e. $P(A \mid V)$ f. $P(V \mid A)$

Cell Phone Provider	Visa Card (V)	No Visa Card (V′)	Row Total
AT&T (A)	32	15	47
Other (A′)	84	27	111
Column Total	116	42	158

5.37 A survey of 156 introductory statistics students showed the following contingency table. Find each event probability. **WebSurvey**

a. $P(D)$ b. $P(R)$ c. $P(D \cap R)$
d. $P(D \cup R)$ e. $P(R \mid D)$ f. $P(R \mid P)$

	Living Where?			
Newspaper Read	Dorm (D)	Parents (P)	Apt (A)	Row Total
Never (N)	13	6	6	25
Occasionally (O)	58	30	21	109
Regularly (R)	8	7	7	22
Column Total	79	43	34	156

5.38 This contingency table describes 200 business students. Find each probability and interpret it in words. **GenderMajor**

a. $P(A)$ b. $P(M)$ c. $P(A \cap M)$ d. $P(F \cap S)$
e. $P(A \mid M)$ f. $P(A \mid F)$ g. $P(F \mid S)$ h. $P(E \cup F)$

	Major			
Gender	Accounting (A)	Economics (E)	Statistics (S)	Row Total
Female (F)	44	30	24	98
Male (M)	56	30	16	102
Column Total	100	60	40	200

5.39 Based on the previous problem, is major independent of gender? Explain the basis for your conclusion.

5.40 The following contingency table shows average yield (rows) and average duration (columns) for 38 bond funds. For a randomly chosen bond fund, find the probability that: **BondFunds**

a. The bond fund is long duration.
b. The bond fund has high yield.
c. The bond fund has high yield given that it is of short duration.
d. The bond fund is of short duration given that it has high yield.

Yield	Average Portfolio Duration Short (D_1)	Intermediate (D_2)	Long (D_3)	Row Total
Small (Y_1)	8	2	0	10
Medium (Y_2)	1	6	6	13
High (Y_3)	2	4	9	15
Column Total	11	12	15	38

5.6 TREE DIAGRAMS

What Is a Tree?

LO 5-7

Interpret a tree diagram.

Events and probabilities can be displayed in the form of a **tree diagram** or *decision tree* to help visualize all possible outcomes. This is a common business planning activity. We begin with a contingency table. Table 5.14 shows a cross-tabulation of expense ratios (low, medium, high) by fund type (bond, stock) for a sample of 21 bond funds and 23 stock funds. For purposes of this analysis, a fund's expense ratio is defined as "low" if it is in the lowest ⅓ of the sample, "medium" if it is in the middle ⅓ of the sample, and "high" if it is in the upper ⅓ of the sample.

TABLE 5.14

Frequency Tabulation of Expense Ratios by Fund Type BondFund

Expense Ratio	Fund Type Bond Fund (B)	Stock Fund (S)	Row Total
Low (L)	11	3	14
Medium (M)	7	9	16
High (H)	3	11	14
Column Total	21	23	44

To label the tree, we need to calculate *conditional probabilities*. Table 5.15 shows conditional probabilities by fund type (i.e., dividing each cell frequency by its column total). For example, $P(L \mid B) = 11/21 = .5238$. This says there is about a 52 percent chance that a fund has a low expense ratio if it is a bond fund. In contrast, $P(L \mid S) = 3/23 = .1304$. This says there is about a 13 percent chance that a fund has a low expense ratio if it is a stock fund.

TABLE 5.15

Conditional Probabilities by Fund Type BondFund

Expense Ratio	Fund Type Bond Fund (B)	Stock Fund (S)
Low (L)	$= P(L \mid B) = 11/21 = .5238$	$= P(L \mid S) = 3/23 = .1304$
Medium (M)	$= P(M \mid B) = 7/21 = .3333$	$= P(M \mid S) = 9/23 = .3913$
High (H)	$= P(H \mid B) = 3/21 = .1429$	$= P(H \mid S) = 11/23 = .4783$
Column Total	1.0000	1.0000

The tree diagram in Figure 5.8 shows all events along with their marginal, conditional, and joint probabilities. To illustrate the calculation of joint probabilities, we make a slight modification of the formula for conditional probability for events A and B:

$$P(A \mid B) = \frac{P(A \cap B)}{P(B)} \quad \text{or} \quad P(A \cap B) = P(B)P(A \mid B)$$

FIGURE 5.8

Tree Diagram for Fund Type and Expense Ratios BondFund

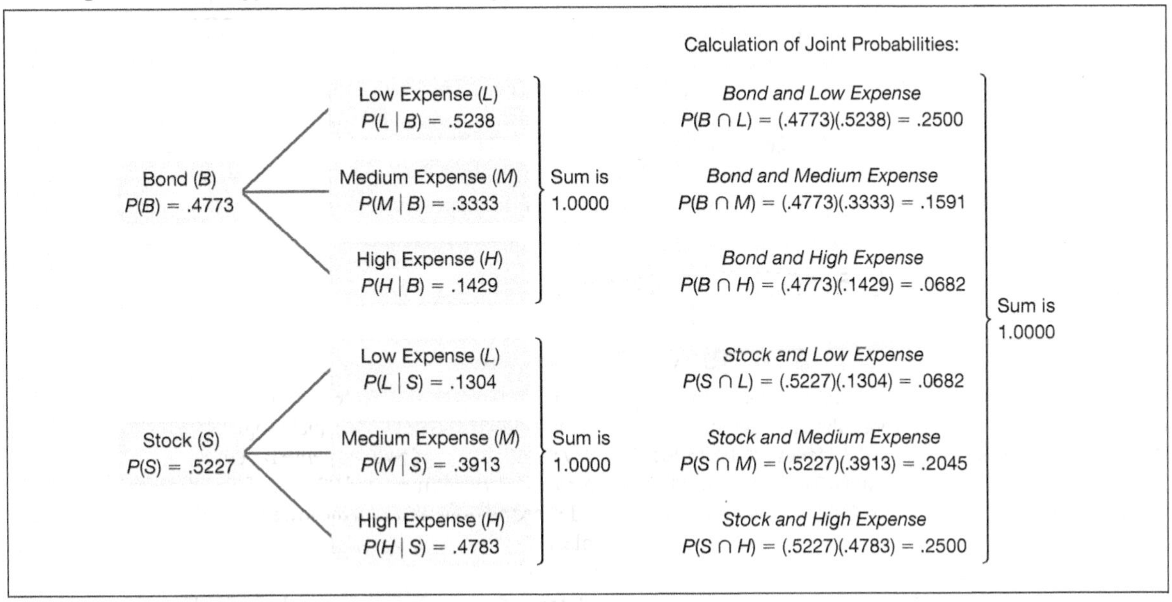

Thus, the joint probability of each terminal event on the tree can be obtained by multiplying the probabilities along its branches. For example, following the top branch of the tree, the joint probability of a bond fund (B) with low expenses (L) is

$$P(B \cap L) = P(B)P(L \mid B) = (.4773)(.5238) = .2500$$

The conditional probabilities sum to 1 *within* each branch, and the joint probabilities also sum to 1 *for all six terminal events.*

SECTION EXERCISES

connect

5.41 Of grocery shoppers who have a shopping cart, 70 percent pay by credit/debit card (event C_1), 20 percent pay cash (event C_2), and 10 percent pay by check (event C_3). Of shoppers without a grocery cart, 50 percent pay by credit/debit card (event C_1), 40 percent pay cash (event C_2), and 10 percent pay by check (event C_3). On Saturday morning, 80 percent of the shoppers take a shopping cart (event S_1) and 20 percent do not (event S_2). (a) Sketch a tree based on these data. (b) Calculate the probability of all joint probabilities (e.g., $S_1 \cap C_1$). (c) Verify that the joint probabilities sum to 1.

5.42 A study showed that 60 percent of *The Wall Street Journal* subscribers watch CNBC every day. Of these, 70 percent watch it outside the home. Only 20 percent of those who don't watch CNBC every day watch it outside the home. Let D be the event "watches CNBC daily" and O be the event "watches CNBC outside the home." (a) Sketch a tree based on these data. (b) Calculate the probability of all joint probabilities (e.g., $D \cap O$). (c) Verify that the joint probabilities sum to 1.

Mini Case 5.2

Can Amazon Read Your Mind?

You go to Amazon.com to purchase a copy of *Eugenie Grandet* by Honore de Balzac. Amazon offers you 714 online choices (new, used, various vendors). But Amazon also recommends that you consider buying a copy of *Hedda Gabler* by Henrik Ibsen or *Madame Bovary* by Gustave Flaubert. How did they decide on these suggestions? The answer is that Amazon has a matrix (like an Excel pivot table) that keeps track of the frequency of *copurchased* items (e.g., books, music, DVDs) for web shoppers. Probabilities derived from the cells in this contingency table are used to recommend products that are likely to be of interest to you, assuming that you are "like" other buyers. While such predictions of your behavior are only probabilistic, even a modest chance of landing extra sales can make a difference in bottom-line profit. There are even more sophisticated logic engines that can track your web clicks. Is this an invasion of your privacy? Does it bother you to think that you may be predictable? Interestingly, many consumers don't seem to mind, and actually find value in this kind of statistical information system.

5.7 BAYES' THEOREM

LO 5-8

Use Bayes' Theorem to calculate revised probabilities.

An important theorem published by Thomas Bayes (1702–1761) provides a method of revising probabilities to reflect new information. The **prior** (unconditional) **probability** of an event B is revised after event A has occurred to yield a **posterior** (conditional) **probability**. We begin with a formula slightly different from the standard definition of conditional probability:

(5.14) $$P(B \mid A) = \frac{P(A \mid B)P(B)}{P(A)}$$

Unfortunately, in some situations $P(A)$ is not given. The most useful and common form of **Bayes' Theorem** replaces $P(A)$ with an expanded formula:

(5.15) $$P(B \mid A) = \frac{P(A \mid B)P(B)}{P(A \mid B)P(B) + P(A \mid B')P(B')}$$

How Bayes' Theorem Works

Bayes' Theorem is best understood by example. Suppose that 10 percent of the women who purchase over-the-counter pregnancy testing kits are actually pregnant. For a particular brand of kit, if a woman is pregnant, the test will yield a positive result 96 percent of the time and a negative result 4 percent of the time (called a "false negative"). If she is not pregnant, the test will yield a positive result 5 percent of the time (called a "false positive") and a negative result 95 percent of the time. Suppose the test comes up positive. What is the probability that she is really pregnant?

We can solve this problem intuitively. If 1,000 women use this test, the results should look like Figure 5.9. Of the 1,000 women, 100 will actually be pregnant and 900 will not. The test yields 4 percent false negatives ($.04 \times 100 = 4$) and 5 percent false positives ($.05 \times 900 = 45$). Therefore, of the 141 women who will test positive ($96 + 45$), only 96 will actually be pregnant, so $P(\text{pregnant} \mid \text{positive test}) = 96/141 = .6809$.

If the test is positive, there is a 68.09 percent chance that a woman is actually pregnant. A common error is to think that the probability should be 96 percent. But that is the probability of a positive test *if* the woman is pregnant, while many of the women who take the test are *not* pregnant. This intuitive calculation (assuming a large number of individuals) can also be arranged in a contingency like Table 5.16.

TABLE 5.16

Bayes' Theorem—Intuitive Method for 1,000 Women

	Positive Test	*Negative Test*	*Row Total*
Pregnant	96	4	100
Not Pregnant	45	855	900
Column Total	141	859	1,000

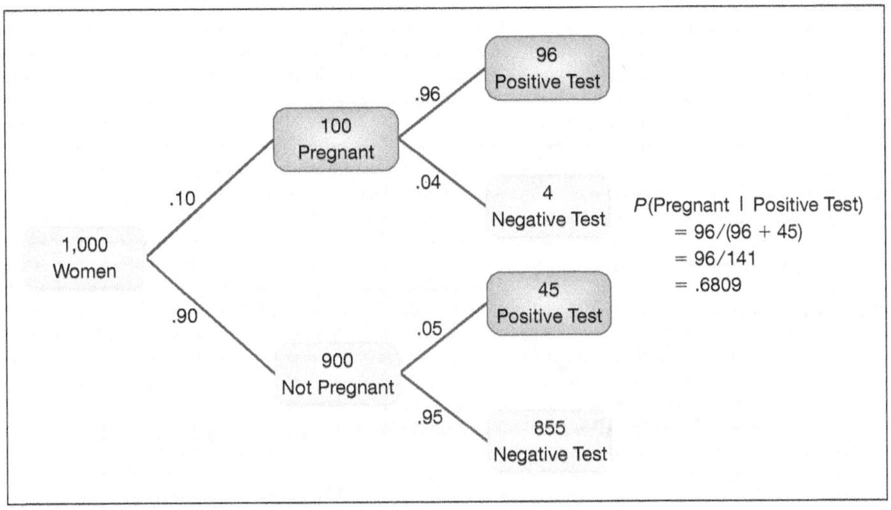

FIGURE 5.9

Bayes' Theorem—Intuitive Method for 1,000 Women

Bayes' Theorem allows us to derive this result more formally. We define these events:

A = positive test $\quad$ B = pregnant

A' = negative test $\quad$ B' = not pregnant

The given facts may be stated as follows:

$$P(A \mid B) = .96 \qquad P(A \mid B') = .05 \qquad P(B) = .10$$

The complement of each event is found by subtracting from 1:

$$P(A' \mid B) = .04 \qquad P(A' \mid B') = .95 \qquad P(B') = .90$$

Applying Bayes' Theorem:

$$P(B \mid A) = \frac{P(A \mid B)P(B)}{P(A \mid B)P(B) + P(A \mid B')P(B')} = \frac{(.96)(.10)}{(.96)(.10) + (.05)(.90)}$$

$$= \frac{.096}{.096 + .045} = \frac{.096}{.141} = .6809$$

There is a 68.09 percent chance that a woman is pregnant, given that the test is positive. This is the same result that we obtained using the intuitive method.

What Bayes' Theorem does is to show us how to revise our *prior* probability of pregnancy (10 percent) to get the *posterior* probability (68.09 percent) after the results of the pregnancy test are known:

Prior (before the test)	*Posterior (after positive test result)*
$P(B) = .10$	$P(B \mid A) = .6809$

The given information did not permit a direct calculation of $P(B \mid A)$ since we only knew the conditional probabilities $P(A \mid B)$ and $P(A \mid B')$. Bayes' Theorem is useful in situations like this.

A probability tree diagram (Figure 5.10) is helpful in visualizing the situation. Only branches 1 and 3 have a positive test, and only in branch 1 is the woman actually pregnant, so $P(B \mid A) = (.096)/(.096 + .045) = .6809$. The conditional probabilities for each branch sum to 1.

The result is the same using either method. While the formal method is somewhat less intuitive, the intuitive method has the drawback that a large number of individuals must be assumed if the resulting frequencies are to be integers. Use whichever method makes sense for the problem at hand.

FIGURE 5.10

Tree Diagram for Home Pregnancy Test
Pregnancy

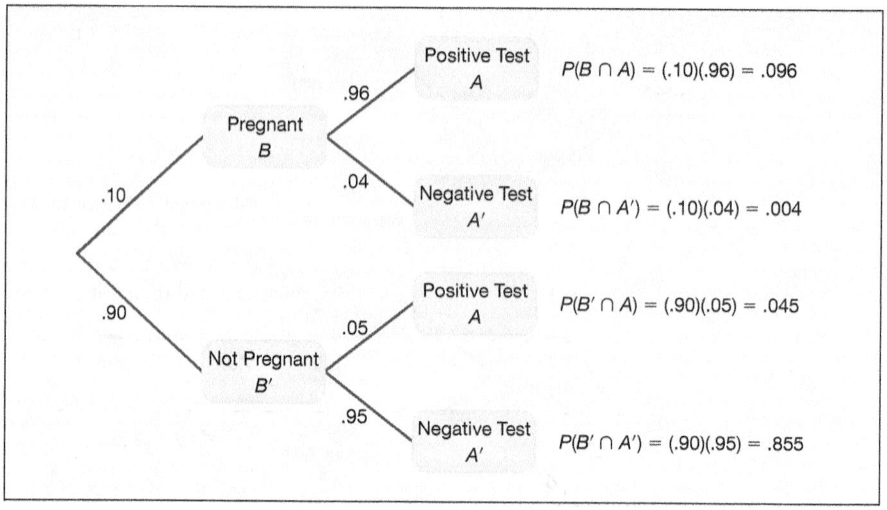

General Form of Bayes' Theorem

A generalization of Bayes' Theorem allows event B to have as many mutually exclusive and collectively exhaustive categories as we wish ($B_1, B_2, \ldots, B_n$) rather than just the two dichotomous categories B and B':

(5.16)
$$P(B_i \mid A) = \frac{P(A \mid B_i)P(B_i)}{P(A \mid B_1)P(B_1) + P(A \mid B_2)P(B_2) + \ldots + P(A \mid B_n)P(B_n)}$$

EXAMPLE 5.8

Hospital Trauma Centers

Based on historical data, three hospital trauma centers have 50, 30, and 20 percent of the cases, respectively. The probability of a case resulting in a malpractice suit in each of the three hospitals is .001, .005, and .008, respectively. If a malpractice suit is filed, what is the probability that it originated in hospital 1? This problem is solved as follows. We define:

Event A = event that a malpractice suit is filed by patient

Event B_i = event that the patient was treated at trauma center i ($i = 1, 2, 3$)

The given information can be presented in a table like Table 5.17.

TABLE 5.17 **Given Information for Hospital Trauma Centers** Malpractice

Hospital	*Marginal*	*Conditional: Suit Filed*
1	$P(B_1) = .50$	$P(A \mid B_1) = .001$
2	$P(B_2) = .30$	$P(A \mid B_2) = .005$
3	$P(B_3) = .20$	$P(A \mid B_3) = .008$

Applying formula 5.16, we can find $P(B_1 \mid A)$ as follows:

$$P(B_1 \mid A) = \frac{P(A \mid B_1)P(B_1)}{P(A \mid B_1)P(B_1) + P(A \mid B_2)P(B_2) + P(A \mid B_3)P(B_3)}$$

$$= \frac{(.001)(.50)}{(.001)(.50) + (.005)(.30) + (.008)(.20)}$$

$$= \frac{.0005}{.0005 + .0015 + .0016} = \frac{.0005}{.0036} = .1389$$

The probability that the malpractice suit was filed in hospital 1 is .1389, or 13.89 percent. Although hospital 1 sees 50 percent of the trauma patients, it is expected to generate less than half the malpractice suits, since the other two hospitals have a much higher incidence of malpractice suits.

There is nothing special about $P(B_1 \mid A)$. In fact, it is easy to calculate *all* the posterior probabilities at once by using a worksheet, as shown in Table 5.18:

$P(B_1 \mid A) = .1389$ (probability that a malpractice lawsuit originated in hospital 1)

$P(B_2 \mid A) = .4167$ (probability that a malpractice lawsuit originated in hospital 2)

$P(B_3 \mid A) = .4444$ (probability that a malpractice lawsuit originated in hospital 3)

TABLE 5.18 **Worksheet for Bayesian Probability of Malpractice Suit**
Malpractice

	Prior (Given)	Given		Posterior (Revised)
Hospital	$P(B_i)$	$P(A \mid B_i)$	$P(B_i \cap A) = P(A \mid B_i)\,P(B_i)$	$P(B_i \mid A) = P(B_i \cap A)/P(A)$
1	.50	.001	(.001)(.50) = .0005	.0005/.0036 = .1389
2	.30	.005	(.005)(.30) = .0015	.0015/.0036 = .4167
3	.20	.008	(.008)(.20) = .0016	.0016/.0036 = .4444
Total	1.00		$P(A)$ = .0036	1.0000

We could also approach the problem intuitively by imagining 10,000 patients, as shown in Table 5.19. First, calculate each hospital's expected number of patients (50, 30, and 20 percent of 10,000). Next, find each hospital's expected number of malpractice suits by multiplying its malpractice rate by its expected number of patients:

TABLE 5.19 **Malpractice Frequencies for 10,000 Hypothetical Patients**
Malpractice

Hospital	*Malpractice Suit Filed*	*No Malpractice Suit Filed*	*Total*
1	5	4,995	5,000
2	15	2,985	3,000
3	16	1,984	2,000
Total	36	9,964	10,000

Hospital 1: $.001 \times 5{,}000 = 5$ (expected malpractice suits at hospital 1)

Hospital 2: $.005 \times 3{,}000 = 15$ (expected malpractice suits at hospital 2)

Hospital 3: $.008 \times 2{,}000 = 16$ (expected malpractice suits at hospital 3)

Refer to Table 5.19. Adding down, the total number of malpractice suits filed is 36. Hence, $P(B_1 \mid A) = 5/36 = .1389$, $P(B_2 \mid A) = 15/36 = .4167$, and $P(B_3 \mid A) = 16/36 = .4444$. These three probabilities add to 1. Overall, there are 36 malpractice suits, so we can also calculate $P(A) = 36/10{,}000 = .0036$. Many people find the table method easier to understand than the formulas. Do you agree?

We could visualize this situation as shown in Figure 5.11. The initial sample space consists of three mutually exclusive and collectively exhaustive events (hospitals B_1, B_2, B_3). As indicated by their relative areas, B_1 is 50 percent of the sample space, B_2 is 30 percent of the sample space, and B_3 is 20 percent of the sample space. But *given* that a malpractice case has been filed (event A), then the relevant sample space is *reduced* to that of event A.

FIGURE 5.11

Illustration of Hospital Trauma Center Example

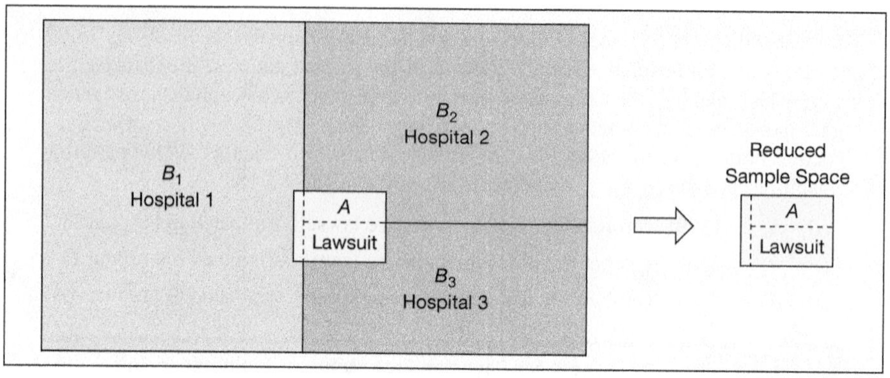

The revised (posterior) probabilities are the relative areas *within* event A:

$P(B_1 \mid A)$ is the proportion of A that lies within $B_1 = 13.89\%$

$P(B_2 \mid A)$ is the proportion of A that lies within $B_2 = 41.67\%$

$P(B_3 \mid A)$ is the proportion of A that lies within $B_3 = 44.44\%$

These percentages were calculated in Table 5.18. A worksheet is still needed to calculate $P(A)$ for the denominator.

SECTION EXERCISES

connect

5.43 A drug test for athletes has a 5 percent false positive rate and a 10 percent false negative rate. Of the athletes tested, 4 percent have actually been using the prohibited drug. If an athlete tests positive, what is the probability that the athlete has actually been using the prohibited drug? Explain your reasoning clearly.

5.44 Half of a set of the parts are manufactured by machine A and half by machine B. Four percent of all the parts are defective. Six percent of the parts manufactured on machine A are defective. Find the probability that a part was manufactured on machine A, given that the part is defective. Explain your reasoning clearly.

5.45 An airport gamma ray luggage scanner coupled with a neural net artificial intelligence program can detect a weapon in suitcases with a false positive rate of 2 percent and a false negative rate of 2 percent. Assume a .001 probability that a suitcase contains a weapon. If a suitcase triggers the alarm, what is the probability that the suitcase contains a weapon? Explain your reasoning.

Mini Case 5.3

Bayes' Theorem and Decision Analysis

Businesses must make decisions that involve uncertainty about future events. For example, a company might want to build a new manufacturing facility in anticipation of sales growth, but the demand for their product and the amount of future sales are uncertain. If they build the facility and demand goes down, they will have built more capacity than needed. However, if they don't build the new facility and demand goes up, then they will lose out on the increased revenue. Tree diagrams and Bayes' Theorem are used to model the uncertainty of future events and allow business managers to quantify how this uncertainty will affect the financial outcome of their decisions.

Baxter Inc. is a medium-sized maker of lawn furniture. Their business is doing well and they are considering building a new manufacturing plant to handle potential increased sales next year. Will next year's demand for lawn furniture be up (U) or down (D)? Baxter's own

FIGURE 5.12

Tree Diagram for Demand and Expert Predictions

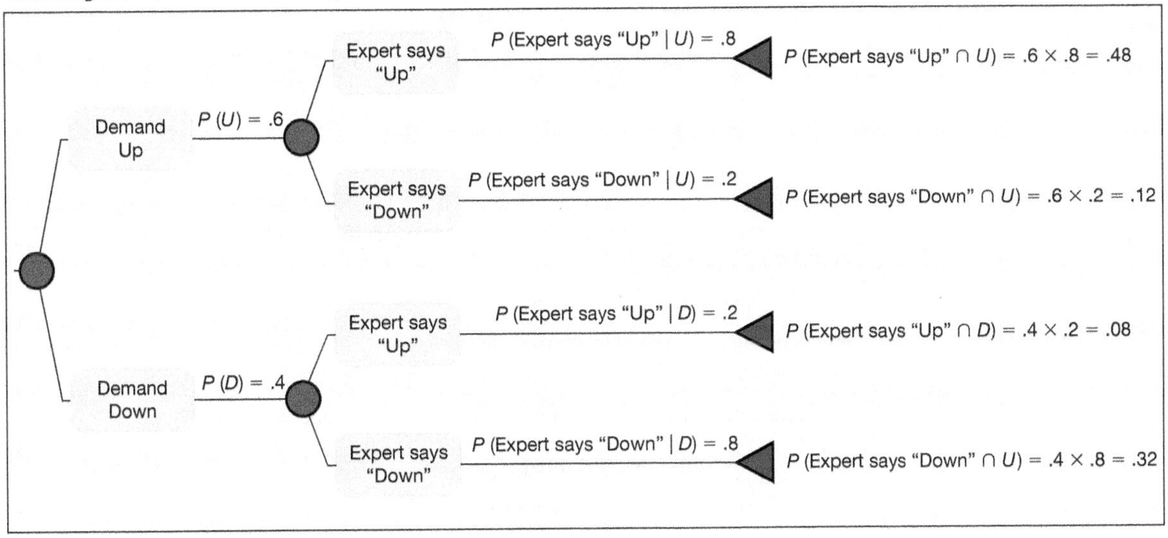

financial staff estimates a 60 percent chance that demand for lawn furniture will be up next year. These are their *prior* probabilities.

$$P(U) = .6 \text{ and } P(D) = 1 - .6 = .4$$

But Baxter's financial staff is not experienced in macroeconomic forecasting. Baxter is considering whether to engage an expert market analyst who has wide experience in forecasting demand for consumer goods. In terms of predicting directional (+ or −) changes in demand, she has been correct 80 percent of the time. If the expert is hired, Baxter could revise its estimate, using two conditional probabilities:

$$P(\text{Expert says "Up"} \mid U) = .8 \text{ and } P(\text{Expert says "Down"} \mid D) = .8$$

Using the complement rule, Baxter could also define two more conditional probabilities:

$$P(\text{Expert says "Down"} \mid U) = .2 \text{ and } P(\text{Expert says "Up"} \mid D) = .2$$

The tree diagram in Figure 5.12 above shows the marginal, conditional, and joint probabilities for these events.

What Baxter really wants to know is the chance the demand will go up *if* the expert says the demand will go up (or conversely). Bayes' Theorem could be used to update probabilities. For example:

$$P(U \mid \text{Expert says "Up"}) = \frac{P(U)P(\text{Expert says "Up"} \mid U)}{P(U)P(\text{Expert says "Up"} \mid U) + P(D)P(\text{Expert says "Up"} \mid D)}$$

$$= \frac{(.60)(.80)}{(.60)(.80) + (.40)(.20)} = \frac{.48}{.48 + .08} = \frac{.48}{.56} = .8571$$

From this calculation, if the expert predicts a rise in demand, the *posterior* probability of demand going up (.8571) would be greater than Baxter's *prior* probability (.6000). Therefore, the expert's added information would be valuable to Baxter.

5.8 COUNTING RULES

LO 5-9

Apply counting rules to calculate possible event arrangements.

Fundamental Rule of Counting

If event A can occur in n_1 ways and event B can occur in n_2 ways, then events A and B can occur in $n_1 \times n_2$ ways. In general, the number of ways that m events can occur is $n_1 \times n_2 \times \cdots \times n_m$.

EXAMPLE 5.9

Stock-Keeping Labels

How many unique stock-keeping unit (SKU) labels can a chain of hardware stores create by using two letters (ranging from *AA* to *ZZ*) followed by four numbers (digits 0 through 9)? For example:

AF1078: hex-head 6 cm bolts—box of 12

RT4855: Lime-A-Way cleaner—16 ounce

LL3119: Rust-Oleum Professional primer—gray 15 ounce

This problem may be viewed as filling six empty boxes, as shown in Figure 5.13.

FIGURE 5.13 **Creating SKU Labels**

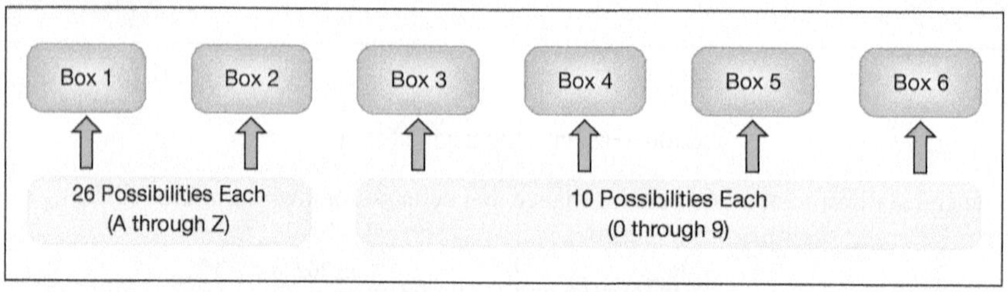

There are 26 ways (letters A through Z) to fill either the first or second box. There are 10 ways (digits 0 through 9) to fill the third through sixth boxes. The number of unique inventory labels is therefore $26 \times 26 \times 10 \times 10 \times 10 \times 10 = 6{,}760{,}000$. Such a system should suffice for a moderately large retail store.

EXAMPLE 5.10

Shirt Inventory

The number of possibilities can be large, even for a very simple counting problem. For example, the L.L. Bean men's cotton chambray shirt comes in six colors (blue, stone, rust, green, plum, indigo), five sizes (*S, M, L, XL, XXL*), and two styles (short sleeve, long sleeve). Their stock, therefore, might include $6 \times 5 \times 2 = 60$ possible shirts. The number of shirts of each type to be stocked will depend on prior demand experience. Counting the outcomes is easy with the counting formula, but even for this simple problem, a tree diagram would be impossible to fit on one page, and the enumeration of them all would be tedious (but necessary for L.L. Bean).

Factorials

The number of unique ways that n items can be arranged in a particular order is n **factorial**, the product of all integers from 1 to n.

(5.17) $$n! = n(n-1)(n-2)\cdots 1$$

This rule is useful for counting the possible arrangements of any n items. There are n ways to choose the first item, $n - 1$ ways to choose the second item, and so on until we reach the last item, as illustrated in Figure 5.14. By definition, $0! = 1$.

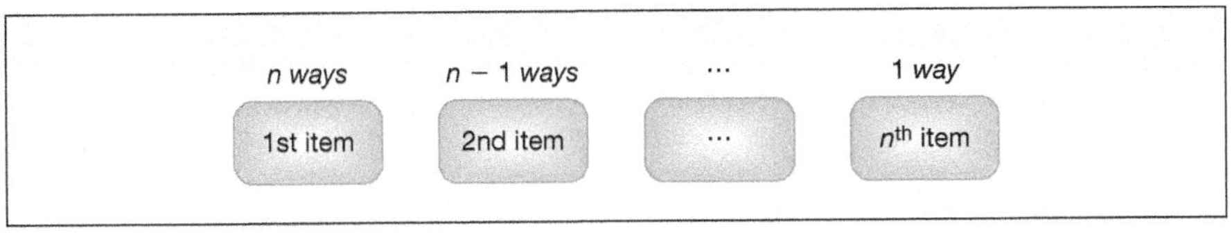

FIGURE 5.14
Choosing n Items

EXAMPLE 5.11
Truck Routing

In very small problems we can actually count the possibilities. For example, a home appliance service truck must make three stops (A, B, C). In how many ways could the three stops be arranged? There are six possible arrangements: {ABC, ACB, BAC, BCA, CAB, CBA}. But if all we want is the *number of possibilities* without listing them all:

$$3! = 3 \times 2 \times 1 = 6$$

Even in moderate-sized problems, listing all the possibilities is not feasible. For example, the number of possible arrangements of nine baseball players in a batting order rotation is:

$$9! = 9 \times 8 \times 7 \times 6 \times 5 \times 4 \times 3 \times 2 \times 1 = 362{,}880$$

You can calculate factorials with your calculator using the key labeled n!. Alternatively, if you have Excel, use the Excel function =FACT(n). If you have Internet access, you can enter n! in the Google search window. For example, 38! would be:

Excel Function	*Google Search Window*
=FACT(38) = 5.23023E+44	38! = 5.23022617 x 10^{44}

Permutations

Choose r items at random without replacement from a group of n items. In how many ways can the r items be arranged, treating each arrangement as a different event (i.e., treating the three-letter sequence XYZ as different from the three-letter sequence ZYX)? A **permutation** is an arrangement of the r sample items *in a particular order*. The number of possible permutations of n items taken r at a time is denoted ${}_nP_r$.

$${}_nP_r = \frac{n!}{(n-r)!} \qquad \textbf{(5.18)}$$

Permutations are used when we are interested in finding how many possible arrangements there are when we select r items from n items, when each possible arrangement of items is a distinct event.

EXAMPLE 5.12
Appliance Service Calls

Five home appliance customers (A, B, C, D, E) need service calls, but the field technician can service only three of them before noon. The order in which they are serviced is important (to the customers, anyway) so each possible arrangement of three service calls is different. The dispatcher must assign the sequence. The number of possible permutations is

$${}_nP_r = \frac{n!}{(n-r)!} = \frac{5!}{(5-3)!} = \frac{5 \cdot 4 \cdot 3 \cdot 2 \cdot 1}{2!} = \frac{120}{2} = 60$$

This may seem a surprisingly large number, but it can be enumerated. There are 10 distinct groups of three customers (two customers must be omitted):

ABC ABD ABE ACD ACE ADE BCD BCE BDE CDE

In turn, each group of three customers can be arranged in six possible orders. For example, the first distinct set of customers $\{A, B, C\}$ could be arranged in six distinct ways:

ABC ACB CAB CBA BAC BCA

We could do the same for each of the other nine groups of three customers. Since there are 10 distinct groups of three customers and six possible arrangements per group, there are $10 \times 6 = 60$ permutations. Clearly, we would prefer not to enumerate sequences like this very often.

As long as n and r are not too large, you can use your calculator's permutation key labeled $_nP_r$. The equivalent Excel function is =PERMUT(n,r). For example, the number of permutations of 49 things taken 9 at a time is:

Excel Function	***Calculator***
=PERMUT(49,9) = 7.45521E+14	$_{49}P_9 = 7.455208604^{14}$

Combinations

A **combination** is a collection of r items chosen at random without replacement from n items where the order of the selected items is *not* important (i.e., treating the three-letter sequence *XYZ* as being the same as the three-letter sequence *ZYX*). The number of possible combinations of r items chosen from n items is denoted $_nC_r$.

(5.19)
$$_nC_r = \frac{n!}{r!(n-r)!}$$

We use combinations when the only thing that matters is which r items are chosen, regardless of how they are arranged.

EXAMPLE 5.13

Appliance Service Calls Revised

Suppose that five customers (A, B, C, D, E) need service calls and the maintenance worker can only service three of them this morning. The customers don't care when they are serviced as long as it's before noon, so the dispatcher does not care who is serviced first, second, or third. In other words, the dispatcher regards *ABC, ACB, BAC, BCA, CAB,* or *CBA* as being the same event because the same three customers (A, B, C) get serviced. The number of combinations is:

$$_nC_r = \frac{n!}{r!(n-r)!} = \frac{5!}{3!(5-3)!} = \frac{5 \cdot 4 \cdot 3 \cdot 2 \cdot 1}{(3 \cdot 2 \cdot 1)(2 \cdot 1)} = \frac{120}{12} = 10$$

This is much smaller than the number of permutations in the previous example where order was important. In fact, the possible combinations can be enumerated easily since there are only 10 distinct groups of three customers:

ABC ABD ABE ACD ACE ADE BCD BCE BDE CDE

For combinations, you can try your calculator's permutation key labeled $_nC_r$. Alternatively, use the Excel function =COMBIN(n,r) or enter n choose r in the Google search window. For example, the number of combinations of 52 things taken 24 at a time is:

Excel Function	***Calculator***	***Google Search Window***
=COMBIN(52,24) = 4.26385E+14	$_{52}C_{24} = 4.26384982^{14}$	52 choose 24 = 4.26384982 x 10^{14}

Permutations or Combinations?

Permutations and combinations both calculate the number of ways we could choose r items from n items. But in permutations *order is important* while in combinations *order does not matter.* The number of permutations ${}_nP_r$ always is at least as great as the number of combinations ${}_nC_r$ in a sample of r items chosen at random from n items.

MegaStat offers computational assistance with factorials, permutations, and combinations. It is exceptionally fast and accurate, even for very large factorials.

SECTION EXERCISES

connect

5.46 (a) Find 8! without a calculator. Show your work. (b) Use your calculator to find 32!. (c) Find 32! by typing "32!" in the Google search window. (d) Which method would you use most often? Why?

5.47 (a) Find ${}_{20}C_5$ without a calculator. Show your work. (b) Use your calculator to find ${}_{20}C_5$. (c) Find ${}_{20}C_5$ by entering "20 choose 5" in the Google search window. (d) Which method would you use most often? Why?

5.48 In the Minnesota Northstar Cash Drawing you pick five different numbers between 1 and 31. What is the probability of picking the winning combination (order does not matter)? *Hint:* Count how many ways you could pick the first number, the second number, and so on, and then divide by the number of permuations of the five numbers.

5.49 American Express Business Travel uses a six-letter record locator number (RLN) for each client's trip (e.g., KEZLFS). (a) How many different RLNs can be created using capital letters (A–Z)? (b) What if they allow any mixture of capital letters (A–Z) and digits (0–9)? (c) What if they allow capital letters and digits but exclude the digits 0 and 1 and the letters O and I because they look too much alike?

5.50 At Oxnard University, a student ID consists of two letters (26 possibilities) followed by four digits (10 possibilities). (a) How many unique student IDs can be created? (b) Would one letter followed by three digits suffice for a university with 40,000 students? (c) Why is extra capacity in student IDs a good idea?

5.51 Until 2005, the UPC bar code had 12 digits (0–9). The first six digits represent the manufacturer, the next five represent the product, and the last is a check digit. (a) How many different manufacturers could be encoded? (b) How many different products could be encoded? (c) In 2005, the EAN bar code replaced the UPC bar code, adding a 13th digit. If this new digit is used for product identification, how many different products could now be encoded?

5.52 Bob has to study for four final exams: accounting (A), biology (B), communications (C), and drama (D). (a) If he studies one subject at a time, in how many different ways could he arrange them? (b) List the possible arrangements in the sample space.

5.53 (a) In how many ways could you arrange seven books on a shelf? (b) Would it be feasible to list the possible arrangements?

5.54 Find the following permutations ${}_nP_r$:

a. $n = 8$ and $r = 3$.
b. $n = 8$ and $r = 5$.
c. $n = 8$ and $r = 1$.
d. $n = 8$ and $r = 8$.

5.55 Find the following combinations ${}_nC_r$:

a. $n = 8$ and $r = 3$.
b. $n = 8$ and $r = 5$.
c. $n = 8$ and $r = 1$.
d. $n = 8$ and $r = 8$.

5.56 A real estate office has 10 sales agents. Each of four new customers must be assigned an agent. (a) Find the number of agent arrangements where order *is* important. (b) Find the number of agent arrangements where order is *not* important. (c) Why is the number of combinations smaller than the number of permutations?

CHAPTER SUMMARY

The **sample space** for a **random experiment** contains all possible outcomes. **Simple events** in a **discrete** sample space can be enumerated, while outcomes of a **continuous** sample space can only be described by a rule. An **empirical** probability is based on relative frequencies, a **classical** probability can be deduced from the nature of the experiment, and a **subjective** probability is based on judgment. An event's **complement** is every outcome except the event. The **odds** are the ratio of an event's probability to the probability of its complement. The **union** of two events is all outcomes in either or both, while the intersection is only those events in both. **Mutually exclusive** events cannot both occur, and **collectively exhaustive** events cover all possibilities. The **conditional probability** of an event is its probability given that another event has occurred. Two events are **independent** if the conditional probability of one is the same as its **unconditional** probability. The **joint probability** of independent events is the product of their probabilities. A **contingency table** is a cross-tabulation of frequencies for two variables with categorical outcomes and can be used to calculate probabilities. A **tree** visualizes events in a sequential diagram. **Bayes' Theorem** shows how to revise a **prior probability** to obtain a **conditional** or **posterior probability** when another event's occurrence is known. The number of arrangements of sampled items drawn from a population is found with the formula for **permutations** (if order is important) or **combinations** (if order does not matter).

KEY TERMS

actuarial science
Bayes' Theorem
binary events
classical approach
collectively exhaustive
combination
complement
compound event
conditional probability
contingency table
dependent
disjoint
empirical approach
empty set
event
factorial
general law of addition
general law of multiplication
independent
intersection
joint probability
law of large numbers
marginal probability
mutually exclusive
odds
permutation
posterior probability
prior probability
probability
random experiment
redundancy
relative frequency approach
sample space
simple event
special law of addition
special law of multiplication
subjective approach
tree diagram
union
Venn diagram

Commonly Used Formulas in Probability

	Odds for A	Odds against A
Odds:	$\dfrac{P(A)}{1-P(A)}$	$\dfrac{1-P(A)}{P(A)}$

General Law of Addition: $P(A \cup B) = P(A) + P(B) - P(A \cap B)$

Special Law of Addition: $P(A \cup B) = P(A) + P(B)$

Conditional probability: $P(A \mid B) = \dfrac{P(A \cap B)}{P(B)}$

General Law of Multiplication: $P(A \cap B) = P(A \mid B)P(B)$

Special Law of Multiplication: $P(A \cap B) = P(A)P(B)$

Bayes' Theorem: $P(B \mid A) = \dfrac{P(A \mid B)P(B)}{P(A \mid B)P(B) + P(A \mid B')P(B')}$

Permutation: ${}_nP_r = \dfrac{n!}{(n-r)!}$

Combination: ${}_nC_r = \dfrac{n!}{r!(n-r)!}$

CHAPTER REVIEW

1. Define (a) random experiment, (b) sample space, (c) simple event, and (d) compound event.
2. What are the three approaches to determining probability? Explain the differences among them.
3. Sketch a Venn diagram to illustrate (a) complement of an event, (b) union of two events, (c) intersection of two events, (d) mutually exclusive events, and (e) dichotomous events.

4. Define *odds*. What does it mean to say that odds are usually quoted against an event?
5. (a) State the general addition law. (b) Why do we subtract the intersection?
6. (a) Write the formula for conditional probability. (b) When are two events independent?
7. (a) What is a contingency table? (b) How do we convert a contingency table into a table of relative frequencies?
8. In a contingency table, explain the concepts of (a) marginal probability and (b) joint probability.
9. Why are tree diagrams useful? Why are they not always practical?
10. What is the main point of Bayes' Theorem?
11. Define (a) fundamental rule of counting, (b) factorial, (c) permutation, and (d) combination.

CHAPTER EXERCISES

Note: Explain answers and show your work clearly. Problems marked * are more difficult.

EMPIRICAL PROBABILITY EXPERIMENTS

5.57 (a) Make your own empirical estimate of the probability that a car is parked "nose first" (as opposed to "backed in"). Choose a local parking lot, such as a grocery store. Let A be the event that a car is parked nose first. Out of n cars examined, let f be the number of cars parked nose first. Then $P(A) = f/n$. (b) Do you feel your sample is large enough to have a reliable empirical probability? (c) If you had chosen a different parking lot (such as a church or a police station), would you expect the estimate of $P(A)$ to be similar? That is, would $P(A \mid \text{church}) = P(A \mid \text{police station})$? Explain.

5.58 (a) Make your own empirical estimate of the probability that a page in this book contains a figure. For n pages sampled (chosen using random numbers or some other random method), let f be the number of pages with a figure. Then $P(A) = f/n$. (b) Do you feel your sample is large enough to have a reliable empirical probability? (c) If you had chosen a different textbook (such as a biology book or an art history book), would you expect $P(A)$ to be similar? That is, would $P(A \mid \text{biology}) = P(A \mid \text{art history})$? Explain.

5.59 (a) Make your own empirical estimate of the probability that a DVD movie from your collection is longer than 2 hours (120 minutes). For the n DVDs in your sample, let f be the number that exceed 2 hours. Then $P(A) = f/n$. (b) Do you feel your sample is large enough to have a reliable empirical probability? (c) If you had chosen a different DVD collection (say, your best friend's), would you expect $P(A)$ to be similar? Explain.

5.60 M&Ms are blended in a ratio of 13 percent brown, 14 percent yellow, 13 percent red, 24 percent blue, 20 percent orange, and 16 percent green. Suppose you choose a sample of two M&Ms at random from a large bag. (a) Show the sample space. (b) What is the probability that both are brown? (c) Both blue? (d) Both green? (e) Find the probability of one brown and one green M&M. (f) Actually take 100 samples of two M&Ms (with replacement) and record the frequency of each outcome listed in (b) and (c) above. How close did your empirical results come to your predictions? (g) Which definition of probability applies in this situation? (Data are from www.mmmars.com.)

PROBLEMS

5.61 For male high school athletes, a news article reported that the probability of receiving a college scholarship is .0139 for basketball players, .0324 for swimmers/divers, and .0489 for lacrosse players. Which type of probabilities (classical, empirical, subjective) do you think these are?

5.62 A judge concludes that there is a 20 percent chance that a certain defendant will fail to appear in court if he is released after paying a full cash bail deposit. Which type of probability (classical, empirical, subjective) do you think this is?

5.63 A survey showed that 44 percent of online Internet shoppers experience some kind of technical failure at checkout (e.g., when submitting a credit card) after loading their shopping cart. Which type of probability (classical, empirical, subjective) do you think this is?

5.64 Bob says he is 50 percent sure he could swim across the Thames River. Which type of probability (classical, empirical, subjective) do you think this is?

5.65 In the first year after its release, 83 percent of emergency room doctors were estimated to have tried Dermabond glue (an alternative to sutures in some situations). Which type of probability (classical, empirical, subjective) do you think this is?

5.66 The U.S. Cesarean section delivery rate in a recent year was estimated at 20.6 percent. Which type of probability (classical, empirical, subjective) do you think this is?

5.67 A recent article states that there is a 2 percent chance that an asteroid 100 meters or more in diameter will strike the earth before 2100. Which type of probability (classical, empirical, subjective) do you think this is?

5.68 If Punxsutawney Phil sees his shadow on February 2, then legend says that winter will last 6 more weeks. In 118 years, Phil has seen his shadow 104 times. (a) What is the probability that Phil will see his shadow on a randomly chosen Groundhog Day? (b) Which type of probability (classical, empirical, subjective) do you think this is?

5.69 On Los Angeles freeways during the rush hour, there is an 18 percent probability that a driver is using a hand-held cell phone. Which type of probability (classical, empirical, subjective) do you think this is?

5.70 Bob owns two stocks. There is an 80 percent probability that stock *A* will rise in price, while there is a 60 percent chance that stock *B* will rise in price. There is a 40 percent chance that both stocks will rise in price. Are the stock prices independent?

5.71 To run its network, the Ramjac Corporation wants to install a system with dual independent servers. Employee Bob grumbled, "But that will double the chance of system failure." Is Bob right? Explain your reasoning with an example.

5.72 A study showed that trained police officers can detect a lie 65 percent of the time, based on controlled studies of videotapes with real-life lies and truths. What are the odds in favor of a lie being detected?

5.73 The probability that a 2011 Audi A8 is stolen is .0048. Find the odds *against* the theft of a 2011 Audi A8. Round your answer to the nearest whole number. (www.nhtsa.gov/theft)

5.74 The probability of being struck by lightning is .00016. Find the odds *against* being struck by lightning. Round your answer to the nearest whole number. (www.lightningsafety.noaa.gov)

5.75 Prior to the start of the 2011 NCAA Men's Basketball playoffs, the reported odds that Butler University would *not* make it to the final game were 200 to 1. What was the implied probability that Butler would make it to the finals in 2011?

5.76 A certain model of remote-control Stanley garage door opener has nine binary (off/on) switches. The homeowner can set any code sequence. (a) How many separate codes can be programmed? (b) If you try to use your door opener on 1,000 other garages, how many times would you expect to succeed?

5.77 (a) In a certain state, license plates consist of three letters (A–Z) followed by three digits (0–9). How many different plates can be issued? (b) If the state allows any six-character mix (in any order) of 26 letters and 10 digits, how many unique plates are possible? (c) Why might some combinations of digits and letters be disallowed? *(d) Would the system described in (b) permit a unique license number for every car in the United States? For every car in the world? Explain your assumptions. *(e) If the letters O and I are not used because they look too much like the numerals 0 and 1, how many different plates can be issued?

5.78 Bob, Mary, and Jen go to dinner. Each orders a different meal. The waiter forgets who ordered which meal, so he randomly places the meals before the three diners. Let *C* be the event that a diner gets the correct meal and let *N* be the event that a diner gets an incorrect meal. Enumerate the sample space and then find the probability that:

a. No diner gets the correct meal.
b. Exactly one diner gets the correct meal.
c. Exactly two diners get the correct meal.
d. All three diners get the correct meal.

5.79 An MBA program offers seven concentrations: accounting (*A*), finance (*F*), human resources (*H*), information systems (*I*), international business (*B*), marketing (*M*), and operations management (*O*). Students in the capstone business policy class are assigned to teams of three. In how many different ways could a team contain exactly one student from each concentration?

5.80 A poker hand (5 cards) is drawn from an ordinary deck of 52 cards. Find the probability of each event, showing your reasoning carefully.

a. The first four cards are the four aces.
b. Any four cards are the four aces.

5.81 Two cards are drawn from an ordinary deck of 52 cards. Find the probability of each event, showing your reasoning carefully.

a. Two aces.
b. Two red cards.
c. Two red aces.
d. Two honor cards (A, K, Q, J, 10).

5.82 A certain airplane has two independent alternators to provide electrical power. The probability that a given alternator will fail on a one-hour flight is .02. What is the probability that (a) both will fail? (b) Neither will fail? (c) One or the other will fail? Show all steps carefully.

5.83 There is a 30 percent chance that a bidding firm will get contract *A* and a 40 percent chance they will get contract *B*. There is a 5 percent chance that they will get both. Are the events independent?

5.84 A couple has two children. What is the probability that both are boys, given that the first is a boy?

5.85 A turboprop aircraft has two attitude gyros, driven from independent electrical sources. On a six-hour flight, assume the probability of failure of each attitude gyroscope is 0.0008. Does this achieve "five-nines" reliability (i.e., a probability of at least 0.99999 that not all gyros will fail)?

5.86 Which are likely to be independent events? For those you think are not, suggest reasons why.

a. Gender of two babies born consecutively in a hospital.
b. Car accident rates and the driver's gender.
c. Phone call arrival rates at a university admissions office and time of day.

5.87 In child-custody cases, about 70 percent of the fathers win the case if they contest it. In the next three custody cases, what is the probability that all three win? What assumption(s) are you making?

***5.88** A web server hosting company advertises 99.999 percent guaranteed network uptime. (a) How many independent network servers would be needed if each has 99 percent reliability? (b) If each has 90 percent reliability?

***5.89** Fifty-six percent of American adults eat at a table-service restaurant at least once a week. Suppose that four American adults are asked if they ate at table-service restaurants last week. What is the probability that all of them say yes?

***5.90** The probability is 1 in 4,000,000 that a single auto trip in the United States will result in a fatality. Over a lifetime, an average U.S. driver takes 50,000 trips. (a) What is the probability of a fatal accident over a lifetime? Explain your reasoning carefully. *Hint:* Assume independent events. (b) Why might the assumption of independence be violated? (c) Why might a driver be tempted not to use a seat belt "just on this trip"?

***5.91** If there are two riders on a city bus, what is the probability that no two have the same birthday? What if there are 10 riders? 20 riders? 50 riders? Hint: Use *LearningStats* from McGraw-Hill's Connect.

***5.92** How many riders would there have to be on a bus to yield (a) a 50 percent probability that at least two will have the same birthday? (b) A 75 percent probability? Hint: Use the *LearningStats* demonstration from McGraw-Hill's Connect.

5.93 Four students divided the task of surveying the types of vehicles in parking lots of four different shopping malls. Each student examined 100 cars in each of four large suburban malls, resulting in the 5 × 4 contingency table shown below. (a) Calculate each probability (i–vi) and explain in words what it means. (b) Do you see evidence that vehicle type is not independent of mall location? Explain. (Data are from an independent project by MBA students Steve Bennett, Alicia Morais, Steve Olson, and Greg Corda.) **Malls**

i. $P(C)$	ii. $P(G)$	iii. $P(V \mid S)$
iv. $P(C \mid J)$	v. $P(C \text{ and } G)$	vi. $P(T \text{ and } O)$

Number of Vehicles of Each Type in Four Shopping Malls

Vehicle Type	*Somerset (S)*	*Oakland (O)*	*Great Lakes (G)*	*Jamestown (J)*	*Row Total*
Car (C)	44	49	36	64	193
Minivan (M)	21	15	18	13	67
Full-size van (F)	2	3	3	2	10
SUV (V)	19	27	26	12	84
Truck (T)	14	6	17	9	46
Column Total	100	100	100	100	400

5.94 Refer to the contingency table shown below. (a) Calculate each probability (i–vi) and explain in words what it means. (b) Do you see evidence that smoking and race are *not* independent? Explain. (c) Do the smoking rates shown here correspond to your experience? (d) Why might public health officials be interested in this type of data? **Smoking2**

i. $P(S)$ ii. $P(W)$ iii. $P(S \mid W)$
iv. $P(S \mid B)$ v. $P(S \text{ and } W)$ vi. $P(N \text{ and } B)$

Smoking by Race for Males Aged 18–24

	Smoker (S)	*Nonsmoker (N)*	*Row Total*
White (W)	290	560	850
Black (B)	30	120	150
Column Total	320	680	1,000

5.95 Analysis of forecasters' interest rate predictions over the period 1982–1990 was intended to see whether the predictions corresponded to what actually happened. The 2 × 2 contingency table below shows the frequencies of actual and predicted interest rate movements. (a) Calculate each probability (i–vi) and explain in words what it means. (b*) Do you think that the forecasters' predictions were accurate? Explain. (Data are from R. A. Kolb and H. O. Steckler, "How Well Do Analysts Forecast Interest Rates?" *Journal of Forecasting* 15, no. 15 [1996], pp. 385–394.) **Forecasts**

i. $P(F-)$ ii. $P(A+)$ iii. $P(A- \mid F-)$
iv. $P(A+ \mid F+)$ v. $P(A+ \text{ and } F+)$ vi. $P(A- \text{ and } F-)$

Interest Rate Forecast Accuracy

	Actual Change		
Forecast Change	*Decline (A−)*	*Rise (A+)*	*Row Total*
Decline (F−)	7	12	19
Rise (F+)	9	6	15
Column Total	16	18	34

5.96 High levels of cockpit noise in an aircraft can damage the hearing of pilots who are exposed to this hazard for many hours. Cockpit noise in a jet aircraft is mostly due to airflow at hundreds of miles per hour. This 3 × 3 contingency table shows 61 observations of data collected by an airline pilot using a handheld sound meter in a certain aircraft cockpit. Noise level is defined as "low" (under 88 decibels), "medium" (88 to 91 decibels), or "high" (92 decibels or more). There are three flight phases (climb, cruise, descent). (a) Calculate each probability (i–vi) and explain in words what it means. (b) Do you see evidence that noise level depends on flight phase? Explain. (c) Where else might ambient noise be an ergonomic issue? (*Hint:* search the web.) Cockpit

i. $P(B)$ ii. $P(L)$ iii. $P(H \mid C)$
iv. $P(H \mid D)$ v. $P(L \text{ and } B)$ vi. $P(L \text{ and } C)$

Cockpit Noise

	Flight Phase			
Noise Level	*Climb (B)*	*Cruise (C)*	*Descent (D)*	*Row Total*
Low (L)	6	2	6	14
Medium (M)	18	3	8	29
High (H)	1	3	14	18
Column Total	25	8	28	61

BAYES' THEOREM

***5.97** A test for ovarian cancer has a 5 percent rate of false positives and a 0 percent rate of false negatives. On average, 1 in every 2,500 American women over age 35 actually has ovarian cancer. If a woman over 35 tests positive, what is the probability that she actually has cancer? *Hint:* Make a contingency table for a hypothetical sample of 100,000 women. Explain your reasoning.

***5.98** A biometric security device using fingerprints erroneously refuses to admit 1 in 1,000 authorized persons from a facility containing classified information. The device will erroneously admit 1 in 1,000,000 unauthorized persons. Assume that 95 percent of those who seek access are authorized. If the alarm goes off and a person is refused admission, what is the probability that the person was really authorized?

***5.99** Dolon Web Security Consultants requires all job applicants to submit to a test for illegal drugs. If the applicant has used illegal drugs, the test has a 90 percent chance of a positive result. If the applicant has not used illegal drugs, the test has an 85 percent chance of a negative result. Actually, 4 percent of the job applicants have used illegal drugs. If an applicant has a positive test, what is the probability that he or she has actually used illegal drugs? *Hint:* Make a 2×2 contingency table of frequencies, assuming 500 job applicants.

RELATED READING

Albert, James H. "College Students' Conceptions of Probability." *The American Statistician* 57, no. 1 (February 2001), pp. 37–45.

CHAPTER 5 More Learning Resources

connect

You can access these *LearningStats* demonstrations through McGraw-Hill's Connect® to help you understand probability.

Topic	*LearningStats Demonstrations*
Contingency tables	Contingency Tables Cross-Tabulations Independent Events
Probability	Birthday Problem System Reliability
Random processes	Law of Large Numbers Dice Rolls Pick a Card Random Names
Bayes' Theorem	Bayes' Theorem

Key: = Excel

Chapter 6. Discrete Probability Distributions

CHAPTER 6 Discrete Probability Distributions

CHAPTER CONTENTS

CHAPTER LEARNING OBJECTIVES

LO

When you finish this chapter you should be able to

LO 6-1 Define a discrete random variable and its probability distribution.

LO 6-2 Solve problems using expected value and variance.

LO 6-3 Define and apply the uniform discrete model.

LO 6-4 Find binomial probabilities using tables, formulas, or Excel.

LO 6-5 Find Poisson probabilities using tables, formulas, or Excel.

LO 6-6 Use the Poisson approximation to the binomial (optional).

LO 6-7 Find hypergeometric probabilities using Excel.

LO 6-8 Use the binomial approximation to the hypergeometric (optional).

LO 6-9 Calculate geometric probabilities (optional).

LO 6-10 Apply rules for transformations of random variables (optional).

This chapter shows how probability can be used to analyze business activities or processes that generate random data. Many business processes create data that can be thought of as random. For example, consider cars being serviced in a quick oil change shop or calls arriving at the L.L. Bean order center. Each car or call can be thought of as an experiment with random outcomes. The variable of interest for the car might be service time. The variable of interest for the call might be amount of the order. Service time and amount of order will vary randomly for each car or call.

A **probability model** assigns a probability to each outcome in the sample space defined by a random process. We use probability models to depict the essential characteristics of a stochastic process, to guide decisions or make predictions. How many service technicians do we need from noon to 1 p.m. on Friday afternoon? To answer this we need to model the process of servicing cars during the lunch hour. Can L.L. Bean predict its total order amount from the next 50 callers? To answer this question L.L. Bean needs to model the process of call orders to its call center. Probability models must be reasonably realistic yet simple enough to be analyzed.

Many random processes can be described by using common probability models whose properties are well known. To correctly use these probability models, it is important that you understand their development. In the following sections we will explain how probability models are developed and describe several commonly used models.

6.1 DISCRETE PROBABILITY DISTRIBUTIONS

Random Variables

LO 6-1

Define a discrete random variable and its probability distribution.

A **random variable** is a function or rule that assigns a numerical value to each outcome in the sample space of a random experiment. We use X when referring to a random variable in general, while specific values of X are shown in lowercase (e.g., x_1). The random variable often is a direct result of an observational experiment (e.g., counting the number of takeoffs in a given hour at O'Hare International Airport). A **discrete random variable** has a countable number of distinct values. Some random variables have a clear upper limit (e.g., number of absences in a class of 40 students) while others do not (e.g., number of text messages you receive in a given hour). Here are some examples of decision problems involving discrete random variables.

Decision Problem	*Discrete Random Variable*
• Oxnard University has space in its MBA program for 65 new students. In the past, 75 percent of those who are admitted actually enroll. The decision is made to admit 80 students. What is the probability that more than 65 admitted students will actually enroll?	• X = number of admitted MBA students who actually enroll ($X = 0, 1, 2, \ldots, 80$)
• On the late morning (9 to 12) work shift, L.L. Bean's order processing center staff can handle up to 5 orders per minute. The mean arrival rate is 3.5 orders per minute. What is the probability that more than 5 orders will arrive in a given minute?	• X = number of phone calls that arrive in a given minute at the L.L. Bean order processing center ($X = 0, 1, 2, \ldots$)
• Rolled steel from a certain supplier averages 0.01 defect per linear meter. Toyota will reject a shipment of 500 linear meters if inspection reveals more than 10 defects. What is the probability that the order will be rejected?	• X = number of defects in 500 meters of rolled steel ($X = 0, 1, 2, \ldots$)

Probability Distributions

A **discrete probability distribution** assigns a probability to each value of a discrete random variable X. The distribution must follow the rules of probability defined in Chapter 5. If X has n distinct values $x_1, x_2, \ldots, x_n$, then:

(6.1) $$0 \leq P(x_i) \leq 1 \quad \text{(the probability for any given value of } X\text{)}$$

(6.2) $$\sum_{i=1}^{n} P(x_i) = 1 \quad \text{(the sum over all values of } X\text{)}$$

Discrete probability distributions follow the rules of functions. More than one sample space outcome can be assigned to the same number, but you cannot assign one outcome to two different numbers. Likewise, more than one random variable value can be assigned to the same probability, but one random variable value cannot have two different probabilities. The probabilities must sum to 1. Figure 6.1 illustrates the relationship between the sample space, the random variable, and the probability distribution function for a simple experiment of rolling a die.

FIGURE 6.1

Random Experiment: Rolling a Die

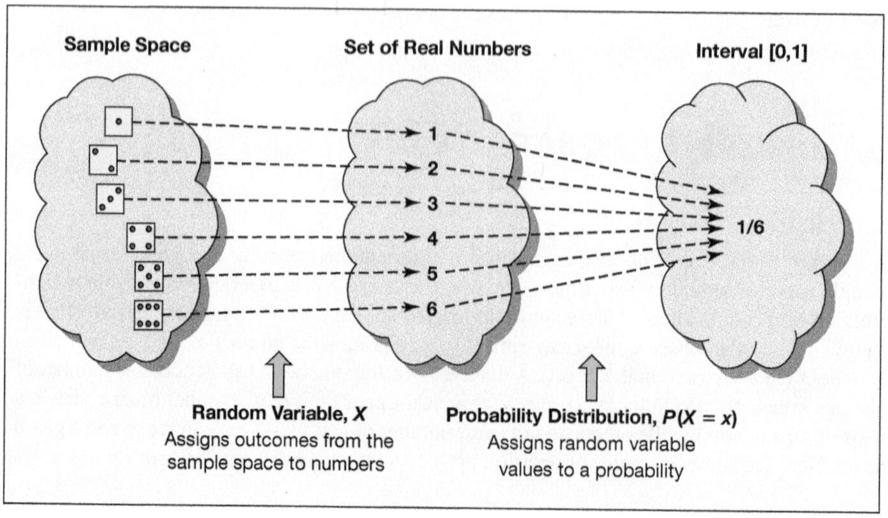

EXAMPLE 6.1

Coin Flips

ThreeCoins

When you flip a fair coin three times, the sample space has eight equally likely simple events: {HHH, HHT, HTH, THH, HTT, THT, TTH, TTT}. If X is the number of heads, then X is a random variable whose probability distribution is shown in Table 6.1 and Figure 6.2.

TABLE 6.1 Probability Distribution for Three Coin Flips

Possible Events	*x*	*P(x)*
TTT	0	1/8
HTT, THT, TTH	1	3/8
HHT, HTH, THH	2	3/8
HHH	3	1/8
Total		1

The values of X need not be equally likely. In this example, $X = 1$ and $X = 2$ are more likely than $X = 0$ or $X = 3$. However, the probabilities sum to 1, as in any probability distribution.

FIGURE 6.2 Probability Distribution for Three Coin Flips

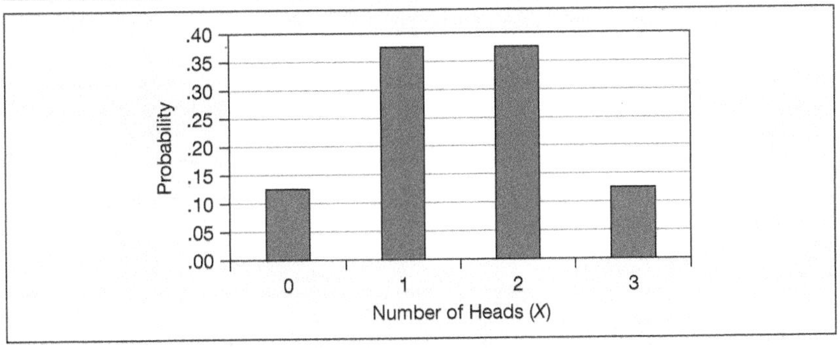

What Is a PDF or a CDF?

A known distribution can be described either by its **probability distribution function** (PDF) or by its **cumulative distribution function** (CDF). The PDF and CDF are defined either by a list of X–values and their probabilities or by mathematical equations. A discrete PDF shows the probability of each X–value, while the CDF shows the cumulative sum of probabilities, adding from the smallest to the largest X–value. Figure 6.3 illustrates a discrete PDF and the corresponding CDF. Notice that the CDF approaches 1, and the PDF values of X will sum to 1.

FIGURE 6.3

Illustration of PDF and CDF

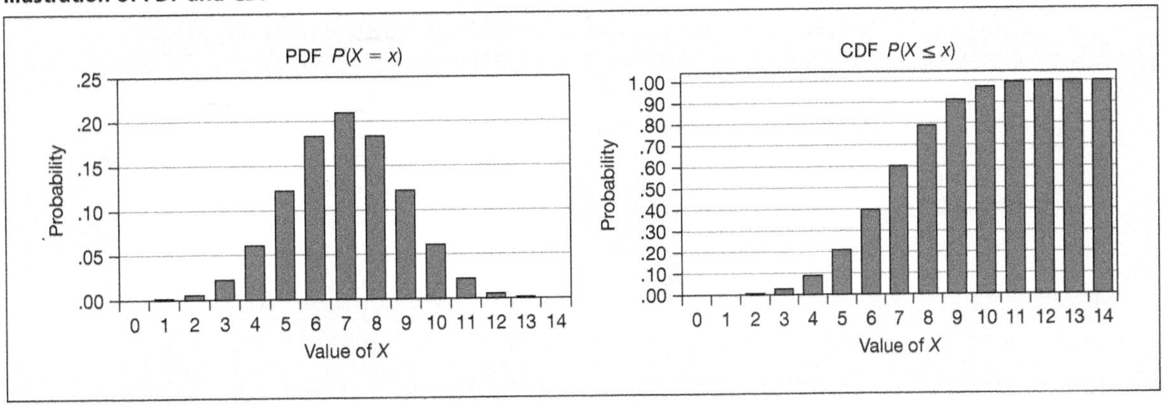

Random variables and their distributions are described by their **parameters**. The equations for the PDF, the CDF, and the characteristics of the distribution (such as the mean and standard deviation) will depend on the parameters of the process. The rest of this chapter explains several well-known discrete distributions and their applications. Many random business processes can be described by these common distributions.

SECTION EXERCISES

connect

6.1 Which of the following could *not* be probability distributions? Explain.

Example A		Example B		Example C	
x	*P(x)*	*x*	*P(x)*	*x*	*P(x)*
0	.80	1	.05	50	.30
1	.20	2	.15	60	.60
		3	.25	70	.40
		4	.40		
		5	.10		

6.2 On hot, sunny, summer days, Jane rents inner tubes by the river that runs through her town. Based on her past experience, she has assigned the following probability distribution to the number of tubes she will rent on a randomly selected day. (a) Find $P(X = 75)$. (b) Find $P(X \leq 75)$. (c) Find $P(X > 50)$. (d) Find $P(X < 100)$. (e) Which of the probability expressions in parts (a)–(d) is a value of the CDF?

x	25	50	75	100	Total
P(x)	.20	.40	.30	.10	1.00

6.3 On the midnight shift, the number of patients with head trauma in an emergency room has the probability distribution shown below. (a) Find $P(X \geq 3)$. (b) Find $P(X \leq 2)$. (c) Find $P(X < 4)$. (d) Find $P(X = 1)$. (e) Which of the probability expressions in parts (a)–(d) is a value of the CDF?

x	0	1	2	3	4	5	Total
P(x)	.05	.30	.25	.20	.15	.05	1.00

6.2 EXPECTED VALUE AND VARIANCE

LO 6-2

Solve problems using expected value and variance.

Recall that a discrete probability distribution is defined only at specific points on the *X*-axis. The **expected value** $E(X)$ of a discrete random variable is the sum of all *X*-values weighted by their respective probabilities. It is a measure of *center*. If there are *N* distinct values of X $(x_1, x_2, \ldots, x_N)$, the expected value is

$$E(X) = \mu = \sum_{i=1}^{N} x_i P(x_i) \qquad \textbf{(6.3)}$$

The expected value is a *weighted* average because outcomes can have different probabilities. Because it is an average, we usually call $E(X)$ the *mean* and use the symbol μ.

EXAMPLE 6.2

Service Calls

ServiceCalls

The distribution of Sunday emergency service calls by Ace Appliance Repair is shown in Table 6.2. The probabilities sum to 1, as must be true for any probability distribution.

The mode (most likely value of *X*) is 2, but the *expected* number of service calls $E(X)$ is 2.75, that is, $\mu = 2.75$. In other words, the "average" number of service calls is 2.75 on Sunday:

$$E(X) = \mu = \sum_{i=1}^{N} x_i P(x_i) = 0P(0) + 1P(1) + 2P(2) + 3P(3) + 4P(4) + 5P(5)$$

$$= 0(.05) + 1(.10) + 2(.30) + 3(.25) + 4(.20) + 5(.10) = 2.75$$

TABLE 6.2 **Probability Distribution of Service Calls**

x	*P(x)*	*xP(x)*
0	.05	0.00
1	.10	0.10
2	.30	0.60
3	.25	0.75
4	.20	0.80
5	.10	0.50
Total	1.00	2.75

In Figure 6.4, we see that this particular probability distribution is not symmetric around the mean $\mu = 2.75$. However, the mean $\mu = 2.75$ is still the balancing point, or fulcrum.

Note that $E(X)$ need not be an observable event. For example, you could have 2 service calls or 3 service calls, but not 2.75 service calls. This makes sense because $E(X)$ is an *average*. It is like saying that "the average American family has 2.1 children" (even though families come only in integer sizes) or "Albert Pujols's batting average is .312" (even though the number of hits by Pujols in a particular game must be an integer).

FIGURE 6.4 **Probability Distribution for Service Calls**

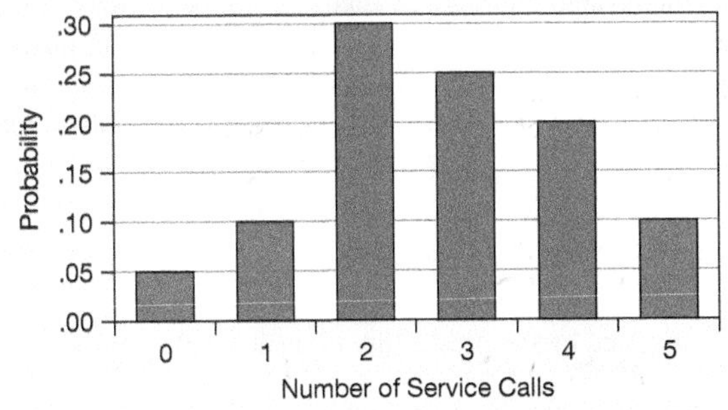

Application: Life Insurance Expected value is the basis of life insurance, a purchase that almost everyone makes. For example, based on U.S. mortality statistics, the probability that a 30-year-old white female will die within the next year is .000642, so the probability of living another year is 1 − .000642 = .999358. What premium should a life insurance company charge to break even on a $500,000 one-year term insurance policy (that is, to achieve zero expected payout)? This situation is shown in Table 6.3. Let X be the amount paid by the company to settle the policy. The expected payout is $321, so the premium should be $321 plus whatever return the company needs to cover its administrative overhead and profit.

TABLE 6.3 **Expected Payout for a One-Year Term Life Policy**

Event	*x*	*P(x)*	*xP(x)*
Live	0	.999358	.00
Die	500,000	.000642	321.00
Total		1.000000	321.00

Source: Centers for Disease Control and Prevention, *National Vital Statistics Reports* 58, no. 19 (2010).

The mortality rate shown here is for *all* 30-year-old women. An insurance quote (e.g., from the web) is likely to yield a lower premium, as long as you are a healthy, educated nonsmoker in a nonrisky occupation. Insurance companies make money by knowing the actuarial probabilities and using them to set their premiums. The task is difficult because actuarial probabilities must be revised as life expectancies change over time.

Application: Raffle Tickets Expected value can be applied to raffles and lotteries. If it costs \$2 to buy a ticket in a raffle to win a new luxury automobile worth \$55,000 and 29,346 raffle tickets are sold, the expected value of a lottery ticket is

$$E(X) = (\text{value if you win})P(\text{win}) + (\text{value if you lose})P(\text{lose})$$

$$= (55{,}000)\left(\frac{1}{29{,}346}\right) + (0)\left(\frac{29{,}345}{29{,}346}\right)$$

$$= (55{,}000)(.000034076) + (0)(.999965924) = \$1.87$$

The raffle ticket is actually worth \$1.87. So why would you pay \$2.00 for it? Partly because you hope to beat the odds, but also because you know that your ticket purchase helps the charity. Since the idea of a raffle is to raise money, the sponsor tries to sell enough tickets to push the expected value of the ticket below its price (otherwise, the charity would lose money on the raffle). If the raffle prize is donated (or partially donated) by a well-wisher, the break-even point may be much less than the full value of the prize.

Like a lottery, an **actuarially fair** insurance program must collect as much in overall revenue as it pays out in claims. This is accomplished by setting the premiums to reflect empirical experience with the insured group. Individuals may gain or lose, but if the pool of insured persons is large enough, the total payout is predictable. Of course, many insurance policies have exclusionary clauses for war and natural disaster (e.g., Hurricane Katrina), to deal with cases where the events are not independent. Actuarial analysis is critical for corporate pension fund planning. Group health insurance is another major application.

Variance and Standard Deviation

The **variance** Var(X) of a discrete random variable is the sum of the squared deviations about its expected value, weighted by the probability of each X-value. If there are N distinct values of X, the variance is

$$\text{Var}(X) = \sigma^2 = \sum_{i=1}^{N}[x_i - \mu]^2 P(x_i) \qquad \textbf{(6.4)}$$

Just as the expected value $E(X)$ is a weighted average that measures *center,* the variance Var(X) is a weighted average that measures variability about the mean. And just as we interchangeably use μ or $E(X)$ to denote the mean of a distribution, we use either σ^2 or Var(X) to denote its variance.

The *standard deviation* is the square root of the variance and is denoted σ:

$$\sigma = \sqrt{\sigma^2} = \sqrt{\text{Var}(X)} \qquad \textbf{(6.5)}$$

EXAMPLE 6.3

Bed and Breakfast

RoomRent

The Bay Street Inn is a seven-room bed-and-breakfast in the sunny California coastal city of Santa Theresa. Demand for rooms generally is strong during February, a prime month for tourists. However, experience shows that demand is quite variable. The probability distribution of room rentals during February is shown in Table 6.4 where X = the number of rooms rented (X = 0, 1, 2, 3, 4, 5, 6, 7). The worksheet shows the calculation of $E(X)$ and Var(X).

TABLE 6.4 **Worksheet for $E(X)$ and $Var(X)$ for February Room Rentals**

x	$P(x)$	$xP(x)$	$x - \mu$	$[x - \mu]^2$	$[x - \mu]^2P(x)$
0	.05	0.00	−4.71	22.1841	1.109205
1	.05	0.05	−3.71	13.7641	0.688205
2	.06	0.12	−2.71	7.3441	0.440646
3	.10	0.30	−1.71	2.9241	0.292410
4	.13	0.52	−0.71	0.5041	0.065533
5	.20	1.00	+0.29	0.0841	0.016820
6	.15	0.90	+1.29	1.6641	0.249615
7	.26	1.82	+2.29	5.2441	1.363466
Total	1.00	$\mu = 4.71$			$\sigma^2 = 4.225900$

The formulas are:

$$E(X) = \mu = \sum_{i=1}^{N} x_i P(x_i) = 4.71$$

$$\text{Var}(X) = \sigma^2 = \sum_{i=1}^{N} [x_i - \mu]^2 P(x_i) = 4.2259$$

$$\sigma = \sqrt{4.2259} = 2.0557$$

This distribution is skewed to the left and bimodal. The mode (most likely value) is 7 rooms rented, but the average is only 4.71 room rentals in February. The standard deviation of 2.06 indicates that there is considerable variation around the mean, as seen in Figure 6.5.

FIGURE 6.5 **Probability Distribution of Room Rentals**

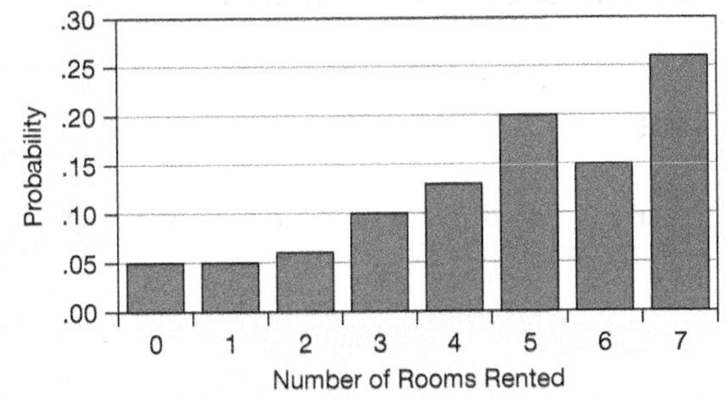

SECTION EXERCISES

connect

6.4 On hot, sunny, summer days, Jane rents inner tubes by the river that runs through her town. Based on her past experience, she has assigned the following probability distribution to the number of tubes she will rent on a randomly selected day. (a) Calculate the expected value and standard deviation of this random variable X by using the PDF shown. (b) Describe the shape of this distribution.

x	25	50	75	100	Total
$P(x)$	.20	.40	.30	.10	1.00

6.5 On the midnight shift, the number of patients with head trauma in an emergency room has the probability distribution shown below. (a) Calculate the mean and standard deviation. (b) Describe the shape of this distribution.

x	0	1	2	3	4	5	Total
$P(x)$	.05	.30	.25	.20	.15	.05	1.00

6.6 Pepsi and Mountain Dew products sponsored a contest giving away a Lamborghini sports car worth $215,000. The probability of winning from a single bottle purchase was .00000884. Find the expected value. Show your calculations clearly. (Data are from J. Paul Peter and Jerry C. Olson, *Consumer Behavior and Marketing Strategy,* 7th ed. [McGraw-Hill/Irwin, 2005], p. 226.)

6.7 Student Life Insurance Company wants to offer an insurance plan with a maximum claim amount of $5,000 for dorm students to cover theft of certain items. Past experience suggests that the probability of a maximum claim is .01. What premium should be charged if the company wants to make a profit of $25 per policy? Assume any student who files a claim files for the maximum amount and there is no deductible. Show your calculations clearly.

6.8 A lottery ticket has a grand prize of $28 million. The probability of winning the grand prize is .000000023. Based on the expected value of the lottery ticket, would you pay $1 for a ticket? Show your calculations and reasoning clearly.

6.9 Oxnard Petro Ltd. is buying hurricane insurance for its off-coast oil drilling platform. During the next five years, the probability of total loss of only the above-water superstructure ($250 million) is .30, the probability of total loss of the facility ($950 million) is .30, and the probability of no loss is .40. Find the expected loss.

6.3 UNIFORM DISTRIBUTION

Characteristics of the Uniform Distribution

LO 6-3

Define and apply the uniform discrete model.

The **uniform distribution** is one of the simplest discrete models. It describes a random variable with a finite number of consecutive integer values from a to b. That is, the entire distribution depends only on the two parameters a and b. Each value is equally likely. Table 6.5 summarizes the characteristics of the uniform discrete distribution.

TABLE 6.5

Uniform Discrete Distribution

Parameters	a = lower limit b = upper limit
PDF	$P(X = x) = \dfrac{1}{b - a + 1}$
CDF	$P(X \leq x) = \dfrac{x - a + 1}{b - a + 1}$
Domain	$x = a, a + 1, a + 2, \ldots, b$
Mean	$\dfrac{a + b}{2}$
Standard deviation	$\sqrt{\dfrac{[(b - a) + 1]^2 - 1}{12}}$
Random data generation in Excel	=RANDBETWEEN(a, b)
Comments	Useful as a benchmark, to generate random integers for sampling, or in simulation models.

When you roll one die, the number of dots forms a uniform discrete random variable with six equally likely integer values 1, 2, 3, 4, 5, 6, shown in the PDF and CDF in Figure 6.6. You can see that the mean (3.5) must be halfway between 1 and 6, but there is no way you could anticipate the standard deviation without using a formula.

For this example, the mean and standard deviation are:

Mean $$\mu = \frac{a + b}{2} = \frac{1 + 6}{2} = 3.5$$

Std. Dev. $$\sigma = \sqrt{\frac{[(b - a) + 1]^2 - 1}{12}} = \sqrt{\frac{[(6 - 1) + 1]^2 - 1}{12}} = 1.708$$

FIGURE 6.6

PDF and CDF for Rolling a Die

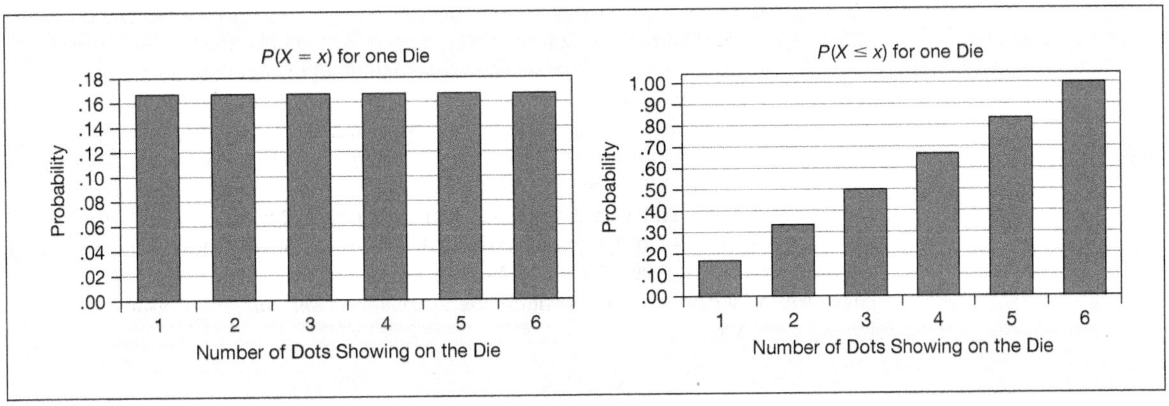

Consider another example of the discrete uniform distribution. When filling your car with gas, the last two digits (pennies) showing on the display of gallons dispensed will be a uniform random integer (assuming you don't "top off" but just let the pump stop automatically) ranging from $a = 00$ to $b = 99$. You could verify the predicted mean and standard deviation shown here by looking at a large sample of fill-ups on your own car:

PDF $$P(X = x) = \frac{1}{b - a + 1} = \frac{1}{99 - 0 + 1} = \frac{1}{100} = .010 \quad \text{for all } x$$

Mean $$\mu = \frac{a + b}{2} = \frac{0 + 99}{2} = 49.5$$

Std. Dev. $$\sigma = \sqrt{\frac{[(b - a) + 1]^2 - 1}{12}} = \sqrt{\frac{[(99 - 0) + 1]^2 - 1}{12}} = 28.87$$

The discrete uniform distribution is often used to generate random integers that are then used to randomly sample from a population. To accomplish this, we can use the Excel function =RANDBETWEEN(a, b). For example, to generate a random integer from 5 through 10, the Excel function would be =RANDBETWEEN(5, 10). The same integer may come up more than once, so to obtain n distinct random integers you would have to generate a few extras and then eliminate the duplicates if you are sampling without replacement (see Chapter 2). This method is useful in accounting and auditing (e.g., to allow the auditor to choose numbered invoices at random).

Mini Case 6.1

The "Daily 3" Lottery

Many states have a "daily 3" lottery. The daily 3 is a uniformly distributed discrete random variable whose values range from 000 through 999. There are 1,000 equally likely outcomes, so the probability of any given three-digit number is 1/1,000. The theoretical characteristics of this lottery are:

$$P(X = x) = \frac{1}{b - a + 1} = \frac{1}{999 - 0 + 1} = \frac{1}{1{,}000} = .001$$

$$\mu = \frac{a + b}{2} = \frac{0 + 999}{2} = 499.5$$

$$\sigma = \sqrt{\frac{(b - a + 1)^2 - 1}{12}} = \sqrt{\frac{(999 - 0 + 1)^2 - 1}{12}} = 288.67$$

In a large sample of three-digit lottery numbers, you would expect the sample mean and standard deviation to be very close to 499.5 and 288.67, respectively. For example, in Michigan's daily three-digit lottery, from January 1, 2010, through December 31, 2010, there were 364 evening drawings. The mean of all the three-digit numbers drawn over that period was 497.1 with a standard deviation of 289.5. These sample results are extremely close to what would be expected. It is the nature of random samples to vary, so no sample is expected to yield statistics identical with the population parameters.

In Michigan, randomization is achieved by drawing a numbered ping-pong ball from each of three bins. Within each bin, the balls are agitated using air flow. Each bin contains 10 ping-pong balls. Each ball has a single digit (0, 1, 2, 3, 4, 5, 6, 7, 8, 9). The drawing is televised, so there is no possibility of bias or manipulation. Lotteries are studied frequently to make sure that they are truly random, using statistical comparisons like these, as well as tests for overall shape and patterns over time.

SECTION EXERCISES

connect

6.10 Find the mean and standard deviation of four-digit uniformly distributed lottery numbers (0000 through 9999).

6.11 The ages of Java programmers at SynFlex Corp. range from 20 to 60. (a) If their ages are uniformly distributed, what would be the mean and standard deviation? (b) What is the probability that a randomly selected programmer's age is at least 40? At least 30? *Hint:* Treat employee ages as integers.

6.12 Use Excel to generate 100 random integers from (a) 1 through 2, inclusive; (b) 1 through 5, inclusive; and (c) 0 through 99, inclusive. (d) In each case, write the Excel formula. (e) In each case, calculate the mean and standard deviation of the sample of 100 integers you generated, and compare them with their theoretical values.

6.4 BINOMIAL DISTRIBUTION

Bernoulli Experiments

LO 6-4

Find binomial probabilities using tables, formulas, or Excel.

A random experiment that has only two outcomes is called a **Bernoulli experiment**, named after Jakob Bernoulli (1654–1705). To create a random variable, we arbitrarily call one outcome a "success" (denoted $X = 1$) and the other a "failure" (denoted $X = 0$). The probability of success is denoted π (the Greek letter "pi," *not* to be confused with the mathematical constant 3.14159).* The probability of failure is $1 - \pi$, so the probabilities sum to 1, that is, $P(0) + P(1) = (1 - \pi) + \pi = 1$. The probability of success, π, remains the same for each trial.

The examples in Table 6.6 show that a success ($X = 1$) may in fact represent something undesirable. Metallurgists look for signs of metal fatigue. Auditors look for expense voucher errors. Bank loan officers look for loan defaults. A success, then, is merely an event of interest.

TABLE 6.6

Examples of Bernoulli Experiments

Bernoulli Experiment	*Possible Outcomes*	*Probability of "Success"*
Flip a coin	1 = heads 0 = tails	$\pi = .50$
Inspect a jet turbine blade	1 = crack found 0 = no crack found	$\pi = .001$
Purchase a tank of gas	1 = pay by credit card 0 = do not pay by credit card	$\pi = .78$
Do a mammogram test	1 = positive test 0 = negative test	$\pi = .0004$

*Some textbooks denote the probability of success p. However, in this textbook, we prefer to use Greek letters for population parameters. In Chapters 8 and 9, the symbol p will be used to denote a *sample* estimate of π.

The probability of success π can be any value between 0 and 1. In flipping a fair coin, π is .50. But in other applications π could be close to 1 (e.g., the probability that a customer's Visa purchase will be approved) or close to 0 (e.g., the probability that an adult male is HIV positive). Table 6.6 is only intended to suggest that π depends on the situation. The definitions of success and failure are arbitrary and can be switched, although we usually define success as the less likely outcome so that π is less than .50.

The only parameter needed to define a Bernoulli process is π. A Bernoulli experiment has mean π and variance $\pi(1 - \pi)$ as we see from the definitions of $E(X)$ and $\text{Var}(X)$:

(6.6) $$E(X) = \sum_{i=1}^{2} x_i P(x_i) = (0)(1 - \pi) + (1)(\pi) = \pi \quad \text{(Bernoulli mean)}$$

$$\text{Var}(X) = \sum_{i=1}^{2} [x_i - E(X)]^2 P(x_i)$$
$$= (0 - \pi)^2(1 - \pi) + (1 - \pi)^2(\pi) = \pi(1 - \pi) \quad \text{(Bernoulli variance)} \quad \textbf{(6.7)}$$

There are many business applications that can be described by the Bernoulli model and it is an important building block for more complex models. We will use the Bernoulli distribution to develop the next model.

Binomial Distribution

Bernoulli experiments lead to an important and more interesting model. The **binomial distribution** arises when a Bernoulli experiment is repeated n times. Each Bernoulli trial is independent so that the probability of success π remains constant on each trial. In a binomial experiment, we are interested in X = the number of success in n trials, so the binomial random variable X is the sum of n independent Bernoulli random variables:

$$X = X_1 + X_2 + \cdots + X_n$$

We can add the n identical Bernoulli means $(\pi + \pi + \cdots + \pi)$ to get the binomial mean $n\pi$. Since the n Bernoulli trials are independent, we can add* the n identical Bernoulli variances $\pi(1 - \pi) + \pi(1 - \pi) + \cdots + \pi(1 - \pi)$ to obtain the binomial variance $n\pi(1 - \pi)$ and hence its standard deviation $\sqrt{n\pi(1 - \pi)}$. The domain of the binomial is $x = 0, 1, 2, \ldots, n$. The binomial probability of a particular number of successes $P(X = x)$ is determined by the two parameters n and π. The characteristics of the binomial distribution are summarized in Table 6.7. The binomial probability function is:

$$P(X = x) = \frac{n!}{x!(n - x)!}\pi^x(1 - \pi)^{n-x}, \quad \text{for } X = 0, 1, 2, 3, 4, \ldots, n. \quad \textbf{(6.8)}$$

Application: Uninsured Patients **Uninsured** On average, 20 percent of the emergency room patients at Greenwood General Hospital lack health insurance. In a random sample of four patients, what is the probability that two will be uninsured? Define X = number of uninsured patients and set $\pi = .20$ (i.e., a 20 percent chance that a given patient will be uninsured) and $1 - \pi = .80$ (i.e., an 80 percent chance that a patient will be insured). The domain is $X = 0, 1, 2, 3, 4$ patients. Applying the binomial formulas, the mean and standard deviation are:

$$\text{Mean} = \mu = n\pi = (4)(.20) = 0.8 \text{ patient}$$

$$\text{Standard deviation} = \sigma = \sqrt{n\pi(1 - \pi)} = \sqrt{(4)(.20)(1 - .20)} = 0.8 \text{ patient}$$

*The last section in this chapter (optional) explains the rules for transforming and summing random variables.

TABLE 6.7
Binomial Distribution

Parameters	n = number of trials π = probability of success
PDF	$P(X = x) = \frac{n!}{x!(n-x)!}\pi^x(1-\pi)^{n-x}$
Excel* PDF	=BINOM.DIST(x, n, π, 0)
Excel* CDF	=BINOM.DIST(x, n, π, 1)
Domain	$x = 0, 1, 2, \ldots, n$
Mean	$n\pi$
Standard deviation	$\sqrt{n\pi(1-\pi)}$
Random data generation in Excel	=BINOM.INV(n, π, RAND()) or use Excel's **Data Analysis Tools**
Comments	Skewed right if $\pi < .50$, skewed left if $\pi > .50$, and symmetric if $\pi = .50$.

*Excel 2010's new function =BINOM.DIST(x, n, π, cumulative) gives the same result as the previous function =BINOMDIST(x, n, π, cumulative). This new function will not work in previous versions of Excel, but the old functions work in all versions of Excel as of the publication date of this textbook.

EXAMPLE 6.4

Servicing Cars at a Quick Oil Change Shop

Consider a shop that specializes in quick oil changes. It is important to this type of business to ensure that a car's service time is not considered "late" by the customer. Therefore, to study this process, we can define service times as being either *late* or *not late* and define the random variable X to be the number of cars that are late out of the total number of cars serviced. We further assume that cars are independent of each other and the chance of a car being late stays the same for each car. Based on our knowledge of the process we know that $P(\text{car is late}) = \pi = .10$.

Now, think of each car as a Bernoulli experiment and let's apply the binomial distribution. Suppose we would like to know the probability that exactly 2 of the next 12 cars serviced are late. In this case, $n = 12$, and we want to know $P(X = 2)$:

$$P(X = 2) = \frac{12!}{2!(12-2)!}(.10)^2(1-.10)^{12-2} = .2301$$

Alternatively, we could calculate this by using the Excel function =BINOM.DIST (2, 12, .1, 0). The fourth parameter, 0, means that we want Excel to calculate $P(X = 2)$ rather than $P(X \leq 2)$.

Binomial Shape

A binomial distribution is skewed right if $\pi < .50$, skewed left if $\pi > .50$, and symmetric only if $\pi = .50$. However, skewness decreases as n increases, regardless of the value of π, as illustrated in Figure 6.7. Notice that $\pi = .20$ and $\pi = .80$ have the same shape, except reversed from left to right. This is true for any values of π and $1 - \pi$.

Binomial Shape

$\pi < .50$	skewed right
$\pi = .50$	symmetric
$\pi > .50$	skewed left

Using the Binomial Formula

The PDF is shown in Table 6.8. We can calculate binomial probabilities by using Excel's binomial formula =BINOM.DIST(x, n, π, cumulative) where cumulative is 0 (if you want a PDF)

FIGURE 6.7

Binomial Distributions

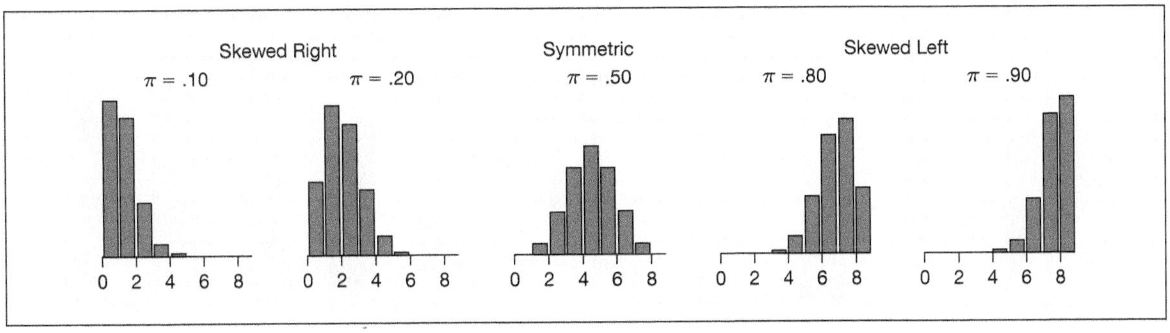

x	PDF P(X = x)	CDF P(X ≤ x)
0	.4096	.4096
1	.4096	.8192
2	.1536	.9728
3	.0256	.9984
4	.0016	1.0000

TABLE 6.8

Binomial Distribution for $n = 4$, $\pi = .20$

or 1 (if you want a CDF). We can also use a calculator to work it out from the mathematical formula with $n = 4$ and $\pi = .20$. For example, the PDF is:

Excel Function

$$P(X=0) = \frac{4!}{0!(4-0)!}(.20)^0(1-.20)^{4-0} = 1 \times .20^0 \times .80^4 = .4096$$ =BINOM.DIST(0, 4, .20, 0)

$$P(X=1) = \frac{4!}{1!(4-1)!}(.20)^1(1-.20)^{4-1} = 4 \times .20^1 \times .80^3 = .4096$$ =BINOM.DIST(1, 4, .20, 0)

$$P(X=2) = \frac{4!}{2!(4-2)!}(.20)^2(1-.20)^{4-2} = 6 \times .20^2 \times .80^2 = .1536$$ =BINOM.DIST(2, 4, .20, 0)

$$P(X=3) = \frac{4!}{3!(4-3)!}(.20)^3(1-.20)^{4-3} = 4 \times .20^3 \times .80^1 = .0256$$ =BINOM.DIST(3, 4, .20, 0)

$$P(X=4) = \frac{4!}{4!(4-4)!}(.20)^4(1-.20)^{4-4} = 1 \times .20^4 \times .80^0 = .0016$$ =BINOM.DIST(4, 4, .20, 0)

As for any discrete probability distribution, the probabilities sum to unity. That is, $P(0) + P(1) + P(2) + P(3) + P(4) = .4096 + .4096 + .1536 + .0256 + .0016 = 1.0000$. Figure 6.8 shows the PDF and CDF. Since $\pi < .50$, the distribution is right-skewed. The mean $\mu = n\pi = 0.8$ would be the balancing point or fulcrum of the PDF.

Compound Events

A compound event is expressed using an inequality. Consider the event that the sample of four patients will contain *at most* two uninsured patients. The probability of this event would be expressed as $P(X \le 2)$. We can add the PDF values shown above:

$$P(X \le 2) = P(X=0) + P(X=1) + P(X=2) = .4096 + .4096 + .1536 = .9728$$

Alternatively, we can calculate this probability using Excel's CDF function:

$P(X \le 2) =$ BINOM.DIST(2, 4, .2, 1) $= .9728$

FIGURE 6.8

Binomial Distribution for $n = 4$, $\pi = .20$

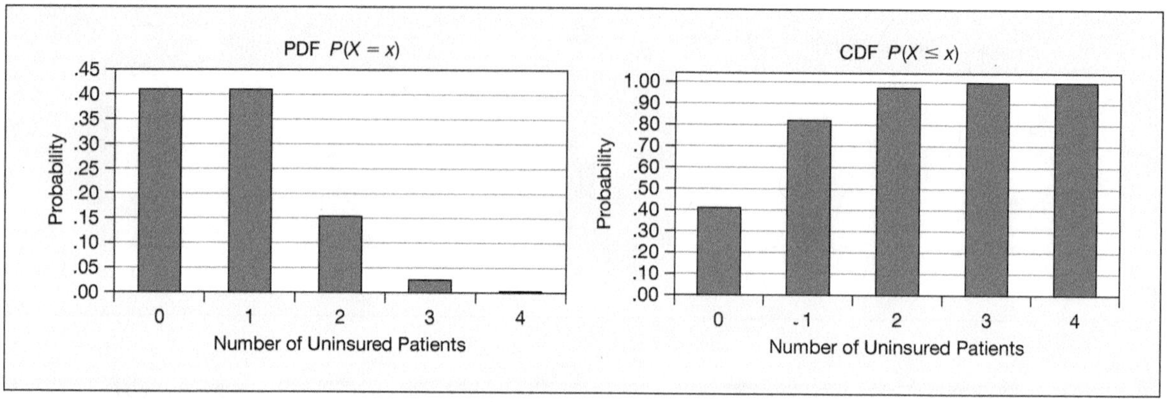

The probability that *fewer than* two patients have insurance is the same as *at most* one patient is uninsured:

$$P(X < 2) = P(X \leq 1) = \text{BINOM.DIST}(1, 4, .2, 1) = .8192$$

Suppose we want to calculate the probability that *at least* two patients are uninsured: $P(X \geq 2)$. Because $P(X \geq 2)$ and $P(X \leq 1)$ are complementary events, we can obtain $P(X \geq 2)$ using our result from above:

$$P(X \geq 2) = 1 - P(X \leq 1) = 1 - \text{BINOM.DIST}(1, 4, .2, 1) = 1 - .8192 = .1808$$

To interpret phrases such as "more than," "at most," or "at least," it is helpful to sketch a diagram, as illustrated in Figure 6.9.

FIGURE 6.9

Diagrams to Illustrate Events

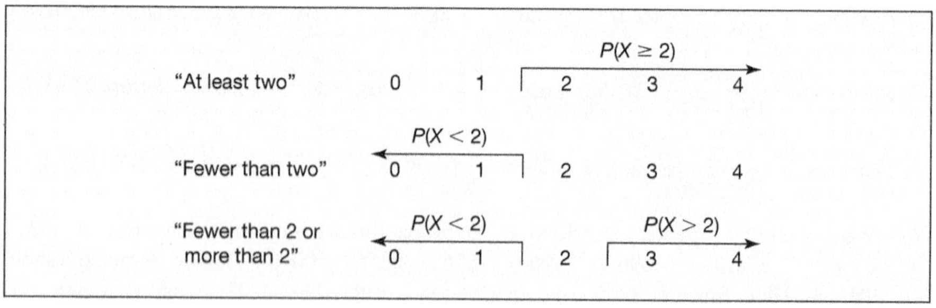

Using Tables: Appendix A

The binomial formula is cumbersome, even for small n, so we prefer to use a computer program (Excel, MINITAB, MegaStat, Visual Statistics, or *LearningStats*) or a calculator with a built-in binomial function. When you have no access to a computer (e.g., taking an exam), you can use Appendix A to look up binomial probabilities for selected values of n and π. An abbreviated portion of Appendix A is shown in Figure 6.10. The probabilities for $n = 4$ and $\pi = .20$ are highlighted. Probabilities in Appendix A are rounded to 4 decimal places so the values may differ slightly from Excel.

FIGURE 6.10

Binomial Probabilities from Appendix A

		π																
n	*X*	.01	.02	.05	.10	.15	.20	.30	.40	.50	.60	.70	.80	.85	.90	.95	.98	.99
2	0	.9801	.9604	.9025	.8100	.7225	.6400	.4900	.3600	.2500	.1600	.0900	.0400	.0225	.0100	.0025	.0004	.0001
	1	.0198	.0392	.0950	.1800	.2550	.3200	.4200	.4800	.5000	.4800	.4200	.3200	.2550	.1800	.0950	.0392	.0198
	2	.0001	.0004	.0025	.0100	.0225	.0400	.0900	.1600	.2500	.3600	.4900	.6400	.7225	.8100	.9025	.9604	.9801
3	0	.9703	.9412	.8574	.7290	.6141	.5120	.3430	.2160	.1250	.0640	.0270	.0080	.0034	.0010	.0001	—	—
	1	.0294	.0576	.1354	.2430	.3251	.3840	.4410	.4320	.3750	.2880	.1890	.0960	.0574	.0270	.0071	.0012	.0003
	2	.0003	.0012	.0071	.0270	.0574	.0960	.1890	.2880	.3750	.4320	.4410	.3840	.3251	.2430	.1354	.0576	.0294
	3	—	—	.0001	.0010	.0034	.0080	.0270	.0640	.1250	.2160	.3430	.5120	.6141	.7290	.8574	.9412	.9703
4	0	.9606	.9224	.8145	.6561	.5220	.4096	.2401	.1296	.0625	.0256	.0081	.0016	.0005	.0001	—	—	—
	1	.0388	.0753	.1715	.2916	.3685	.4096	.4116	.3456	.2500	.1536	.0756	.0256	.0115	.0036	.0005	—	—
	2	.0006	.0023	.0135	.0486	.0975	.1536	.2646	.3456	.3750	.3456	.2646	.1536	.0975	.0486	.0135	.0023	.0006
	3	—	—	.0005	.0036	.0115	.0256	.0756	.1536	.2500	.3456	.4116	.4096	.3685	.2916	.1715	.0753	.0388
	4	—	—	—	.0001	.0005	.0016	.0081	.0256	.0625	.1296	.2401	.4096	.5220	.6561	.8145	.9224	.9606

Using Software

Figure 6.11 shows Excel's Formulas > Insert Function menu to calculate the probability of $x = 67$ successes in $n = 1{,}024$ trials with success probability $\pi = .048$. Alternatively, you could just enter the formula =BINOM.DIST(67, 1024, 0.048, 0) in the spreadsheet cell.

MegaStat will compute an entire binomial PDF (not just a single point probability) for any n and π that you specify, and also show you a graph of the PDF. This is even easier than entering your own Excel functions.

If you need binomial random data, Excel's Data Analysis or MegaStat will generate random binomial values. A third option is to use the function =BINOM.INV(4, .20, RAND()) to create a binomial random variable value.

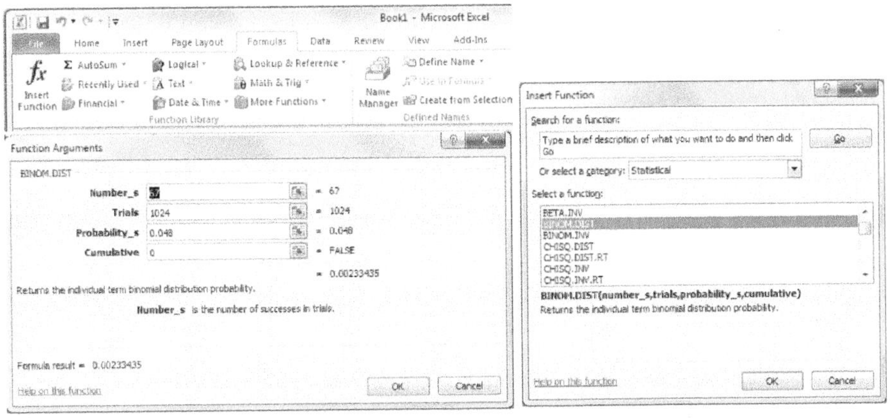

FIGURE 6.11

Excel Binomial Probability Function

Recognizing Binomial Applications

Can you recognize a binomial situation? The binomial distribution has five main characteristics.

- There are a fixed number of trials (n).
- There are only two outcomes for each trial: *success* or *failure*.
- The probability of success for each trial (π) remains constant.
- The trials are independent of each other.
- The random variable (X) is the number of successes.

Ask yourself if the five characteristics above make sense in the following examples.

In a sample of 20 friends, how many are left-handed?

In a sample of 50 cars in a parking lot, how many have hybrid engines?

In a sample of 10 emergency patients with chest pain, how many will be uninsured?

Even if you don't know π, you may have a binomial experiment. In practice, the value of π would be estimated from experience, but in this chapter it will be given.

SECTION EXERCISES

connect

6.13 List the X values that are included in each italicized event.

a. You can miss *at most* 2 quizzes out of 16 quizzes (X = number of missed quizzes).
b. You go to Starbuck's *at least* 4 days a week (X = number of Starbuck's visits).
c. You are penalized if you have *more than* 3 absences out of 10 lectures (X = number of absences).

6.14 Write the probability of each italicized event in symbols (e.g., $P(X \geq 5)$).

a. *At least* 7 correct answers on a 10-question quiz (X = number of correct answers).
b. *Fewer than* 4 "phishing" e-mails out of 20 e-mails (X = number of phishing e-mails).
c. *At most* 2 no-shows at a party where 15 guests were invited (X = number of no-shows).

6.15 Find the mean and standard deviation for each binomial random variable:

a. $n = 8, \pi = .10$ b. $n = 10, \pi = .40$ c. $n = 12, \pi = .50$

6.16 Find the mean and standard deviation for each binomial random variable:

a. $n = 30, \pi = .90$ b. $n = 80, \pi = .70$ c. $n = 20, \pi = .80$

6.17 Calculate each binomial probability:

a. $X = 5, n = 9, \pi = .90$ b. $X = 0, n = 6, \pi = .20$ c. $X = 9, n = 9, \pi = .80$

6.18 Calculate each binomial probability:

a. $X = 2, n = 8, \pi = .10$
b. $X = 1, n = 10, \pi = .40$
c. $X = 3, n = 12, \pi = .70$

6.19 Calculate each compound event probability:

a. $X \leq 3, n = 8, \pi = .20$
b. $X > 7, n = 10, \pi = .50$
c. $X < 3, n = 6, \pi = .70$

6.20 Calculate each compound event probability:

a. $X \leq 10, n = 14, \pi = .95$
b. $X > 2, n = 5, \pi = .45$
c. $X \leq 1, n = 10, \pi = .15$

6.21 Calculate each binomial probability:

a. More than 10 successes in 16 trials with an 80 percent chance of success.
b. At least 4 successes in 8 trials with a 40 percent chance of success.
c. No more than 2 successes in 6 trials with a 20 percent chance of success.

6.22 Calculate each binomial probability:

a. Fewer than 4 successes in 12 trials with a 10 percent chance of success.
b. At least 3 successes in 7 trials with a 40 percent chance of success.
c. At most 9 successes in 14 trials with a 60 percent chance of success.

6.23 In the Ardmore Hotel, 20 percent of the customers pay by American Express credit card. (a) Of the next 10 customers, what is the probability that none pay by American Express? (b) At least two? (c) Fewer than three? (d) What is the expected number who pay by American Express? (e) Find the standard deviation. (f) Construct the probability distribution (using Excel or Appendix A). (g) Make a graph of its PDF, and describe its shape.

6.24 Historically, 5 percent of a mail-order firm's repeat charge-account customers have an incorrect current address in the firm's computer database. (a) What is the probability that none of the next 12 repeat customers who call will have an incorrect address? (b) One customer? (c) Two customers?

(d) Fewer than three? (e) Construct the probability distribution (using Excel or Appendix A), make a graph of its PDF, and describe its shape.

6.25 At a Noodles & Company restaurant, the probability that a customer will order a nonalcoholic beverage is .38. Use Excel to find the probability that in a sample of 5 customers (a) none of the 5 will order a nonalcoholic beverage, (b) at least 2 will, (c) fewer than 4 will, (d) all 5 will order a nonalcoholic beverage.

6.26 J.D. Power and Associates says that 60 percent of car buyers now use the Internet for research and price comparisons. (a) Find the probability that in a sample of 8 car buyers, all 8 will use the Internet; (b) at least 5; (c) more than 4. (d) Find the mean and standard deviation of the probability distribution. (e) Sketch the PDF (using Excel or Appendix A) and describe its appearance (e.g., skewness). (Data are from J. Paul Peter and Jerry C. Olson, *Consumer Behavior and Marketing Strategy,* 7th ed. [McGraw-Hill/Irwin, 2005], p. 188.)

6.27 There is a 70 percent chance that an airline passenger will check bags. In the next 16 passengers that check in for their flight at Denver International Airport, find the probability that (a) all will check bags; (b) fewer than 10 will check bags; (c) at least 10 will check bags.

6.28 Police records in the town of Saratoga show that 15 percent of the drivers stopped for speeding have invalid licenses. If 12 drivers are stopped for speeding, find the probability that (a) none will have an invalid license; (b) exactly one will have an invalid license; (c) at least 2 will have invalid licenses.

6.5 POISSON DISTRIBUTION

LO 6-5

Find Poisson probabilities using tables, formulas, or Excel.

LO 6-6

Use the Poisson approximation to the binomial (optional).

Poisson Processes

Named for the French mathematician Siméon-Denis Poisson (1781–1840), the **Poisson distribution** describes the number of occurrences within a randomly chosen unit of time (e.g., minute, hour) or space (e.g., square foot, linear mile). For the Poisson distribution to apply, the events must occur randomly and independently over a continuum of time or space, as illustrated in Figure 6.12. We will call the continuum "time" since the most common Poisson application is modeling **arrivals** *per unit of time*. Each dot (•) is an occurrence of the event of interest.

FIGURE 6.12

Poisson Events Distributed over Time

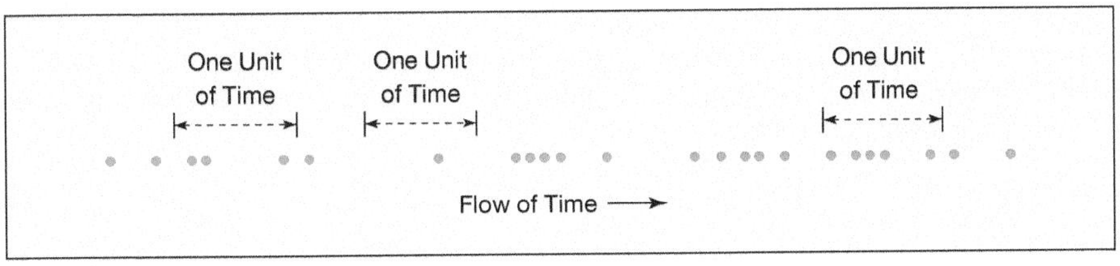

Let X = the number of events per unit of time. The value of X is a random variable that depends on when the unit of time is observed. Figure 6.12 shows that we could get $X = 3$ or $X = 1$ or $X = 5$ events, depending on where the randomly chosen unit of time happens to fall.

We often call the Poisson distribution the *model of arrivals* (customers, defects, accidents). Arrivals can reasonably be regarded as Poisson events if each event is **independent** (i.e., each event's occurrence has no effect on the probability of other events occurring). Some situations lack this characteristic. For example, computer users know that a power interruption often presages another within seconds or minutes. But, as a practical matter, the Poisson assumptions often are met sufficiently to make it a useful model of reality. For example:

- X = number of customers arriving at a bank ATM in a given minute.
- X = number of file server virus infections at a data center during a 24-hour period.
- X = number of asthma patient arrivals in a given hour at a walk-in clinic.

- X = number of Airbus 330 aircraft engine shutdowns per 100,000 flight hours.
- X = number of blemishes per sheet of white bond paper.

The Poisson model has only one parameter denoted λ (the lowercase Greek letter "lambda") representing the *mean number of events per unit of time or space*. The unit of time usually is chosen to be short enough that the mean arrival rate is not large (typically $\lambda < 20$). For this reason, the Poisson distribution is sometimes called the *model of* **rare events**. If the mean is large, we can reformulate the time units to yield a smaller mean. For example, $\lambda = 90$ events per hour is the same as $\lambda = 1.5$ events per minute. However, the Poisson model works for any λ as long as its assumptions are met.

Characteristics of the Poisson Distribution

All characteristics of the Poisson model are determined by its mean λ, as shown in Table 6.9. The constant e (the base of the natural logarithm system) is approximately 2.71828 (to see a more precise value of e, use your calculator's e^x function with $x = 1$). The mean of the Poisson distribution is λ, and its standard deviation is the square root of the mean. The simplicity of the Poisson formulas makes it an attractive model (easier than the binomial, for example). Unlike the binomial, X has no obvious limit, that is, the number of events that can occur in a given unit of time is not bounded. However, Poisson probabilities taper off toward zero as X increases, so the effective range is usually small.

TABLE 6.9

Poisson Distribution

Parameter	λ = mean arrivals per unit of time or space
PDF	$P(X = x) = \dfrac{\lambda^x e^{-\lambda}}{x!}$
Excel* PDF	=POISSON.DIST(x, λ, 0)
Excel* CDF	=POISSON.DIST(x, λ, 1)
Domain	$x = 0, 1, 2, \ldots$ (no obvious upper limit)
Mean	λ
Standard deviation	$\sqrt{\lambda}$
Comments	Always right-skewed, but less so for larger λ.

*Excel 2010's new function =POISSON.DIST(x, λ, cumulative) gives the same result as the old function =POISSONDIST(x, λ, cumulative).

Table 6.10 shows some Poisson PDFs. Going down each column, the probabilities must sum to 1.0000 (except for rounding, since these probabilities are only accurate to four decimals). The Poisson probability function is:

(6.9)
$$P(X = x) = \frac{\lambda^x e^{-\lambda}}{x!}, \quad \text{for } X = 1, 2, 3, 4, \ldots$$

TABLE 6.10

Poisson Probabilities for Various Values of λ

x	λ = 0.1	λ = 0.5	λ = 0.8	λ = 1.6	λ = 2.0
0	.9048	.6065	.4493	.2019	.1353
1	.0905	.3033	.3595	.3230	.2707
2	.0045	.0758	.1438	.2584	.2707
3	.0002	.0126	.0383	.1378	.1804
4	—	.0016	.0077	.0551	.0902
5	—	.0002	.0012	.0176	.0361
6	—	—	.0002	.0047	.0120
7	—	—	—	.0011	.0034
8	—	—	—	.0002	.0009
9	—	—	—	—	.0002
Sum	1.0000	1.0000	1.0000	1.0000	1.0000

Note: Probabilities less than .0001 have been omitted. Columns may not sum to 1 due to rounding.

Poisson distributions are always right-skewed (long right tail) but become less skewed and more bell-shaped as λ increases, as illustrated in Figure 6.13.

FIGURE 6.13

Poisson Becomes Less Skewed for Larger λ

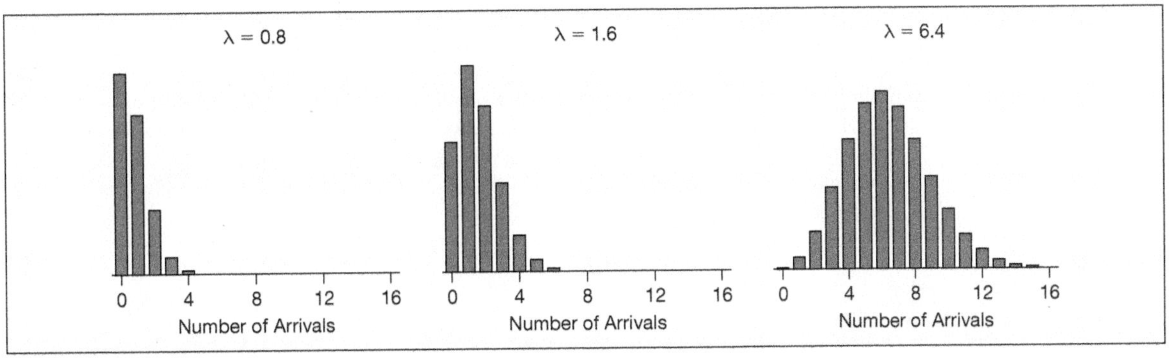

EXAMPLE 6.5

Credit Union Customers

CreditUnion

On Thursday morning between 9 a.m. and 10 a.m customers arrive at a mean rate of 1.7 customers per minute at the Oxnard University Credit Union and enter the queue (if any) for the teller windows. Using the Poisson formulas with $\lambda = 1.7$, the equations for the PDF, mean, and standard deviation are:

$$\text{PDF: } P(X = x) = \frac{\lambda^x e^{-\lambda}}{x!} = \frac{(1.7)^x e^{-1.7}}{x!}$$

$$\text{Mean: } \lambda = 1.7$$

$$\text{Standard deviation: } \sigma = \sqrt{\lambda} = \sqrt{1.7} = 1.304$$

TABLE 6.11

Probability Distribution for λ = 1.7

x	P(X = x)	P(X ≤ x)
0	.1827	.1827
1	.3106	.4932
2	.2640	.7572
3	.1496	.9068
4	.0636	.9704
5	.0216	.9920
6	.0061	.9981
7	.0015	.9996
8	.0003	.9999
9	.0001	1.0000

Using the Poisson Formula

Table 6.11 shows the probabilities for each value of X. The probabilities for individual X-values can be calculated by inserting $\lambda = 1.7$ into the Poisson PDF or by using Excel's Poisson function =POISSON.DIST(x, λ, cumulative) where cumulative is 0 (if you want a PDF) or 1 (if you want a CDF).

PDF Formula	*Excel Function*
$P(X = 0) = \frac{1.7^0 e^{-1.7}}{0!} = .1827$	=POISSON.DIST(0, 1.7, 0)
$P(X = 1) = \frac{1.7^1 e^{-1.7}}{1!} = .3106$	=POISSON.DIST(1, 1.7, 0)
$P(X = 2) = \frac{1.7^2 e^{-1.7}}{2!} = .2640$	=POISSON.DIST(2, 1.7, 0)
⋮	⋮

$$P(X = 8) = \frac{1.7^8 e^{-1.7}}{8!} = .0003 \quad \text{=POISSON.DIST(8, 1.7, 0)}$$

$$P(X = 9) = \frac{1.7^9 e^{-1.7}}{9!} = .0001 \quad \text{=POISSON.DIST(9, 1.7, 0)}$$

Poisson probabilities must sum to 1 (except due to rounding) as with any discrete probability distribution. Beyond $X = 9$, the probabilities are below .0001. Graphs of the PDF and CDF are shown in Figure 6.14. The most likely event is one arrival (probability .3106, or a 31.1 percent chance), although two arrivals is almost as likely (probability .2640, or a 26.4 percent chance). This PDF would help the credit union schedule its tellers for the Thursday morning work shift.

FIGURE 6.14

Poisson PDF and CDF for λ = 1.7

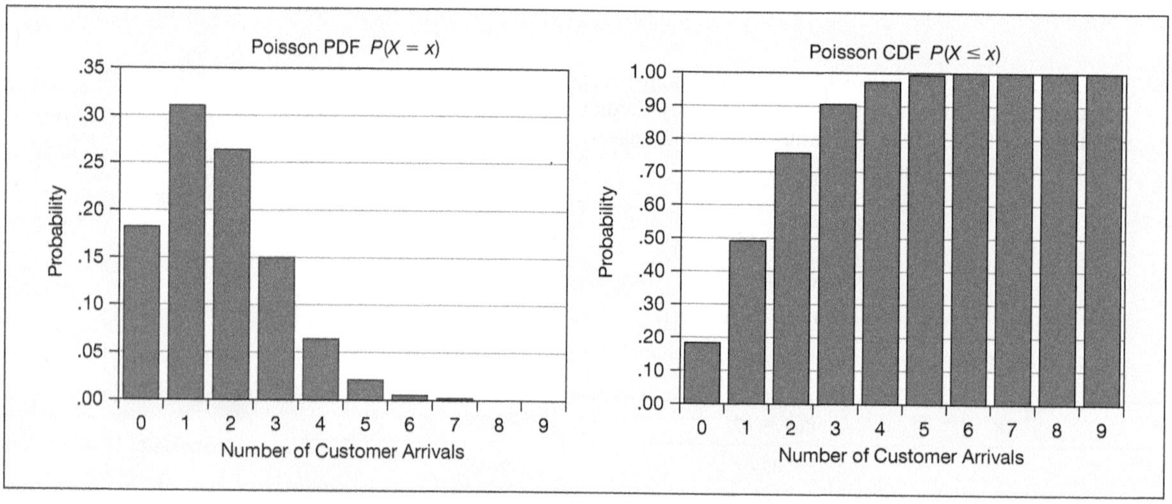

Compound Events

Cumulative probabilities can be evaluated by summing individual X probabilities. For example, the probability that *at most* two customers will arrive in a given minute is the sum of probabilities for several events:

$$P(X \le 2) = P(X = 0) + P(X = 1) + P(X = 2) = .1827 + .3106 + .2640 = .7572$$

Alternatively, we could calculate this probability using Excel's CDF function:

$$P(X \le 2) = \text{POISSON.DIST(2, 1.7, 1)} = .7572$$

We could then calculate the probability of *at least* three customers (the complementary event):

$$P(X \ge 3) = 1 - P(X \le 2) = 1 - \text{POISSON.DIST(2, 1.7, 1)} = 1 - .7572 = .2428$$

Using Tables (Appendix B)

Appendix B facilitates Poisson calculations, as illustrated in Figure 6.15 with highlighted probabilities for the terms in the sum for $P(X \ge 3)$. Appendix B doesn't go beyond $\lambda = 20$, partly because the table would become huge, but mainly because we have Excel.

Using Software

Tables are helpful for taking statistics exams (when you may not have access to Excel). However, tables contain only selected λ values, and in real-world problems, we cannot expect λ

FIGURE 6.15

Poisson Probabilities for $P(X \geq 3)$ from Appendix B

	λ					
X	*1.6*	*1.7*	*1.8*	*1.9*	*2.0*	*2.1*
0	.2019	.1827	.1653	.1496	.1353	.1225
1	.3230	.3106	.2975	.2842	.2707	.2572
2	.2584	.2640	.2678	.2700	.2707	.2700
3	.1378	.1496	.1607	.1710	.1804	.1890
4	.0551	.0636	.0723	.0812	.0902	.0992
5	.0176	.0216	.0260	.0309	.0361	.0417
6	.0047	.0061	.0078	.0098	.0120	.0146
7	.0011	.0015	.0020	.0027	.0034	.0044
8	.0002	.0003	.0005	.0006	.0009	.0011
9	—	.0001	.0001	.0001	.0002	.0003
10	—	—	—	—	—	.0001
11	—	—	—	—	—	—

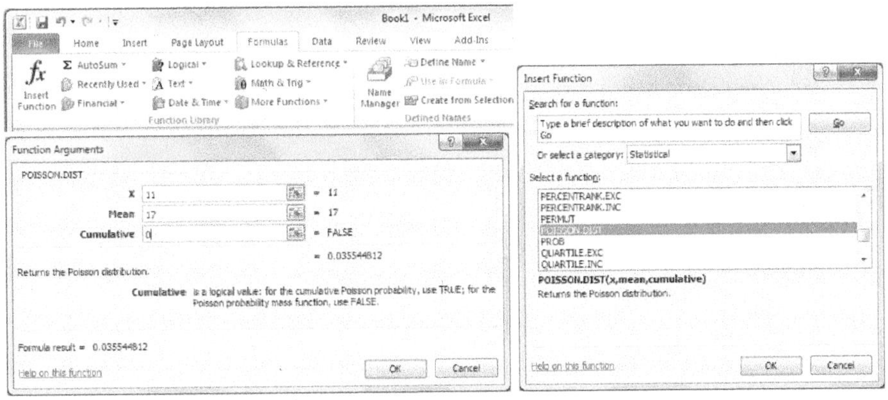

FIGURE 6.16

Excel Poisson Probability Function

always to be a nice round number. Excel's menus are illustrated in Figure 6.16. In this example, Excel calculates =POISSON.DIST(11, 17, 0) as .035544812, which is more accurate than Appendix B.

Recognizing Poisson Applications

Can you recognize a Poisson situation? The Poisson distribution has four main characteristics.

- An event of interest occurs randomly over time or space.
- The average arrival rate (λ) remains constant.
- The arrivals are independent of each other.
- The random variable (*X*) is the number of events within an observed time interval.

Ask yourself if the four characteristics above make sense in the following examples.

In the last week, how many credit card applications did you receive by mail?

In the last week, how many checks did you write?

In the last week, how many e-mail viruses did your firewall deflect?

It may be a Poisson process, even if you don't know the mean (λ). In business applications, the value of λ would have to be estimated from experience, but in this chapter λ will be given.

SECTION EXERCISES

connect

6.29 Find the mean and standard deviation for each Poisson:

a. $\lambda = 1.0$
b. $\lambda = 2.0$
c. $\lambda = 4.0$

6.30 Find the mean and standard deviation for each Poisson:

a. $\lambda = 9.0$
b. $\lambda = 12.0$
c. $\lambda = 7.0$

6.31 Calculate each Poisson probability:

a. $P(X = 6), \lambda = 4.0$
b. $P(X = 10), \lambda = 12.0$
c. $P(X = 4), \lambda = 7.0$

6.32 Calculate each Poisson probability:

a. $P(X = 2), \lambda = 0.1$
b. $P(X = 1), \lambda = 2.2$
c. $P(X = 3), \lambda = 1.6$

6.33 Calculate each compound event probability:

a. $P(X \leq 3), \lambda = 4.3$
b. $P(X > 7), \lambda = 5.2$
c. $P(X < 3), \lambda = 2.7$

6.34 Calculate each compound event probability:

a. $P(X \leq 10), \lambda = 11.0$
b. $P(X > 3), \lambda = 5.2$
c. $P(X < 2), \lambda = 3.7$

6.35 Calculate each Poisson probability:

a. More than 10 arrivals with $\lambda = 8.0$.
b. No more than 5 arrivals with $\lambda = 4.0$.
c. At least 2 arrivals with $\lambda = 5.0$

6.36 Calculate each Poisson probability:

a. Fewer than 4 arrivals with $\lambda = 5.8$.
b. At least 3 arrivals with $\lambda = 4.8$.
c. At most 9 arrivals with $\lambda = 7.0$.

6.37 According to J.D. Power and Associates' 2006 Initial Quality Study, consumers reported on average 1.7 problems per vehicle with new 2006 Volkswagens. In a randomly selected new Volkswagen, find the probability of (a) at least one problem; (b) no problems; (c) more than three problems. (d) Construct the probability distribution using Excel or Appendix B, make a graph of its PDF, and describe its shape. (Data are from J.D. Power and Associates 2006 Initial Quality Study^{SM}.)

6.38 At an outpatient mental health clinic, appointment cancellations occur at a mean rate of 1.5 per day on a typical Wednesday. Let X be the number of cancellations on a particular Wednesday. (a) Justify the use of the Poisson model. (b) What is the probability that no cancellations will occur on a particular Wednesday? (c) One? (d) More than two? (e) Five or more?

NOODLES & COMPANY

6.39 The average number of items (such as a drink or dessert) ordered by a Noodles & Company customer in addition to the meal is 1.4. These items are called *add-ons*. Define X to be the number of add-ons ordered by a randomly selected customer. (a) Justify the use of the Poisson model. (b) What is the probability that a randomly selected customer orders at least 2 add-ons? (c) No add-ons? (d) Construct the probability distribution using Excel or Appendix B, make a graph of its PDF, and describe its shape.

6.40 (a) Why might the number of yawns per minute by students in a warm classroom not be a Poisson event? (b) Give two additional examples of events per unit of time that might violate the assumptions of the Poisson model, and explain why.

Poisson Approximation to Binomial (Optional)

The binomial and Poisson are close cousins. The Poisson distribution may be used to approximate a binomial by setting $\lambda = n\pi$. This approximation is helpful when the binomial calculation is difficult (e.g., when n is large) and when Excel is not available. For example, suppose 1,000 women are screened for a rare type of cancer that has a nationwide incidence of 6 cases per 10,000 (i.e., $\pi = .0006$). What is the probability of finding two or fewer cases? The number of cancer cases would follow a binomial distribution with $n = 1{,}000$ and $\pi = .0006$. However, the binomial formula would involve awkward factorials. To use a Poisson approximation, we set the Poisson mean (λ) equal to the binomial mean ($n\pi$):

$$\lambda = n\pi = (1000)(.0006) = 0.6$$

To calculate the probability of x successes, we can then use Appendix B or the Poisson PDF $P(X = x) = \lambda^x e^{-\lambda}/x!$, which is simpler than the binomial PDF $P(X = x) = \frac{n!}{x!(n-x)!}\pi^x(1-\pi)^{n-x}$. The Poisson approximation of the desired probability is $P(X \le 2) = P(0) + P(1) + P(2) = .5488 + .3293 + .0988 = .9769$.

Poisson Approximation	*Actual Binomial Probability*
$P(X = 0) = 0.6^0 e^{-0.6}/0! = .5488$	$P(X = 0) = \frac{1000!}{0!(1000-0)!}.0006^0(1-.0006)^{1000-0} = .5487$
$P(X = 1) = 0.6^1 e^{-0.6}/1! = .3293$	$P(X = 1) = \frac{1000!}{1!(1000-1)!}.0006^1(1-.0006)^{1000-1} = .3294$
$P(X = 2) = 0.6^2 e^{-0.6}/2! = .0988$	$P(X = 2) = \frac{1000!}{2!(1000-2)!}.0006^2(1-.0006)^{1000-2} = .0988$

The Poisson calculations are easy and (at least in this example) the Poisson approximation is accurate. The Poisson approximation does a good job in this example, but when is it "good enough" in other situations? The general rule for a good approximation is that n should be "large" and π should be "small." A common rule of thumb says the approximation is adequate if $n \ge 20$ and $\pi \le .05$.

SECTION EXERCISES

connect

6.41 An experienced order taker at the L.L. Bean call center has a .003 chance of error on each keystroke (i.e., $\pi = .003$). In 500 keystrokes, find the approximate probability of (a) at least two errors and (b) fewer than four errors. (c) Is the Poisson approximation justified?

6.42 The probability of a manufacturing defect in an aluminum beverage can is .00002. If 100,000 cans are produced, find the approximate probability of (a) at least one defective can and (b) two or more defective cans. (c) Is the Poisson approximation justified?

6.43 Three percent of the letters placed in a certain postal drop box have incorrect postage. Suppose 200 letters are mailed. (a) For this binomial, what is the expected number with incorrect postage? (b) For this binomial, what is the standard deviation? (c) What is the approximate probability that at least 10 letters will have incorrect postage? (d) Fewer than five? (e) Is the Poisson approximation justified?

6.44 In a string of 100 Christmas lights, there is a .01 chance that a given bulb will fail within the first year of use (if one bulb fails, it does not affect the others). Find the approximate probability that two or more bulbs will fail within the first year.

6.45 The probability that a passenger's bag will be mishandled on a U.S. airline is .0046. During spring break, suppose that 500 students fly from Minnesota to various southern destinations. (a) What is the expected number of mishandled bags? (b) What is the approximate probability of no mishandled bags? More than two? (c) Would you expect the approximation to be accurate (cite a rule of thumb)?

LO 6-7

Find hypergeometric probabilities using Excel.

6.6 HYPERGEOMETRIC DISTRIBUTION

LO 6-8

Use the binomial approximation to the hypergeometric (optional).

Characteristics of the Hypergeometric Distribution

The **hypergeometric distribution** is similar to the binomial except that sampling is *without replacement* from a finite population of N items. Therefore, the trials are not independent and the probability of success is *not* constant from trial to trial. The hypergeometric distribution has three parameters: N (the number of items in the population), n (the number of items in the sample), and s (the number of successes in the population). The distribution of X (the number of successes in the sample) is hypergeometric, with the characteristics shown in Table 6.12. The hypergeometric distribution may be skewed right or left, and is symmetric only if $s/N = .50$ (i.e., if the proportion of successes in the population is 50 percent).

TABLE 6.12

Hypergeometric Distribution

Parameters	N = number of items in the population n = sample size s = number of successes in population
PDF	$P(X = x) = \frac{{}_sC_x \, {}_{N-s}C_{n-x}}{{}_NC_n}$
Excel* PDF	=HYPGEOM.DIST(*x, n, s, N*, 0)
Domain	$\max(0, n - N + s) \le X \le \min(s, n)$
Mean	$n\pi$ where $\pi = s/N$
Standard deviation	$\sqrt{n\pi(1-\pi)}\sqrt{\frac{N-n}{N-1}}$
Comments	Similar to binomial, but sampling is without replacement from a finite population. It can be approximated by a binomial with $\pi = s/N$ if $n/N < 0.05$, and is symmetric if $s/N = 0.50$.

*Excel 2010's new function =HYPGEOM.DIST(*x, n, s, N*, cumulative) gives the same result as the old function =HYPGEOMDIST(*x, n, s, N*) when *cumulative* = 0. The CDF value is returned when *cumulative* = 1.

The hypergeometric PDF, shown in formula 6.10, uses the formula for combinations:

(6.10)
$$P(X = x) = \frac{{}_sC_x \, {}_{N-s}C_{n-x}}{{}_NC_n}$$

where

$${}_sC_x = \text{the number of ways to choose } x \text{ successes from } s \text{ successes in the population}$$

$${}_{N-s}C_{n-x} = \text{the number of ways to choose } n - x \text{ failures from } N - s \text{ failures in the population}$$

$${}_NC_n = \text{the number of ways to choose } n \text{ items from } N \text{ items in the population}$$

and $N - s$ is the number of failures in the population, x is the number of successes in the sample, and $n - x$ is the number of failures in the sample. For a review of combinations see Chapter 5.

EXAMPLE 6.6

Damaged iPods

In a shipment of 10 iPods, 2 are damaged and 8 are good. The receiving department at Best Buy tests a sample of 3 iPods at random to see if they are defective. The number of damaged iPods in the sample is a random variable X. The problem description is:

$N = 10$	(number of iPods in the shipment)
$n = 3$	(sample size drawn from the shipment)
$s = 2$	(number of damaged iPods in the shipment, i.e., successes in population)
$N - s = 8$	(number of nondamaged iPods in the shipment)
$x = ?$	(number of damaged iPods in the sample, i.e., successes in sample)
$n - x = ?$	(number of nondamaged iPods in the sample)

It is tempting to think of this as a binomial problem with $n = 3$ and $\pi = s/N = 2/10 = .20$. But π is not constant. On the first draw, the probability of a damaged iPod is indeed $\pi_1 = 2/10$. But on the second draw, the probability of a damaged iPod could be $\pi_2 = 1/9$ (if the first draw contained a damaged iPod) or $\pi_2 = 2/9$ (if the first draw did not contain a damaged iPod). On the third draw, the probability of a damaged iPod could be $\pi_3 = 0/8$, $\pi_3 = 1/8$, or $\pi_3 = 2/8$ depending on what happened in the first two draws.

Using the Hypergeometric Formula

For the iPod example, the only possible values of x are 0, 1, and 2 since there are only 2 damaged iPods in the population. The probabilities are:

PDF Formula — *Excel Function*

$$P(X=0) = \frac{{}_2C_0\,{}_8C_3}{{}_{10}C_3} = \frac{\left(\frac{2!}{0!2!}\right)\left(\frac{8!}{3!5!}\right)}{\left(\frac{10!}{3!7!}\right)} = \frac{56}{120} = \frac{7}{15} = .4667$$ =HYPGEOM.DIST(0, 3, 2, 10, 0)

$$P(X=1) = \frac{{}_2C_1\,{}_8C_2}{{}_{10}C_3} = \frac{\left(\frac{2!}{1!1!}\right)\left(\frac{8!}{2!6!}\right)}{\left(\frac{10!}{3!7!}\right)} = \frac{56}{120} = \frac{7}{15} = .4667$$ =HYPGEOM.DIST(1, 3, 2, 10, 0)

$$P(X=2) = \frac{{}_2C_2\,{}_8C_1}{{}_{10}C_3} = \frac{\left(\frac{2!}{2!0!}\right)\left(\frac{8!}{1!7!}\right)}{\left(\frac{10!}{3!7!}\right)} = \frac{8}{120} = \frac{1}{15} = .0667$$ =HYPGEOM.DIST(2, 3, 2, 10, 0)

The values of $P(X)$ sum to 1, as they should: $P(0) + P(1) + P(2) = 7/15 + 7/15 + 1/15 = 1$. We can also find the probability of compound events. For example, the probability of at least one damaged iPod is $P(X \geq 1) = P(1) + P(2) = 7/15 + 1/15 = 8/15 = .533$, or 53.3 percent. The PDF and CDF are illustrated in Figure 6.17.

FIGURE 6.17

Hypergeometric PDF and CDF Illustrated with $N = 10$, $n = 3$, and $S = 2$

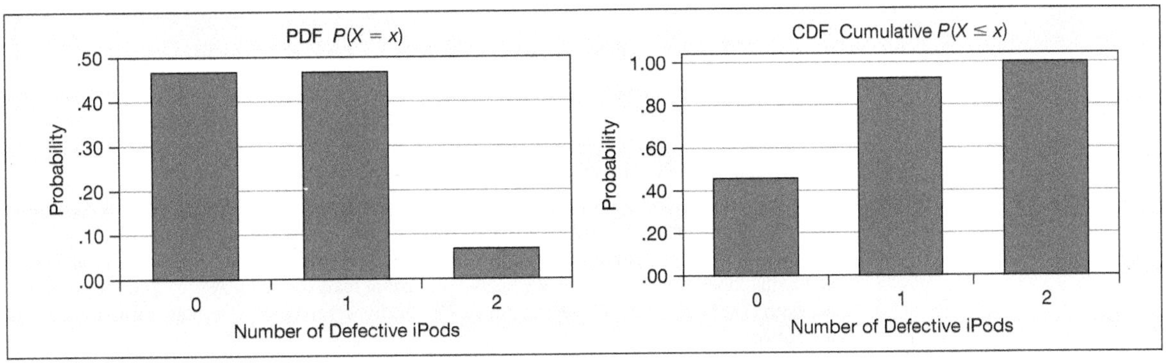

Using Software

Excel The hypergeometric formula is tedious and tables are impractical because there are three parameters, so we prefer Excel's hypergeometric function =HYPGEOM.DIST(*x*, *n*, *s*, *N*, 0). For example, using $X = 5$, $n = 10$, $s = 82$, $N = 194$, the formula =HYPGEOM.DIST(5, 10, 82, 194, 0) gives .222690589, as illustrated in Figure 6.18. You can also get hypergeometric probabilities from MegaStat or Minitab (menus not shown).

FIGURE 6.18

Excel Hypergeometric Probability Function

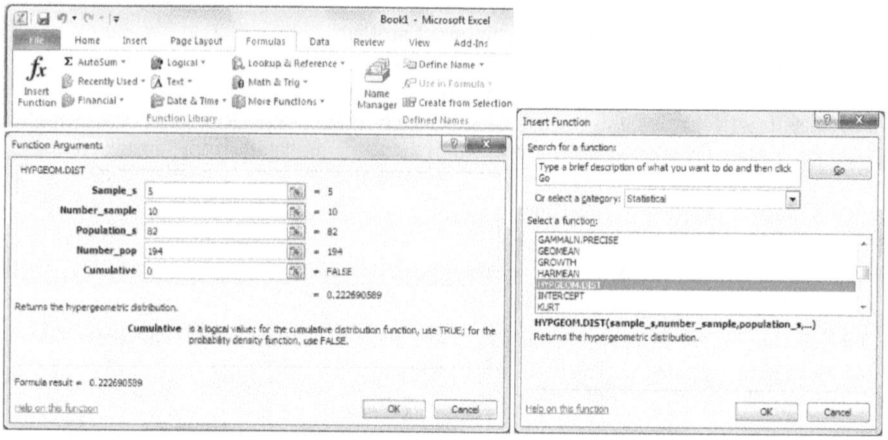

Recognizing Hypergeometric Applications

Look for a finite population (N) containing a known number of successes (s) and *sampling without replacement* (n items in the sample) where the probability of success is not constant for each sample item drawn. For example:

- Forty automobiles are to be inspected for California emissions compliance. Thirty-two are compliant but 8 are not. A sample of 7 cars is chosen at random. What is the probability that all are compliant? At least 5?
- A law enforcement agency must process 500 background checks for firearms purchasers. Fifty applicants are convicted felons. Through a computer error, 10 applicants are approved without a background check. What is the probability that none is a felon? At least two are?
- A medical laboratory receives 40 blood specimens to check for HIV. Eight actually contain HIV. A worker is accidentally exposed to 5 specimens. What is the probability that none contained HIV?

SECTION EXERCISES

6.46 (a) State the values that X can assume in each hypergeometric scenario. (b) Use the hypergeometric PDF formula to find the probability requested. (c) Check your answer by using Excel.

i. $N = 10, n = 3, s = 4, P(X = 3)$
ii. $N = 20, n = 5, s = 3, P(X = 2)$
iii. $N = 36, n = 4, s = 9, P(X = 1)$
iv. $N = 50, n = 7, s = 10, P(X = 3)$

6.47 ABC Warehouse has eight refrigerators in stock. Two are side-by-side models and six are top-freezer models. (a) Using Excel, calculate the entire hypergeometric probability distribution for the number of top-freezer models in a sample of four refrigerators chosen at random. (b) Make an Excel graph of the PDF for this probability distribution and describe its appearance.

6.48 A statistics textbook chapter contains 60 exercises, 6 of which are essay questions. A student is assigned 10 problems. Define X to be the number of essay questions the student receives. (a) Use Excel to calculate the entire hypergeometric probability distribution for X. (b) What is the probability that none of the questions are essay? (c) That at least one is essay? (d) That two or more are essay? (e) Make an Excel graph of the PDF of the hypergeometric distribution and describe its appearance.

6.49 Fifty employee travel expense reimbursement vouchers were filed last quarter in the finance department at Ramjac Corporation. Of these, 20 contained errors. A corporate auditor inspects five vouchers at random. Let X be the number of incorrect vouchers in the sample. (a) Use Excel to calculate the entire hypergeometric probability distribution. (b) Find $P(X = 0)$. (c) Find $P(X = 1)$. (d) Find $P(X \geq 3)$. (e) Make an Excel graph of the PDF of the hypergeometric distribution and describe its appearance.

6.50 A medical laboratory receives 40 blood specimens to check for HIV. Eight actually contain HIV. A worker is accidentally exposed to five specimens. (a) Use Excel to calculate the entire hypergeometric probability distribution. (b) What is the probability that none contained HIV? (c) Fewer than three? (d) At least two? (e) Make an Excel graph of the PDF of the hypergeometric distribution and describe its appearance.

Binomial Approximation to the Hypergeometric (Optional)

There is a strong similarity between the binomial and hypergeometric models. Both involve samples of size n and both treat X as the number of successes in the sample. If you replaced each item after it was selected, then you would have a binomial distribution instead of a hypergeometric distribution. If the size of the sample (n) is small in relation to the population (N), then the probability of success is nearly constant on each draw, so the two models are almost the same if we set $\pi = s/N$. A common *rule of thumb* is that the binomial is a safe approximation to the hypergeometric whenever $n/N < 0.05$. In other words, if we sample less than 5 percent of the population, π will remain essentially constant, even if we sample without replacement. For example, suppose we want $P(X = 6)$ for a hypergeometric with $N = 400$, $n = 10$, and $s = 200$. Since $n/N = 10/400 = .025$, the binomial approximation would be acceptable. Set $\pi = s/N = 200/400 = .50$ and use Appendix A to obtain $P(X = 6) = .2051$. But in the iPod example, the binomial approximation would be unacceptable because we sampled more than 5 percent of the population (i.e., $n/N = 3/10 = .30$ for the iPod problem).

Rule of Thumb

If $n/N < .05$, it is safe to use the binomial approximation to the hypergeometric, using sample size n and success probability $\pi = s/N$.

SECTION EXERCISES

connect

6.51 (a) Check whether the binomial approximation is acceptable in each of the following hypergeometric situations. (b) Find the binomial approximation (using Appendix A) for each probability requested. (c) Check the accuracy of your approximation by using Excel to find the actual hypergeometric probability.

a. $N = 100, n = 3, s = 40, P(X = 3)$
b. $N = 200, n = 10, s = 60, P(X = 2)$
c. $N = 160, n = 12, s = 16, P(X = 1)$
d. $N = 500, n = 7, s = 350, P(X = 5)$

6.52 Two hundred employee travel expense reimbursement vouchers were filed last year in the finance department at Ramjac Corporation. Of these, 20 contained errors. A corporate auditor audits a sample of five vouchers. Let X be the number of incorrect vouchers in the sample. (a) Justify the use of the binomial approximation. (b) Find the probability that the sample contains no erroneous vouchers. (c) Find the probability that the sample contains at least two erroneous vouchers.

6.53 A law enforcement agency processes 500 background checks for firearms purchasers. Fifty applicants are convicted felons. Through a clerk's error, 10 applicants are approved without checking for felony convictions. (a) Justify the use of the binomial approximation. (b) What is the probability that none of the 10 is a felon? (c) That at least 2 of the 10 are convicted felons? (d) That fewer than 4 of the 10 are convicted felons?

6.54 Four hundred automobiles are to be inspected for California emissions compliance. Of these, 320 actually are compliant but 80 are not. A random sample of 6 cars is chosen. (a) Justify the use of the binomial approximation. (b) What is the probability that all are compliant? (c) At least 4?

6.7 GEOMETRIC DISTRIBUTION (OPTIONAL)

LO 6-9

Calculate geometric probabilities (optional).

Characteristics of the Geometric Distribution

The **geometric distribution** is related to the binomial. It describes the number of Bernoulli trials until the first success is observed. But the number of trials is not fixed. We define X as the number of trials until the first success, and π as the constant *probability* of a success on each trial. The geometric distribution depends only on the parameter π (i.e., it is a one-parameter model). The domain of X is $\{1, 2, \ldots\}$ since we must have at least one trial to obtain our first success, but there is no limit on how many trials may be necessary. The characteristics of the geometric distribution are shown in Table 6.13. It is always skewed to the right. It can be shown that the geometric probabilities sum to 1 and that the mean and standard deviation are nearly the same when π is small. Probabilities diminish as X increases, but not rapidly.

TABLE 6.13

Geometric Distribution

Parameter	π = probability of success
PDF	$P(X = x) = \pi(1 - \pi)^{x-1}$
CDF	$P(X \le x) = 1 - (1 - \pi)^x$
Domain	$x = 1, 2, \ldots$
Mean	$1/\pi$
Standard deviation	$\sqrt{\frac{1-\pi}{\pi^2}}$
Random data in Excel	=1+INT(LN(1–RAND())/LN(1 – π))
Comments	Describes the number of trials before the first success. Highly skewed.

EXAMPLE 6.7

Telefund Calling

At Faber University, 15 percent of the alumni (the historical percentage) make a donation or pledge during the annual telefund. What is the probability that the first donation will come within the first five calls? To calculate this geometric probability, we would set $\pi = .15$, apply the PDF formula $P(X = x) = \pi(1 - \pi)^{x-1}$, and then sum the probabilities:

$$P(1) = (.15)(1 - .15)^{1-1} = (.15)(.85)^0 = .1500$$

$$P(2) = (.15)(1 - .15)^{2-1} = (.15)(.85)^1 = .1275$$

$$P(3) = (.15)(1 - .15)^{3-1} = (.15)(.85)^2 = .1084$$

$$P(4) = (.15)(1 - .15)^{4-1} = (.15)(.85)^3 = .0921$$

$$P(5) = (.15)(1 - .15)^{5-1} = (.15)(.85)^4 = .0783$$

Then $P(X \le 5) = P(1) + P(2) + P(3) + P(4) + P(5) = .5563$. Alternately, we can use the CDF to get $P(X \le 5) = 1 - (1 - .15)^5 = 1 - .4437 = .5563$. The CDF is a much easier method when sums are required. The PDF and CDF are illustrated in Figure 6.19.

The expected number of phone calls until the first donation is

$$\mu = 1/\pi = 1/(.15) = 6.67 \text{ calls}$$

On the average, we expect to call between 6 and 7 alumni until the first donation. However, the standard deviation is rather large:

$$\sigma = [(1 - \pi)/\pi^2]^{1/2} = [(1 - .15)/(.15)^2]^{1/2} = 6.15 \text{ calls}$$

The large standard deviation is a signal that it would be unwise to regard the mean as a good prediction of how many trials will be needed until the first donation.

FIGURE 6.19

Geometric PDF and CDF for $\pi = .15$

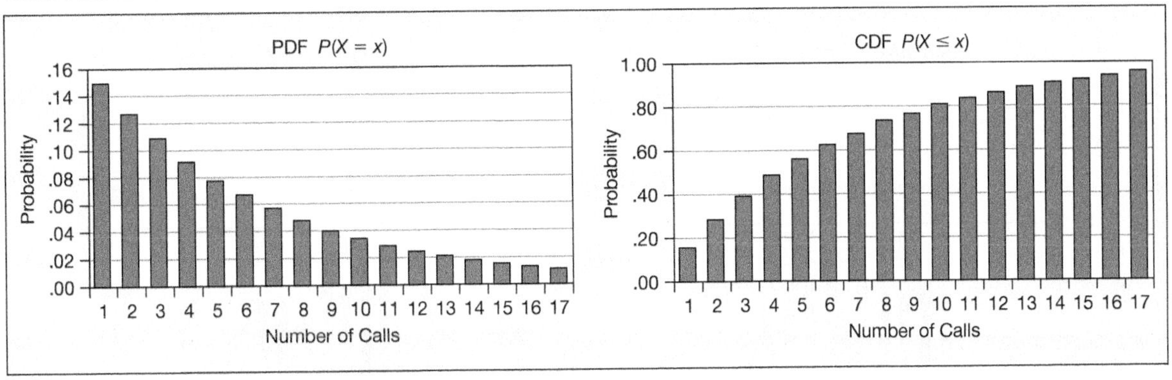

SECTION EXERCISES

connect

6.55 Find each geometric probability.

a. $P(X = 5)$ when $\pi = .50$
b. $P(X = 3)$ when $\pi = .25$
c. $P(X = 4)$ when $\pi = .60$

6.56 In the Ardmore Hotel, 20 percent of the guests (the historical percentage) pay by American Express credit card. (a) What is the expected number of guests until the next one pays by American Express credit card? (b) What is the probability that the first guest to use an American Express is within the first 10 to checkout?

6.57 In a certain Kentucky Fried Chicken franchise, half of the customers request "crispy" instead of "original," on average. (a) What is the expected number of customers before the next customer requests "crispy"? (b) What is the probability of serving more than 10 customers before the first request for "crispy"?

6.8 TRANSFORMATIONS OF RANDOM VARIABLES (OPTIONAL)

Linear Transformation

LO 6-10

Apply rules for transformations of random variables (optional).

A **linear transformation** of a random variable X is performed by adding a constant, multiplying by a constant, or both. Below are two useful rules about the mean and variance of a transformed random variable $aX + b$, where a and b are any constants ($a \ge 0$). Adding a constant shifts the mean but does not affect the standard deviation. Multiplying by a constant affects both the mean and the standard deviation.

Rule 1: $\mu_{aX+b} = a\mu_X + b$ (mean of a transformed variable)

Rule 2: $\sigma_{aX+b} = a\sigma_X$ (standard deviation of a transformed variable)

Application: Exam Scores Professor Hardtack gave a tough exam whose raw scores had $\mu = 40$ and $\sigma = 10$, so he decided to raise the mean by 20 points. One way to increase the mean to 60 is to shift the curve by adding 20 points to every student's score. Rule 1 says that adding a constant to all X-values will *shift the mean* but will leave the standard deviation unchanged, as illustrated in the left-side graph in Figure 6.20 using $a = 1$ and $b = 20$.

Alternatively, Professor Hardtack could multiply every exam score by 1.5, which would also accomplish the goal of raising the mean from 40 to 60. However, Rule 2 says that the standard deviation would rise from 10 to 15, thereby also *increasing the dispersion*. In other words, this policy would "spread out" the students' exam scores. Some scores might even exceed 100, as illustrated in the right-side graph in Figure 6.20.

FIGURE 6.20

Effect of Adding a Constant to X

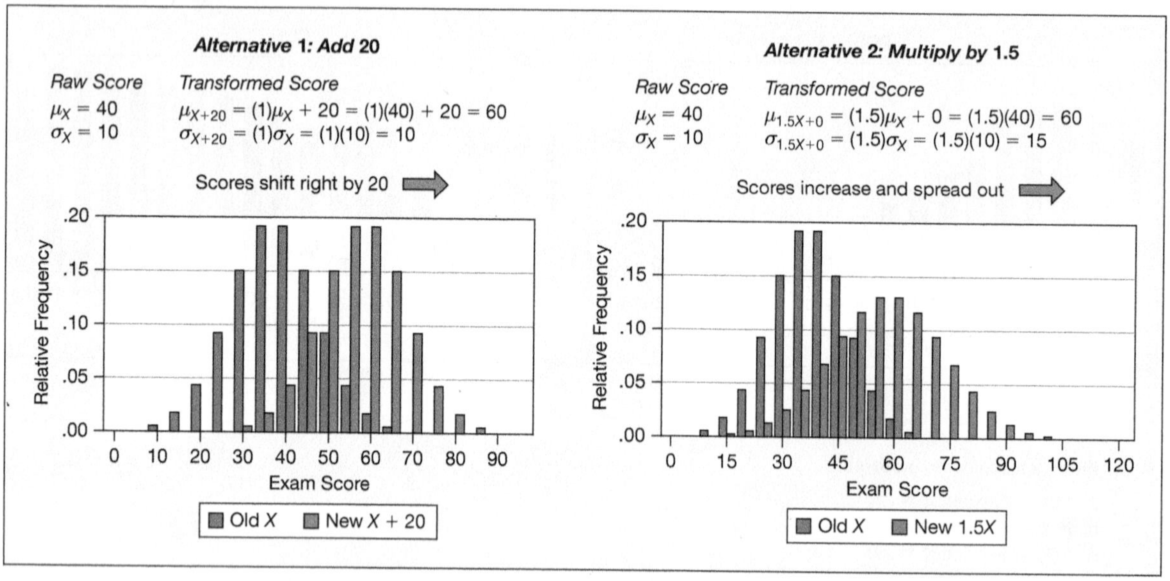

Application: Total Cost A linear transformation useful in business is the calculation of total cost as a function of quantity produced: $C = vQ + F$, where C is total cost, v is variable cost per unit, Q is the number of units produced, and F is fixed cost. Sonoro Ltd. is a small firm that manufactures kortholts. Its variable cost per unit is $v = \$35$, its annual fixed cost is $F = \$24{,}000$, and its monthly order quantity Q is a random variable with mean $\mu_Q = 500$ units and standard deviation $\sigma_Q = 40$. Total cost C is a random variable $C = vQ + F$, so we can apply Rules 1 and 2:

$$\text{Mean of total cost: } \mu_{vQ+F} = v\mu_Q + F = (35)(500) + 24{,}000 = \$41{,}500$$

$$\text{Std. Dev. of total cost: } \sigma_{vQ+F} = v\sigma_Q = (35)(40) = \$1{,}400$$

Sums of Random Variables

Below are two useful rules that apply to **sums of random variables**. Rule 3 says that the means can be added. Rule 4 says that the variances can be added *if* the variables are independent. These rules apply to the sum of any number of variables and are useful for analyzing situations where we must combine random variables. For example, if a firm has k different products, each with a known stochastic demand, then total revenue R is the sum of the revenue for each of the k product: $R = R_1 + R_2 + R_3 + \cdots + R_k$.

Rule 3: $\mu_{X+Y} = \mu_X + \mu_Y$ (mean of sum of two random variables X and Y)

Rule 4: $\sigma_{X+Y} = \sqrt{\sigma_X^2 + \sigma_Y^2}$ (standard deviation of sum if X and Y are independent)

Application: Gasoline Expenses The daily gasoline expense of Apex Movers, Inc., is a random variable with mean $\mu = \$125$ and standard deviation $\sigma = \$35$ ($\sigma^2 = 1225$). If we define Y to be the gasoline expense *per year,* and there are 250 working days per year at Apex Movers, then

$$\mu_Y = \mu + \cdots + \mu = \underbrace{\$125 + \cdots + \$125}_{250 \text{ times}} = \$31{,}250$$

$$\sigma_Y = \sqrt{\sigma^2 + \cdots + \sigma^2} = \underbrace{\sqrt{1225 + \cdots + 1225}}_{250 \text{ times}} = \$553$$

This assumes that daily gasoline expenses are independent of each other.

Application: Project Scheduling The initial phase of a construction project entails three activities that must be undertaken sequentially (that is, the second activity cannot begin until the first is complete, and so on) and the time (in days) to complete each activity is a random variable with a known mean and standard deviation:

Excavation	*Foundations*	*Structural Steel*
$\mu_1 = 25$ days	$\mu_2 = 14$ days	$\mu_3 = 58$ days
$\sigma_1 = 3$ days	$\sigma_2 = 2$ days	$\sigma_3 = 7$ days

By Rule 3, the mean time to complete the whole project is the sum of the task means (even if the task times are not independent):

$$\mu = \mu_1 + \mu_2 + \mu_3 = 25 + 14 + 58 = 97 \text{ days}$$

By Rule 4, if the times to complete each activity are *independent,* the overall variance for the project is the sum of the task variances, so the standard deviation for the entire project is:

$$\sigma = \sqrt{\sigma_1^2 + \sigma_2^2 + \sigma_3^2} = \sqrt{3^2 + 2^2 + 7^2} = \sqrt{62} = 7.874 \text{ days}$$

From this information, we can construct $\mu \pm 1\sigma$ or $\mu \pm 2\sigma$ intervals for the entire project:

$97 \pm (1)(7.874)$, or between 89.1 and 104.9 days
$97 \pm (2)(7.874)$, or between 81.3 and 112.8 days

So the *Empirical Rule* would imply that there is about a 95 percent chance that the project will take between 81.3 and 112.8 days. This calculation could help the construction firm estimate upper and lower bounds for the project completion time. Of course, if the distribution is not normal, the Empirical Rule may not apply.

Covariance

If X and Y are *not* independent (i.e., if X and Y are *correlated*), then we cannot use Rule 4 to find the standard deviation of their sum. Recall from Chapter 4 that the **covariance** of two random variables, denoted Cov(X,Y) or σ_{XY}, describes how the variables vary in relation to each other. A positive covariance indicates that the two variables tend to move in the same direction while a negative covariance indicates that the two variables move in opposite directions. We use both the covariance and the variances of X and Y to calculate the standard deviation of the sum of X and Y.

$$\textit{Rule 5:} \quad \sigma_{X+Y} = \sqrt{\sigma_X^2 + \sigma_Y^2 + 2\sigma_{XY}}$$

Finance is one area where the covariance measure has important applications because a portfolio's income is the sum of the incomes of the assets in the portfolio. If two asset returns have a positive covariance, the variance in total return will be *greater* than the sum of the two variances (i.e., risk is increased) while if the two asset returns have a negative covariance, the variance in total return will be *less* (i.e., risk is decreased). If the asset returns are uncorrelated, then their variances can just be summed (Rule 4). The point is that investors can reduce portfolio risk (i.e., smaller variance) by choosing assets appropriately.

Application: Centralized vs. Decentralized Warehousing The design of an optimal distribution network is critical for the operations of a firm. High demand variation means there will be a high need for inventory safety stock. Lower demand variation decreases the amount of safety stock needed at a distribution center. A firm can centralize their distribution centers (DC) so that one DC services all markets, or they can decentralize their network so each market has its own DC. The demand patterns will dictate whether a centralized or decentralized network is best. Suppose a firm has two markets to service. The parameters of the two distributions on demand for each market are given below as well as their covariance.

Market X Demand	*Market Y Demand*
$\mu_X = 500$ units/day	$\mu_Y = 250$ units/day
$\sigma_X = 45$ units	$\sigma_Y = 35$ units

$$\sigma_{XY} = -882 \text{ units}$$

Applying Rule 3, the average *aggregate* demand for both markets combined would be

$$\mu_D = \mu_X + \mu_Y = 500 + 250 = 750 \text{ units}$$

Given that the two markets have a negative covariance, by Rule 5 the standard deviation in aggregate demand would be

$$\sigma_D = \sqrt{\sigma_X^2 + \sigma_Y^2 + 2\sigma_{XY}} = \sqrt{45^2 + 35^2 + 2(-882)} = \sqrt{1486} = 38.55 \text{ units}$$

Note that the variation in aggregate demand is less than the variation for market *X* demand and close to the variation for market *Y* demand. This means a centralized DC could be the best solution because the firm would need less safety inventory on hand. (Of course the cost savings would need to be compared to possibly increased transportation costs.)

SECTION EXERCISES

connect

6.58 The height of a Los Angeles Lakers basketball player averages 6 feet 7.6 inches (i.e., 79.6 inches) with a standard deviation of 3.24 inches. To convert from inches to centimeters, we multiply by 2.54. (a) In centimeters, what is the mean? (b) In centimeters, what is the standard deviation? (c) Which rules did you use?

6.59 July sales for Melodic Kortholt, Ltd., average μ_1 = \$9,500 with σ_1^2 = \$1,250. August sales average μ_2 = \$7,400 with σ_2^2 = \$1,425. September sales average μ_3 = \$8,600 with σ_3^2 = \$1,610. (a) Find the mean and standard deviation of total sales for the third quarter. (b) What assumptions are you making?

6.60 The mean January temperature in Fort Collins, CO, is 37.1° F with a standard deviation of 10.3° F. Express these Fahrenheit parameters in degrees Celsius using the transformation C = 5/9F − 17.78.

6.61 There are five accounting exams. Bob's typical score on each exam is a random variable with a mean of 80 and a standard deviation of 5. His final grade is based on the sum of his exam scores. (a) Find the mean and standard deviation of Bob's point total assuming his performances on exams are independent of each other. (b) By the Empirical Rule (see Chapter 4), would you expect that Bob would earn at least 450 points (the required total for an "A")?

CHAPTER SUMMARY

A **random variable** assigns a numerical value to each outcome in the sample space of a random process. A **discrete random variable** has a countable number of distinct values. Probabilities in a **discrete probability distribution** must be between zero and one, and must sum to one. The **expected value** is the mean of the distribution, measuring center, and its **variance** is a measure of variability. A known distribution is described by its **parameters**, which imply its **probability distribution function** (PDF) and its **cumulative distribution function** (CDF).

As summarized in Table 6.14 the **uniform distribution** has two parameters (a, b) that define its domain. The **Bernoulli distribution** has one parameter (π, the probability of success) and two outcomes (0 or 1). The **binomial distribution** has two parameters (n, π). It describes the sum of n independent Bernoulli random experiments with constant probability of success. It may be skewed left ($\pi > .50$) or right ($\pi < .50$) or be symmetric ($\pi = .50$) but becomes less skewed as n increases. The **Poisson distribution** has one parameter (λ, the mean arrival rate). It describes arrivals of independent events per unit of time

TABLE 6.14 **Comparison of Models**

Model	*Parameters*	*Mean*	*Variance*	*Characteristics*
Bernoulli	π	π	$\pi(1-\pi)$	Used to generate the binomial.
Binomial	n, π	$n\pi$	$n\pi(1-\pi)$	Skewed right if $\pi < .50$, left if $\pi > .50$.
Geometric	π	$1/\pi$	$(1-\pi)/\pi^2$	Always skewed right and leptokurtic.
Hypergeometric	N, n, s	$n\pi$ where $\pi = s/N$	$n\pi(1-\pi)[(N-n)/(N-1)]$	Like binomial except sampling without replacement from a finite population.
Poisson	λ	λ	λ	Always skewed right and leptokurtic.
Uniform	a, b	$(a+b)/2$	$[(b-a+1)^2-1]/12$	Always symmetric and platykurtic.

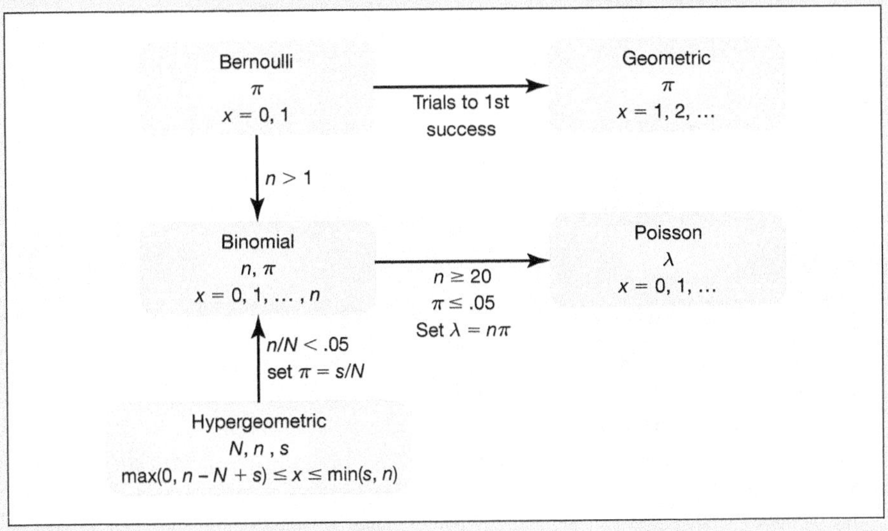

FIGURE 6.21
Relationships among Discrete Models

or space. It is always right-skewed, becoming less so as λ increases. The **hypergeometric distribution** has three parameters (N, n, s). It is like a binomial, except that sampling of n items is without replacement from a finite population of N items containing s successes. The **geometric distribution** is a one-parameter model (π, the probability of success) that describes the number of trials until the first success. Figure 6.21 shows the relationships among these five discrete models.

Rules for **linear transformations** of random variables say that adding a constant to a random variable shifts the distribution but does not change its variance, while multiplying a random variable by a constant changes both its mean and its variance. Rules for summing random variables permit adding of their means, but their variances can be summed only if the random variables are independent.

KEY TERMS

actuarially fair
arrivals (Poisson)
Bernoulli experiment
binomial distribution
covariance
cumulative distribution function
discrete probability distribution
discrete random variable
expected value
geometric distribution
hypergeometric distribution
independent
linear transformation (of a random variable)
parameters
Poisson distribution
probability distribution function
probability model
random variable
rare events (Poisson)
sums of random variables
uniform distribution
variance

Commonly Used Formulas in Discrete Distributions

Total probability: $\sum_{i=1}^{N} P(x_i) = 1$

Expected value: $E(X) = \mu = \sum_{i=1}^{N} x_i P(x_i)$

Variance: $\text{Var}(X) = \sigma^2 = \sum_{i=1}^{N} [x_i - \mu]^2 P(x_i)$

(if there are N distinct values $x_1, x_2, \ldots, x_N$)

Uniform PDF: $P(X = x) = \dfrac{1}{b - a + 1}$ $\quad x = a, a + 1, \ldots, b$

Binomial PDF: $P(X = x) = \dfrac{n!}{x!(n - x)!} \pi^x (1 - \pi)^{n-x}$ $\quad x = 0, 1, 2, \ldots, n$

Poisson PDF: $P(X = x) = \dfrac{\lambda^x e^{-\lambda}}{x!}$ $\quad x = 0, 1, 2, \ldots$

Hypergeometric PDF: $P(X = x) = \dfrac{{}_sC_x \, {}_{N-s}C_{n-x}}{{}_NC_n}$ $\quad \max(0, n - N + s) \le x \le \min(s, n)$

Geometric PDF: $P(X = x) = \pi (1 - \pi)^{x-1}$ $\quad x = 1, 2, \ldots$

CHAPTER REVIEW

Note: Questions marked * are harder or rely on optional material from this chapter.

1. Define (a) random process; (b) random variable; (c) discrete random variable; and (d) probability distribution.
2. Without using formulas, explain the meaning of (a) expected value of a random variable; (b) actuarial fairness; and (c) variance of a random variable.
3. What is the difference between a PDF and a CDF? Sketch a picture of each.
4. (a) What are the two parameters of a uniform distribution? (b) Why is the uniform distribution the first one considered in this chapter?
5. (a) Describe a Bernoulli experiment and give two examples. (b) What is the connection between a Bernoulli experiment and a binomial distribution?
6. (a) What are the parameters of a binomial distribution? (b) What is the mean of a binomial distribution? The standard deviation? (c) When is a binomial skewed right? Skewed left? Symmetric? (d) Suggest a data-generating situation that might be binomial.
7. (a) What are the parameters of a Poisson distribution? (b) What is the mean of a Poisson distribution? The standard deviation? (c) Is a Poisson ever symmetric? (d) Suggest a data-generating situation that might be Poisson.
8. In the binomial and Poisson models, why is the assumption of independent events important?

* 9. (a) When are we justified in using the Poisson approximation to the binomial? (b) Why would we want to do this approximation?

10. (a) Explain a situation when we would need the hypergeometric distribution. (b) What are the three parameters of the hypergeometric distribution? (c) How does it differ from a binomial distribution?

*11. When are we justified in using (a) the Poisson approximation to the binomial? (b) The binomial approximation to the hypergeometric?

12. (a) Name a situation when we would need the (a) hypergeometric distribution; (b)* geometric distribution; (c) uniform distribution.

*13. What do Rules 1 and 2 say about transforming a random variable?

*14. What do Rules 3 and 4 say about sums of several random variables?

*15. In Rule 5, what does the covariance measure? What happens to the variance of the sum of two random variables when the covariance is (a) positive? (b) negative? (c) zero?

CHAPTER EXERCISES

connect

Note: Show your work clearly. Problems marked * are harder or rely on optional material from this chapter.

6.62 The probability that a 30-year-old white male will live another year is .99863. What premium would an insurance company charge to break even on a one-year $1 million term life insurance policy?

6.63 As a birthday gift, you are mailing a new personal digital assistant (PDA) to your cousin in Toledo. The PDA cost $250. There is a 2 percent chance it will be lost or damaged in the mail. Is it worth $4 to insure the mailing? Explain, using the concept of expected value.

6.64 Use Excel to generate 1,000 random integers in the range 1 through 5. (a) What are the expected mean and standard deviation? (b) What are your sample mean and standard deviation? (c) Is your sample consistent with the uniform model? Discuss. (d) Show the Excel formula you used.

6.65 Consider the Bernoulli model. What would be a typical probability of success (π) for (a) free throw shooting by a good college basketball player? (b) Hits by a good baseball batter? (c) Passes completed by a good college football quarterback? (d) Incorrect answers on a five-part multiple choice exam if you are guessing? (e) Can you suggest reasons why independent events might not be assumed in some of these situations? Explain.

6.66 There is a 14 percent chance that a Noodles & Company customer will order bread with the meal. Use Excel to find the probability that in a sample of 10 customers (a) more than five will order bread; (b) no more than two will; (c) none of the 10 will order bread. (d) Is the distribution skewed left or right?

6.67 In a certain year, on average 10 percent of the vehicles tested for emissions failed the test. Suppose that five vehicles are tested. (a) What is the probability that all pass? (b) All but one pass? (c) Sketch the probability distribution and discuss its shape.

6.68 The probability that an American CEO can transact business in a foreign language is .20. Ten American CEOs are chosen at random. (a) What is the probability that none can transact business in a foreign language? (b) That at least two can? (c) That all 10 can?

6.69 In a certain Kentucky Fried Chicken franchise, half of the customers typically request "crispy" instead of "original." (a) What is the probability that none of the next four customers will request "crispy"? (b) At least two? (c) At most two? (d) Construct the probability distribution (Excel or Appendix A), make a graph of its PDF, and describe its shape.

6.70 On average, 40 percent of U.S. beer drinkers order light beer. (a) What is the probability that none of the next eight customers who order beer will order light beer? (b) That one customer will? (c) Two customers? (d) Fewer than three? (e) Construct the probability distribution (Excel or Appendix A), make a graph of its PDF, and describe its shape.

6.71 Write the Excel binomial formula for each probability.

a. Three successes in 20 trials with a 30 percent chance of success.
b. Seven successes in 50 trials with a 10 percent chance of success.
c. Six or fewer successes in 80 trials with a 5 percent chance of success.
d. At least 30 successes in 120 trials with a 20 percent chance of success.

6.72 Tired of careless spelling and grammar, a company decides to administer a test to all job applicants. The test consists of 20 sentences. Applicants must state whether each sentence contains any grammar or spelling errors. Half the sentences contain errors. The company requires a score of 14 or more. (a) If an applicant guesses randomly, what is the probability of passing? (b) What minimum score would be required to reduce the probability of "passing by guessing" to 5 percent or less?

6.73 The default rate on government-guaranteed student loans at a certain private 4-year institution is 7 percent. The college extends 10 such loans. (a) What is the probability that none of them will default? (b) That at least three will default? (c) What is the expected number of defaults?

6.74 Experience indicates that 8 percent of the pairs of men's trousers dropped off for dry cleaning will have an object in the pocket that should be removed before cleaning. Suppose that 14 pairs of pants are dropped off and the cleaner forgets to check the pockets. What is the probability that no pair has an object in the pocket?

6.75 A study by the Parents' Television Council showed that 80 percent of movie commercials aired on network television between 8 and 9 p.m. (the prime family viewing hour) were for R-rated films. (a) Find the probability that in 16 commercials during this time slot at least 10 will be for R-rated films. (b) Find the probability of fewer than 8 R-rated films.

6.76 Write the Excel formula for each Poisson probability, using a mean arrival rate of 10 arrivals per hour.

a. Seven arrivals. b. Three arrivals. c. Fewer than five arrivals. d. At least 11 arrivals.

6.77 A small feeder airline knows that the probability is .10 that a reservation holder will not show up for its daily 7:15 a.m. flight into a hub airport. The flight carries 10 passengers. (a) If the flight is fully booked, what is the probability that all those with reservations will show up? (b) If the airline overbooks by selling 11 seats, what is the probability that no one will have to be bumped? (c) That more than one passenger will be bumped? *(d) The airline wants to overbook the flight by enough seats to ensure a 95 percent chance that the flight will be full, even if some passengers may be bumped. How many seats would it sell?

6.78 Although television HDTV converters are tested before they are placed in the installer's truck, the installer knows that 20 percent of them still won't work properly. The driver must install eight converters today in an apartment building. (a) Ten converters are placed in the truck. What is the probability that the driver will have enough working converters? *(b) How many boxes should the driver load to ensure a 95 percent probability of having enough working converters?

6.79 (a) Why might the number of calls received per minute at a fire station not be a Poisson event? (b) Name two other events per unit of time that might violate the assumptions of the Poisson model.

6.80 Software filters rely heavily on "blacklists" (lists of known "phishing" URLs) to detect fraudulent e-mails. But such filters typically catch only 20 percent of phishing URLs. Jason receives 16 phishing e-mails. (a) What is the expected number that would be caught by such a filter? (b) What is the chance that such a filter would detect none of them?

6.81 Lunch customers arrive at a Noodles & Company restaurant at an average rate of 2.8 per minute. Define X to be the number of customers to arrive during a randomly selected minute during the lunch hour and assume X has a Poisson distribution. (a) Calculate the probability that exactly five customers will arrive in a minute during the lunch hour. (b) Calculate the probability that no more than five customers will arrive in a minute. (c) What is the average customer arrival rate for a 5-minute interval? (d) What property of the Poisson distribution did you use to find this arrival rate?

6.82 In a major league baseball game, the average is 1.0 broken bat per game. Find the probability of (a) no broken bats in a game; (b) at least 2 broken bats.

6.83 In the last 50 years, the average number of deaths due to alligators in Florida is 0.3 death per year. Assuming no change in this average, in a given year find the probability of (a) no alligator deaths; (b) at least 2 alligator deaths.

6.84 In a recent year, potentially dangerous commercial aircraft incidents (e.g., near collisions) averaged 1.2 per 100,000 flying hours. Let X be the number of incidents in a 100,000-hour period. (a) Justify the use of the Poisson model. (b) What is the probability of at least one incident? (c) More than three incidents? (d) Construct the probability distribution (Excel or Appendix B) and make a graph of its PDF.

6.85 At an outpatient mental health clinic, appointment cancellations occur at a mean rate of 1.5 per day on a typical Wednesday. Let X be the number of cancellations on a particular Wednesday. (a) Justify the use of the Poisson model. (b) What is the probability that no cancellations will occur on a particular Wednesday? (c) That one will? (d) More than two? (e) Five or more?

6.86 Car security alarms go off at a mean rate of 3.8 per hour in a large Costco parking lot. Find the probability that in an hour there will be (a) no alarms; (b) fewer than four alarms; and (c) more than five alarms.

6.87 In a certain automobile manufacturing paint shop, paint defects on the hood occur at a mean rate of 0.8 defect per square meter. A hood on a certain car has an area of 3 square meters. (a) Justify the use of the Poisson model. (b) If a customer inspects a hood at random, what is the probability that there will be no defects? (c) One defect? (d) Fewer than two defects?

6.88 Past insurance company audits have found that 2 percent of dependents claimed on an employee's health insurance actually are ineligible for health benefits. An auditor examines a random sample of 7 claimed dependents. (a) What is the probability that all are eligible? (b) That at least one is ineligible?

***6.89** A "rogue wave" (one far larger than others surrounding a ship) can be a threat to ocean-going vessels (e.g., naval vessels, container ships, oil tankers). The European Centre for Medium-Range Weather Forecasts issues a warning when such waves are likely. The average for this rare event is estimated to be .0377 rogue wave per hour in the South Atlantic. Find the probability that a ship will encounter at least one rogue wave in a 5-day South Atlantic voyage (120 hours).

6.90 In Northern Yellowstone Lake, earthquakes occur at a mean rate of 1.2 quakes per year. Let X be the number of quakes in a given year. (a) Justify the use of the Poisson model. (b) What is the probability of fewer than three quakes? (c) More than five quakes? (d) Construct the probability distribution (Excel or Appendix B) and make a graph of its PDF.

6.91 On New York's Verrazano Narrows bridge, traffic accidents occur at a mean rate of 2.0 crashes per day. Let X be the number of crashes in a given day. (a) Justify the use of the Poisson model. (b) What is the probability of at least one crash? (c) Fewer than five crashes? (d) Construct the probability distribution (Excel or Appendix B), make a graph of its PDF, and describe its shape.

APPROXIMATIONS

***6.92** Leaks occur in a pipeline at a mean rate of 1 leak per 1,000 meters. In a 2,500-meter section of pipe, what is the probability of (a) no leaks? (b) Three or more leaks? (c) What is the expected number of leaks?

***6.93** Among live deliveries, the probability of a twin birth is .02. (a) In 200 live deliveries, how many would be expected to have twin births? (b) What is the probability of no twin births? (c) One twin birth? (d) Calculate these probabilities both with and without an approximation. (e) Is the approximation justified? Discuss fully.

***6.94** The probability is .03 that a passenger on United Airlines Flight 9841 is a Platinum flyer (50,000 miles per year). If 200 passengers take this flight, use Excel to find the binomial probability of (a) no Platinum flyers, (b) one Platinum flyer, and (c) two Platinum flyers. (d) Calculate the same probabilities using a Poisson approximation. (e) Is the Poisson approximation justified? Explain.

***6.95** The probability of being "bumped" (voluntarily or involuntarily) on a U.S. airline was .00128. The average number of passengers traveling through Denver International Airport each hour is 5,708. (a) What is the expected number of bumped passengers per hour? (b) What is the approximate Poisson probability of fewer than 10 bumped passengers? More than 5? (c) Would you expect the approximation likely to be accurate (cite a rule of thumb)?

***6.96** On average, 2 percent of all persons who are given a breathalyzer test by the state police pass the test (blood alcohol under .08 percent). Suppose that 500 breathalyzer tests are given. (a) What is the expected number who pass the test? (b) What is the approximate Poisson probability that 5 or fewer will pass the test?

***6.97** The probability of an incorrect call by an NFL referee is .025 (e.g., calling a pass complete, but the decision reversed on instant replays). In a certain game, there are 150 plays. (a) What is the probability of at least 4 incorrect calls by the referees? (b) Justify any assumptions that you made.

***6.98** In CABG surgery, there is a .00014 probability of a retained foreign body (e.g., a sponge or a surgical instrument) left inside the patient. (a) In 100,000 CABG surgeries, what is the expected number of retained foreign bodies? (b) What is the Poisson approximation to the binomial probability of five or fewer retained foreign bodies in 100,000 CABG surgeries? (c) Look up CABG on the Internet if you are unfamiliar with the acronym. (See *AHRQ News*, No. 335, July 2008, p. 3.)

GEOMETRIC

***6.99** The probability of a job offer in a given interview is .25. (a) What is the expected number of interviews until the first job offer? (b) What is the probability the first job offer occurs within the first six interviews?

***6.100** The probability that a bakery customer will order a birthday cake is .04. (a) What is the expected number of customers until the first birthday cake is ordered? (b) What is the probability the first cake order occurs within the first 20 customers?

***6.101** In a certain city, 8 percent of the cars have a burned-out headlight. (a) What is the expected number that must be inspected before the first one with a burned-out headlight is found? (b) What is the probability of finding the first one within the first five cars? *Hint:* Use the CDF.

***6.102** For patients aged 81 to 90, the probability is .07 that a coronary bypass patient will die soon after the surgery. (a) What is the expected number of operations until the first fatality? (b) What is the probability of conducting 20 or more operations before the first fatality? *Hint:* Use the CDF.

***6.103** Historically, 5 percent of a mail-order firm's regular charge-account customers have an incorrect current address in the firm's computer database. (a) What is the expected number of customer orders until the first one with an incorrect current address places an order? (b) What is the probability of mailing 30 bills or more until the first one is returned with a wrong address? *Hint:* Use the CDF.

***6.104** At a certain clinic, 2 percent of all pap smears show signs of abnormality. What is the expected number of pap smears that must be inspected before the first abnormal one is found?

TRANSFORMATIONS AND COVARIANCE

***6.105** The weight of a Los Angeles Lakers basketball player averages 233.1 pounds with a standard deviation of 34.95 pounds. To express these measurements in terms a European would understand, we could convert from pounds to kilograms by multiplying by .4536. (a) In kilograms, what is the mean? (b) In kilograms, what is the standard deviation?

***6.106** The Rejuvo Corp. manufactures granite countertop cleaner and polish. Quarterly sales Q is a random variable with a mean of 25,000 bottles and a standard deviation of 2,000 bottles. Variable cost is \$8 per unit and fixed cost is \$150,000. (a) Find the mean and standard deviation of Rejuvo's total cost. (b) If all bottles are sold, what would the selling price have to be to break even, on average? To make a profit of \$20,000?

***6.107** A manufacturer fills one-gallon cans (3,785 ml) on an assembly line in two independent steps. First, a high-volume spigot injects most of the paint rapidly. Next, a more precise but slower spigot tops off the can. The fill amount in each step is a normally distributed random variable. For step one, $\mu_1 = 3{,}420$ ml and $\sigma_2 = 10$ ml, while for step two $\mu_2 = 390$ ml and $\sigma_2 = 2$ ml. Find the mean and standard deviation of the total fill $X_1 + X_2$.

***6.108** A manufacturing project has five independent phases whose completion must be sequential. The time to complete each phase is a random variable. The mean and standard deviation of the time for each phase are shown below. (a) Find the expected completion time. (b) Make a 2-sigma interval around the mean completion time ($\mu \pm 2\sigma$).

Phase	*Mean (hours)*	*Std. Dev. (hours)*
Set up dies and other tools	20	4
Milling and machining	10	2
Finishing and painting	14	3
Packing and crating	6	2
Shipping	48	6

***6.109** In September, demand for industrial furnace boilers at a large plumbing supply warehouse has a mean of 7 boilers with a standard deviation of 2 boilers. The warehouse pays a unit cost of \$2,225 per boiler plus a fee of \$500 per month to act as dealer for these boilers. Boilers are sold for \$2,850 each. (a) Find the mean and standard deviation of September profit (revenue minus cost). (b) Which rules did you use?

***6.110** A certain outpatient medical procedure has five steps that must be performed in sequence. (a) Assuming that the time (in minutes) required for each step is an independent random variable, find the mean and standard deviation for the total time. (b) Why might the assumption of independence be doubtful?

Step	*Mean (minutes)*	*Standard Deviation (minutes)*
Patient check-in	15	4
Pre-op preparation	30	6
Medical procedure	25	5
Recovery	45	10
Check-out and discharge	20	5

***6.111** Malaprop Ltd. sells two products. Daily sales of product *A* have a mean of $70 with a standard deviation of $10, while sales of product *B* have a mean of $200 with a standard deviation of $30. Sales of the products tend to rise and fall at the same time, having a positive covariance of 400. (a) Find the mean daily sales for both products together. (b) Find the standard deviation of total sales of both products. (c) Is the variance of the total sales greater than or less than the sum of the variances for the two products?

RELATED READING

Forbes, Catherine; Merran Evans; Nicholas Hastings; and Brian Peacock. *Statistical Distributions.* 4th ed. John Wiley & Sons, 2011.

CHAPTER 6 More Learning Resources

You can access these *LearningStats* demonstrations through McGraw-Hill's Connect® to help you understand visual data displays.

Topic	*LearningStats Demonstrations*
Discrete distributions	Probability Calculator Random Discrete Data Binomial/Poisson Approximation
Tables	Table A—Binomial Probabilities Table B—Poisson Probabilities
Applications	Covariance in Asset Portfolios: A Simulation Expected Value: Life Expectancy

Key: [Excel icon] = Excel

Chapter 7. Continuous Probability Distributions

CHAPTER 7

Continuous Probability Distributions

CHAPTER CONTENTS

CHAPTER LEARNING OBJECTIVES

LO

When you finish this chapter you should be able to

LO 7-1 Define a continuous random variable.

LO 7-2 Calculate uniform probabilities.

LO 7-3 Know the form and parameters of the normal distribution.

LO 7-4 Find the normal probability for a given *z* or *x* using tables or Excel.

LO 7-5 Solve for *z* or *x* for a given normal probability using tables or Excel.

LO 7-6 Use the normal approximation to a binomial or a Poisson.

LO 7-7 Find the exponential probability for a given *x*.

LO 7-8 Solve for *x* for a given exponential probability.

LO 7-9 Use the triangular distribution for "what-if" analysis (optional).

In Chapter 6, you learned about probability models and discrete random variables. We will now expand our discussion of probability models to include models that describe **continuous random variables.** Recall that a discrete random variable usually arises from *counting* something such as the number of customer arrivals in the next minute. In contrast, a continuous random variable usually arises from *measuring* something such as the waiting time until the next customer arrives. Unlike a discrete variable, a continuous random variable can have noninteger (decimal) values.

Probability for a discrete variable is defined at a point such as $P(X = 3)$ or as a sum over a series of points such as $P(X \leq 2) = P(0) + P(1) + P(2)$. But when X is a continuous variable (e.g., waiting time), it does not make sense to speak of probability "at" a particular X-value (e.g., $X = 54$ seconds) because the values of X are not a set of discrete points. Rather, probabilities are defined as *areas under a curve* called the *probability density function* (PDF). Probabilities for a continuous random variable are defined on intervals such as $P(53.5 \leq X \leq 54.5)$ or $P(X < 54)$ or $P(X \geq 53)$. Figure 7.1 illustrates the differences between discrete and continuous random variables. This chapter explains how to recognize data-generating situations that produce continuous random variables, how to calculate event probabilities, and how to interpret the results.

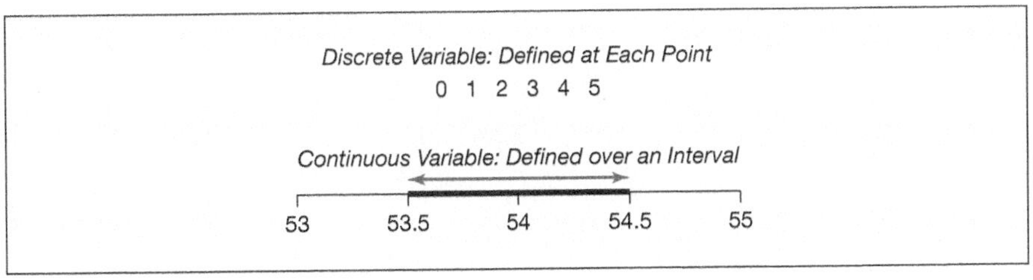

FIGURE 7.1
Discrete and Continuous Events

7.1 CONTINUOUS PROBABILITY DISTRIBUTIONS

PDFs and CDFs

LO 7-1
Define a continuous random variable.

A probability distribution can be described either by its **probability density function (PDF)** or by its **cumulative distribution function (CDF)**. For a continuous random variable, the PDF is an equation that shows the height of the curve $f(x)$ at each possible value of X. Any continuous PDF must be nonnegative and the area under the entire PDF must be 1. The mean, variance, and shape of the distribution depend on the PDF and its *parameters*. The CDF is denoted $F(x)$ and shows $P(X \leq x)$, the cumulative *area* to the left of a given value of X. The CDF is useful for probabilities, while the PDF reveals the *shape* of the distribution. There are Excel functions for many common PDFs or CDFs.

For example, Figure 7.2 shows a hypothetical PDF and CDF for a distribution of freeway speeds. The random variable *miles per hour* is a continuous variable that can be expressed with any level of precision we choose. The curves are smooth, with the PDF showing the probability density at points along the X-axis. The CDF shows the *cumulative* probability of speeds, gradually approaching 1 as X approaches 90. In this illustration, the distribution is symmetric and bell-shaped (normal or Gaussian) with a mean of 75 and a standard deviation of 5.

FIGURE 7.2

Freeway Speed Examples

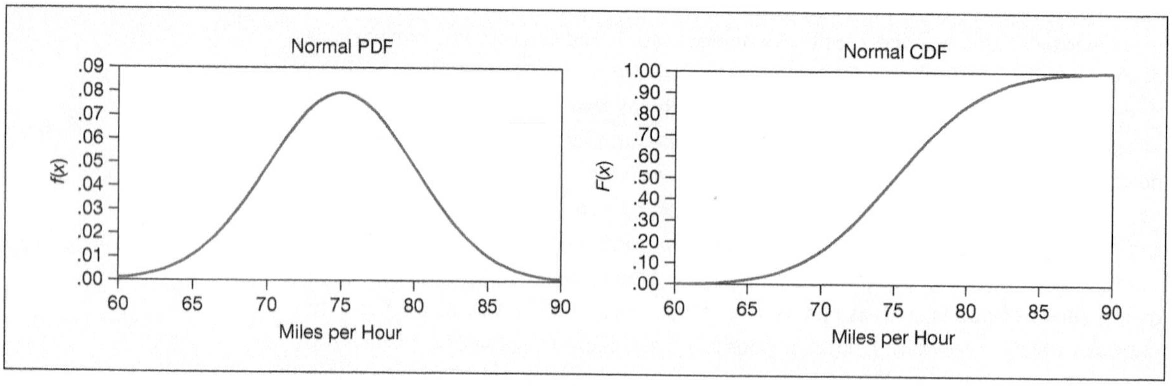

Probabilities as Areas

With discrete random variables, we take sums of probabilities over groups of points. But continuous probability functions are smooth curves, so the area *at* any point would be zero. Instead of taking sums of probabilities, we speak of *areas under curves*. In calculus terms, we would say that $P(a < X < b)$ is the **integral** of the probability density function $f(x)$ over the interval from a to b. Because $P(X = a) = 0$ the expression $P(a < X < b)$ is equal to $P(a \leq X \leq b)$. Figure 7.3 shows the area under a continuous PDF. The entire area under any PDF must be 1.

FIGURE 7.3

Probability as an Area

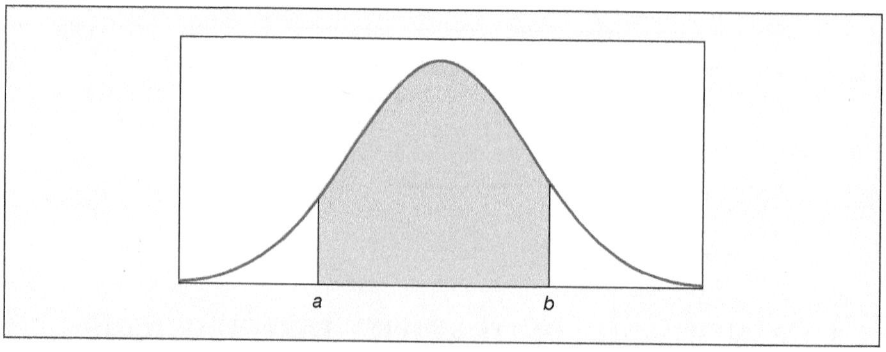

Expected Value and Variance

The mean and variance of a continuous random variable are analogous to $E(X)$ and Var(X) for a discrete random variable, except that the integral sign $\int$ replaces the summation sign Σ. Integrals are taken over all X-values. The mean is still the balancing point or fulcrum for the entire distribution, and the variance is still a measure of dispersion about the mean. The mean is still the average of all X-values weighted by their probabilities, and the variance is still the weighted average of all squared deviations around the mean. The standard deviation is still the square root of the variance.

	Continuous Random Variable	*Discrete Random Variable*	
Mean	$E(X) = \mu = \int_{-\infty}^{+\infty} x f(x)\, dx$	$E(X) = \mu = \sum_{\text{all } x} x P(x)$	**(7.1)**
Variance	$\text{Var}(X) = \sigma^2 = \int_{-\infty}^{+\infty} (x - \mu)^2 f(x)\, dx$	$\text{Var}(X) = \sigma^2 = \sum_{\text{all } x} [x - \mu]^2 P(x)$	**(7.2)**

Calculus notation is used here for the benefit of those who have studied it. But statistics can be learned without calculus, if you are willing to accept that others have worked out the details by using calculus. If you decide to become an actuary, you *will* use calculus (so don't sell your calculus book). However, in this chapter, the means and variances are presented *without* proof for the distributions that you are most likely to see applied to business situations.

SECTION EXERCISES

connect

7.1 Flight 202 is departing Los Angeles. Is each random variable discrete (D) or continuous (C)?

a. Number of airline passengers traveling with children under age 3.
b. Proportion of passengers traveling without checked luggage.
c. Weight of a randomly chosen passenger on Flight 202.

7.2 It is Saturday morning at Starbucks. Is each random variable discrete (D) or continuous (C)?

a. Temperature of the coffee served to a randomly chosen customer.
b. Number of customers who order only coffee with no food.
c. Waiting time before a randomly chosen customer is handed the order.

7.3 Which of the following could *not* be probability density functions for a continuous random variable? Explain. *Hint:* Find the area under the function $f(x)$.

a. $f(x) = .25$ for $0 \le x \le 1$
b. $f(x) = .25$ for $0 \le x \le 4$
c. $f(x) = x$ for $0 \le x \le 2$

7.4 For a continuous PDF, why can't we sum the probabilities of all x-values to get the total area under the curve?

7.2 UNIFORM CONTINUOUS DISTRIBUTION

Characteristics of the Uniform Distribution

LO 7-2

Calculate uniform probabilities.

The **uniform continuous distribution** is perhaps the simplest model one can imagine. If X is a random variable that is uniformly distributed between a and b, its PDF has constant height, as shown in Figure 7.4. The uniform continuous distribution is sometimes denoted $U(a, b)$ for short. Its mean and standard deviation are shown in Table 7.1.

Since the PDF is rectangular, you can easily verify that the area under the curve is 1 by multiplying its base $(b - a)$ by its height $1/(b - a)$. Its CDF increases linearly to 1, as shown in Figure 7.4. Since events can easily be shown as rectangular areas, we rarely need to refer to the CDF, whose formula is just $P(X \le x) = (x - a)/(b - a)$.

The continuous uniform distribution is similar to the discrete uniform distribution if the x-values cover a wide range. For example, three-digit lottery numbers ranging from 000 to 999 would closely resemble a continuous uniform with $a = 0$ and $b = 999$.

FIGURE 7.4

Uniform Distribution

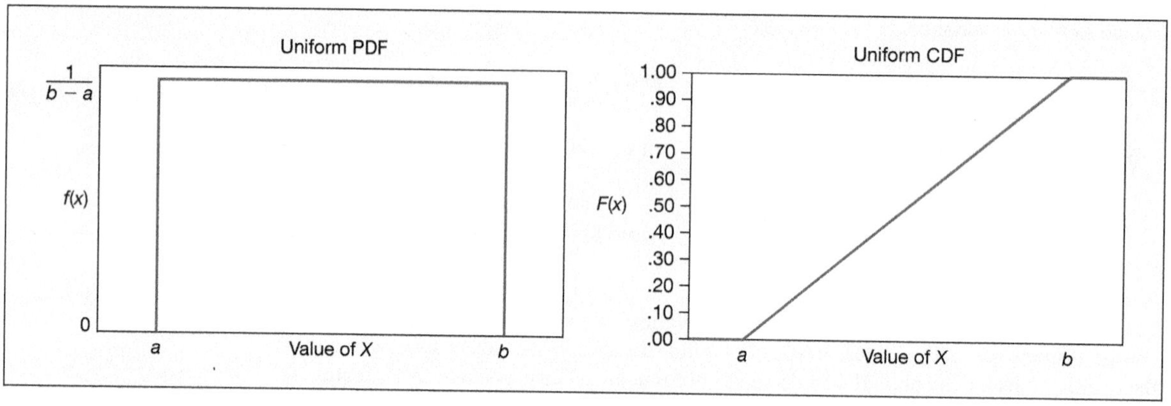

TABLE 7.1

Uniform Continuous Distribution

Parameters	a = lower limit b = upper limit
PDF	$f(x) = \dfrac{1}{b-a}$
CDF	$P(X \le x) = \dfrac{x-a}{b-a}$
Domain	$a \le x \le b$
Mean	$\dfrac{a+b}{2}$
Standard deviation	$\sqrt{\dfrac{(b-a)^2}{12}}$
Shape	Symmetric with no mode.
Random data in Excel	=a+(b–a)*RAND()
Comments	Used as a conservative what-if benchmark and in simulation.

EXAMPLE 7.1

Anesthesia Effectiveness

An oral surgeon injects a painkiller prior to extracting a tooth. Given the varying characteristics of patients, the dentist views the time for anesthesia effectiveness as a uniform random variable that takes between 15 minutes and 30 minutes. In short notation, we could say that X is $U(15, 30)$. Setting $a = 15$ and $b = 30$, we obtain the mean and standard deviation:

$$\mu = \frac{a+b}{2} = \frac{15+30}{2} = 22.5 \text{ minutes}$$

$$\sigma = \sqrt{\frac{(b-a)^2}{12}} = \sqrt{\frac{(30-15)^2}{12}} = 4.33 \text{ minutes}$$

An event probability is simply an interval width expressed as a proportion of the total. Thus, the probability of taking between c and d minutes is

(7.3) $P(c < X < d) = (d - c)/(b - a)$ (area between c and d in a uniform model)

For example, the probability that the anesthetic takes between 20 and 25 minutes is

$$P(20 < X < 25) = (25 - 20)/(30 - 15) = 5/15 = 0.3333, \text{ or } 33.3\%.$$

This situation is illustrated in Figure 7.5.

FIGURE 7.5 **Uniform Probability $P(20 < X < 25)$**

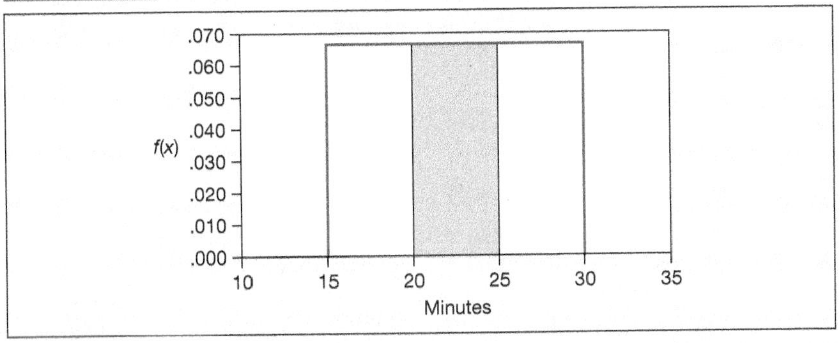

A special case of the continuous uniform distribution, denoted $U(0, 1)$, has limits $a = 0$ and $b = 1$, is shown in Figure 7.6. Using the formulas for the mean and standard deviation, you can easily show that this distribution has $\mu = 0.5000$ and $\sigma = 0.2887$. This special case is important because Excel's function =RAND() uses this distribution. If you create random numbers by using =RAND(), you know what their mean and standard deviation should be. This important distribution is discussed in more detail in later chapters on simulation and goodness-of-fit tests.

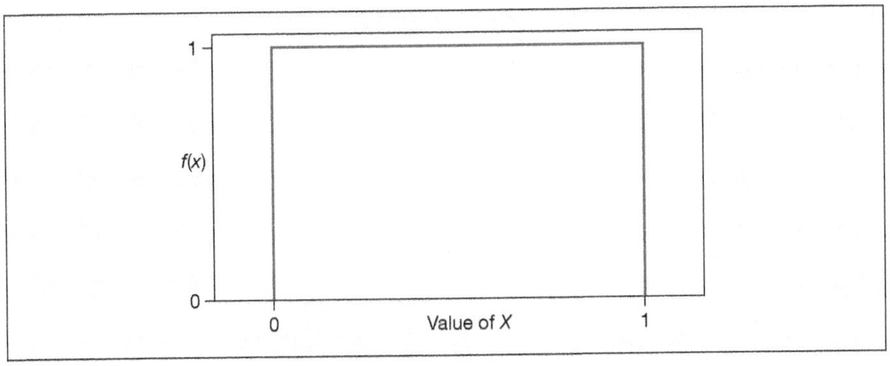

FIGURE 7.6 **Unit $U(0, 1)$ Distribution**

Uses of the Uniform Model

The uniform model $U(a, b)$ is used only when you have no reason to imagine that any X-values are more likely than others. The uniform distribution can be useful in business for what-if analysis, in situations where you know the "worst" and "best" range, but don't want to make any assumptions about the distribution in between. That may sound like a conservative approach. But bear in mind that if the data-generating situation has any central tendency at all, the assumption of a uniform distribution would lead to a higher standard deviation than might be appropriate.

SECTION EXERCISES

connect

7.5 Find the mean and standard deviation for each uniform continuous model.

a. $U(0, 10)$ b. $U(100, 200)$ c. $U(1, 99)$

7.6 Find each uniform continuous probability and sketch a graph showing it as a shaded area.

a. $P(X < 10)$ for $U(0, 50)$
b. $P(X > 500)$ for $U(0, 1{,}000)$
c. $P(25 < X < 45)$ for $U(15, 65)$

7.7 For a continuous uniform distribution, why is $P(25 < X < 45)$ the same as $P(25 \le X \le 45)$?

7.8 Assume the weight of a randomly chosen American passenger car is a uniformly distributed random variable ranging from 2,500 pounds to 4,500 pounds. (a) What is the mean weight of a randomly chosen vehicle? (b) The standard deviation? (c) What is the probability that a vehicle will weigh less than 3,000 pounds? (d) More than 4,000 pounds? (e) Between 3,000 and 4,000 pounds?

7.3 NORMAL DISTRIBUTION

Characteristics of the Normal Distribution

LO 7-3

Know the form and parameters of the normal distribution.

The **normal** or **Gaussian distribution**, named for German mathematician Karl Gauss (1777–1855), has already been mentioned several times. Its importance gives it a major role in our discussion of continuous models. A normal probability distribution is defined by two parameters, μ and σ. It is often denoted $N(\mu, \sigma)$. The domain of a normal random variable is $-\infty < x < +\infty$. However, as a practical matter, the interval $[\mu - 3\sigma, \mu + 3\sigma]$ includes almost all the area (as you know from the Empirical Rule in Chapter 4). Besides μ and σ, the normal probability density function $f(x)$ depends on the constants e (approximately 2.71828) and π (approximately 3.14159). The expected value of a normal random variable is μ and its variance is σ^2. The normal distribution is always symmetric. Table 7.2 summarizes its main characteristics.

TABLE 7.2

Normal Distribution

Parameters	μ = population mean σ = population standard deviation
PDF	$f(x) = \frac{1}{\sigma\sqrt{2\pi}} e^{-\frac{1}{2}\left(\frac{x-\mu}{\sigma}\right)^2}$
Domain	$-\infty < x < +\infty$
Mean	μ
Std. Dev.	σ
Shape	Symmetric, mesokurtic, and bell-shaped.
PDF in Excel*	=NORM.DIST(x,μ,σ,0)
CDF in Excel*	=NORM.DIST(x,μ,σ,1)
Random data in Excel	=NORM.INV(RAND(),μ,σ)

*Excel 2010's new functions =NORM.DIST(x,μ,σ, cumulative) and =NORM.INV(area,μ,σ) give the same result as =NORMDIST(x,μ,σ, cumulative) and =NORMINV(area,μ,σ).

The normal probability density function $f(x)$ reaches a maximum at μ and has points of inflection at $\mu \pm \sigma$ as shown in the left chart in Figure 7.7. Despite its appearance, $f(x)$ does not reach the X-axis beyond $\mu \pm 3\sigma$, but is merely asymptotic to it. Its single peak and symmetry cause some observers to call it "mound-shaped" or "bell-shaped." Its CDF has a "lazy-S" shape, as shown in the right chart in Figure 7.7. It approaches, but never reaches, 1.

FIGURE 7.7

Normal PDF and CDF

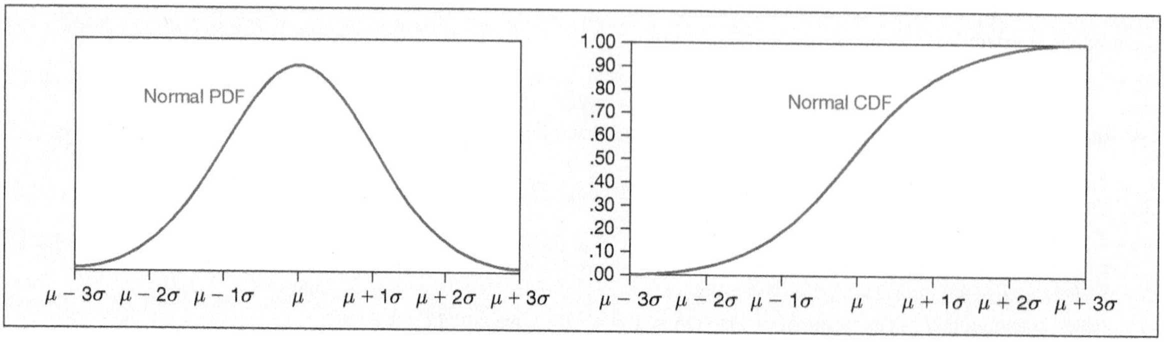

A normal distribution with mean μ and standard deviation σ is sometimes denoted $N(\mu, \sigma)$ for short. All normal distributions have the same general shape, differing only in the axis scales. For example, the left chart in Figure 7.8 shows the distribution of diameters of golf balls from a manufacturing process that produces normally distributed diameters with a mean diameter of $\mu = 42.70$ mm and a standard deviation $\sigma = 0.01$ mm, or $N(42.70, 0.01)$ in short notation. The right chart in Figure 7.8 shows the distribution of scores on the CPA theory exam, assumed to be normal with a mean of $\mu = 70$ and a standard deviation $\sigma = 10$, or $N(70, 10)$ in short notation. Although the shape of each PDF is the same, notice that the horizontal and vertical axis scales differ.

FIGURE 7.8

All Normal Distributions Look Alike Except for Scaling

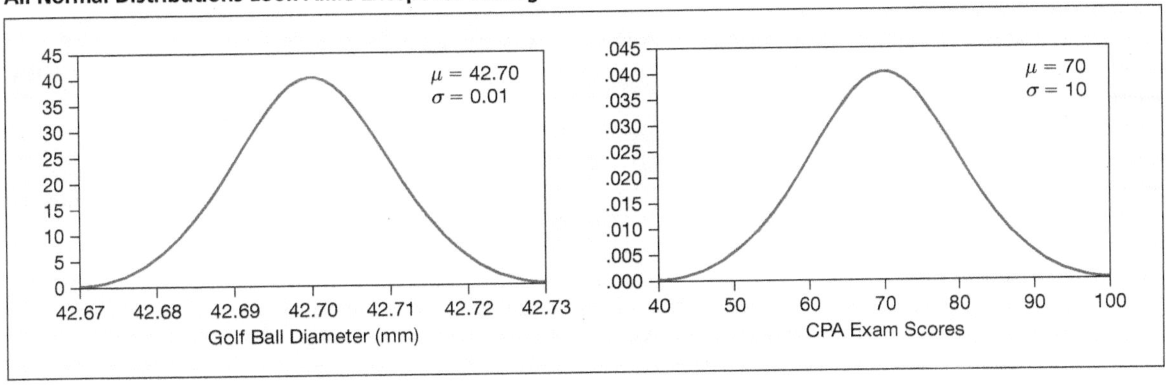

It is a common misconception that $f(x)$ must be smaller than 1, but in the left chart in Figure 7.8 you can see that this is not the case. Because the area under the entire curve must be 1, when X has a small range (e.g., the golf ball diameter range is about 0.06 mm), the height of $f(x)$ is large (about 40 for the golf ball diameters). Conversely, as shown in the right chart in Figure 7.8, when X has a large range (e.g., the CPA exam range is about 60 points), the height of $f(x)$ is small (about 0.40 for the exam scores).

What Is Normal?

Many physical measurements in engineering and the sciences resemble normal distributions. Normal random variables also can be found in economic and financial data, behavioral measurement scales, marketing research, and operations analysis. The normal distribution is especially important as a sampling distribution for estimation and hypothesis testing. To be regarded as a candidate for normality, a random variable should:

- Be measured on a continuous scale.
- Possess a clear center.
- Have only one peak (unimodal).
- Exhibit tapering tails.
- Be symmetric about the mean (equal tails).

When the range is large, we often treat a discrete variable as continuous. For example, exam scores are discrete (range from 0 to 100) but are often treated as continuous data. Here are some random variables that *might* be expected to be approximately normally distributed:

- X = quantity of beverage in a 2-liter bottle of Diet Pepsi.
- X = cockpit noise level in a Boeing 777 at the captain's left ear during cruise.
- X = diameter in millimeters of a manufactured steel ball bearing.

Each of these variables would tend toward a certain mean but would exhibit random variation. For example, even with excellent quality control, not every bottle of a soft drink will have exactly the same fill (even if the variation is only a few milliliters). The mean and standard deviation depend on the nature of the data-generating process. Precision manufacturing can achieve very small σ in relation to μ (e.g., steel ball bearing diameter), while other data-generating situations produce relatively large σ in relation to μ (e.g., your driving fuel mileage). Thus, each normally distributed random variable may have a different coefficient of variation, even though they may share a common shape.

There are statistical tests to see whether a sample came from a normal population. In Chapter 4, for example, you saw that a histogram can be used to assess normality in a general way. More precise tests will be discussed in Chapter 15. For now, our task is to learn more about the normal distribution and its applications.

SECTION EXERCISES

connect

7.9 If all normal distributions have the same shape, how do they differ?

7.10 (a) At what x value does $f(x)$ reach a maximum for a normal distribution $N(75, 5)$? (b) Does $f(x)$ touch the X-axis at $\mu \pm 3\sigma$?

7.11 State the Empirical Rule for a normal distribution (see Chapter 4).

7.12 Discuss why you would or would not expect each of the following variables to be normally distributed. *Hint:* Would you expect a single central mode and tapering tails? Would the distribution be roughly symmetric? Would one tail be longer than the other?

a. Shoe sizes of adult males.
b. Years of higher education of 30-year-old employed women.
c. Days from mailing home utility bills to receipt of payment.
d. Time to process insurance claims for residential fire damage.

7.4 STANDARD NORMAL DISTRIBUTION

Characteristics of the Standard Normal

LO 7-4

Find the normal probability for a given z or x using tables or Excel.

LO 7-5

Solve for z or x for a given normal probability using tables or Excel.

Since there is a different normal distribution for every pair of values of μ and σ, we often transform the variable by subtracting the mean and dividing by the standard deviation to produce a *standardized variable,* just as in Chapter 4, except that now we are talking about a population distribution instead of sample data. This important transformation is shown in formula 7.4.

(7.4) $$z = \frac{x - \mu}{\sigma}$$ (transformation of each x-value to a z-value)

If X is normally distributed $N(\mu, \sigma)$, the standardized variable Z has a **standard normal distribution**. Its mean is 0 and its standard deviation is 1, denoted $N(0, 1)$. The maximum height of $f(z)$ is at 0 (the mean) and its points of inflection are at ± 1 (the standard deviation). The shape of the distribution is unaffected by the z transformation. Table 7.3 summarizes the main characteristics of the standard normal distribution.

TABLE 7.3

Standard Normal Distribution

Parameters	μ = population mean σ = population standard deviation
PDF	$f(z) = \frac{1}{\sqrt{2\pi}} e^{-z^2/2}$ where $z = \frac{x - \mu}{\sigma}$
Domain	$-\infty < z < +\infty$
Mean	0
Standard deviation	1
Shape	Symmetric, mesokurtic, and bell-shaped.
CDF in Excel*	=NORM.S.DIST(z,1)
Random data in Excel	=NORM.S.INV(RAND())
Comment	There is no simple formula for a normal CDF, so we need normal tables or Excel to find areas.

*Excel 2010's new functions =NORM.S.DIST(*z*) and =NORM.S.INV(*area*) give the same result as =NORMSDIST(*z*) and =NORMSINV(*area*).

Notation

Use an uppercase variable name like Z or X when speaking in general, and a lowercase variable name like z or x to denote a particular value of Z or X.

Since every transformed normal distribution will look the same, we can use a common scale, usually labeled from −3 to +3, as shown in Figure 7.9. Since $f(z)$ is a probability density function, the entire area under the curve is 1, as you can approximately verify by treating it as a triangle (area = ½ base × height). As a rule, we are not interested in the height of the function $f(z)$ but rather in areas under the curve (although Excel will provide either). The probability of an event $P(z_1 < z < z_2)$ is a definite integral of $f(z)$. Although there is no simple integral for $f(z)$, a normal area can be approximated to any desired degree of accuracy using various methods (e.g., covering the area from 0 to $f(z)$ with many narrow rectangles and summing their areas). You do not need to worry about this because tables or Excel functions are available.

FIGURE 7.9

Standard Normal PDF and CDF

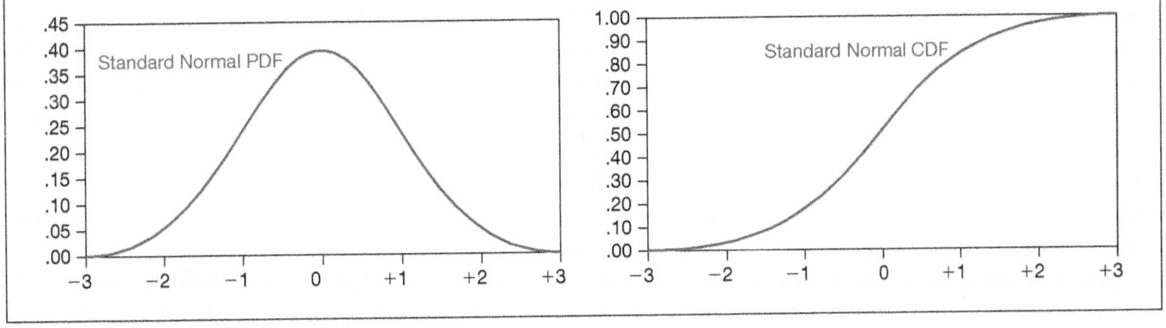

Normal Areas from Appendix C-1

Tables of normal probabilities have been prepared so you can look up any desired normal area. Such tables have many forms. Table 7.4 illustrates Appendix C-1, which shows areas from 0 to z using increments of 0.01 from $z = 0$ to $z = 3.69$ (beyond this range, areas are very small). For example, to calculate $P(0 < Z < 1.96)$, you select the row for $z = 1.9$ and the column for 0.06 (since 1.96 = 1.90 + 0.06). This row and column are shaded in Table 7.4. At the intersection of the shaded row and column, we see $P(0 < Z < 1.96) = .4750$. This area is illustrated in Figure 7.10. Since half the total area under the curve lies to the right of the mean, we can find a right-tail area by subtraction. For example, $P(Z > 1.96) = .5000 - P(0 < Z < 1.96) = .5000 - .4750 = .0250$.

Suppose we want a middle area such as $P(-1.96 < Z < +1.96)$. Because the normal distribution is symmetric, we also know that $P(-1.96 < Z < 0) = .4750$. Adding these areas, we get

$$P(-1.96 < Z < +1.96) = P(-1.96 < Z < 0) + P(0 < Z < 1.96)$$
$$= .4750 + .4750 = .9500$$

So the interval $-1.96 < Z < 1.96$ encloses 95 percent of the area under the normal curve. Figure 7.11 illustrates this calculation.

Inequalities–Strict (<) or Inclusive (≤)?

Because a point has no area in a continuous distribution, the probability $P(-1.96 \le Z \le +1.96)$ is the same as $P(-1.96 < Z < +1.96)$, so, for simplicity, we sometimes omit the equality.

TABLE 7.4

Normal Area from 0 to z (from Appendix C-1)

z	*0.00*	*0.01*	*0.02*	*0.03*	*0.04*	*0.05*	*0.06*	*0.07*	*0.08*	*0.09*
0.0	.0000	.0040	.0080	.0120	.0160	.0199	.0239	.0279	.0319	.0359
0.1	.0398	.0438	.0478	.0517	.0557	.0596	.0636	.0675	.0714	.0753
0.2	.0793	.0832	.0871	.0910	.0948	.0987	.1026	.1064	.1103	.1141
⋮	⋮	⋮	⋮	⋮	⋮	⋮	⋮	⋮	⋮	⋮
1.6	.4452	.4463	.4474	.4484	.4495	.4505	.4515	.4525	.4535	.4545
1.7	.4554	.4564	.4573	.4582	.4591	.4599	.4608	.4616	.4625	.4633
1.8	.4641	.4649	.4656	.4664	.4671	.4678	.4686	.4693	.4699	.4706
1.9	.4713	.4719	.4726	.4732	.4738	.4744	**.4750**	.4756	.4761	.4767
2.0	.4772	.4778	.4783	.4788	.4793	.4798	.4803	.4808	.4812	.4817
2.1	.4821	.4826	.4830	.4834	.4838	.4842	.4846	.4850	.4854	.4857
2.2	.4861	.4864	.4868	.4871	.4875	.4878	.4881	.4884	.4887	.4890
2.3	.4893	.4896	.4898	.4901	.4904	.4906	.4909	.4911	.4913	.4916
⋮	⋮	⋮	⋮	⋮	⋮	⋮	⋮	⋮	⋮	⋮
3.6	.49984	.49985	.49985	.49986	.49986	.49987	.49987	.49988	.49988	.49989
3.7	.49989	.49990	.49990	.49990	.49991	.49991	.49992	.49992	.49992	.49992

FIGURE 7.10

Finding Areas Using Appendix C-1

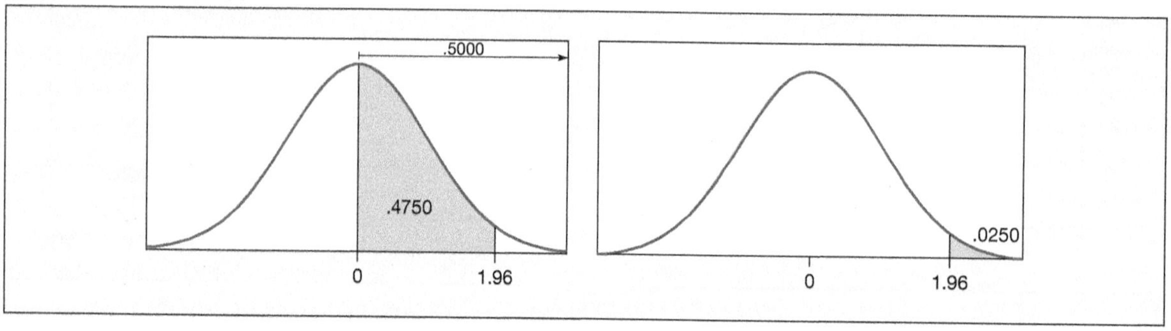

FIGURE 7.11

Finding Areas by Using Appendix C-1

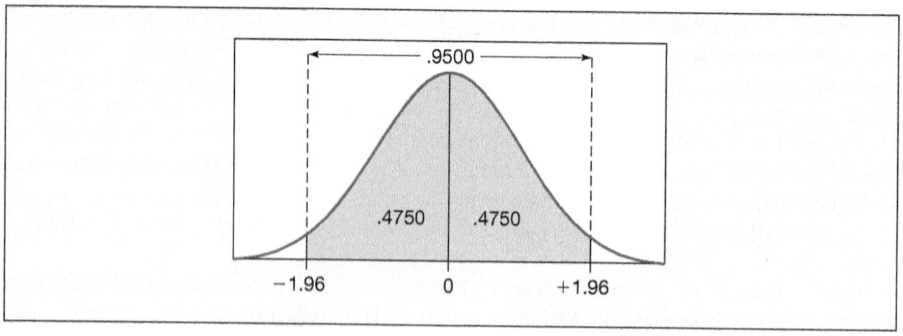

From Appendix C-1 we can see the basis for the Empirical Rule, illustrated in Figure 7.12. These are the "*k*-sigma" intervals mentioned in Chapter 4 and used by statisticians for quick reference to the normal distribution. Thus, it is *approximately* correct to say that a "2-sigma interval" contains 95 percent of the area (actually $z = 1.96$ would yield a 95 percent area):

$$P(-1.00 < Z < +1.00) = 2 \times P(0 < Z < 1.00) = 2 \times .3413 = .6826, \text{ or } 68.26\%$$

$$P(-2.00 < Z < +2.00) = 2 \times P(0 < Z < 2.00) = 2 \times .4772 = .9544, \text{ or } 95.44\%$$

$$P(-3.00 < Z < +3.00) = 2 \times P(0 < Z < 3.00) = 2 \times .49865 = .9973, \text{ or } 99.73\%$$

FIGURE 7.12

Normal Areas within $\mu \pm k\sigma$

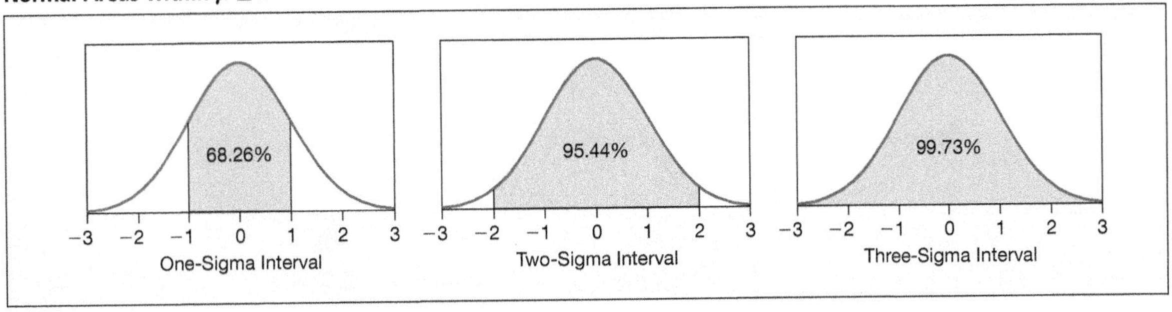

Normal Areas from Appendix C-2

Table 7.5 illustrates another kind of table. Appendix C-2 shows cumulative normal areas from the left to z. You can think of Appendix C-2 as the CDF for the normal distribution. This corresponds to the way Excel calculates normal areas. Using this approach, we see that $P(Z < -1.96) = .0250$ and $P(Z < +1.96) = .9750$. By subtraction, we get

$$P(-1.96 < Z < +1.96) = P(Z < +1.96) - P(Z < -1.96) = .9750 - .0250 = .9500$$

The result is identical to that obtained previously. The interval $-1.96 < Z < 1.96$ encloses 95 percent of the area under the normal curve. This calculation is illustrated in Figure 7.13.

Since Appendix C-1 and Appendix C-2 yield identical results, you should use whichever table is easier for the area you are trying to find. Appendix C-1 is often easier for "middle

TABLE 7.5

Cumulative Normal Area from Left to z (from Appendix C-2)

z	*0.00*	*0.01*	*0.02*	*0.03*	*0.04*	*0.05*	*0.06*	*0.07*	*0.08*	*0.09*
−3.7	.00011	.00010	.00010	.00010	.00009	.00009	.00008	.00008	.00008	.00008
−3.6	.00016	.00015	.00015	.00014	.00014	.00013	.00013	.00012	.00012	.00011
⋮	⋮	⋮	⋮	⋮	⋮	⋮	⋮	⋮	⋮	⋮
−2.3	.0107	.0104	.0102	.0099	.0096	.0094	.0091	.0089	.0087	.0084
−2.2	.0139	.0136	.0132	.0129	.0125	.0122	.0119	.0116	.0113	.0110
−2.1	.0179	.0174	.0170	.0166	.0162	.0158	.0154	.0150	.0146	.0143
−2.0	.0228	.0222	.0217	.0212	.0207	.0202	.0197	.0192	.0188	.0183
−1.9	.0287	.0281	.0274	.0268	.0262	.0256	.0250	.0244	.0239	.0233
−1.8	.0359	.0351	.0344	.0336	.0329	.0322	.0314	.0307	.0301	.0294
−1.7	.0446	.0436	.0427	.0418	.0409	.0401	.0392	.0384	.0375	.0367
−1.6	.0548	.0537	.0526	.0516	.0505	.0495	.0485	.0475	.0465	.0455
⋮	⋮	⋮	⋮	⋮	⋮	⋮	⋮	⋮	⋮	⋮
0.0	.5000	.5040	.5080	.5120	.5160	.5199	.5239	.5279	.5319	.5359
0.1	.5398	.5438	.5478	.5517	.5557	.5596	.5636	.5675	.5714	.5753
0.2	.5793	.5832	.5871	.5910	.5948	.5987	.6026	.6064	.6103	.6141
⋮	⋮	⋮	⋮	⋮	⋮	⋮	⋮	⋮	⋮	⋮
1.6	.9452	.9463	.9474	.9484	.9495	.9505	.9515	.9525	.9535	.9545
1.7	.9554	.9564	.9573	.9582	.9591	.9599	.9608	.9616	.9625	.9633
1.8	.9641	.9649	.9656	.9664	.9671	.9678	.9686	.9693	.9699	.9706
1.9	.9713	.9719	.9726	.9732	.9738	.9744	.9750	.9756	.9761	.9767
2.0	.9772	.9778	.9783	.9788	.9793	.9798	.9803	.9808	.9812	.9817
2.1	.9821	.9826	.9830	.9834	.9838	.9842	.9846	.9850	.9854	.9857
2.2	.9861	.9864	.9868	.9871	.9875	.9878	.9881	.9884	.9887	.9890
2.3	.9893	.9896	.9898	.9901	.9904	.9906	.9909	.9911	.9913	.9916
⋮	⋮	⋮	⋮	⋮	⋮	⋮	⋮	⋮	⋮	⋮
3.6	.99984	.99985	.99985	.99986	.99986	.99987	.99987	.99988	.99988	.99989
3.7	.99989	.99990	.99990	.99990	.99991	.99991	.99992	.99992	.99992	.99992

FIGURE 7.13

Finding Areas by Using Appendix C-2

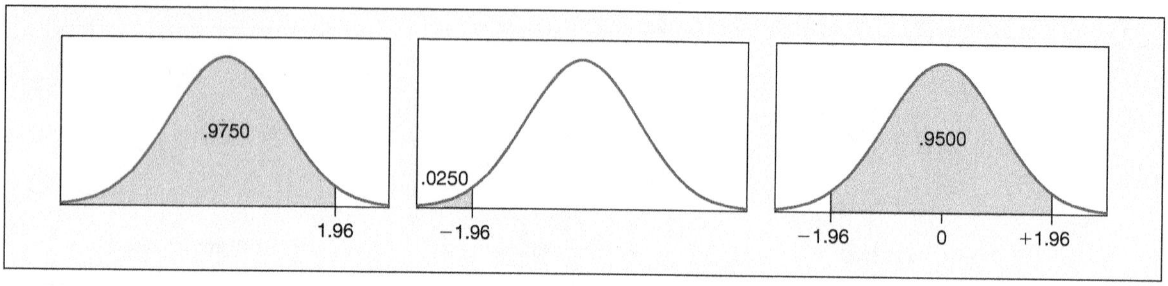

areas." It also has the advantage of being more compact (it fits on one page), which is one reason why it has traditionally been used for statistics exams and in other textbooks (e.g., marketing). But Appendix C-2 is easier for left-tail areas and some complex areas. Further, Appendix C-2 corresponds to the way Excel calculates normal areas. When subtraction is required for a right-tail or middle area, either table is equally convenient.

SECTION EXERCISES

connect

Note: Use Appendix C-1 or C-2 for these exercises.

7.13 Find the standard normal area for each of the following, showing your reasoning clearly and indicating which table you used.

a. $P(0 < Z < 0.50)$ b. $P(-0.50 < Z < 0)$ c. $P(Z > 0)$ d. $P(Z = 0)$

7.14 Find the standard normal area for each of the following, showing your reasoning clearly and indicating which table you used.

a. $P(1.22 < Z < 2.15)$ b. $P(2.00 < Z < 3.00)$ c. $P(-2.00 < Z < 2.00)$ d. $P(Z > 0.50)$

7.15 Find the standard normal area for each of the following, showing your reasoning clearly and indicating which table you used.

a. $P(-1.22 < Z < 2.15)$ b. $P(-3.00 < Z < 2.00)$ c. $P(Z < 2.00)$ d. $P(Z = 0)$

7.16 Find the standard normal area for each of the following. Sketch the normal curve and shade in the area represented below.

a. $P(Z < -1.96)$ b. $P(Z > 1.96)$ c. $P(Z < 1.65)$ d. $P(Z > -1.65)$

7.17 Find the standard normal area for each of the following. Sketch the normal curve and shade in the area represented below.

a. $P(Z < -1.28)$ b. $P(Z > 1.28)$ c. $P(-1.96 < Z < 1.96)$ d. $P(-1.65 < Z < 1.65)$

7.18 Bob's exam score was 2.17 standard deviations above the mean. The exam was taken by 200 students. Assuming a normal distribution, how many scores were higher than Bob's?

7.19 Joan's finishing time for the Bolder Boulder 10K race was 1.75 standard deviations faster than the women's average for her age group. There were 405 women who ran in her age group. Assuming a normal distribution, how many women ran faster than Joan?

Finding *z* for a Given Area

We can also use the tables to find the z-value that corresponds to a given area. For example, what z-value defines the top 1 percent of a normal distribution? Since half the area lies above the mean, an upper area of 1 percent implies that 49 percent of the area must lie between 0 and z. Searching Appendix C-1 for an area of .4900 we see that $z = 2.33$ yields an area of .4901. Without interpolation, that is as close as we can get to 49 percent. This is illustrated in Table 7.6 and Figure 7.14.

We can find other important areas in the same way. Since we are often interested in the top 25 percent, 10 percent, 5 percent, 1 percent, etc., or the middle 50 percent, 90 percent, 95 percent, 99 percent, and so forth, it is convenient to record these important z-values for quick reference.

TABLE 7.6

Normal Area from 0 to z (from Appendix C-1)

z	0.00	0.01	0.02	0.03	0.04	0.05	0.06	0.07	0.08	0.09
0.0	.0000	.0040	.0080	.0120	.0160	.0199	.0239	.0279	.0319	.0359
0.1	.0398	.0438	.0478	.0517	.0557	.0596	.0636	.0675	.0714	.0753
0.2	.0793	.0832	.0871	.0910	.0948	.0987	.1026	.1064	.1103	.1141
⋮	⋮	⋮	⋮	⋮	⋮	⋮	⋮	⋮	⋮	⋮
1.6	.4452	.4463	.4474	.4484	.4495	.4505	.4515	.4525	.4535	.4545
1.7	.4554	.4564	.4573	.4582	.4591	.4599	.4608	.4616	.4625	.4633
1.8	.4641	.4649	.4656	.4664	.4671	.4678	.4686	.4693	.4699	.4706
1.9	.4713	.4719	.4726	.4732	.4738	.4744	.4750	.4756	.4761	.4767
2.0	.4772	.4778	.4783	.4788	.4793	.4798	.4803	.4808	.4812	.4817
2.1	.4821	.4826	.4830	.4834	.4838	.4842	.4846	.4850	.4854	.4857
2.2	.4861	.4864	.4868	.4871	.4875	.4878	.4881	.4884	.4887	.4890
2.3	.4893	.4896	.4898	.4901	.4904	.4906	.4909	.4911	.4913	.4916
⋮	⋮	⋮	⋮	⋮	⋮	⋮	⋮	⋮	⋮	⋮
3.6	.49984	.49985	.49985	.49986	.49986	.49987	.49987	.49988	.49988	.49989
3.7	.49989	.49990	.49990	.49990	.49991	.49991	.49992	.49992	.49992	.49992

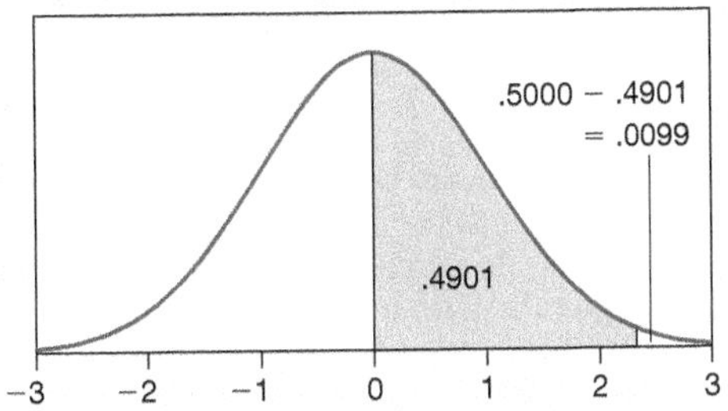

FIGURE 7.14

Finding Areas by Using Appendix C-1

TABLE 7.7

Important Normal Areas

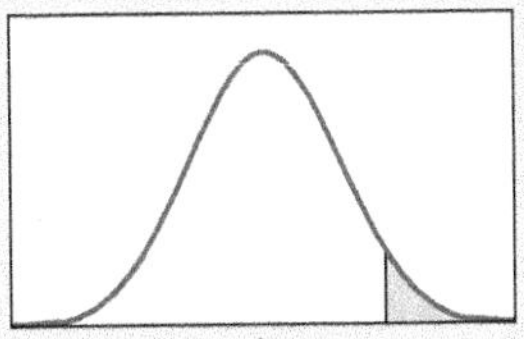

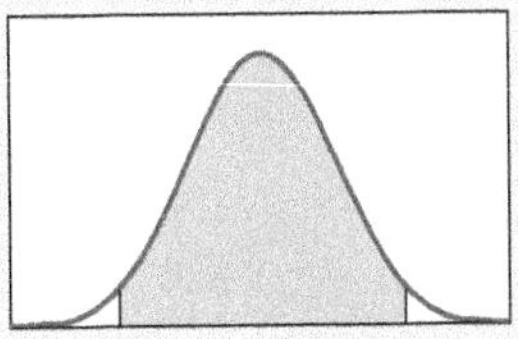

z	*Right Tail Area*	*Middle Area*
0.675	.25	.50
1.282	.10	.80
1.645	.05	.90
1.960	.025	.95
2.326	.01	.98
2.576	.005	.99

Table 7.7 summarizes some important normal areas. For greater accuracy, these z-values are shown to three decimals (they were obtained from Excel).

SECTION EXERCISES

connect

Note: For each problem below, without interpolating you may only be able to approximate the actual area.

7.20 Find the associated z-score for each of the following standard normal areas.

a. Highest 10 percent b. Lowest 50 percent c. Highest 7 percent

7.21 Find the associated z-score for each of the following standard normal areas.
a. Lowest 6 percent b. Highest 40 percent c. Lowest 7 percent

7.22 Find the associated z-score or scores that represent the following standard normal areas.
a. Middle 50 percent b. Lowest 5 percent c. Middle 90 percent

7.23 Find the associated z-score or scores that represent the following standard normal areas.
a. Middle 60 percent b. Highest 2 percent c. Middle 95 percent

7.24 High school students across the nation compete in a financial capability challenge each year by taking a National Financial Capability Challenge Exam. Students who score in the top 20 percent are recognized publicly for their achievement by the Department of the Treasury. Assuming a normal distribution, how many standard deviations above the mean does a student have to score to be publicly recognized?

7.25 The fastest 10 percent of runners who complete the Nosy Neighbor 5K race win a gift certificate to a local running store. Assuming a normal distribution, how many standard deviations below the mean must a runner's time be in order to win the gift certificate?

Finding Areas by Using Standardized Variables

John took an economics exam and scored 86 points. The class mean was 75 with a standard deviation of 7. What percentile is John in? That is, what is $P(X < 86)$? We need first to calculate John's standardized Z-score:

$$z_{\text{John}} = \frac{x_{\text{John}} - \mu}{\sigma} = \frac{86 - 75}{7} = \frac{11}{7} = 1.57$$

This says that John's score is 1.57 standard deviations above the mean. From Appendix C-2 we get $P(X < 86) = P(Z < 1.57) = .9418$, so John is approximately in the 94th percentile. That means that his score was better than 94 percent of the class, as illustrated in Figure 7.15. The table gives a slightly different value from Excel due to rounding.

FIGURE 7.15
Two Equivalent Areas

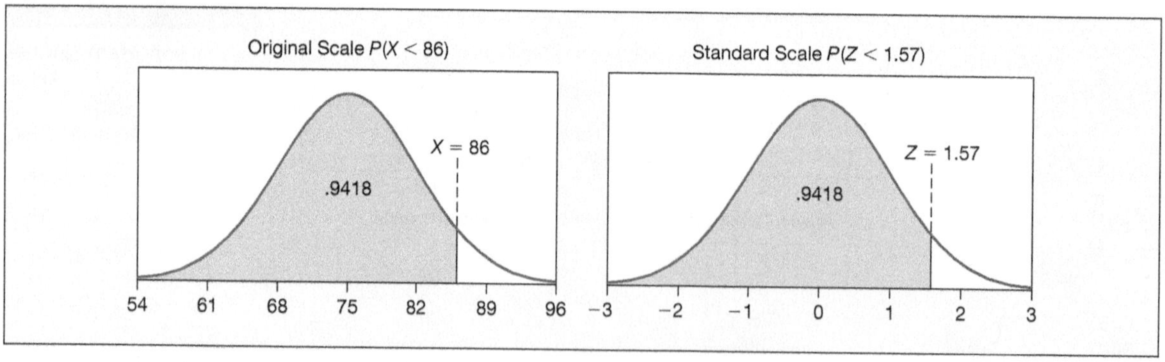

On this exam, what is the probability that a randomly chosen test-taker would have a score of at least 65? We begin by standardizing:

$$z = \frac{x - \mu}{\sigma} = \frac{65 - 75}{7} = \frac{-10}{7} = -1.43$$

Using Appendix C-1 we can calculate $P(X \geq 65) = P(Z \geq -1.43)$ as

$$\begin{aligned} P(Z \geq -1.43) &= P(-1.43 < Z < 0) + .5000 \\ &= .4236 + .5000 = .9236, \text{ or } 92.4\% \end{aligned}$$

Using Appendix C-2 we can calculate $P(X \geq 65) = P(Z \geq -1.43)$ as

$$P(Z \geq -1.43) = 1 - P(Z < -1.43) = 1 - .0764 = .9236, \text{ or } 92.4\%$$

FIGURE 7.16

Two Ways to Find an Area

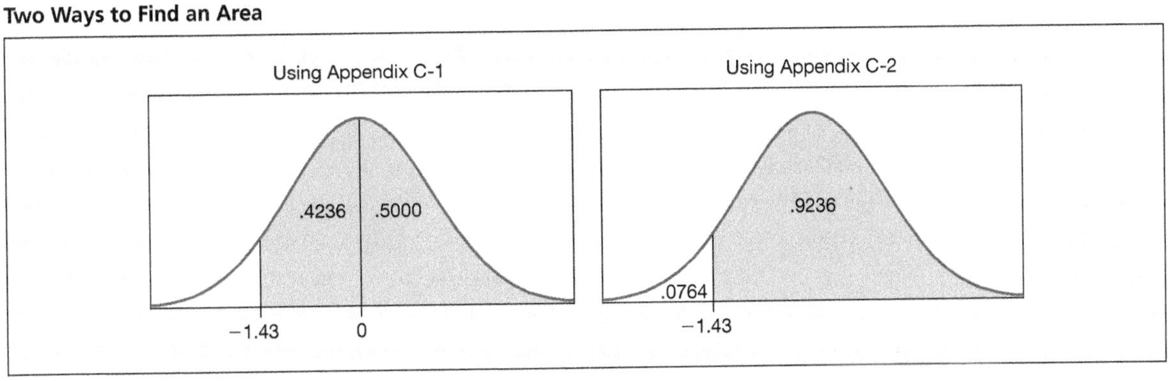

Using either method, there is a 92.4 percent chance that a student scores 65 or above on this exam. These calculations are illustrated in Figure 7.16.

Finding Normal Areas with Excel

Excel offers several functions for the normal and standard normal distributions, as shown in Figure 7.17.

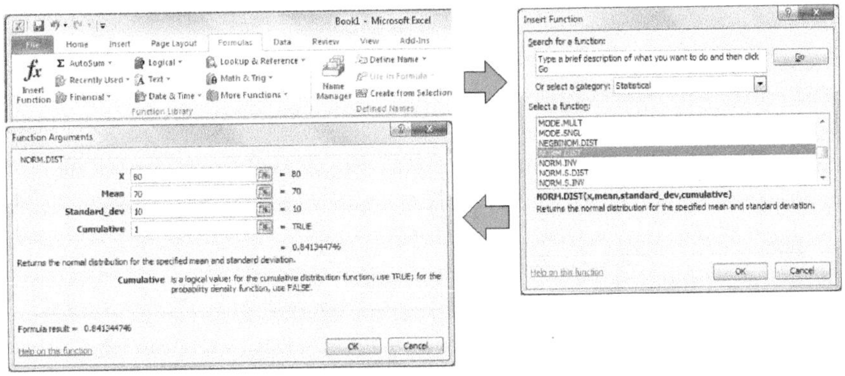

FIGURE 7.17

Inserting Excel Normal Functions

Table 7.8 illustrates Excel functions that return left-tail normal areas for a given value of x or z. Excel is more accurate than a table; however, you must be careful of syntax. It is a good idea to sketch a normal curve and shade the desired area to help you *visualize* the answer you expect, so that you will recognize if you are getting an unreasonable answer from Excel. In Table 7.8, note that the cumulative argument is set to 1 (or TRUE) because we want the CDF (left-tail area) rather than the PDF (height of the normal curve).

TABLE 7.8

Excel Normal CDF Functions

	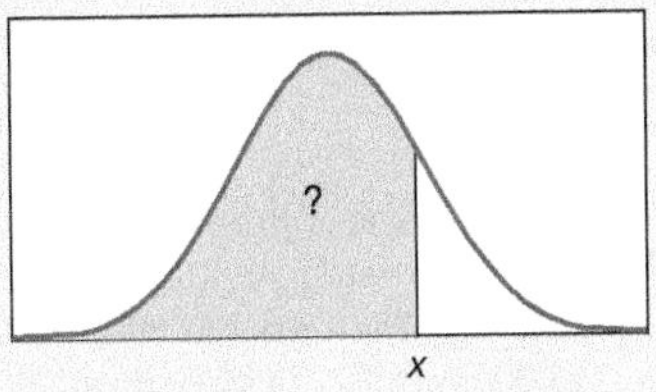 	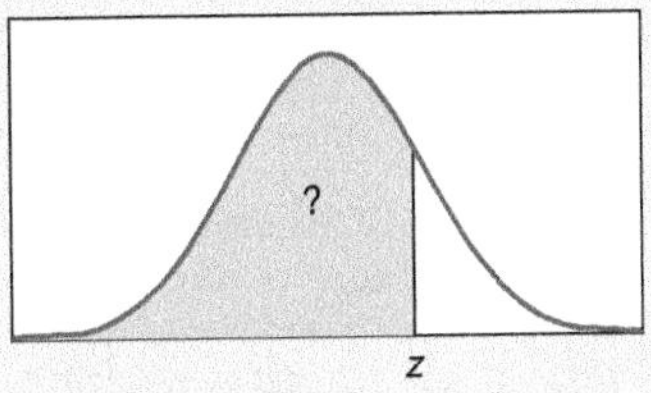
Syntax:	=NORM.DIST(x, μ, σ, cumulative)	=NORM.S.DIST(z,1)
Example:	=NORM.DIST(80,75,7,1) = 0.762475	=NORM.S.DIST(1.96.1) = 0.975002
What it does:	Area to the left of x for given μ and σ. Here, 76.25% of the exam-takers score 80 or less if $\mu = 75$ and $\sigma = 7$.	Area to the left of z in a standard normal. Here, we see that 97.50% of the area is to the left of $z = 1.96$.

Excel's NORM.DIST and NORM.INV functions let us evaluate areas and inverse areas *without* standardizing. For example, let X be the diameter of a manufactured steel ball bearing whose mean diameter is $\mu = 2.040$ cm and whose standard deviation $\sigma = .001$ cm. What is the probability that a given steel bearing will have a diameter between 2.039 and 2.042 cm? We use Excel's function =NORM.DIST(x,μ,σ,cumulative) where cumulative is TRUE.

Since Excel gives left-tail areas, we first calculate $P(X < 2.039)$ and $P(X < 2.042)$ as in Figure 7.18. We then obtain the area between by subtraction, as illustrated in Figure 7.19. The desired area is approximately 81.9 percent. Of course, we could do exactly the same thing by using Appendix C-2:

$$P(2.039 < X < 2.042) = P(X < 2.042) - P(X < 2.039)$$
$$= \text{NORM.DIST}(2.042,2.04,.001,1) - \text{NORM.DIST}(2.039,2.04,.001,1)$$
$$= .9772 - .1587 = .8185, \text{ or } 81.9\%$$

FIGURE 7.18

Left-Tail Areas Using Excel Normal CDF

Excel's $P(X < 2.039)$ | Excel's $P(X < 2.042)$

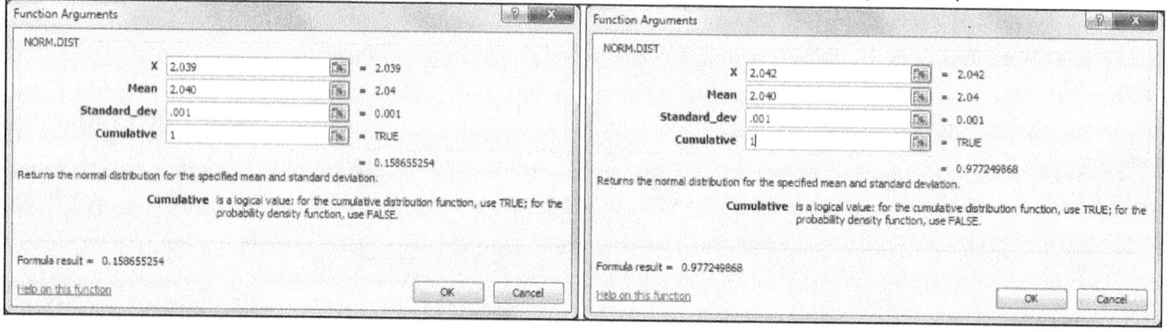

FIGURE 7.19

Cumulative Areas from Excel's NORM.DIST

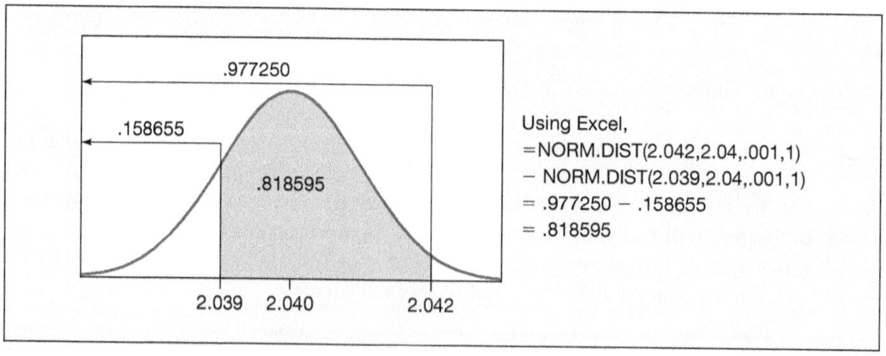

SECTION EXERCISES

connect

7.26 Daily output of Marathon's Garyville, Lousiana, refinery is normally distributed with a mean of 232,000 barrels of crude oil per day with a standard deviation of 7,000 barrels. (a) What is the probability of producing at least 232,000 barrels? (b) Between 232,000 and 239,000 barrels? (c) Less than 239,000 barrels? (d) Less than 245,000 barrels? (e) More than 225,000 barrels?

7.27 Assume that the number of calories in a McDonald's Egg McMuffin is a normally distributed random variable with a mean of 290 calories and a standard deviation of 14 calories. (a) What is the probability that a particular serving contains fewer than 300 calories? (b) More than 250 calories? (c) Between 275 and 310 calories? Show all work clearly. (Data are from McDonalds.com)

7.28 The weight of a miniature Tootsie Roll is normally distributed with a mean of 3.30 grams and standard deviation of 0.13 gram. (a) Within what weight range will the middle 95 percent of all miniature Tootsie Rolls fall? (b) What is the probability that a randomly chosen miniature Tootsie Roll will weigh more than 3.50 grams? (Data are from a project by MBA student Henry Scussel.)

7.29 The pediatrics unit at Carver Hospital has 24 beds. The number of patients needing a bed at any point in time is $N(19.2, 2.5)$. What is the probability that the number of patients needing a bed will exceed the pediatric unit's bed capacity?

7.30 The cabin of a business jet has a cabin height 5 feet 9 inches high. If a business traveler's height is $N(5'10'', 2.7'')$, what percentage of the business travelers will have to stoop?

7.31 On January 1, 2011, a new standard for baseball bat "liveliness" called BBCOR (Ball-Bat Coefficient of Restitution) was adopted for teams playing under NCAA rules. A higher BBCOR allows the ball to travel farther when hit, so bat manufacturers want a high BBCOR. The maximum allowable BBCOR is 0.500. BigBash Inc. produces bats whose BBCOR is $N(0.480, 0.008)$. What percentage of their bats will exceed the BBCOR standard? (See http://batrollingblog.com.)

7.32 Last year's freshman class at Big State University totaled 5,324 students. Of those, 1,254 received a merit scholarship to help offset tuition costs their freshman year (although the amount varied per student). The amount a student received was $N(\$3{,}456, \$478)$. If the cost of tuition was \$4,200 last year, what percentage of students did *not* receive enough to cover their full tuition?

Inverse Normal

How can we find the various normal percentiles (5th, 10th, 25th, 75th, 90th, 95th, etc.) known as the **inverse normal**? That is, how can we find X for a given area? We simply turn the standardizing transformation around:

$$x = \mu + z\sigma \qquad \left(\text{solving for } x \text{ in } z = \frac{x - \mu}{\sigma}\right) \tag{7.5}$$

Using Table 7.7 (or looking up the areas in Excel) we obtain the results shown in Table 7.9. Note that to find a lower tail area (such as the lowest 5 percent), we must use negative Z-values.

TABLE 7.9 Percentiles for Desired Normal Area

Percentile	z	$x = \mu + z\sigma$	x (to nearest integer)
95th (highest 5%)	1.645	$x = 75 + (1.645)(7)$	86.52, or 87 (rounded)
90th (highest 10%)	1.282	$x = 75 + (1.282)(7)$	83.97, or 84 (rounded)
75th (highest 25%)	0.675	$x = 75 + (0.675)(7)$	79.73, or 80 (rounded)
25th (lowest 25%)	−0.675	$x = 75 - (0.675)(7)$	70.28, or 70 (rounded)
10th (lowest 10%)	−1.282	$x = 75 - (1.282)(7)$	66.03, or 66 (rounded)
5th (lowest 5%)	−1.645	$x = 75 - (1.645)(7)$	63.49, or 63 (rounded)

Using the two Excel functions =NORM.INV() and =NORM.S.INV() shown in Table 7.10, we can solve for the value of x or z that corresponds to a given normal area. Also, for a given area and x, we might want to solve for μ or σ.

TABLE 7.10 Excel Inverse Normal Functions

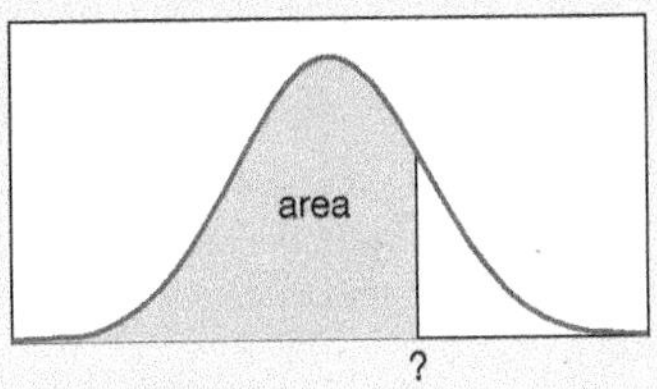

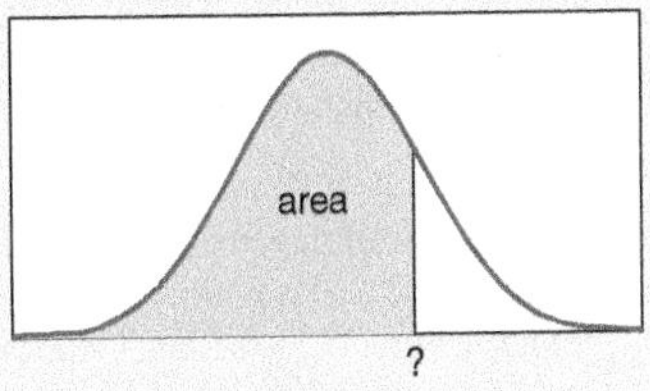

Syntax:	=NORM.INV(area, μ, σ)	=NORM.S.INV(area)
Example:	=NORM.INV(0.99,75,7) = 91.2844	=NORM.S.INV(0.75) = 0.674490
What it does:	Value of x for given left-tail area. If $\mu = 75$ and $\sigma = 7$, the 99th percentile for exam-takers is a score of 91.28 or 91 to the nearest integer.	Value of z corresponding to a given left-tail area. Here, the 75th percentile (third quartile) of a standard normal is $z = 0.675$.

For example, suppose that John's economics professor has decided that any student who scores below the 10th percentile must retake the exam. The exam scores are normal with $\mu = 75$ and $\sigma = 7$. What is the score that would require a student to retake the exam? We need to find the value of x that satisfies $P(X < x) = .10$. The approximate z-score for the 10th percentile is $z = -1.28$. The steps to solve the problem are:

- Use Appendix C or Excel to find $z = -1.28$ to satisfy $P(Z < -1.28) = .10$.
- Substitute the given information into $z = \dfrac{x - \mu}{\sigma}$ to get $-1.28 = \dfrac{x - 75}{7}$.
- Solve for x to get $x = 75 - (1.28)(7) = 66.04$ (or 66 after rounding)

Students who score below 66 points on the economics exam will be required to retake the exam.

SECTION EXERCISES

connect

7.33 The time required to verify and fill a common prescription at a neighborhood pharmacy is normally distributed with a mean of 10 minutes and a standard deviation of 3 minutes. Find the time for each event. Show your work.

a. Highest 10 percent
b. Middle 50 percent
c. Highest 80 percent
d. Lowest 10 percent

7.34 The time required to cook a pizza at a neighborhood pizza joint is normally distributed with a mean of 12 minutes and a standard deviation of 2 minutes. Find the time for each event. Show your work.

a. Highest 5 percent
b. Lowest 50 percent
c. Middle 95 percent
d. Lowest 80 percent

7.35 The weight of a McDonald's cheeseburger is normally distributed with a mean of 114 ounces and a standard deviation of 7 ounces. Find the weight that corresponds to each event. Show your work.

a. Highest 5 percent
b. Lowest 50 percent
c. Middle 95 percent
d. Lowest 80 percent

7.36 The weight of a small Starbucks coffee is a normally distributed random variable with a mean of 360 grams and a standard deviation of 9 grams. Find the weight that corresponds to each event. Show your work.

a. Highest 10 percent
b. Middle 50 percent
c. Highest 80 percent
d. Lowest 10 percent

7.37 The weights of newborn babies in Foxboro Hospital are normally distributed with a mean of 6.9 pounds and a standard deviation of 1.2 pounds. (a) How unusual is a baby weighing 8.0 pounds or more? (b) What would be the 90th percentile for birth weight? (c) Within what range would the middle 95 percent of birth weights lie?

7.38 The credit scores of 35-year-olds applying for a mortgage at Ulysses Mortgage Associates are normally distributed with a mean of 600 and a standard deviation of 100. (a) Find the credit score that defines the upper 5 percent. (b) Seventy-five percent of the customers will have a credit score higher than what value? (c) Within what range would the middle 80 percent of credit scores lie?

7.39 The number of patients needing a bed at any point in time in the pediatrics unit at Carver Hospital is $N(19.2, 2.5)$. Find the middle 50 percent of the number of beds needed (round to the next higher integer since a "bed" is indivisible).

7.40 Vail Resorts pays part-time seasonal employees at ski resorts on an hourly basis. At a certain mountain, the hourly rates have a normal distribution with $\sigma = \$3.00$. If 20 percent of all part-time seasonal employees make more than \$13.16 an hour, what is the average hourly pay rate at this mountain?

7.41 The average cost of an IRS Form 1040 tax filing at Thetis Tax Service is \$157.00. Assuming a normal distribution, if 70 percent of the filings cost less than \$171.00, what is the standard deviation?

EXAMPLE 7.2

Service Times in a Quick Oil Change Shop: Four Worked Problems

After studying the process of changing oil, the shop's manager has found that the distribution of service times, X, is normal with a mean $\mu = 28$ minutes and a standard deviation $\sigma = 5$ minutes, that is, $X \sim N(28, 5)$. This information can now be used to answer questions about normal probabilities.

To answer these types of questions it is helpful to follow a few basic steps. (1) Draw a picture and label the picture with the information you know. (2) Shade in the area that will answer your question. (3) Standardize the random variable. (4) Find the area by using one of the tables or Excel.

Worked Problem #1 *What proportion of cars will be finished in less than half an hour?*

- **Steps 1 and 2:** Draw a picture and shade the area to the left of 30 minutes.

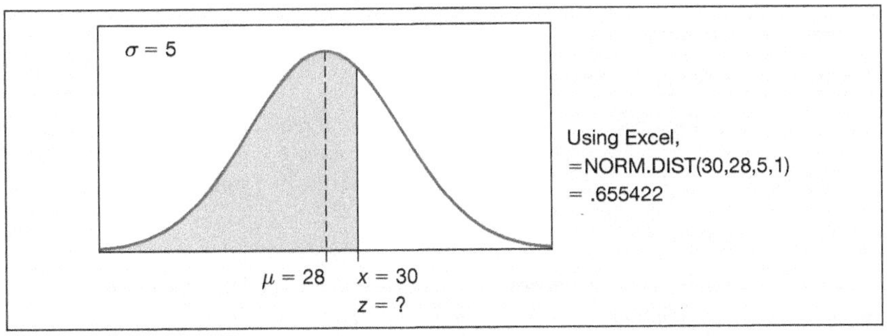

- **Step 3:** $z = \dfrac{30 - 28}{5} = 0.40$
- **Step 4:** Using Appendix C-2 or Excel we find that $P(Z < 0.40) = .6554$.

Approximately 66 percent of the cars will be finished in less than half an hour.

Worked Problem # 2 *What is the chance that a randomly selected car will take longer than 40 minutes to complete?*

- **Steps 1 and 2:** Draw a picture and shade the area to the right of 40 minutes.

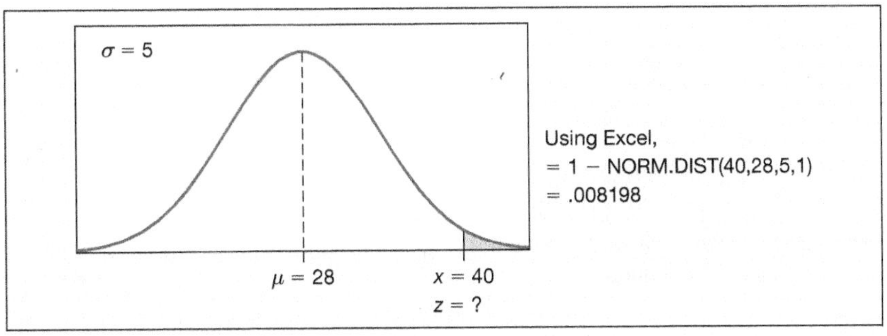

- **Step 3:** $z = \dfrac{40 - 28}{5} = 2.4$
- **Step 4:** Using Appendix C-2 or Excel we find that $P(Z > 2.4) = 1 - P(Z \leq 2.4) = 1 - .9918 = .0082$.

There is less than a 1 percent chance that a car will take longer than 40 minutes to complete.

Worked Problem # 3 *What service time corresponds to the 90th percentile?*

- **Steps 1 and 2:** Draw a picture and shade the desired area.

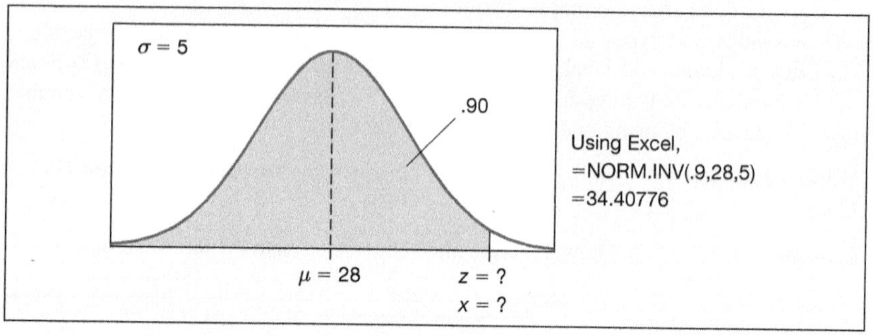

In this case, steps 3 and 4 need to be reversed.

- **Step 3:** Find $z = 1.28$ by using the tables or Excel.
- **Step 4:** $1.28 = \dfrac{x - 28}{5}$, so $x = 28 + 5(1.28) = 34.4$ minutes.

Ninety percent of the cars will be finished in 34.4 minutes or less.

Worked Problem #4 *The manager wants to be able to service 80 percent of the vehicles within 30 minutes. What must the mean service time be to accomplish this goal?*

- **Steps 1 and 2:** Draw a curve and shade the desired area.

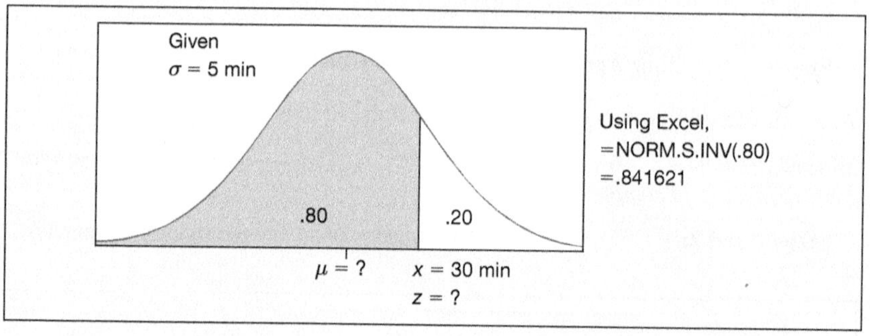

- **Step 3:** Use tables or Excel to find $z = 0.84$ (approximately) for an upper tail area of .20 (lower tail area of .80).
- **Step 4:** Substitute into $z = \dfrac{x - \mu}{\sigma}$ to get $0.84 = \dfrac{30 - \mu}{5}$ and solve for $\mu = 30 - 0.84(5) = 25.8$.

The mean service time would have to be 25.8 minutes to ensure that 80 percent are serviced within 30 minutes.

SECTION EXERCISES

connect

7.42 Use Excel to find each probability.

a. $P(X < 110)$ for $N(100, 15)$
b. $P(X < 2.00)$ for $N(0, 1)$
c. $P(X < 5{,}000)$ for $N(6000, 1000)$
d. $P(X < 450)$ for $N(600, 100)$

7.43 Use Excel to find each probability.

a. $P(80 < X < 110)$ for $N(100, 15)$
b. $P(1.50 < X < 2.00)$ for $N(0, 1)$
c. $P(4{,}500 < X < 7{,}000)$ for $N(6000, 1000)$
d. $P(225 < X < 450)$ for $N(600, 100)$

7.44 The weight of a small Starbucks coffee is a normal random variable with a mean of 360 g and a standard deviation of 9 g. Use Excel to find the weight corresponding to each percentile of weight.

a. 10th percentile b. 32nd percentile c. 75th percentile
d. 90th percentile e. 99.9th percentile f. 99.99th percentile

7.45 A study found that the mean waiting time to see a physician at an outpatient clinic was 40 minutes with a standard deviation of 28 minutes. Use Excel to find each probability. (a) What is the probability of more than an hour's wait? (b) Less than 20 minutes? (c) At least 10 minutes.

7.46 High-strength concrete is supposed to have a compressive strength greater than 6,000 pounds per square inch (psi). A certain type of concrete has a mean compressive strength of 7,000 psi, but due to variability in the mixing process it has a standard deviation of 420 psi. Assume a normal distribution. What is the probability that a given pour of concrete from this mixture will fail to meet the high-strength criterion? In your judgment, does this mixture provide an adequate margin of safety?

7.5 NORMAL APPROXIMATIONS

Normal Approximation to the Binomial

LO 7-6

Use the normal approximation to a binomial or a Poisson.

We have seen that (unless we are using Excel) binomial probabilities may be difficult to calculate when n is large, particularly when many terms must be summed. Instead, we can use a normal approximation. The logic of this approximation is that as n becomes large, the discrete binomial bars become more like a smooth, continuous, normal curve. Figure 7.20 illustrates this idea for 4, 16, and 64 flips of a fair coin with X defined as the number of heads in n tries. As sample size increases, it becomes easier to visualize a smooth, bell-shaped curve overlaid on the bars.

As a rule of thumb, when $n\pi \geq 10$ and $n(1 - \pi) \geq 10$, it is safe to use the normal approximation to the binomial, setting the normal μ and σ equal to the binomial mean and standard deviation:

$$\mu = n\pi \qquad (7.6)$$

$$\sigma = \sqrt{n\pi(1 - \pi)} \qquad (7.7)$$

FIGURE 7.20

Binomial Approaches Normal as n Increases

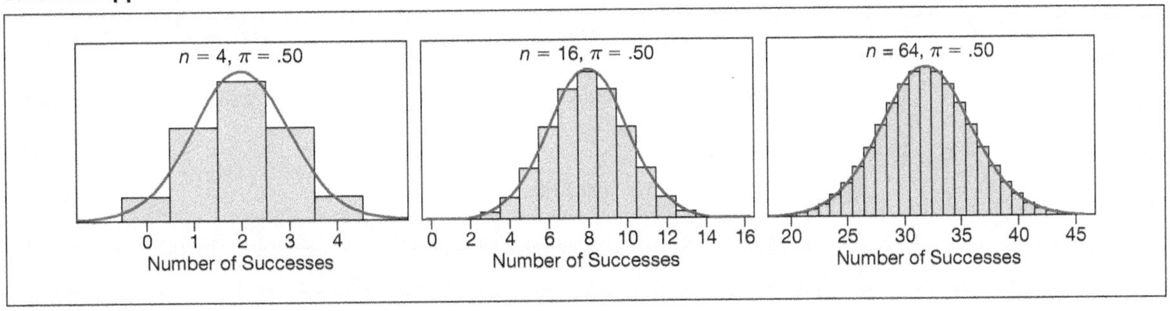

EXAMPLE 7.3

Coin Flips

What is the probability of more than 17 heads in 32 flips of a fair coin? In binomial terms, this would be $P(X \geq 18) = P(18) + P(19) + \cdots + P(32)$, which would be a tedious sum even if we had a table. Could the normal approximation be used? With $n = 32$ and $\pi = .50$, we clearly meet the requirement that $n\pi \geq 10$ and $n(1 - \pi) \geq 10$. However, when translating a discrete scale into a continuous scale we must be careful about individual points. The event "more than 17" actually falls halfway *between* 17 and 18 on a discrete scale, as shown in Figure 7.21.

You don't need to draw the entire distribution. All you need is a little diagram (ignoring the low and high ends of the scale since they are not relevant) to show the event "more than 17" visually:

. . . 14 15 16 17 *18 19 20 21 22 23* . . .

FIGURE 7.21 **Normal Approximation to $P(X \geq 18)$**

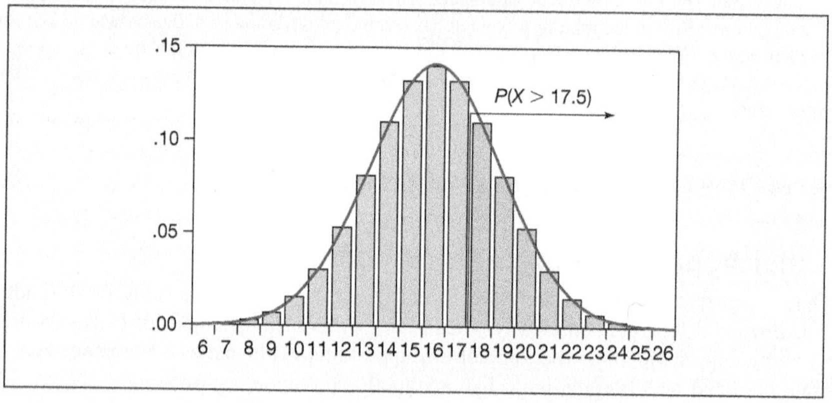

If you make a diagram like this, you can *see* the correct cutoff point. Since the cutoff point for "more than 17" is halfway between 17 and 18, the normal approximation is $P(X > 17.5)$. The 0.5 is an adjustment called the **continuity correction**. The normal parameters are

$$\mu = n\pi = (32)(0.5) = 16$$

$$\sigma = \sqrt{n\pi(1-\pi)} = \sqrt{(32)(0.5)(1-0.5)} = 2.82843$$

We then perform the usual standardizing transformation with the continuity-corrected X-value:

$$z = \frac{x-\mu}{\sigma} = \frac{17.5-16}{2.82843} = .53$$

From Appendix C-1 we find $P(Z > .53) = .5000 - P(0 < Z < .53) = .5000 - .2019 = .2981$. Alternately, we could use Appendix C-2 to get $P(Z > .53)$ which, by the symmetry of the normal distribution, is the same as $P(Z < -.53) = .2981$. The calculations are illustrated in Figure 7.22.

FIGURE 7.22 **Normal Area for $P(Z > .53)$**

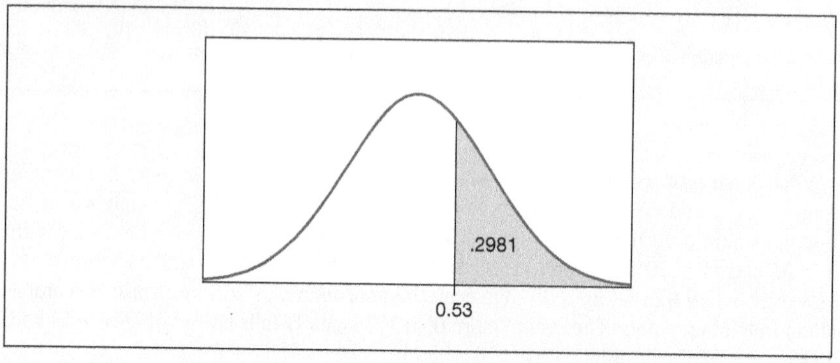

How accurate is this normal approximation to the binomial $P(X \geq 18)$ in our coin flip example? We can check it by using Excel. Since Excel's function is cumulative to the left, we find $P(X \leq 17)$ with the Excel function =BINOM.DIST(17,32,0.5,1) and then subtract from 1:

$$P(X \geq 18) = 1 - P(X \leq 17) = 1 - .7017 = .2983$$

In this case, the normal approximation (.2981) is very close to the binomial probability (.2983), partly because this binomial is roughly symmetric (π is near .50). The rule of thumb results in an error of less than .01 in the approximation. (For a demonstration of this result see *LearningStats* and other Learning Resources at the end of this chapter.)

When a binomial distribution is badly skewed (π near 0 or 1), the normal approximation is less accurate, *ceteris paribus*. But when n is large, the normal approximation improves, regardless of π. In a *right-skewed* binomial (when $\pi < .50$), the rule $n\pi \geq 10$ ensures that the mean $\mu = n\pi$ is far enough above 0 to prevent severe truncation. In a *left-skewed* binomial distribution (when $\pi > .50$), the rule that $n(1 - \pi) \geq 10$ guards against severe truncation at the upper end of the scale by making sure that the mean is well below n. That is why both rules are needed.

To be sure you understand the continuity correction, consider the events in the table below. We sketch a diagram to find the correct cutoff point to approximate a discrete model with a continuous one.

Event	*Relevant Values of X*	*Normal Cutoff*
At least 17	. . . 14 15 16 ***17 18 19 20*** . . .	Use $x = 16.5$
More than 15	. . . 14 15 ***16 17 18 19 20*** . . .	Use $x = 15.5$
Fewer than 19	. . . ***14 15 16 17 18*** 19 20 . . .	Use $x = 18.5$

SECTION EXERCISES

Note: Use Appendix C-2 for these exercises.

7.47 The default rate on government-guaranteed student loans at a certain public four-year institution is 7 percent. (a) If 1,000 student loans are made, what is the probability of fewer than 50 defaults? (b) More than 100? Show your work carefully.

7.48 In a certain store, there is a .03 probability that the scanned price in the bar code scanner will not match the advertised price. The cashier scans 800 items. (a) What is the expected number of mismatches? The standard deviation? (b) What is the probability of at least 20 mismatches? (c) What is the probability of more than 30 mismatches? Show your calculations clearly.

7.49 The probability is .90 that a vending machine in the Oxnard University Student Center will dispense the desired item when correct change is inserted. If 200 customers try the machine, find the probability that (a) at least 175 will receive the desired item and (b) that fewer than 190 will receive the desired item. Explain.

7.50 When confronted with an in-flight medical emergency, pilots and crew can consult staff physicians at a global response center located in Arizona. If the global response center is called, there is a 4.8 percent chance that the flight will be diverted for an immediate landing. Suppose the response center is called 8,465 times in a given year. (a) What is the expected number of diversions? (b) What is the probability of at least 400 diversions? (c) Fewer than 450 diversions? Show your work carefully.

Normal Approximation to the Poisson

The normal approximation for the Poisson works best when λ is fairly large. If you can't find λ in Appendix B (which only goes up to $\lambda = 20$), you are reasonably safe in using the normal approximation. Some textbooks allow the approximation when $\lambda \geq 10$, which is comparable to the rule that the binomial mean must be at least 10. To use the normal approximation to the Poisson we set the normal μ and σ equal to the Poisson mean and standard deviation:

$$\mu = \lambda \tag{7.8}$$

$$\sigma = \sqrt{\lambda} \tag{7.9}$$

EXAMPLE 7.4

Utility Bills

On Wednesday between 10 a.m. and noon, customer billing inquiries arrive at a mean rate of 42 inquiries per hour at Consumers Energy. What is the probability of receiving more than 50 calls? Call arrivals presumably follow a Poisson model, but the mean $\lambda = 42$ is too large to use Appendix B. The formula would entail an infinite sum $P(51) + P(52) + \cdots$ whose terms gradually become negligible (recall that the Poisson has no upper limit), but the calculation would be tedious at best. However, the normal approximation is simple. We set

$$\mu = \lambda = 42$$
$$\sigma = \sqrt{\lambda} = \sqrt{42} = 6.48074$$

The continuity-corrected cutoff point for $X \geq 51$ is $X = 50.5$ (halfway between 50 and 51):

. . . 46 47 48 49 50 *51 52 53 . . .*

The standardized Z-value for the event "more than 50" is $P(X > 50.5) = P(Z > 1.31)$ since

$$z = \frac{x - \mu}{\sigma} = \frac{50.5 - 42}{6.48074} \cong 1.31$$

Using Appendix C-2 we look up $P(Z < -1.31) = .0951$, which is the same as $P(Z > 1.31)$ because the normal distribution is symmetric. We can check the actual Poisson probability by using Excel's cumulative function =POISSON.DIST(50,42,1) and subtracting from 1:

$$P(X \geq 51) = 1 - P(X \leq 50) = 1 - .9025 = .0975$$

In this case, the normal approximation (.0951) comes fairly close to the Poisson result (.0975). Of course, if you have access to Excel, you don't need the approximation at all.

SECTION EXERCISES

connect

Note: Use Appendix C-2 for these exercises.

7.51 On average, 28 patients per hour arrive in the Foxboro 24-Hour Walk-in Clinic on Friday between 6 p.m. and midnight. (a) What is the approximate probability of more than 35 arrivals? (b) What is the approximate probability of fewer than 25 arrivals? (c) Is the normal approximation justified? Show all calculations. (d) Use Excel to calculate the actual Poisson probabilities. How close were your approximations?

7.52 For a large Internet service provider (ISP), web virus attacks occur at a mean rate of 150 per day. (a) Estimate the probability of at least 175 attacks in a given day. (b) Estimate the probability of fewer than 125 attacks. (c) Is the normal approximation justified? Show all calculations. (d) Use Excel to calculate the actual Poisson probabilities. How close were your approximations?

LO 7-7

Find the exponential probability for a given *x*.

LO 7-8

Solve for *x* for a given exponential probability.

7.6 EXPONENTIAL DISTRIBUTION

Characteristics of the Exponential Distribution

In Chapter 6 we introduced the idea of a *random process*. For example, consider the process of customers arriving at a Noodles & Company restaurant, illustrated in Figure 7.23. There are two different variables that could be used to describe this process. We could count the number of customers who arrive in a randomly selected minute, or we could measure the

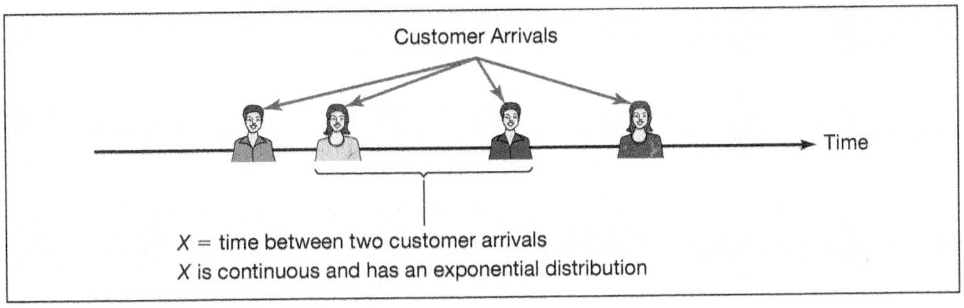

FIGURE 7.23

Customer Arrival Process at a Noodles & Company Restaurant

time between two customer arrivals. As you learned in Chapter 6, the *count* of customer arrivals is a discrete random variable and typically has a Poisson distribution. When the count of customer arrivals has a Poisson distribution, the distribution of the time between two customer arrivals will have an **exponential distribution**, detailed in Table 7.11. In the exponential model, the focus is on the waiting time until the next event, a continuous

TABLE 7.11

Exponential Distribution

Parameter	λ = mean arrival rate per unit of time or space (same as Poisson mean)
PDF	$f(x) = \lambda e^{-\lambda x}$
CDF	$P(X \le x) = 1 - e^{-\lambda x}$
Domain	$x \ge 0$
Mean	$1/\lambda$
Standard deviation	$1/\lambda$
Shape	Always right-skewed.
CDF in Excel	=EXPON.DIST(x, λ,1)
Random data in Excel	=–LN(RAND())/λ
Comments	Waiting time is exponential when arrivals follow a Poisson model. Often $1/\lambda$ is given (mean time between events) rather than λ. The value of e is approximately 2.71828.

variable. The exponential probability density function approaches zero as x increases, and is very skewed, as shown in Figure 7.24.

We are usually not interested in the height of the function $f(x)$ but rather in areas under the curve. Fortunately, the CDF is simple; no tables are needed, just a calculator that has the

FIGURE 7.24

Exponential Areas

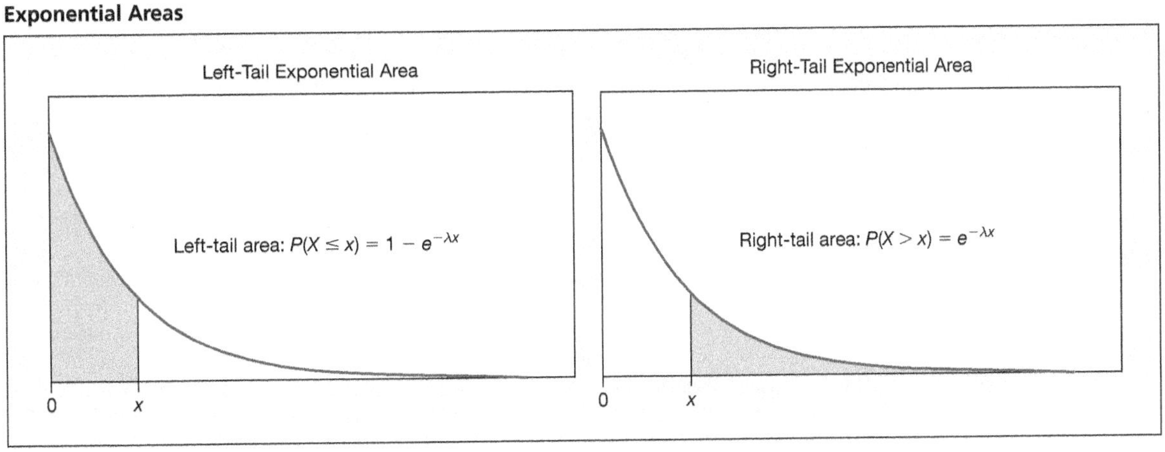

e^x function key. The probability of waiting more than x units of time until the next arrival is $e^{-\lambda x}$, while the probability of waiting x units of time or less is $1 - e^{-\lambda x}$.

$$P(X \le x) = 1 - e^{-\lambda x} \quad \text{(probability of waiting } x \text{ or less)} \tag{7.10}$$

$$P(X > x) = e^{-\lambda x} \quad \text{(probability of waiting } more \text{ than } x\text{)} \tag{7.11}$$

Recall that $P(X \le x)$ is the same as $P(X < x)$ since the point x has no area. For this reason, we could use either $<$ or $\le$ in formula 7.10.

EXAMPLE 7.5

Customer Waiting Time

Between 2 p.m. and 4 p.m. on Wednesday, patient insurance inquiries arrive at Blue Choice insurance at a mean rate of 2.2 calls per minute. What is the probability of waiting more than 30 seconds for the next call? We set $\lambda = 2.2$ events per minute and $x = 0.50$ minute. Note that we must convert 30 seconds to 0.50 minute since λ is expressed in minutes, and the units of measurement must be the same. We have

$$P(X > 0.50) = e^{-\lambda x} = e^{-(2.2)(0.50)} = .3329, \text{ or } 33.29\%$$

There is about a 33 percent chance of waiting more than 30 seconds before the next call arrives. Since $x = 0.50$ is a *point* that has no area in a continuous model, $P(X \ge 0.50)$ and $P(X > 0.50)$ refer to the same event (unlike, say, a binomial model, in which a point *does* have a probability). The probability that 30 seconds or less (0.50 minute) will be needed before the next call arrives is

$$P(X \le 0.50) = 1 - e^{-(2.2)(0.50)} = 1 - .3329 = .6671$$

These calculations are illustrated in Figure 7.25.

FIGURE 7.25

Exponential Tail Areas for $\lambda = 2.2$

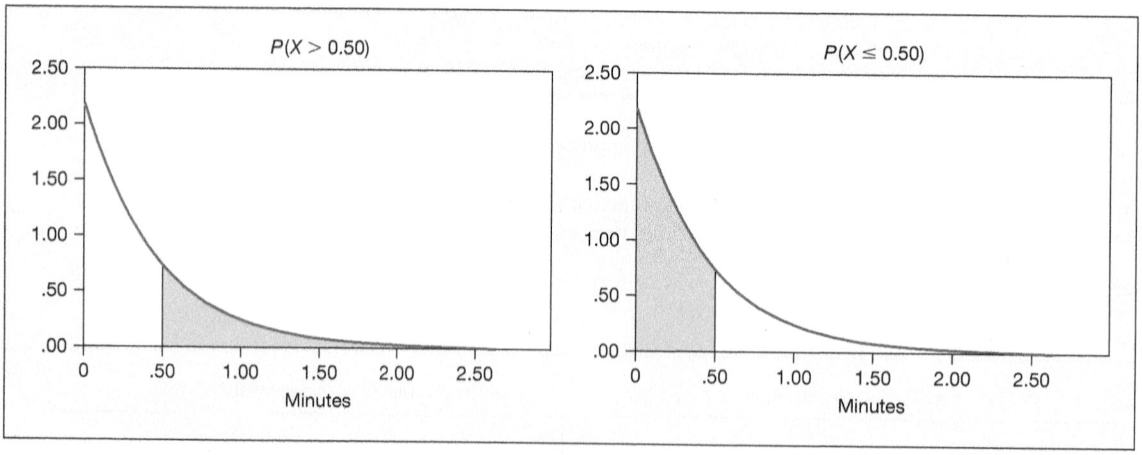

SECTION EXERCISES

connect

7.53 In Santa Theresa, false alarms are received at the downtown fire station at a mean rate of 0.3 per day. (a) What is the probability that more than 7 days will pass before the next false alarm arrives? (b) Less than 2 days? (c) Explain fully.

7.54 Between 11 p.m. and midnight on Thursday night, Mystery Pizza gets an average of 4.2 telephone orders per hour. Find the probability that (a) at least 30 minutes will elapse before the next telephone order; (b) less than 15 minutes will elapse; and (c) between 15 and 30 minutes will elapse.

7.55 A passenger metal detector at Chicago's Midway Airport gives an alarm 2.1 times a minute. What is the probability that (a) less than 60 seconds will pass before the next alarm? (b) More than 30 seconds? (c) At least 45 seconds?

7.56 The Johnson family uses a propane gas grill for cooking outdoors. During the summer they need to replace their tank on average every 30 days. At a randomly chosen moment, what is the probability that they can grill out (a) at least 40 days before they need to replace their tank; (b) no more than 20 days?

7.57 At a certain Noodles & Company restaurant, customers arrive during the lunch hour at a rate of 2.8 per minute. What is the probability that (a) at least 30 seconds will pass before the next customer walks in; (b) no more than 15 seconds; (c) more than 1 minute?

Inverse Exponential

We can use the exponential area formula in reverse. If the mean arrival rate is 2.2 calls per minute, we want the 90th percentile for waiting time (the top 10 percent of waiting time) as illustrated in Figure 7.26. We want to find the x-value that defines the upper 10 percent.

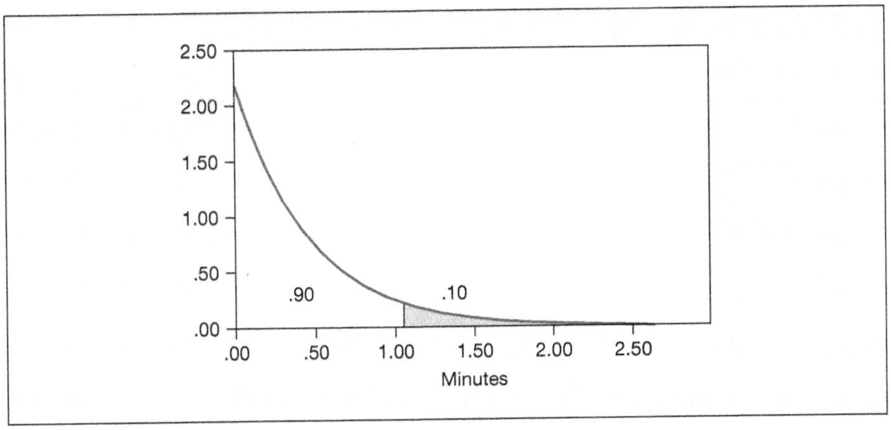

FIGURE 7.26

Finding x for the Upper 10 Percent

Call the unknown time x. Since $P(X \leq x) = .90$ implies $P(X > x) = .10$, we set the right-tail area to .10, take the natural logarithm of both sides, and solve for x:

$$P(X \leq x) = 1 - e^{-\lambda x} = .90$$
$$\text{so} \quad e^{-\lambda x} = .10$$
$$-\lambda x = \ln(.10)$$
$$-(2.2)x = -2.302585$$
$$x = 2.302585/2.2$$
$$x = 1.0466 \text{ minutes}$$

So 90 percent of the calls will arrive within 1.0466 minutes (or 62.8 seconds). We can find any percentile in the same way. For example, Table 7.12 illustrates similar calculations to find the quartiles (25 percent, 50 percent, 75 percent) of waiting time.

TABLE 7.12 **Quartiles for Exponential with $\lambda = 2.2$**

First Quartile Q_1	*Second Quartile Q_2 (median)*	*Third Quartile Q_3*
$P(X \leq x) = 1 - e^{-\lambda x} = .25$	$P(X \leq x) = 1 - e^{-\lambda x} = .50$	$P(X \leq x) = 1 - e^{-\lambda x} = .75$
so $e^{-\lambda x} = .75$	so $e^{-\lambda x} = .50$	so $e^{-\lambda x} = .25$
$-\lambda x = \ln(.75)$	$-\lambda x = \ln(.50)$	$-\lambda x = \ln(.25)$
$-(2.2)x = -0.2876821$	$-(2.2)x = -0.6931472$	$-(2.2)x = -1.386294$
$x = 0.2876821/2.2$	$x = 0.6931472/2.2$	$x = 1.386294/2.2$
$x = 0.1308$ minute, or 7.9 seconds	$x = 0.3151$ minute, or 18.9 seconds	$x = 0.6301$ minute, or 37.8 seconds

The calculations in Table 7.12 show that the mean waiting time is $1/\lambda = 1/2.2 = 0.4545$ minute, or 27 seconds. It is instructive to note that the median waiting time (18.9 seconds) is less than the mean. Since the exponential distribution is highly right-skewed, we would expect the mean waiting time to be above the median, which it is.

Mean Time between Events

Exponential waiting times are often described in terms of the **mean time between events** (MTBE) rather than in terms of Poisson arrivals per unit of time. In other words, we might be given $1/\lambda$ instead of λ.

$$\text{MTBE} = 1/\lambda = \textit{mean time between events} \text{ (units of time per event)}$$

$$1/\text{MTBE} = \lambda = \text{mean } \textit{events per unit of time} \text{ (events per unit of time)}$$

For example, if the mean time between patient arrivals in an emergency room is 20 minutes, then $\lambda = 1/20 = 0.05$ arrival per minute (or $\lambda = 3.0$ arrivals per hour). We could work a problem using either hours or minutes, as long as we are careful to make sure that x and λ are expressed in the same units when we calculate $e^{-\lambda x}$. For example, $P(X > 12 \text{ minutes}) = e^{-(0.05)(12)} = e^{-0.60}$ is the same as $P(X > 0.20 \text{ hour}) = e^{-(3)(0.20)} = e^{-0.60}$.

EXAMPLE 7.6

Flat-Panel Displays

The NexGenCo color flat-panel display in an aircraft cockpit has a mean time between failures (MTBF) of 22,500 flight hours. What is the probability of a failure within the next 10,000 flight hours? Since 22,500 hours per failure implies $\lambda = 1/22{,}500$ failures per hour, we calculate:

$$P(X < 10{,}000) = 1 - e^{-\lambda x} = 1 - e^{-(1/22{,}500)(10{,}000)} = 1 - e^{-0.4444} = 1 - .6412 = .3588$$

There is a 35.88 percent chance of failure within the next 10,000 hours of flight. This assumes that failures follow the Poisson model.

EXAMPLE 7.7

Warranty Period

A manufacturer of GPS navigation receivers for boats knows that their mean life under typical maritime conditions is 7 years. What warranty should be offered in order that not more than 30 percent of the GPS units will fail before the warranty expires? The situation is illustrated in Figure 7.27.

FIGURE 7.27 **Finding *x* for the Lower 30 Percent**

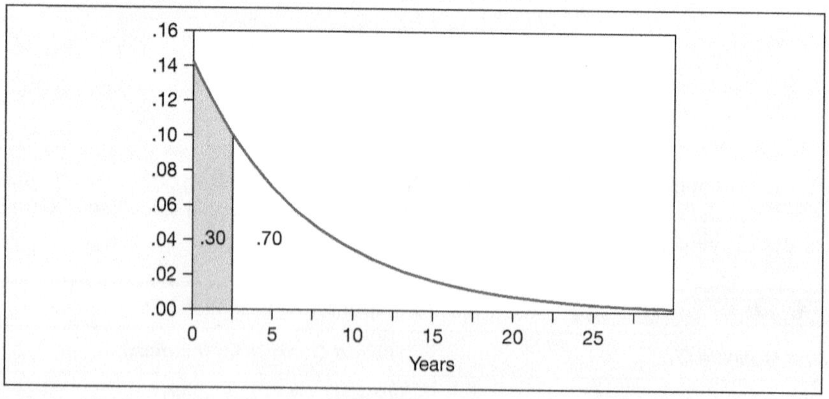

Let x be the length of the warranty. To solve this problem, we note that if 30 percent fail before the warranty expires, 70 percent will fail afterward. That is, $P(X > x) = 1 - P(X \le x) = 1 - 0.30 = .70$.

We set $P(X > x) = e^{-\lambda x} = .70$ and solve for x by taking the natural log of both sides of the equation:

$$e^{-\lambda x} = .70$$
$$-\lambda x = \ln(.70)$$
$$-\lambda x = -0.356675$$
$$x = (0.356675)/\lambda$$

But in this case, we are not given λ but rather its reciprocal MTBF $= 1/\lambda$. Seven years *mean time between failures* is the same as saying $\lambda = 1/7$ *failures per year*. So we plug in $\lambda = 1/7 = 0.1428571$ to finish solving for x:

$$x = (0.356675)/(0.142857) = 2.497 \text{ years}$$

Thus, the firm would offer a 30-month warranty.

It may seem paradoxical that such a short warranty would be offered for something that lasts 7 years. However, the right tail is very long. A few long-lived GPS units will pull up the mean. This is typical of electronic equipment, which helps explain why your laptop computer may have only a 1-year warranty when we know that laptops often last for many years. Similarly, automobiles typically outlast their warranty period (although competitive pressures have recently led to warranties of 5 years or more, even though it may result in a loss on a few warranties). In general, warranty periods are a policy tool used by business to balance costs of expected claims against the competitive need to offer contract protection to consumers.

Using Excel

The Excel function =EXPON.DIST(x,Lambda,1) will return the left-tail area $P(X \leq x)$. The "1" indicates a cumulative area. If you enter 0 instead of 1, you will get the height of the PDF instead of the left-tail area for the CDF.

Every situation with Poisson arrivals over time is associated with an exponential waiting time. Both models depend solely on the parameter λ = mean arrival rate per unit of time. These two closely related distributions are summarized in Table 7.13.

TABLE 7.13 Relation between Exponential and Poisson Models

Model	*Random Variable*	*Parameter*	*Mean*	*Domain*	*Variable Type*
Poisson	X = number of arrivals per unit of time	$\lambda = \frac{\text{mean arrivals}}{\text{unit of time}}$	λ	$x = 0, 1, 2, \ldots$	Discrete
Exponential	X = waiting time until next arrival	$\lambda = \frac{\text{mean arrivals}}{\text{unit of time}}$	$1/\lambda$	$x \geq 0$	Continuous

The exponential model may also remind you of the geometric model, which describes the number of items that must be sampled until the first success. In spirit, they are similar. However, the models are different because the geometric model tells us the number of *discrete* events until the next success, while the exponential model tells the *continuous* waiting time until the next arrival of an event.

SECTION EXERCISES

connect

7.58 The time it takes a ski patroller to respond to an accident call has an exponential distribution with an average equal to 5 minutes. (a) In what time will 90 percent of all ski accident calls be responded to? (b) If the ski patrol would like to be able to respond to 90 percent of the accident calls within 10 minutes, what does the average response time need to be?

7.59 Between 11 p.m. and midnight on Thursday night, Mystery Pizza gets an average of 4.2 telephone orders per hour. (a) Find the median waiting time until the next telephone order. (b) Find the upper quartile of waiting time before the next telephone order. (c) What is the upper 10 percent of waiting time until the next telephone order? Show all calculations clearly.

7.60 A passenger metal detector at Chicago's Midway Airport gives an alarm 0.5 time a minute. (a) Find the median waiting time until the next alarm. (b) Find the first quartile of waiting time before the next alarm. (c) Find the 30th percentile waiting time until the next alarm. Show all calculations clearly.

7.61 Between 2 a.m. and 4 a.m. at an all-night pizza parlor, the mean time between arrival of telephone pizza orders is 20 minutes. (a) Find the median wait for pizza order arrivals. (b) Explain why the median is not equal to the mean. (c) Find the upper quartile.

7.62 The mean life of a certain computer hard disk in continual use is 8 years. (a) How long a warranty should be offered if the vendor wants to ensure that not more than 10 percent of the hard disks will fail within the warranty period? (b) Not more than 20 percent?

7.7 TRIANGULAR DISTRIBUTION (OPTIONAL)

Characteristics of the Triangular Distribution

LO 7-9

Use the triangular distribution for "what-if" analysis (optional).

Table 7.14 shows the characteristics of the **triangular distribution**. Visually, it is a simple distribution, as you can see in Figure 7.28. It can be symmetric or skewed. Its X values must lie within the interval $[a, c]$. But unlike the uniform, it has a mode or "peak." The peak is reminiscent of a normal, which also has a single maximum. But unlike the normal, the triangular does not go on forever, since its X values are confined by a and c. The triangular distribution is sometimes denoted $T(a, b, c)$ or $T(\text{min, mode, max})$.

TABLE 7.14

Triangular Distribution

Parameters	a = lower limit b = mode c = upper limit
PDF	$f(x) = \dfrac{2(x-a)}{(b-a)(c-a)}$ for $a \le x \le b$ $f(x) = \dfrac{2(c-x)}{(c-a)(c-b)}$ for $b \le x \le c$
CDF	$P(X \le x) = \dfrac{(x-a)^2}{(b-a)(c-a)}$ for $a \le x \le b$ $P(X \le x) = 1 - \dfrac{(c-x)^2}{(c-a)(c-b)}$ for $b \le x \le c$
Domain	$a \le x \le c$
Mean	$\dfrac{a+b+c}{3}$
Standard deviation	$\sqrt{\dfrac{a^2+b^2+c^2-ab-ac-bc}{18}}$
Shape	Positively skewed if $b < (a + c)/2$. Negatively skewed if $b > (a + c)/2$.
Comments	Practical model, useful in business what-if analysis. A symmetric triangular is the sum of two identically distributed uniform variates.

FIGURE 7.28

Triangular PDFs

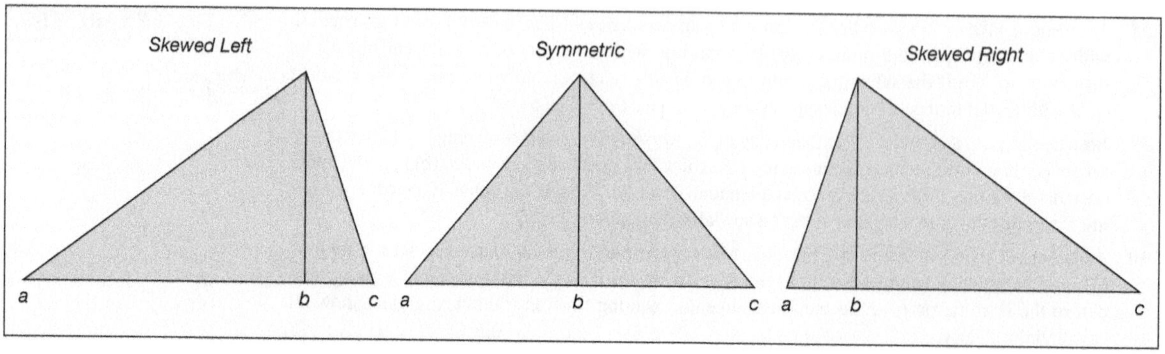

EXAMPLE 7.8

Anesthesia Effectiveness Using Triangular Distribution

An oral surgeon injects a painkiller prior to extracting a tooth. Given the varying characteristics of patients, the dentist views the time for anesthesia effectiveness as a triangular random variable that takes between 15 minutes and 30 minutes, with 20 minutes as the most likely time. Setting $a = 15$, $b = 20$, and $c = 30$, we obtain

$$\mu = \frac{a+b+c}{3} = \frac{15+20+30}{3} = 21.7 \text{ minutes}$$

$$\sigma = \sqrt{\frac{a^2+b^2+c^2-ab-ac-bc}{18}}$$

$$= \sqrt{\frac{15^2+20^2+30^2-(15)(20)-(15)(30)-(20)(30)}{18}}$$

$$= 3.12 \text{ minutes}$$

Using the cumulative distribution function or CDF, we can calculate the probability of taking less than x minutes:

$$P(X \le x) = \frac{(x-a)^2}{(b-a)(c-a)} \quad \text{for } a \le x \le b \qquad \textbf{(7.12)}$$

$$P(X \le x) = 1 - \frac{(c-x)^2}{(c-a)(c-b)} \quad \text{for } b \le x \le c \qquad \textbf{(7.13)}$$

For example, the probability that the anesthetic takes less than 25 minutes is

$$P(X \le 25) = 1 - \frac{(30-25)^2}{(30-15)(30-20)} = .8333$$

Basically, we are finding the small triangle's area (½ base × height) and then subtracting from 1. This situation is illustrated in Figure 7.29. In contrast, assuming a uniform distribution with parameters $a = 15$ and $b = 30$ would yield $P(X \le 25) = .6667$. Why is it different? Because the triangular, with mode 20, has more probability on the low end, making it more likely that a patient will be fully anesthetized within 25 minutes. Assuming a uniform distribution may seem conservative, but it could lead to patients sitting around longer waiting to be sure the anesthetic has taken effect. Only experience could tell us which model is more realistic.

FIGURE 7.29 **Triangular $P(X \le 25)$**

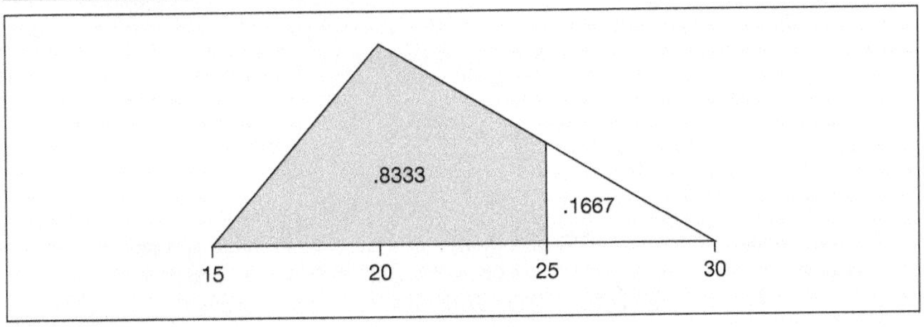

Special Case: Symmetric Triangular

An interesting special case is a **symmetric triangular distribution** centered at 0, whose lower limit is identical to its upper limit except for sign (e.g., from $-c$ to $+c$) with mode 0 (halfway between $-c$ and $+c$). If you set $c = 2.45$, the distribution $T(-2.45, 0, +2.45)$ closely resembles a standard normal distribution $N(0, 1)$.

Figure 7.30 compares these two distributions. Unlike the normal $N(0, 1)$, the triangular distribution $T(-2.45, 0, +2.45)$ always has values within the range $-2.45 \le X \le +2.45$. Yet over

FIGURE 7.30

Symmetric Triangular Is Approximately Normal

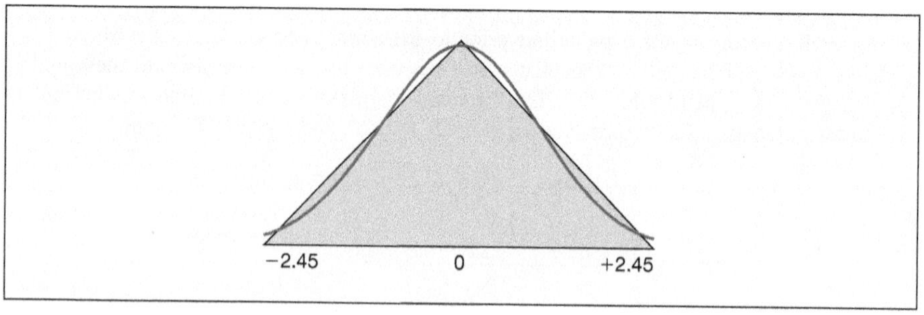

much of the range, the distributions are alike, and random samples from $T(-2.45, 0, +2.45)$ are surprisingly similar to samples from a normal $N(0, 1)$ distribution. It is easy to generate symmetric triangular random data in Excel by summing two $U(0, 1)$ random variables using the function =2.45 *(RAND()+RAND()-1).

Uses of the Triangular

The triangular distribution is a way of thinking about variation that corresponds rather well to what-if analysis in business. It is not surprising that business analysts are attracted to the triangular model. Its finite range and simple form are more understandable than a normal distribution. It is more versatile than a normal because it can be skewed in either direction. Yet it has some of the nice properties of a normal, such as a distinct mode. The triangular model is especially handy for what-if analysis when the business case depends on predicting a stochastic variable (e.g., the price of a raw material, an interest rate, a sales volume). If the analyst can anticipate the range (a to c) and most likely value (b), it will be possible to calculate probabilities of various outcomes. Many times, such distributions will be skewed, so a normal wouldn't be much help. The triangular distribution is often used in simulation modeling software such as Arena. In Chapter 18, we will explore what-if analysis using the triangular $T(a, b, c)$ model in simulations.

SECTION EXERCISES

connect

7.63 Suppose that the distribution of order sizes (in dollars) at L.L. Bean has a distribution that is $T(0, 25, 75)$. (a) Find the mean. (b) Find the standard deviation. (c) Find the probability that an order will be less than \$25. (d) Sketch the distribution and shade the area for the event in part (c).

7.64 Suppose that the distribution of oil prices (\$/bbl) is forecast to be $T(50, 65, 105)$. (a) Find the mean. (b) Find the standard deviation. (c) Find the probability that the price will be greater than \$75. (d) Sketch the distribution and shade the area for the event in part (c).

CHAPTER SUMMARY

The **probability density function (PDF)** of a **continuous random variable** is a smooth curve, and probabilities are *areas* under the curve. The area under the entire PDF is 1. The **cumulative distribution function (CDF)** shows the area under the PDF to the left of X, approaching 1 as X increases. The mean $E(X)$ and variance $\text{Var}(X)$ are integrals, rather than sums, as for a discrete random variable. The **uniform continuous distribution,** denoted $U(a, b)$, has two parameters a and b that enclose the range. It is a simple what-if model with applications in simulation. The **normal distribution,** denoted $N(\mu, \sigma)$, is symmetric and bell-shaped. It has two parameters, the mean μ and standard deviation σ. It serves as a benchmark. Because there is a different normal distribution for every possible μ and σ, we apply the transformation $z = (x - \mu)/\sigma$ to get a new random variable that follows a **standard normal distribution,** denoted $N(0, 1)$, with mean 0 and standard deviation 1. There is no simple formula for normal areas, but tables or Excel functions are available to find an area under the curve for given z-values or to find z-values that give a specified area (the "inverse normal"). As shown in Figure 7.31, a **normal approximation** for a binomial or Poisson probability is acceptable when the mean is at least 10. The **exponential distribution** describes *waiting time* until the next Poisson arrival. Its one parameter is λ

(the mean arrival rate) and its right tail area is $e^{-\lambda x}$ (the probability of waiting at least x time units for the next arrival). It is strongly right-skewed and is used to predict warranty claims or to schedule facilities. The **triangular distribution** $T(a, b, c)$ has three parameters (a and c enclose the range, and b is the mode). It may be symmetric or skewed in either direction. It is easy to visualize and is a useful model for what-if simulation. Table 7.15 compares these five models.

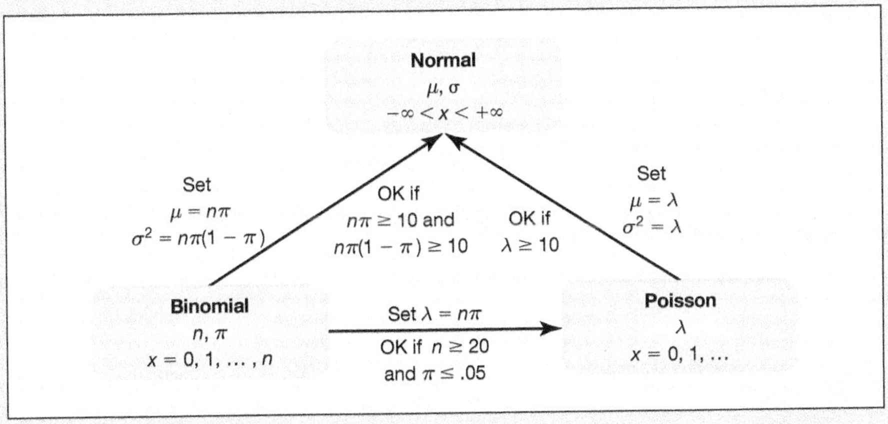

FIGURE 7.31

Relationships among Three Models

TABLE 7.15 **Comparison of Models**

Model	*Parameters*	*Mean*	*Variance*	*Characteristics*
Uniform	a, b	$(a + b)/2$	$(b - a)^2/12$	Always symmetric.
Normal	μ, σ	μ	σ^2	Symmetric. Useful as reference benchmark.
Standard normal	μ, σ	0	1	Special case of the normal with $z = (x - \mu)/\sigma$.
Exponential	λ	$1/\lambda$	$1/\lambda^2$	Always skewed right. Right-tail area is $e^{-\lambda x}$ for waiting times.
Triangular	a, b, c	$(a + b + c)/3$	$(a^2 + b^2 + c^2 - ab - ac - bc)/18$	Useful for what-if business modeling.

KEY TERMS

continuity correction
continuous random variable
cumulative distribution function
exponential distribution
Gaussian distribution
integral
inverse normal
mean time between events
normal distribution
probability density function
standard normal distribution
symmetric triangular distribution
triangular distribution
uniform continuous distribution

Commonly Used Formulas in Continuous Distributions

Uniform CDF: $P(X \le x) = \dfrac{x - a}{b - a}$ for $a \le x \le b$

Standard Normal Transformation: $z = \dfrac{x - \mu}{\sigma}$ for $-\infty < x < +\infty$

Normal-Binomial Approximation: $\mu = n\pi \quad \sigma = \sqrt{n\pi(1 - \pi)}$ for $n\pi \ge 10$ and $n(1 - \pi) \ge 10$

Normal-Poisson Approximation: $\mu = \lambda \quad \sigma = \sqrt{\lambda}$ for $\lambda \ge 10$

Exponential CDF: $P(X \le x) = 1 - e^{-\lambda x}$ for $x \ge 0$

CHAPTER REVIEW

1. (a) Why does a point have zero probability in a continuous distribution? (b) Why are probabilities areas under curves in a continuous distribution?
2. Define (a) parameter, (b) PDF, and (c) CDF.
3. For the uniform distribution: (a) tell how many parameters it has; (b) indicate what the parameters represent; (c) describe its shape; and (d) explain when it would be used.
4. For the normal distribution: (a) tell how many parameters it has; (b) indicate what the parameters represent; (c) describe its shape; and (d) explain why all normal distributions are alike despite having different μ and σ.
5. (a) What features of a stochastic process might lead you to anticipate a normal distribution? (b) Give two examples of random variables that might be considered normal.
6. (a) What is the transformation to standardize a normal random variable? (b) Why do we standardize a variable to find normal areas? (c) How does a standard normal distribution differ from any other normal distribution, and how is it similar?
7. (a) Explain the difference between Appendix C-1 and Appendix C-2. (b) List advantages of each type of table. (c) Which table do you expect to use, and why? (d) Why not always use Excel?
8. Write an example of each of the four normal functions in Excel and tell what each function does.
9. List the standard normal z-values for several common areas (tail and/or middle). *You will use them often.*
10. For the exponential distribution: (a) tell how many parameters it has; (b) indicate what the parameters represent; (c) describe its shape; and (d) explain when it would be used.
11. When does the normal give an acceptable approximation (a) to a binomial and (b) to a Poisson? (c) Why might you never need these approximations? (d) When might you need them?
12. For the triangular distribution: (a) tell how many parameters it has; (b) indicate what the parameters represent; (c) describe its shape in a general way (e.g., skewness); and (d) explain when it would be used.

CHAPTER EXERCISES

connect

Note: Show your work clearly. Problems with * are harder or based on optional material.

7.65 Which of the following is a continuous random variable?

a. Number of Honda Civics sold in a given day at a car dealership.
b. Amount of gasoline used for a 200-mile trip in a Honda Civic.
c. Distance driven on a particular Thursday by the owner of a Honda Civic.

7.66 Which of the following could be probability density functions for a continuous random variable? Explain.

a. $f(x) = .50$ for $0 \le x \le 2$
b. $f(x) = 2 - x$ for $0 \le x \le 2$
c. $f(x) = .5x$ for $0 \le x \le 2$

7.67 Applicants for a night caretaker position are uniformly distributed in age between 25 and 65. (a) What is the mean age of an applicant? (b) The standard deviation? (c) What is the probability that an applicant will be over 45? (d) Over 55? (e) Between 30 and 60?

7.68 Passengers using New York's MetroCard system must swipe the card at a rate between 10 and 40 inches per second, or else the card must be re-swiped through the card reader. Research shows that actual swipe rates by subway riders are uniformly distributed between 5 and 50 inches per second. (a) What is the mean swipe rate? (b) What is the standard deviation of the swipe rate? (c) What are the quartiles? (d) What percentage of subway riders must re-swipe the card because they were outside the acceptable range?

7.69 Discuss why you would or would not expect each of the following variables to be normally distributed. *Hint:* Would you expect a single central mode and tapering tails? Would the distribution be roughly symmetric? Would one tail be longer than the other?

a. Time for households to complete the U.S. Census short form.
b. Size of automobile collision damage claims.
c. Diameters of randomly chosen circulated quarters.
d. Weight of contents of 16-ounce boxes of elbow macaroni.

7.70 Why might the following *not* be normally distributed? (a) The time it takes you to drive to the airport. (b) The annual income for a randomly chosen Major League Baseball player. (c) The annual hurricane losses suffered by homeowners in Florida.

7.71 Scores on a certain accounting exam were normally distributed with a mean of 75 and a standard deviation of 7. Find the percentile for each individual using Excel's =NORM.S.DIST function. (a) Bob's score was 82; (b) Phyllis's score was 93; (c) Tom's score was 63.

7.72 Chlorine concentration in a municipal water supply is a uniformly distributed random variable that ranges between 0.74 ppm and 0.98 ppm. (a) What is the mean chlorine concentration? (b) The standard deviation? (c) What is the probability that the chlorine concentration will exceed 0.80 ppm on a given day? (d) Will be under 0.85 ppm? (e) Will be between 0.80 ppm and 0.90 ppm?

7.73 The weekly demand for Baked Lay's potato chips at a certain Subway sandwich shop is a random variable with mean 450 and standard deviation 80. Find the value(s) of X for each event. Show your work.

a. Highest 50 percent
b. Lowest 25 percent
c. Middle 80 percent
d. 5th percentile

7.74 The weekly demand for Papa Chubby's pizzas on a Friday night is a random variable with mean 235 and standard deviation 10. Find the value(s) of X for each event. Show your work.

a. Lowest 50 percent
b. Highest 25 percent
c. 90th percentile
d. Middle 80 percent

7.75 The amounts spent by customers at a Noodles & Company restaurant during lunch are normally distributed with a mean equal to \$7.00 and a standard deviation equal to \$0.35. (a) What amount is the first quartile? (b) The second quartile? (c) The 90th percentile?

7.76 The length of a Colorado brook trout is normally distributed. (a) What is the probability that a brook trout's length exceeds the mean? (b) Exceeds the mean by at least 1 standard deviation? (c) Exceeds the mean by at least 2 standard deviations? (d) Is within 2 standard deviations?

7.77 The caffeine content of a cup of home-brewed coffee is a normally distributed random variable with a mean of 115 mg with a standard deviation of 20 mg. (a) What is the probability that a randomly chosen cup of home-brewed coffee will have more than 130 mg of caffeine? (b) Less than 100 mg? (c) A very strong cup of tea has a caffeine content of 91 mg. What is the probability that a cup of coffee will have less caffeine than a very strong cup of tea?

7.78 The fracture strength of a certain type of manufactured glass is normally distributed with a mean of 579 MPa with a standard deviation of 14 MPa. (a) What is the probability that a randomly chosen sample of glass will break at less than 579 MPa? (b) More than 590 MPa? (c) Less than 600 MPa?

7.79 Tire pressure in a certain car is a normally distributed random variable with mean 30 psi (pounds per square inch) and standard deviation 2 psi. The manufacturer's recommended correct inflation range is 28 psi to 32 psi. A motorist's tire is inspected at random. (a) What is the probability that the tire's inflation is within the recommended range? (b) What is the probability that the tire is underinflated? *(c) A company has developed a microchip that will warn when a tire is 25 percent below the recommended mean, to warn of dangerously low tire pressure. How often would such an alarm be triggered?

7.80 In a certain microwave oven on the high power setting, the time it takes a randomly chosen kernel of popcorn to pop is normally distributed with a mean of 140 seconds and a standard deviation of 25 seconds. What percentage of the kernels will fail to pop if the popcorn is cooked for (a) 2 minutes? (b) Three minutes? (c) If you wanted 95 percent of the kernels to pop, what time would you allow? (d) If you wanted 99 percent to pop?

7.81 Procyon Manufacturing produces tennis balls. Their manufacturing process has a mean ball weight of 2.035 ounces with a standard deviation of 0.03 ounce. Regulation tennis balls are required to have a weight between 1.975 ounces and 2.095 ounces. What proportion of Procyon's production will fail to meet these specifications?

7.82 Shower temperature at the Oxnard Health Club showers is regulated automatically. The heater kicks in when the temperature falls to 99°F and shuts off when the temperature reaches 107°F. Water temperature then falls slowly until the heater kicks in again. At a given moment, the water temperature is a uniformly distributed random variable $U(99,107)$. (a) Find the mean temperature. (b) Find the standard deviation of the temperature. (c) Find the 75th percentile for water temperature.

7.83 Tests show that, on average, the Li-ion Hitachi stick driver can drive 207 drywall screws on a single charge. Bob needs to drive 230 drywall screws. If the standard deviation is 14 screws, find the probability that Bob can finish his job without recharging. *Hint:* Assume a normal distribution and treat the data as continuous.

7.84 The time it takes to give a man a shampoo and haircut is normally distributed with mean 22 minutes and standard deviation 3 minutes. Customers are scheduled every 30 minutes. (a) What is the probability that a male customer will take longer than the allotted time? *(b) If three male customers are scheduled sequentially on the half-hour, what is the probability that all three will be finished within their allotted half-hour times?

7.85 The length of a time-out during a televised professional football game is normally distributed with a mean of 84 seconds and a standard deviation of 10 seconds. If the network runs consecutive commercials totaling 90 seconds, what is the probability that play will resume before the commercials are over?

7.86 If the weight (in grams) of cereal in a box of Lucky Charms is $N(470,5)$, what is the probability that the box will contain less than the advertised weight of 453 g?

7.87 Demand for residential electricity at 6:00 p.m. on the first Monday in October in Santa Theresa County is normally distributed with a mean of 4,905 MW (megawatts) and a standard deviation of 355 MW. Due to scheduled maintenance and unexpected system failures in a generating station, the utility can supply a maximum of 5,200 MW at that time. What is the probability that the utility will have to purchase electricity from other utilities or allow brownouts?

7.88 Jim's systolic blood pressure is a random variable with a mean of 145 mmHg and a standard deviation of 20 mmHg. For Jim's age group, 140 is the threshold for high blood pressure. (a) If Jim's systolic blood pressure is taken at a randomly chosen moment, what is the probability that it will be 135 or less? (b) 175 or more? (c) Between 125 and 165? (d) Discuss the implications of variability for physicians who are trying to identify patients with high blood pressure.

7.89 A statistics exam was given. Calculate the percentile for each of the following four students.

a. John's z-score was -1.62.
b. Mary's z-score was 0.50.
c. Zak's z-score was 1.79.
d. Frieda's z-score was 2.48.

7.90 Are the following statements true or false? Explain your reasoning.

a. "If we see a standardized z-value beyond ± 3, the variable cannot be normally distributed."
b. "If X and Y are two normally distributed random variables measured in different units (e.g., X is in pounds and Y is in kilograms), then it is not meaningful to compare the standardized z-values."
c. "Two machines fill 2-liter soft drink bottles by using a similar process. Machine A has $\mu = 1{,}990$ ml and $\sigma = 5$ ml while Machine B has $\mu = 1{,}995$ ml and $\sigma = 3$ ml. The variables cannot both be normally distributed since they have different standard deviations."

***7.91** John can take either of two routes (A or B) to LAX airport. At midday on a typical Wednesday the travel time on either route is normally distributed with parameters $\mu_A = 54$ minutes, $\sigma_A = 6$ minutes, $\mu_B = 60$ minutes, and $\sigma_B = 3$ minutes. (a) Which route should he choose if he must be at the airport in 54 minutes to pick up his spouse? (b) Sixty minutes? (c) Sixty-six minutes? Explain carefully.

7.92 The amount of fill in a half-liter (500 ml) soft drink bottle is normally distributed. The process has a standard deviation of 5 ml. The mean is adjustable. (a) Where should the mean be set to ensure a 95 percent probability that a half-liter bottle will not be underfilled? (b) A 99 percent probability? (c) A 99.9 percent probability? Explain.

7.93 The length of a certain kind of Colorado brook trout is normally distributed with a mean of 12.5 inches and a standard deviation of 1.2 inches. What minimum size limit should the Department of Natural Resources set if it wishes to allow people to keep 80 percent of the trout they catch?

7.94 Times for a surgical procedure are normally distributed. There are two methods. Method A has a mean of 28 minutes and a standard deviation of 4 minutes, while method B has a mean of 32 minutes and a standard deviation of 2 minutes. (a) Which procedure is preferred if the procedure must be completed within 28 minutes? (b) Thirty-eight minutes? (c) Thirty-six minutes? Explain your reasoning fully.

7.95 The length of a brook trout is normally distributed. Two brook trout are caught. (a) What is the probability that both exceed the mean? (b) Neither exceeds the mean? (c) One is above the mean and one is below? (d) Both are equal to the mean?

APPROXIMATIONS

7.96 Among live deliveries, the probability of a twin birth is .02. (a) In 2,000 live deliveries, what is the probability of at least 50 twin births? (b) Fewer than 35?

7.97 Nationwide, the probability that a rental car is from Hertz is 25 percent. In a sample of 100 rental cars, what is the probability that fewer than 20 are from Hertz?

7.98 The probability of being in a car accident when driving more than 10 miles over the speed limit in a residential neighborhood is .06. Of the next 1,000 cars that pass through a particular neighborhood, what are the first and third quartiles for the number of car accidents in this neighborhood?

7.99 A multiple-choice exam has 100 questions. Each question has four choices. (a) What minimum score should be required to reduce the chance of passing by random guessing to 5 percent? (b) To 1 percent? (c) Find the quartiles for a guesser.

7.100 The probability that a certain kind of flower seed will germinate is .80. (a) If 200 seeds are planted, what is the probability that fewer than 150 will germinate? (b) That at least 150 will germinate?

7.101 On a cold morning the probability is .02 that a given car will not start in the small town of Eureka. Assume that 1,500 cars are started each cold morning. (a) What is the probability that at least 25 cars will not start? (b) More than 40?

7.102 At a certain fire station, false alarms are received at a mean rate of 0.2 per day. In a year, what is the probability that fewer than 60 false alarms are received?

EXPONENTIAL DISTRIBUTION

7.103 The HP dvd1040i 20X Multiformat DVD Writer has an MTBF of 70,000 hours. (a) Assuming continuous operation, what is the probability that the DVD writer will last more than 100,000 hours? (b) Less than 50,000 hours? (c) At least 50,000 hours but not more than 80,000 hours? (Product specifications are from www.hp.com.)

7.104 Automobile warranty claims for engine mount failure in a Troppo Malo 2000 SE are rare at a certain dealership, occurring at a mean rate of 0.1 claim per month. (a) What is the probability that the dealership will wait at least 6 months until the next claim? (b) At least a year? (c) At least 2 years? (d) At least 6 months but not more than 1 year?

7.105 Suppose the average time to service a Noodles & Company customer at a certain restaurant is 3 minutes and the service time follows an exponential distribution. (a) What is the probability that a customer will be serviced in less than 3 minutes? (b) Why is your answer more than 50 percent? Shouldn't exactly half the area be below the mean?

7.106 Systron Donner Inertial manufactures inertial subsystems for automotive, commercial/industrial, and aerospace and defense applications. The sensors use a one-piece, micromachined inertial sensing element to measure angular rotational velocity or linear acceleration. The MTBF for a single axis sensor is 400,000 hours. (a) Find the probability that a sensor lasts at least 30 years, assuming continuous operation. (b) Would you be surprised if a sensor has failed within the first 3 years? Explain. (Product specifications are from www.systron.com/techsupp_A.asp.)

TRIANGULAR DISTRIBUTION

***7.107** The price (dollars per 1,000 board feet) of Douglas fir from western Washington and Oregon varies according to a triangular distribution $T(300, 350, 490)$. (a) Find the mean. (b) Find the standard deviation. (c) What is the probability that the price will exceed 400?

***7.108** The distribution of scores on a statistics exam is $T(50, 60, 95)$. (a) Find the mean. (b) Find the standard deviation. (c) Find the probability that a score will be less than 75. (d) Sketch the distribution and shade the area for the event in part (c).

***7.109** The distribution of beach condominium prices in Santa Theresa ($ thousands) is $T(500, 700, 2{,}100)$. (a) Find the mean. (b) Find the standard deviation. (c) Find the probability that a condo price will be greater than $750K. (d) Sketch the distribution and shade the area for the event in part (c).

PROJECTS AND DISCUSSION

7.110 (a) Write an Excel formula to generate a random normal deviate from $N(0, 1)$ and copy the formula into 10 cells. (b) Find the mean and standard deviation of your sample of 10 random data values. Are you satisfied that the random data have the desired mean and standard deviation? (c) Press F9 to generate 10 more data values and repeat question (b).

7.111 (a) Write an Excel formula to generate a random normal deviate from $N(4000, 200)$ and copy the formula into 100 cells. (b) Find the mean and standard deviation of your sample of 100 random data values. Are you satisfied that the random data have the desired mean and standard deviation? (c) Make a histogram of your sample. Does it appear normal?

7.112 On a police sergeant's examination, the historical mean score was 80 with a standard deviation of 20. Four officers who were alleged to be cronies of the police chief scored 195, 171, 191, and 189, respectively, on the test. This led to allegations of irregularity in the exam. (a) Convert these four officers' scores to standardized z-values. (b) Do you think there was sufficient reason to question these four exam scores? What assumptions are you making?

RELATED READING

Balakrishnan, N., and V. B. Nevzorov. *A Primer on Statistical Distributions*. Wiley, 2003.

Forbes, Catherine; Merran Evans; Nicholas Hastings; and Brian Peacock. *Statistical Distributions*. 4th ed. Wiley, 2011.

CHAPTER 7 More Learning Resources

You can access these *LearningStats* demonstrations through McGraw-Hill's Connect® to help you understand probability.

Topic	*LearningStats Demonstrations*
Calculations	Normal Areas Probability Calculator
Normal approximations	Evaluating Rules of Thumb Why the Rule of 10?
Random data	Random Continuous Data Visualizing Random Normal Data
Tables	Table C—Normal Probabilities

Key: = Excel = PDF

EXAM REVIEW QUESTIONS FOR CHAPTERS 5–7

1. Which type of probability (empirical, classical, subjective) is each of the following?
   a. On a given Friday, the probability that Flight 277 to Chicago is on time is 23.7%.
   b. Your chance of going to Disney World next year is 10%.
   c. The chance of rolling a 3 on two dice is 1/8.
2. For the following contingency table, find (a) $P(H \cap T)$; (b) $P(S \mid G)$; (c) $P(S)$

	R	*S*	*T*	*Row Total*
G	10	50	30	90
H	20	50	40	110
Col Total	30	100	70	200

3. If $P(A) = .30$, $P(B) = .70$, and $P(A \cap B) = .25$, are A and B independent events? Explain.
4. Which statement is *false*? Explain.
   a. If $P(A) = .05$, then the odds against event A's occurrence are 19 to 1.
   b. If A and B are mutually exclusive events, then $P(A \cup B) = 0$.
   c. The number of permutations of 5 things taken 2 at a time is 20.
5. Which statement is *true*? Why not the others?
   a. The Poisson distribution has two parameters.
   b. The binomial distribution assumes dependent random trials.
   c. The uniform distribution has two parameters.

6. If the payoff of a risky investment has three possible outcomes ($1,000, $2,000, $5,000) with probabilities .60, .30, and .10 respectively, find the expected value.

   a. $1,500 b. $2,300 c. $1,700

7. Assuming independent arrivals with a mean of 2.5 arrivals per minute, find the probability that in a given minute there will be (a) exactly 2 arrivals; (b) at least 3 arrivals; (c) fewer than 4 arrivals. (d) Which probability distribution did you use and why?
8. If a random experiment whose success probability is .20 is repeated 8 times, find the probability of (a) exactly 3 successes; (b) more than 3 successes; (c) at most 2 successes. (d) Which probability distribution did you use and why?
9. In a random experiment with 50 independent trials with constant probability of success .30, find the mean and standard deviation of the number of successes.
10. Which probability distribution (uniform, binomial, Poisson) is most nearly appropriate to describe each situation (assuming you knew the relevant parameters)?

    a. The number of dimes older than 10 years in a random sample of 8 dimes.
    b. The number of hospital patients admitted during a given minute on Tuesday morning.
    c. The last digit of a randomly chosen student's Social Security number.

11. Which statement is *false*? Explain.

    a. In the hypergeometric distribution, sampling is done without replacement.
    b. The mean of the uniform distribution is always $(a + b)/2$.
    c. We use the geometric distribution to find probabilities of arrivals per unit of time.

12. Which statement is *false*? Explain.

    a. To find probabilities in a continuous distribution, we add up the probabilities at each point.
    b. A uniform continuous model $U(5,21)$ has mean 13 and standard deviation 4.619.
    c. A uniform PDF is constant for all values within the interval $a \leq X \leq b$.

13. Which statement is *true* for a normal distribution? Why not the others?

    a. The shape of the PDF is always symmetric regardless of μ and σ.
    b. The shape of the CDF resembles a bell-shaped curve.
    c. When no tables are available, areas may be found by a simple formula.

14. If freeway speeds are normally distributed with a mean of $\mu = 70$ mph and $\sigma = 7$ mph, find the probability that the speed of a randomly chosen vehicle (a) exceeds 78 mph; (b) is between 65 and 75 mph; (c) is less than 70 mph.
15. In the previous problem, calculate (a) the 95th percentile of vehicle speeds (i.e., 95 percent below); (b) the lowest 10 percent of speeds; (c) the highest 25 percent of speeds (3rd quartile).
16. Which of the following Excel formulas would be a correct way to calculate $P(X < 450)$ given that X is $N(500, 60)$?

    a. =NORM.DIST(450, 500, 60, 1) b. =NORM.S.DIST(450, 60) c. =1–NORM.DIST(450, 500, 60, 0)

17. If arrivals follow a Poisson distribution with mean 1.2 arrivals per minute, find the probability that the waiting time until the next arrival will be (a) less than 1.5 minutes; (b) more than 30 seconds; (c) between 1 and 2 minutes.
18. In the previous problem, find (a) the 95th percentile of waiting times (i.e., 95 percent below); (b) the first quartile of waiting times; (c) the mean time between arrivals.
19. Which statement is *correct* concerning the normal approximation? Why not the others?

    a. The normal Poisson approximation is acceptable when $\lambda \geq 10$.
    b. The normal binomial approximation is better when n is small and π is large.
    c. Normal approximations are needed since Excel lacks discrete probability functions.

20. Which statement is *incorrect*? Explain.

    a. The triangular always has a single mode.
    b. The mean of the triangular is $(a + b + c)/3$.
    c. The triangular cannot be skewed left or right.

Chapter 8. Sampling Distributions and Estimation

CHAPTER 8 Sampling Distributions and Estimation

CHAPTER CONTENTS

CHAPTER LEARNING OBJECTIVES

LO

When you finish this chapter you should be able to

LO 8-1 Define sampling error, parameter, and estimator.

LO 8-2 Explain the desirable properties of estimators.

LO 8-3 State and apply the Central Limit Theorem for a mean.

LO 8-4 Explain how sample size affects the standard error.

LO 8-5 Construct a confidence interval for a population mean using *z*.

LO 8-6 Know when and how to use Student's *t* instead of *z* to estimate a mean.

LO 8-7 Construct a confidence interval for a population proportion.

LO 8-8 Know how to modify confidence intervals when the population is finite.

LO 8-9 Calculate sample size to estimate a mean.

LO 8-10 Calculate sample size to estimate a proportion

LO 8-11 Construct a confidence interval for a variance (optional).

8.1 SAMPLING AND ESTIMATION

LO 8-1

Define sampling error, parameter, and estimator.

LO 8-2

Explain the desirable properties of estimators.

A sample statistic is a *random variable* whose value depends on which population items happen to be included in the *random sample*. Some samples may represent the population well, while other samples could differ greatly from the population (particularly if the sample size is small). To illustrate **sampling variation**, let's draw some random samples from a large population of GMAT scores for MBA applicants. The population *parameters* are $\mu = 520.78$ and $\sigma = 86.80$. Figure 8.1 shows a dot plot of the entire population.

FIGURE 8.1

Dot Plot of GMAT Population GMAT

Source: Data for 2,637 MBA applicants at a medium-sized public university located in the Midwest.

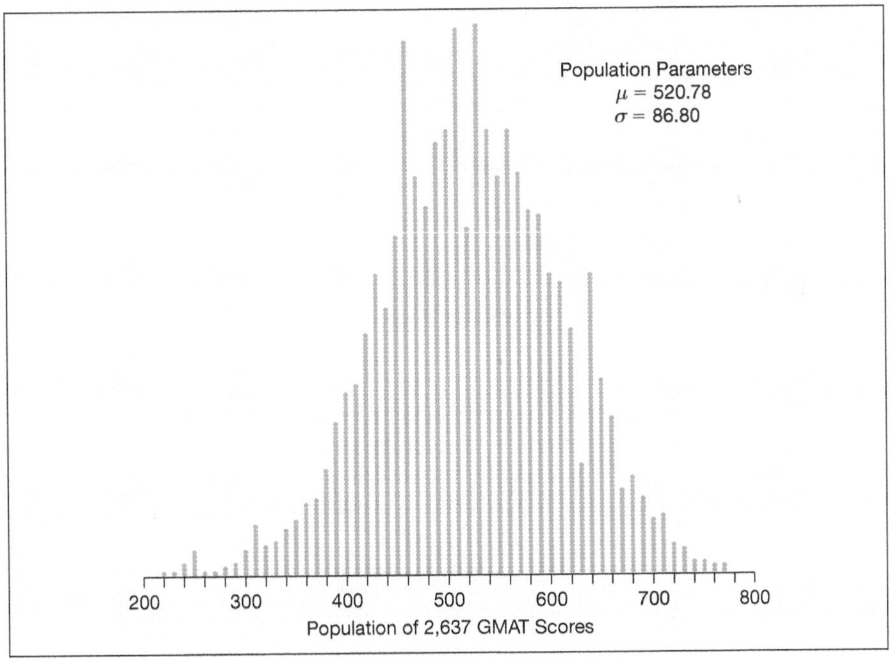

Figure 8.2 on the next page shows several random samples of $n = 5$ from this population. The *individual* items that happen to be included in the samples vary. Sampling variation is inevitable, yet there is a tendency for the sample *means* to be close to the population mean ($\mu = 520.78$) shown as a dashed line in Figure 8.2. In larger samples, the sample means would tend to be even closer to μ. This fact is the basis for **statistical estimation**.

FIGURE 8.2

Dot Plots of Eight Sample Means

GMAT

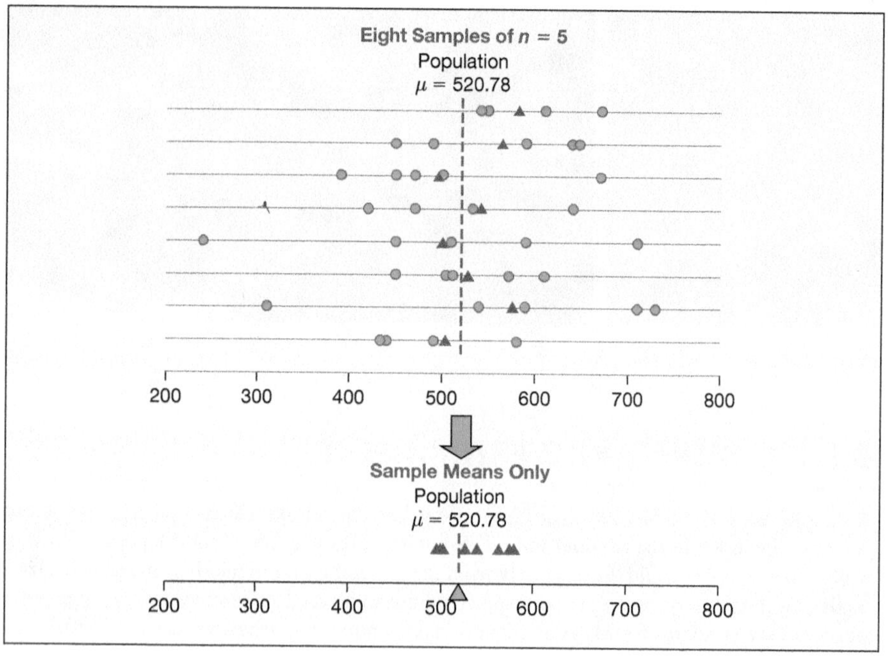

From Figure 8.2 we see that the sample *means* (red markers) have much less variation than the *individual* sample items (blue dots). This is because the mean is an *average*. To see this more clearly, we can remove the *individual* sample items (blue dots) and just look at the sample *means* (lower diagram). This chapter describes the behavior of the sample mean and other statistical estimators of population parameters, and explains how to make *inferences* about a population that take into account four factors:

- Sampling variation (uncontrollable).
- Population variation (uncontrollable).
- Sample size (controllable).
- Desired *confidence* in the estimate (controllable).

Estimators

An **estimator** is a statistic derived from a sample to infer the value of a population **parameter**. An **estimate** is the value of the estimator in a particular sample. Table 8.1 and Figure 8.3 show some common estimators. We usually denote a population parameter by a lowercase Greek letter (e.g., μ, σ, or π). The corresponding sample estimator is usually a Roman letter (e.g., $\bar{x}$, s, or p) or

TABLE 8.1

Examples of Estimators

Estimator	*Formula*	*Parameter*
Sample mean	$\bar{x} = \frac{1}{n}\sum_{i=1}^{n} x_i$ where x_i is the ith data value and n is the sample size	μ
Sample proportion	$p = x/n$ where x is the number of successes in the sample and n is the sample size	π
Sample standard deviation	$s = \sqrt{\frac{\sum_{i=1}^{n}(x_i - \bar{x})^2}{n-1}}$ where x_i is the ith data value and n is the sample size	σ

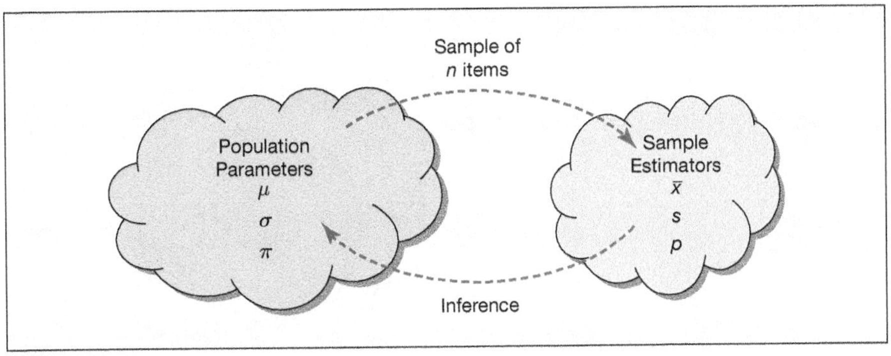

FIGURE 8.3
Sample Estimators of Population Parameters

a Greek letter with a "hat" (e.g., $\hat{\mu}$, $\hat{\sigma}$, or $\hat{\pi}$). Statistics books may use different symbols for these things. That's because the science of statistics developed over many decades and its founders had various ways of expressing their ideas.

Sampling Error

Random samples vary, so an estimator is a *random variable*. The **sampling error** is the difference between an estimate and the corresponding population parameter. For example, for the population mean:

$$\text{Sampling Error} = \bar{x} - \mu \qquad \textbf{(8.1)}$$

Sampling error exists because different samples will yield different values for $\bar{x}$, depending on which population items happen to be included in the sample. For example, we happen to know the true mean GMAT score, so we could calculate the sampling error for any given sample on the previous page. For Sample 1, the sample mean ($\bar{x} = 504.00$) is less than the population mean ($\mu = 520.78$) and its sampling error is $\bar{x} - \mu = 504.00 - 520.78 = -16.78$. For Sample 2, the sample mean ($\bar{x} = 576.00$) is greater than the population mean ($\mu = 520.78$) and its sampling error is $\bar{x} - \mu = 576.00 - 520.78 = +55.22$. Usually the parameter we are estimating is unknown, so we cannot calculate the sampling error. What we do know is that the sample mean $\bar{X}$ is a random variable that correctly estimates μ on average because the sample means that overestimate μ will tend to be offset by those that underestimate μ.

Properties of Estimators

Bias The **bias** is the difference between the expected value (i.e., the average value) of the estimator and the true parameter. For the mean:

$$\text{Bias} = E(\bar{X}) - \mu \qquad \textbf{(8.2)}$$

An estimator is *unbiased* if its expected value is the parameter being estimated. We say $\bar{X}$ is an unbiased estimate of μ because $E(\bar{X}) = \mu$. There can be sampling error in a particular sample, but an **unbiased estimator** neither overstates nor understates the true parameter *on average*. You cannot observe bias in a sample because you do not know the true population parameter, but bias can be studied mathematically or by simulation experiments.

The sample mean ($\bar{x}$) and sample proportion (p) are unbiased estimators of μ and π, respectively. But we can find examples of biased estimators. For example, if you use Excel's population standard deviation formula =STDEV.P(Data) instead of its sample standard deviation formula =STDEV.S(Data) to estimate σ, you will get a biased estimate. By using the population formula we will tend to underestimate the true value of σ *on average*. Sampling error is an inevitable risk in statistical sampling. You cannot *know* whether you have sampling error without knowing the population parameter (and if you knew it, you wouldn't be taking a sample). It is more important to understand that a large sample will yield a more reliable estimate and to take the sample scientifically (see Chapter 2, "Data Collection").

FIGURE 8.4

Illustration of Bias

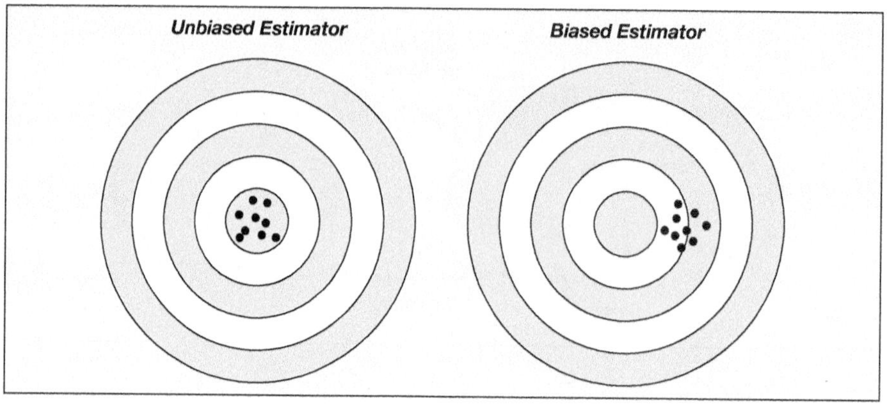

Sampling error is *random* whereas bias is *systematic*. Consider an analogy with target shooting, illustrated in Figure 8.4. An expert whose rifle sights are correctly aligned will produce a target pattern like the one on the left. The same expert shooting a rifle with misaligned sights might produce the pattern on the right. Both targets show sampling variation, but the unbiased estimator is correctly *aimed*. Some samples may happen to hit closer to the bull's-eye than others, but at least an unbiased estimator avoids *systematic* error.

Efficiency **Efficiency** refers to the variance of the estimator's sampling distribution. Smaller variance means a more efficient estimator. Among all unbiased estimators, we prefer the **minimum variance estimator**, referred to as MVUE (minimum variance unbiased estimator). Figure 8.5 shows two unbiased estimators. Both patterns are centered on the bull's-eye, but the estimator on the left has less variation. A more efficient estimator is closer *on average* to the true value of the parameter. You cannot assess efficiency from one sample, but it can be studied either mathematically or by simulation. While an MVUE does not exist for every parameter of every distribution, statisticians have proved that, for a normal distribution, $\bar{x}$ and s^2 are minimum variance estimators of μ and σ^2, respectively (i.e., no other estimators can have smaller variance). Similarly, the sample proportion p is an MVUE of the population proportion π. That is one reason these statistics are widely used.

FIGURE 8.5

Illustration of Efficiency

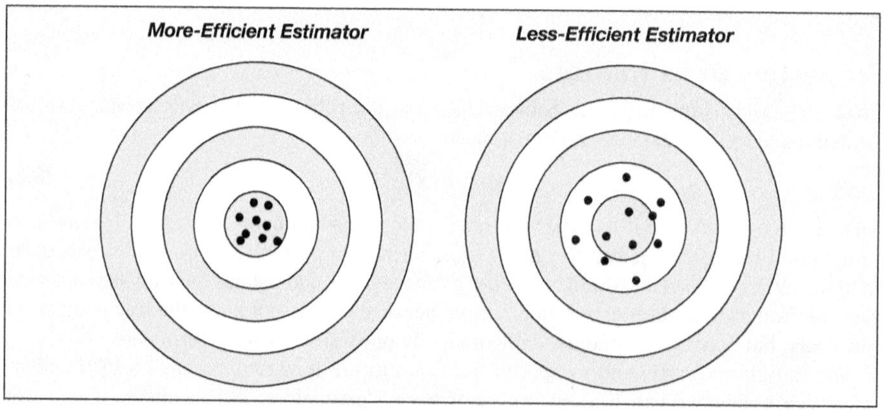

Consistency A **consistent estimator** converges toward the parameter being estimated as the sample size increases. That is, the sampling distribution collapses on the true parameter, as illustrated in Figure 8.6. It seems logical that in larger samples $\bar{x}$ ought to be closer to μ, p ought to be closer to π, and s ought to be closer to σ. In fact, it can be shown that the variances of these three estimators diminish as n increases, so all are consistent estimators. Figure 8.6 illustrates the importance of a large sample because in a large sample your estimated mean is likely to be closer to μ.

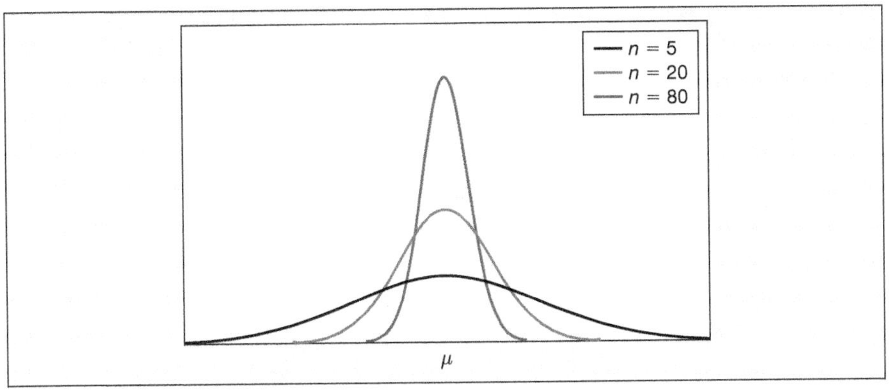

FIGURE 8.6
Illustration of Consistency

8.2 CENTRAL LIMIT THEOREM

LO 8-3
State and apply the Central Limit Theorem for a mean.

The **sampling distribution** of an estimator is the probability distribution of all possible values the statistic may assume when a random sample of size n is taken. An estimator has a probability distribution with a mean and variance.

Consider the sample mean $\bar{X}$ used to estimate the population mean μ. Our objective is to use the sampling distribution of $\bar{X}$ to say something about the population that we are studying. To describe the sampling distribution, we need to know the mean, variance, and shape of the distribution. As we've already learned, the sample mean is an unbiased estimator for μ; therefore,

$$E(\bar{X}) = \mu \quad \text{(expected value of the mean)} \tag{8.3}$$

We've also learned that $\bar{X}$ is a *random variable* whose value will change whenever we take a different sample. And as long as our samples are *random samples,* the only type of error we will have in our estimating process is *sampling error.* The sampling error of the sample mean is described by its standard deviation. This value has a special name, the **standard error of the mean.** Notice that the standard error of the mean decreases as the sample size increases:

$$\sigma_{\bar{x}} = \frac{\sigma}{\sqrt{n}} \quad \text{(standard error of the mean)} \tag{8.4}$$

Suppose the average price, μ, of a 2 GB MP3 player is \$80.00 with a standard deviation, σ, equal to \$10.00. What will be the mean and standard error of $\bar{x}$ from a sample of 20 MP3 players?

$$\mu_{\bar{x}} = \$80.00, \qquad \sigma_{\bar{x}} = \frac{\$10.00}{\sqrt{20}} = \$2.236$$

Furthermore, if the population is normal, then the sample mean follows a normal distribution for any sample size. Unfortunately, the population may not have a normal distribution, or we may simply not know *what* the population distribution looks like. What can we do in these circumstances? We can use one of the most fundamental laws of statistics, the *Central Limit Theorem.*

Central Limit Theorem for a Mean

If a random sample of size n is drawn from a population with mean μ and standard deviation σ, the distribution of the sample mean $\bar{X}$ approaches a normal distribution with mean μ and standard deviation $\sigma_{\bar{x}} = \sigma/\sqrt{n}$ as the sample size increases.

The **Central Limit Theorem** (CLT) is a powerful result that allows us to approximate the shape of the sampling distribution of $\bar{X}$ even when we don't know what the population looks like. Here are three important facts about the sample mean.

1. If the population is normal, the sample mean has a normal distribution centered at μ, with a standard error equal to $\sigma/\sqrt{n}$.

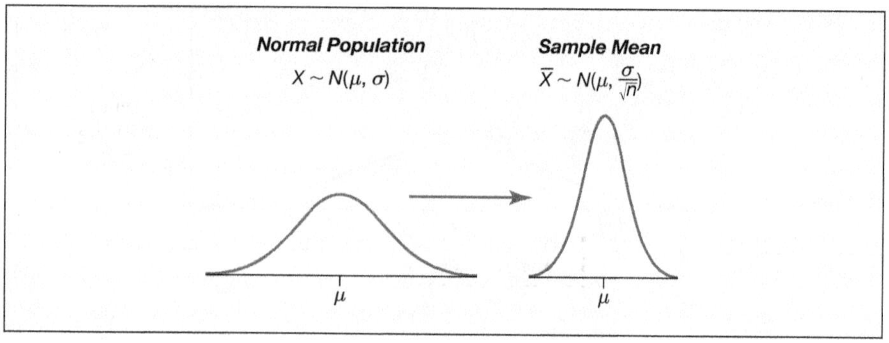

2. As sample size n increases, the distribution of sample means converges to the population mean μ (i.e., the *standard error of the mean* $\sigma_{\bar{x}} = \sigma/\sqrt{n}$ gets smaller).

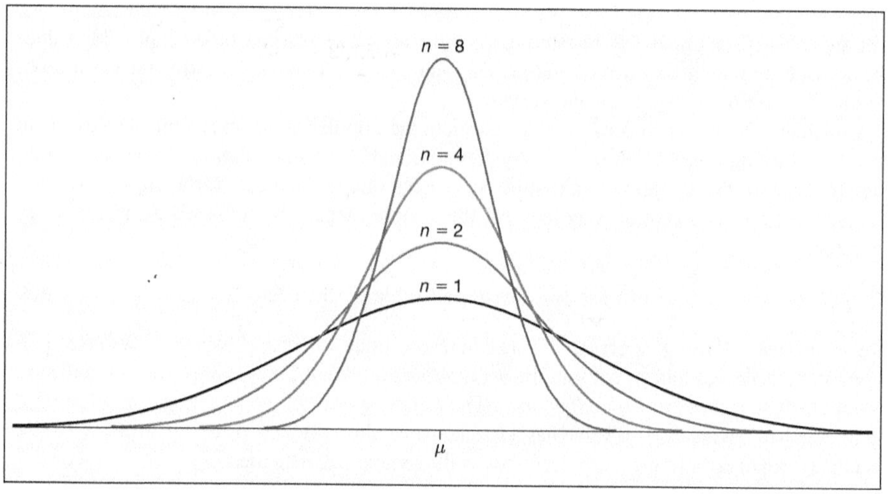

3. Even if your population is *not* normal, by the Central Limit Theorem, if the sample size is large enough, the sample means will have approximately a normal distribution.

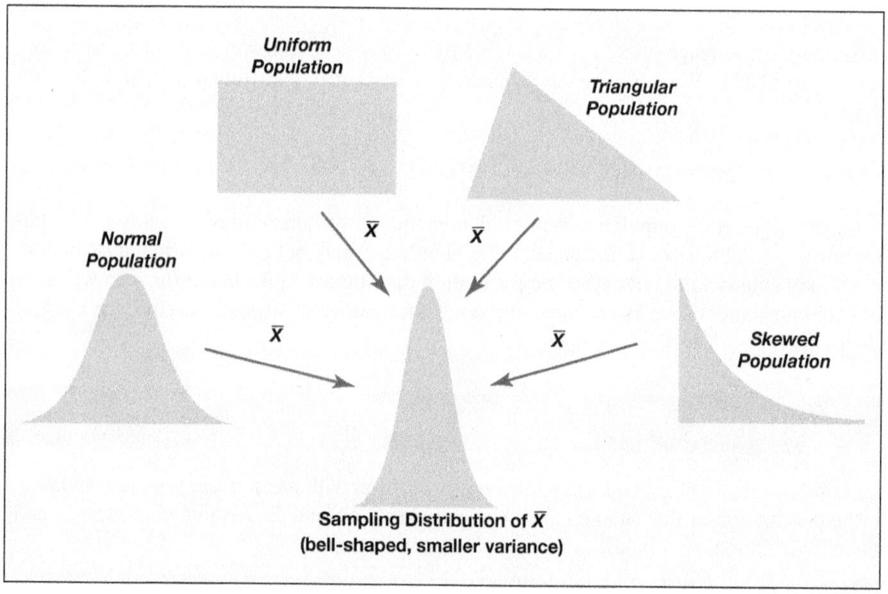

Applying the Central Limit Theorem

Uniform Population You may have heard the rule of thumb that $n \geq 30$ is required to ensure a normal distribution for the sample mean, but actually a much smaller n will suffice if the population is symmetric. You can demonstrate this by performing your own simulations in *LearningStats* (see More Learning Resources at the end of this chapter). For example, consider a uniform population $U(0,1000)$ with mean $\mu = 500$ and standard deviation $\sigma = 288.7$. The Central Limit Theorem predicts that the distribution of sample means drawn from the population will be approximately normal. Also, the standard error of the sample mean will decrease as sample size increases. $\bar{\bar{x}}$ is the notation used to represent the average of many $\bar{x}$'s and $s_{\bar{x}}$ represents the standard deviation of many $\bar{x}$'s. This is illustrated in Table 8.2.

TABLE 8.2 **Samples from a Uniform Population** CLTPopulations

	Sampling Distribution Parameters		Simulation Results for 2,000 Sample Means	
$n = 1$	$\mu = 500$	$\sigma_{\bar{x}} = \sigma/\sqrt{n} = 288.7/\sqrt{1} = 288.7$	$\bar{\bar{x}} = 508.7$	$s_{\bar{x}} = 290.7$
$n = 2$	$\mu = 500$	$\sigma_{\bar{x}} = \sigma/\sqrt{n} = 288.7/\sqrt{2} = 204.1$	$\bar{\bar{x}} = 497.9$	$s_{\bar{x}} = 202.6$
$n = 4$	$\mu = 500$	$\sigma_{\bar{x}} = \sigma/\sqrt{n} = 288.7/\sqrt{4} = 144.3$	$\bar{\bar{x}} = 498.4$	$s_{\bar{x}} = 145.2$
$n = 8$	$\mu = 500$	$\sigma_{\bar{x}} = \sigma/\sqrt{n} = 288.7/\sqrt{8} = 102.1$	$\bar{\bar{x}} = 498.8$	$s_{\bar{x}} = 100.2$

Figure 8.7 shows histograms of the actual means of many samples drawn from this uniform population. There is sampling variation, but the means and standard deviations of the sample

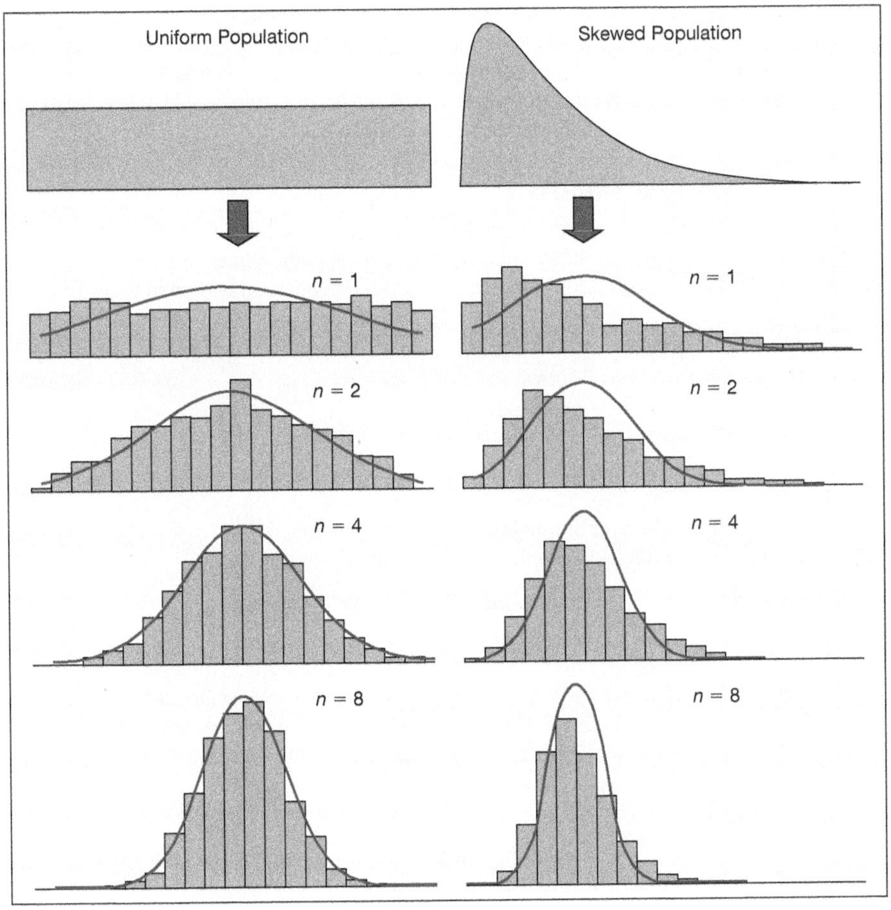

FIGURE 8.7

Illustrations of Central Limit Theorem

means are very close to the predictions in Table 8.2. When $n = 1$, the "means" are simply individual population items, so the histogram looks like the population, and is not normal. For $n = 2$, the histogram of means is triangular, while for $n = 4$ and $n = 8$ we clearly see the approach to a bell-shaped histogram and decreasing variance of the sample mean as sample size increases.

Skewed Population A symmetric, uniform population does not pose much of a challenge for the Central Limit Theorem. But what if the population is severely skewed? For example, consider a strongly skewed population (e.g., waiting times at airport security screening). The Central Limit Theorem predicts that *for any population* the distribution of sample means drawn from this population will approach normality. The standard error of the sample mean will diminish as sample size increases, as illustrated in Table 8.3.

TABLE 8.3 Samples from a Skewed Population CLTPopulations

	Sampling Distribution Parameters		Simulation Results for 2,000 Sample Means	
$n = 1$	$\mu = 3.000$	$\sigma_{\bar{x}} = \sigma/\sqrt{n} = 2.449/\sqrt{1} = 2.449$	$\bar{\bar{x}} = 3.050$	$s_{\bar{x}} = 2.517$
$n = 2$	$\mu = 3.000$	$\sigma_{\bar{x}} = \sigma/\sqrt{n} = 2.449/\sqrt{2} = 1.732$	$\bar{\bar{x}} = 2.982$	$s_{\bar{x}} = 1.704$
$n = 4$	$\mu = 3.000$	$\sigma_{\bar{x}} = \sigma/\sqrt{n} = 2.449/\sqrt{4} = 1.225$	$\bar{\bar{x}} = 2.973$	$s_{\bar{x}} = 1.196$
$n = 8$	$\mu = 3.000$	$\sigma_{\bar{x}} = \sigma/\sqrt{n} = 2.449/\sqrt{8} = 0.866$	$\bar{\bar{x}} = 3.005$	$s_{\bar{x}} = 0.868$

Figure 8.7 shows histograms of the actual means of many samples drawn from this skewed population. Despite the skewness, the means and standard deviations of the sample means are very close to the CLT's predictions. When $n = 1$, the "means" are simply individual population items, so the histogram of means looks just like the skewed parent population. In contrast to the uniform population example, $n = 2$ and $n = 4$ do *not* produce bell-shaped histograms, although the variance does decrease. When $n = 8$ the histogram begins to look normal, but a larger sample might be preferable. In highly skewed populations, even $n \geq 30$ will not ensure normality, although in general it is not a bad rule. In severely skewed populations, recall that the mean is a poor measure of center to begin with due to outliers.

Range of Sample Means

The Central Limit Theorem permits us to define an interval within which the sample means are expected to fall. As long as the sample size n is large enough, we can use the normal distribution regardless of the population shape (or any n if the population is normal to begin with):

Expected Range of Sample Means

(8.5)
$$\mu \pm z\frac{\sigma}{\sqrt{n}}$$

We use the familiar z-values for the standard normal distribution. If we know μ and σ, the CLT allows us to predict the range of sample means for samples of size n:

90% Interval	*95% Interval*	*99% Interval*
$\mu \pm 1.645\frac{\sigma}{\sqrt{n}}$	$\mu \pm 1.960\frac{\sigma}{\sqrt{n}}$	$\mu \pm 2.576\frac{\sigma}{\sqrt{n}}$

For example, within what interval would we expect GMAT sample means to fall for samples of $n = 5$ applicants (see Figure 8.1)? The population is approximately normal with parameters $\mu = 520.78$ and $\sigma = 86.80$, so the predicted range for 95 percent of the sample means is

$$520.78 \pm 1.960\frac{86.80}{\sqrt{5}} \quad \text{or} \quad 520.78 \pm 76.08 \quad \text{or} \quad [444.70, 596.86]$$

Our eight sample means for $n = 5$ (see Figure 8.2) drawn from this population fall within this interval (roughly 444 to 597), as predicted by the Central Limit Theorem.

EXAMPLE 8.1

Bottle Filling: Variation in $\bar{X}$

The amount of liquid in a half-liter (500 ml) bottle of Diet Coke is normally distributed with mean $\mu = 505$ ml and standard deviation $\sigma = 1.2$ ml. Since the population is normal, the sample mean $\bar{X}$ will be a normally distributed random variable for any sample size. If we sample a single bottle (i.e., $n = 1$) and measure its fill, the sample "mean" is just X, which should lie within the ranges shown in Table 8.4. It appears that the company has set the mean far enough above 500 ml that essentially all bottles contain at least the advertised half-liter quantity. If we increase the sample size to $n = 4$ bottles, we expect the sample means to lie within a narrower range, as shown in Table 8.4, because when we average 4 items, we *reduce the variability* in the sample mean.

TABLE 8.4 Expected 95 Percent Range of the Sample Mean

$n = 1$	$n = 4$
$\mu \pm 1.960 \frac{\sigma}{\sqrt{n}}$	$\mu \pm 1.960 \frac{\sigma}{\sqrt{n}}$
$505 \pm 1.960 \frac{1.2}{\sqrt{1}}$	$505 \pm 1.960 \frac{1.2}{\sqrt{4}}$
505 ± 2.352	505 ± 1.176
[502.6, 507.4]	[503.8, 506.2]

If this experiment were repeated a large number of times, we would expect that the sample means would lie within the limits shown above. For example, if we took 1,000 samples and computed the mean fill for each sample, we would expect that approximately 950 of the sample means would lie within the 95 percent limits. But we don't really take 1,000 samples (except in a computer simulation). We actually take only *one* sample. The importance of the CLT is that it *predicts* what will likely happen with that *one* sample.

SECTION EXERCISES

connect

8.1 Find the interval $\left[\mu - z\frac{\sigma}{\sqrt{n}}, \mu + z\frac{\sigma}{\sqrt{n}}\right]$ within which 90 percent of the sample means would be expected to fall, assuming that each sample is from a normal population.

a. $\mu = 100, \sigma = 12, n = 36$
b. $\mu = 2{,}000, \sigma = 150, n = 9$
c. $\mu = 500, \sigma = 10, n = 25$

8.2 Find the interval $\left[\mu - z\frac{\sigma}{\sqrt{n}}, \mu + z\frac{\sigma}{\sqrt{n}}\right]$ within which 95 percent of the sample means would be expected to fall, assuming that each sample is from a normal population.

a. $\mu = 200, \sigma = 12, n = 36$
b. $\mu = 1{,}000, \sigma = 15, n = 9$
c. $\mu = 50, \sigma = 1, n = 25$

8.3 The diameter of bushings turned out by a manufacturing process is a normally distributed random variable with a mean of 4.035 mm and a standard deviation of 0.005 mm. A sample of 25 bushings is taken once an hour. (a) Within what interval should 95 percent of the bushing diameters fall? (b) Within what interval should 95 percent of the sample *means* fall? (c) What conclusion would you reach if you saw a sample mean of 4.020? A sample mean of 4.055?

8.4 Concerns about climate change and CO_2 reduction have initiated the commercial production of blends of biodiesel (e.g., from renewable sources) and petrodiesel (from fossil fuel). Random samples of 35 blended fuels are tested in a lab to ascertain the bio/total carbon ratio. (a) If the true mean is .9480 with a standard deviation of 0.0060, within what interval will 95 percent of the sample means fall? (b) What is the sampling distribution of $\bar{X}$? In other words, state the shape, center, and variability of the distribution of $\bar{X}$. (c) What theorem did you use to answer part (b)?

8.3 SAMPLE SIZE AND STANDARD ERROR

LO 8-4

Explain how sample size affects the standard error.

Even if the population standard deviation σ is large, the sample means will fall within a narrow interval as long as n is large. The key is the *standard error of the mean:* $\sigma_{\bar{x}} = \sigma/\sqrt{n}$. The standard error decreases as n increases. Figure 8.8 illustrates how increasing n reduces the standard error (expressed in this diagram as a fraction of σ). For example, when $n = 4$ the standard error is halved. To halve it again requires $n = 16$, and to halve it again requires $n = 64$. To *halve* the standard error, you must *quadruple* the sample size (the law of diminishing returns).

Sample Size	*Standard Error*
$n = 4$	$\sigma_{\bar{x}} = \sigma/\sqrt{4} = \sigma/2$
$n = 16$	$\sigma_{\bar{x}} = \sigma/\sqrt{16} = \sigma/4$
$n = 64$	$\sigma_{\bar{x}} = \sigma/\sqrt{64} = \sigma/8$

You can make the interval $\mu \pm z\sigma/\sqrt{n}$ as small as you want by increasing n. Thus, the mean of sample means converges to the true population mean μ as n increases.

FIGURE 8.8

Standard Error Declines as *n* Increases

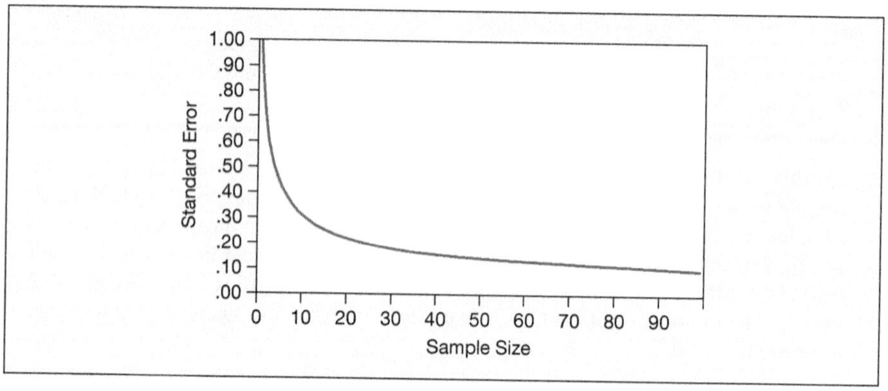

To help visualize the meaning of the Central Limit Theorem, consider a discrete uniform population consisting of the integers {0, 1, 2, 3}. The population parameters are $\mu = 1.5$ and $\sigma = 1.118$ (using the population definition of σ).

$$\mu = \frac{1}{N}\sum_{i=1}^{N} x_i = \frac{0+1+2+3}{4} = 1.5$$

$$\sigma = \sqrt{\frac{\sum_{i=1}^{n}(x_i - \mu)^2}{N}} = \sqrt{\frac{(0-1.5)^2 + (1-1.5)^2 + (2-1.5)^2 + (3-1.5)^2}{4}} = 1.118$$

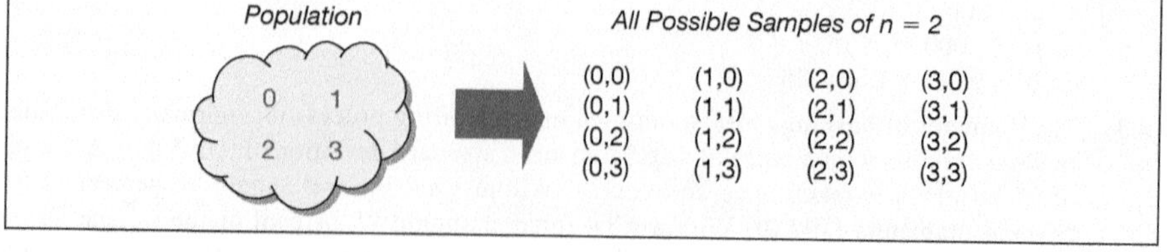

Take all possible random samples of $n = 2$ items *with replacement*. There are 16 equally likely outcomes (x_1, x_2). Each sample mean is $\bar{x} = (x_1 + x_2)/2$:

$\bar{x} = (0 + 0)/2 = 0.0$	$\bar{x} = (1 + 0)/2 = 0.5$	$\bar{x} = (2 + 0)/2 = 1.0$	$\bar{x} = (3 + 0)/2 = 1.5$
$\bar{x} = (0 + 1)/2 = 0.5$	$\bar{x} = (1 + 1)/2 = 1.0$	$\bar{x} = (2 + 1)/2 = 1.5$	$\bar{x} = (3 + 1)/2 = 2.0$
$\bar{x} = (0 + 2)/2 = 1.0$	$\bar{x} = (1 + 2)/2 = 1.5$	$\bar{x} = (2 + 2)/2 = 2.0$	$\bar{x} = (3 + 2)/2 = 2.5$
$\bar{x} = (0 + 3)/2 = 1.5$	$\bar{x} = (1 + 3)/2 = 2.0$	$\bar{x} = (2 + 3)/2 = 2.5$	$\bar{x} = (3 + 3)/2 = 3.0$

TABLE 8.5

Sampling Distribution of $\bar{X}$ for $n = 2$

Sample Mean ($\bar{x}$)	Frequency	Relative Frequency
0.0	1	0.0625
0.5	2	0.1250
1.0	3	0.1875
1.5	4	0.2500
2.0	3	0.1875
2.5	2	0.1250
3.0	1	0.0625
Total	16	1.0000

FIGURE 8.9

Population and Sampling Distribution of $\bar{X}$ for $n = 2$

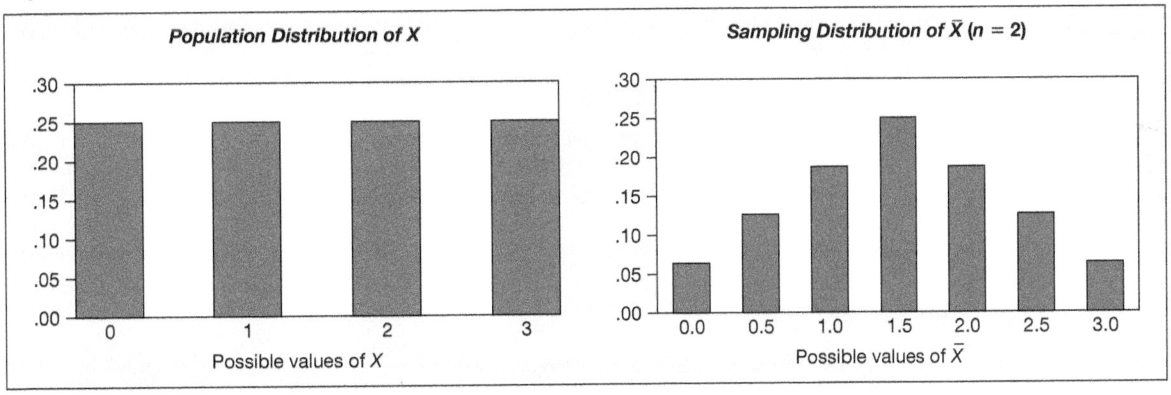

The population is uniform (0, 1, 2, 3 are equally likely) yet the distribution of all possible sample means has a peaked triangular shape, as shown in Table 8.5 and Figure 8.9. The distribution of sample means is approaching a bell shape or normal distribution, as predicted by the Central Limit Theorem.

The predictions for the mean and standard error are

$$\mu_{\bar{x}} = \mu = 1.5 \quad \text{and} \quad \sigma_{\bar{x}} = \frac{\sigma}{\sqrt{n}} = \frac{1.11803}{\sqrt{2}} = 0.7906$$

These theoretical predictions are borne out exactly for all 16 possible sample means. The mean of *means* $\bar{\bar{x}}$ is

$$\bar{\bar{x}} = \frac{1(0.0) + 2(0.5) + 3(1.0) + 4(1.5) + 3(2.0) + 2(2.5) + 1(3.0)}{16} = 1.5$$

The standard deviation of *all possible sample means* is

$$\sigma_{\bar{x}} = \sqrt{\frac{\left[\begin{array}{l} 1(0.0-1.5)^2 + 2(0.5-1.5)^2 + 3(1.0-1.5)^2 + 4(1.5-1.5)^2 \\ \quad + 3(2.0-1.5)^2 + 2(2.5-1.5)^2 + 1(3.0-1.5)^2 \end{array}\right]}{16}} = 0.7906$$

SECTION EXERCISES

connect

8.5 (a) Find the standard error of the mean for each sampling situation (assuming a normal population). (b) What happens to the standard error each time you quadruple the sample size?

a. $\sigma = 32, n = 4$
b. $\sigma = 32, n = 16$
c. $\sigma = 32, n = 64$

8.6 (a) Find the standard error of the mean for each sampling situation (assuming a normal population). (b) What happens to the standard error each time you quadruple the sample size?

a. $\sigma = 24, n = 9$
b. $\sigma = 24, n = 36$
c. $\sigma = 24, n = 144$

8.7 The fat content of a pouch of Keebler Right Bites© Fudge Shoppe© Mini-Fudge Stripes is normally distributed with a mean of 3.50 grams. Assume a known standard deviation of 0.25 gram. (a) What is the standard error of $\bar{X}$, the mean weight from a random sample of 10 pouches of cookies? (b) Within what interval would you expect the sample mean to fall, with 95 percent probability? (Source: http://www.keebler.com.)

8.8 The fuel economy of a 2011 Lexus RX 350 2WD 6 cylinder 3.5 L automatic 5-speed using premium fuel is a normally distributed random variable with a mean of $\mu = 25.0$ MPG and a standard deviation of $\sigma = 1.25$ MPG. (a) What is the standard error of $\bar{X}$, the mean from a random sample of 16 fill-ups by one driver? (b) Within what interval would you expect the sample mean to fall, with 90 percent probability? (Source: www.fueleconomy.gov.)

8.4 CONFIDENCE INTERVAL FOR A MEAN (μ) WITH KNOWN σ

What Is a Confidence Interval?

LO 8-5

Construct a confidence interval for a population mean using *z*.

A sample mean $\bar{x}$ calculated from a random sample $x_1, x_2, \ldots, x_n$ is a **point estimate** of the unknown population mean μ. Because samples vary, we need to indicate our uncertainty about the true value of μ. Based on our knowledge of the sampling distribution of $\bar{X}$, we can create an **interval estimate** for μ. We construct a **confidence interval** for the unknown mean μ by adding and subtracting a **margin of error** from $\bar{x}$, the mean of our random sample. The **confidence level** for this interval is expressed as a percentage such as 90, 95, or 99 percent.

Confidence Interval for a Mean μ with Known σ

(8.6) $$\bar{x} \pm z_{\alpha/2}\frac{\sigma}{\sqrt{n}} \quad \text{where } \frac{\sigma}{\sqrt{n}} \text{ is the standard error of the mean}$$

If samples are drawn from a normal population (or if the sample is large enough that $\bar{X}$ is approximately normal by the Central Limit Theorem) and σ is known, then the margin of error is calculated using the standard normal distribution. The value $z_{\alpha/2}$ is determined by the desired level of confidence, which we call $1 - \alpha$. Because the sampling distribution is symmetric, $\alpha/2$ is the area in each tail of the normal distribution as shown in Figure 8.10.

The middle area shows the confidence level. The remaining area is divided into two symmetrical tails, each having area equal to $\alpha/2$. The value of $z_{\alpha/2}$ will depend on the level of

FIGURE 8.10

Confidence Level Using *z*

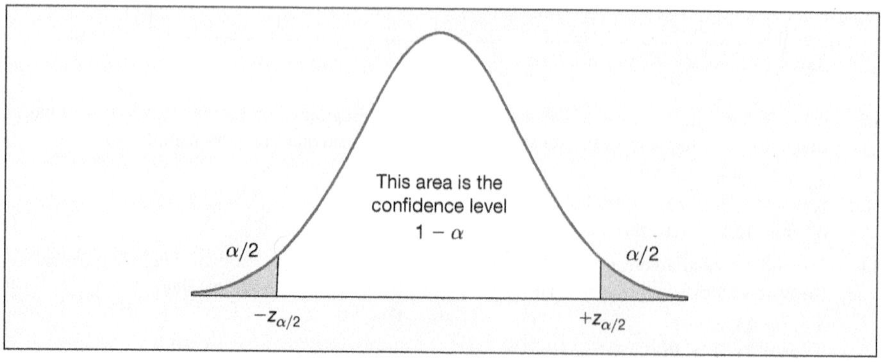

FIGURE 8.11

90 Percent and 95 Percent Confidence Levels Compared

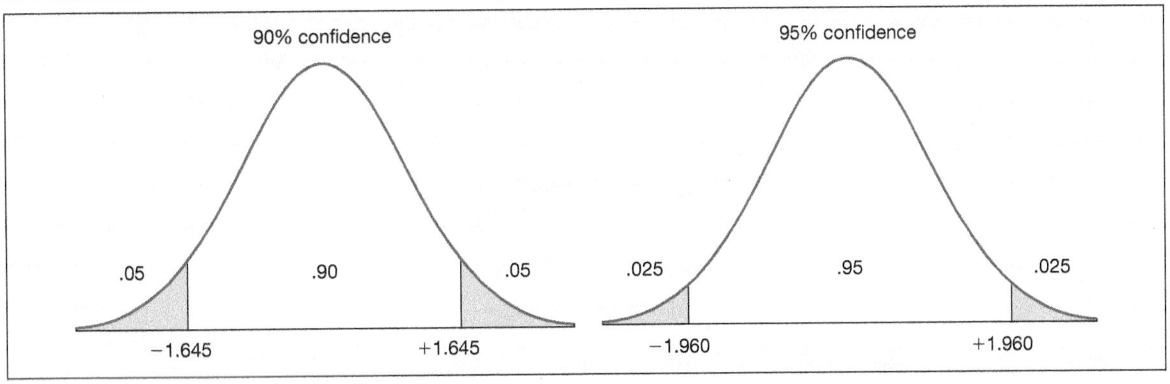

confidence desired. For example, if the chosen confidence level is 90 percent ($1 - \alpha = .90$ and $\alpha = .10$), we would use $z_{\alpha/2} = z_{.10/2} = z_{.05} = 1.645$ for an upper tail area of .05. Similarly, for a 95 percent confidence level ($1 - \alpha = .95$ and $\alpha = .05$), we would use $z_{\alpha/2} = z_{.05/2} = z_{.025} = 1.960$ for an upper tail area of .025, as illustrated in Figure 8.11. Notice that the 95 percent confidence interval is *wider* than the 90 percent confidence interval.

EXAMPLE 8.2

Bottle Filling: Confidence Intervals for μ

The volume of liquid in a half-liter bottle of Diet Coke is a normally distributed random variable. The standard deviation of volume is known to be $\sigma = 1.20$ ml. A sample of 10 bottles gives a sample mean volume $\bar{x} = 503.4$ ml. Since the population is normal, the sample mean is a normally distributed random variable for any sample size, so we can use the z distribution to construct a confidence interval for μ.

For a 90 percent confidence interval, we insert $z_{\alpha/2} = 1.645$ in formula 8.6.

90% confidence interval: $\bar{x} \pm z_{\alpha/2}\dfrac{\sigma}{\sqrt{n}}$ or $503.4 \pm 1.645\dfrac{1.20}{\sqrt{10}}$ or $[502.78, 504.02]$

For a 95 percent confidence interval, we would use $z_{\alpha/2} = 1.960$:

95% confidence interval: $\bar{x} \pm z_{\alpha/2}\dfrac{\sigma}{\sqrt{n}}$ or $503.4 \pm 1.96\dfrac{1.20}{\sqrt{10}}$ or $[502.66, 504.14]$

For a 99 percent confidence interval, we would use $z_{\alpha/2} = 2.576$ in the formula:

99% confidence interval: $\bar{x} \pm z_{\alpha/2}\dfrac{\sigma}{\sqrt{n}}$ or $503.4 \pm 2.576\dfrac{1.2}{\sqrt{10}}$ or $[502.42, 504.38]$

Notice that lower bounds for all three of the confidence intervals are well above 500, indicating that the mean of the bottle-filling process is safely above the required minimum half liter (500 ml).

Choosing a Confidence Level

You might be tempted to assume that a higher confidence level gives a "better" estimate. However, confidence is not free—there is a trade-off that must be made. A higher confidence level leads to a wider confidence interval, as illustrated in Example 8.2. The 95 percent confidence interval is *wider* than the 90 percent confidence interval. In order to gain confidence, we must accept a wider range of possible values for μ. Greater confidence implies loss of precision (i.e., a greater margin of error). Table 8.6 shows several common confidence levels and their associated z-values. A 95 percent confidence level is often used because it is a reasonable compromise between confidence and precision.

TABLE 8.6

Common Confidence Levels and z-Values

Confidence Level	$1-\alpha$	α	$\alpha/2$	$z_{\alpha/2}$
90%	.90	.10	.05	$z_{.05} = 1.645$
95%	.95	.05	.025	$z_{.025} = 1.960$
99%	.99	.01	.005	$z_{.005} = 2.576$

Interpretation

Before actually taking a random sample we can think of the confidence level $1 - \alpha$ as a *probability on the procedure* used to calculate the confidence interval.

(8.7) $$P\left(\bar{X} - z_{\alpha/2}\frac{\sigma}{\sqrt{n}} < \mu < \bar{X} + z_{\alpha/2}\frac{\sigma}{\sqrt{n}}\right) = 1 - \alpha$$

This is a statement about the *random variable* $\bar{X}$. It is not a statement about a *specific* sample mean $\bar{x}$. If you took 100 random samples from the same population and used exactly this procedure to construct 100 confidence intervals using a 95 percent confidence level, approximately 95 of the intervals would contain the true mean μ, while approximately 5 intervals would not. Figure 8.12 illustrates this idea using 20 samples (note that one interval does not contain μ).

FIGURE 8.12

Twenty 95 Percent Confidence Intervals for μ

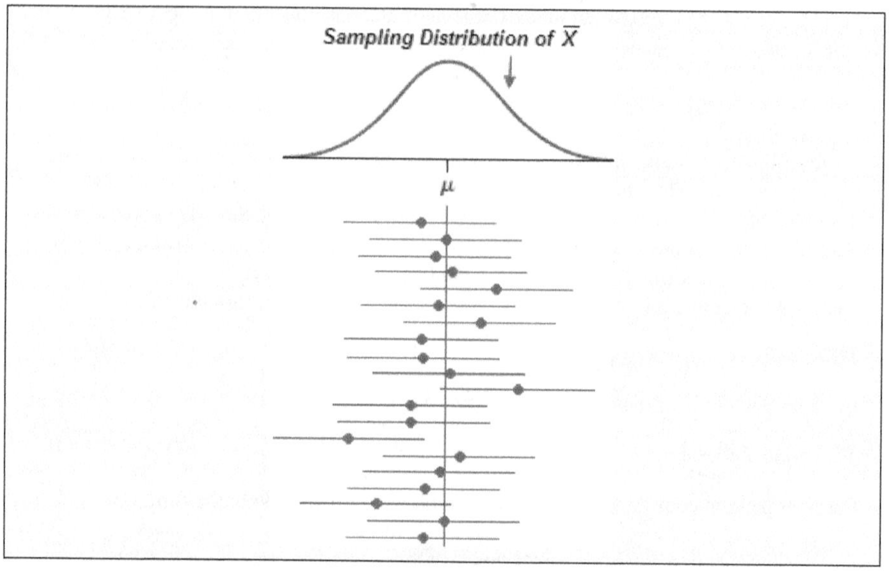

Once you've taken a random sample and have calculated $\bar{x}$ and the corresponding confidence interval, the confidence level $1 - \alpha$ no longer is thought of as a probability. The confidence interval you've calculated either does or does not contain μ. Because you only do it once, you won't know if your specific interval contains the true mean μ or not. You can only say that $1 - \alpha$ is now your level of *confidence* that the interval contains μ.

When Can We Assume Normality?

If σ is known and the population is normal, then we can safely use formula 8.6 to construct the confidence interval for μ. If σ is known but we do not know whether the population is normal, a common rule of thumb is that $n \geq 30$ is sufficient to assume a normal distribution for $\bar{X}$ (by the CLT) as long as the population is reasonably symmetric and has no outliers. However, a larger n may be needed to assume normality if you are sampling from a strongly skewed population or one with outliers. When σ is *unknown*, a different approach is used, as described in the next section.

Is σ Ever Known?

Yes, but not very often. In quality control applications with ongoing manufacturing processes, it may be reasonable to assume that σ stays the same over time. The type of confidence interval just seen is therefore important because it is used to construct *control charts* to track the mean of a process (such as bottle filling) over time. However, the case of unknown σ is more typical, and will be examined in the next section.

SECTION EXERCISES

connect

8.9 Construct a confidence interval for μ assuming that each sample is from a normal population.

a. $\bar{x} = 14$, $\sigma = 4$, $n = 5$, 90 percent confidence
b. $\bar{x} = 37$, $\sigma = 5$, $n = 15$, 99 percent confidence
c. $\bar{x} = 121$, $\sigma = 15$, $n = 25$, 95 percent confidence

8.10 Construct a confidence interval for μ assuming that each sample is from a normal population.

a. $\bar{x} = 24$, $\sigma = 3$, $n = 10$, 90 percent confidence
b. $\bar{x} = 125$, $\sigma = 8$, $n = 25$, 99 percent confidence
c. $\bar{x} = 12.5$, $\sigma = 1.2$, $n = 50$, 95 percent confidence

8.11 Use the sample information $\bar{x} = 2.4$, $\sigma = 0.15$, $n = 9$ to calculate the following confidence intervals for μ assuming the sample is from a normal population: (a) 90 percent confidence; (b) 95 percent confidence; (c) 99 percent confidence. (d) Describe how the intervals change as you increase the confidence level.

8.12 Use the sample information $\bar{x} = 37$, $\sigma = 5$, $n = 15$ to calculate the following confidence intervals for μ assuming the sample is from a normal population: (a) 90 percent confidence; (b) 95 percent confidence; (c) 99 percent confidence. (d) Describe how the intervals change as you increase the confidence level.

8.13 A random sample of 25 items is drawn from a population whose standard deviation is known to be $\sigma = 40$. The sample mean is $\bar{x} = 270$.

a. Construct an interval estimate for μ with 95 percent confidence.
b. Repeat part a assuming that $n = 50$.
c. Repeat part a assuming that $n = 100$.
d. Describe how the confidence interval changes as n increases.

8.14 A random sample of 100 items is drawn from a population whose standard deviation is known to be $\sigma = 50$. The sample mean is $\bar{x} = 850$.

a. Construct an interval estimate for μ with 95 percent confidence.
b. Repeat part a assuming that $\sigma = 100$.
c. Repeat part a assuming that $\sigma = 200$.
d. Describe how the confidence interval changes as σ increases.

8.15 The fuel economy of a 2011 Lexus RX 350 2WD 6 cylinder 3.5 L automatic 5-speed using premium fuel is normally distributed with a known standard deviation of 1.25 MPG. If a random sample of 10 tanks of gas yields a mean of 21.0 MPG, find the 95 percent confidence interval for the true mean MPG. (Source: www.fueleconomy.gov.)

8.16 Guest ages at a Vail Resorts ski mountain typically have a right-skewed distribution. Assume the standard deviation (σ) of *age* is 14.5 years. (a) Even though the population distribution of age is right-skewed, what will be the shape of the distribution of $\bar{X}$, the average age, in a random sample of 40 guests? (b) From a random sample of 40 guests, the sample mean is 36.4 years. Calculate a 99 percent confidence interval for μ, the true mean age of Vail Resorts ski mountain guests.

8.17 The Ball Corporation's beverage can manufacturing plant in Fort Atkinson, Wisconsin, uses a metal supplier that provides metal with a known thickness standard deviation $\sigma = .000959$ mm. If a random sample of 58 sheets of metal resulted in $\bar{x} = 0.2731$ mm, calculate the 99 percent confidence interval for the true mean metal thickness.

8.5 CONFIDENCE INTERVAL FOR A MEAN (μ) WITH UNKNOWN σ

Student's *t* Distribution

LO 8-6

Know when and how to use Student's *t* instead of *z* to estimate a mean.

In situations where the population is normal but its standard deviation σ is unknown, the **Student's *t* distribution** should be used instead of the normal z distribution. This is particularly important when the sample size is small. When σ is unknown, the formula for a confidence interval resembles the formula for known σ except that t replaces z and s replaces σ.

Confidence Interval for a Mean μ with Unknown σ

(8.8) $\bar{x} \pm t_{\alpha/2}\frac{s}{\sqrt{n}}$ where $\frac{s}{\sqrt{n}}$ is the *estimated* standard error of the mean

The interpretation of the confidence interval is the same as when σ is known, as illustrated in Figure 8.13. However, the confidence intervals will be wider (other things being the same) because $t_{\alpha/2}$ is always greater than $z_{\alpha/2}$. Intuitively, our confidence interval will be wider because we face added uncertainty when we use the sample standard deviation s to estimate the unknown population standard deviation σ.

FIGURE 8.13

Confidence Level Using Student's *t*

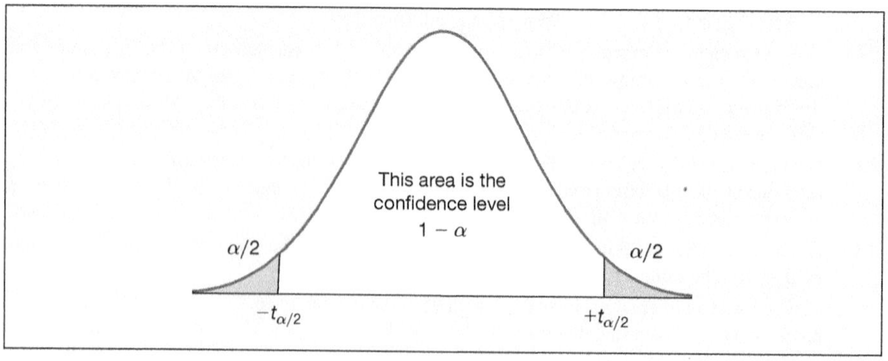

The Student's t distributions were proposed by a Dublin brewer named W. S. Gossett (1876–1937) who published his research under the name "Student" because his employer did not approve of publishing research based on company data. The t distributions are symmetric and shaped very much like the standard normal distribution, except they are somewhat less peaked and have thicker tails. Note that the t distributions are a class of distributions, each of which is dependent on the size of the sample we are using. Figure 8.14 shows how the tails of the distributions change as the sample size increases. A closer look reveals that the t distribution's tails lie *above* the normal (i.e., the t distribution always has longer tails).

FIGURE 8.14

Comparison of Normal and Student's *t*

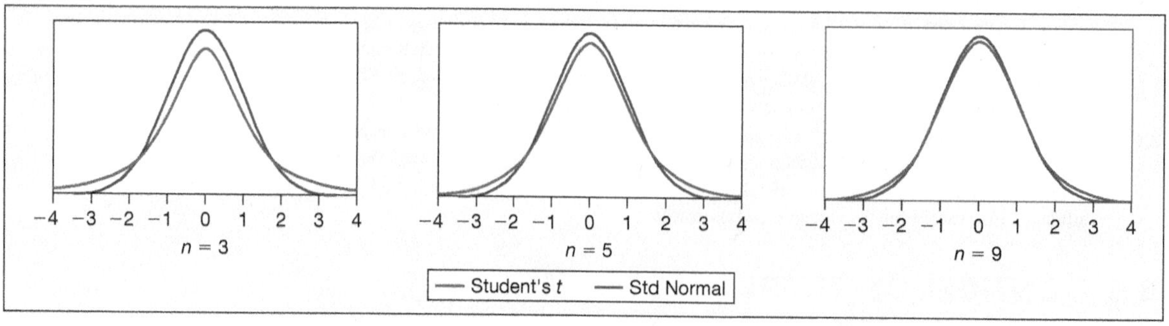

Degrees of Freedom

Knowing the sample size allows us to calculate a parameter called **degrees of freedom** (sometimes abbreviated *d.f.*). This parameter is used to determine the value of the t statistic used in the confidence interval formula. The degrees of freedom tell us how many observations we used to calculate s, the sample standard deviation, less the number of intermediate estimates we used in our calculation. Recall that the formula for s uses all n individual values from the sample and also $\bar{x}$, the sample mean. Therefore, the degrees of freedom are equal to the sample size minus 1.

$$d.f. = n - 1 \quad \text{(degrees of freedom for a confidence interval for } \mu) \tag{8.9}$$

For large degrees of freedom, the t distribution approaches the shape of the normal distribution, as illustrated in Figure 8.14. However, in small samples, the difference is important. For example, in Figure 8.14 the lower axis scale range extends out to ±4, while a range of ±3 would cover most of the area for a standard normal distribution. We have to go out further into the tails of the t distribution to enclose a given area, so for a given confidence level, *t is always larger than z* so the confidence interval is always *wider* than if z were used.

Comparison of *z* and *t*

Table 8.7 (taken from Appendix D) shows that for very small samples the t-values differ substantially from the normal z values. But for a given confidence level, as degrees of freedom increase, the t-values approach the familiar normal z-values (shown at the bottom of each column corresponding to an infinitely large sample). For example, for $n = 31$, we would have degrees of freedom $d.f. = 31 - 1 = 30$, so for a 90 percent confidence interval, we would use $t = 1.697$, which is only slightly larger than $z = 1.645$. It might seem tempting to use the z-values to avoid having to look up the correct degrees of freedom, but this would not be conservative (because the resulting confidence interval would be too narrow).

TABLE 8.7

Student's *t*-values for Selected Degrees of Freedom

	Confidence Level				
d.f.	*80%*	*90%*	*95%*	*98%*	*99%*
1	3.078	6.314	12.706	31.821	63.656
2	1.886	2.920	4.303	6.965	9.925
3	1.638	2.353	3.182	4.541	5.841
4	1.533	2.132	2.776	3.747	4.604
5	1.476	2.015	2.571	3.365	4.032
10	1.372	1.812	2.228	2.764	3.169
20	1.325	1.725	2.086	2.528	2.845
30	1.310	1.697	2.042	2.457	2.750
40	1.303	1.684	2.021	2.423	2.704
60	1.296	1.671	2.000	2.390	2.660
100	1.290	1.660	1.984	2.364	2.626
∞	1.282	1.645	1.960	2.326	2.576

Note: The bottom row shows the z-values for each confidence level.

EXAMPLE 8.3

GMAT Scores

GMATScores

Consider a random sample of GMAT scores submitted by 20 applicants to an MBA program. A dot plot of this sample is shown in Figure 8.15.

530	450	600	570	360
550	640	490	460	550
480	440	530	470	560
500	430	640	420	530

FIGURE 8.15 **Dot Plot and 90 Percent Confidence Interval (n = 20 Scores)**

GMATScores

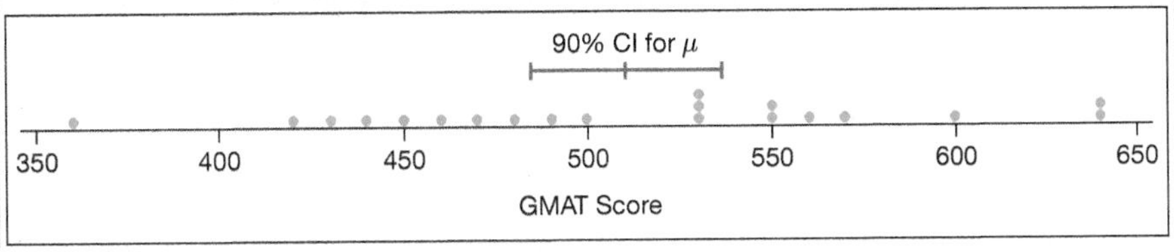

We will construct a 90 percent confidence interval for the mean GMAT score of all MBA applicants. The sample mean is $\bar{x} = 510$ and the sample standard deviation is $s = 73.77$. Since the population standard deviation σ is unknown, we will use the Student's t for our confidence interval with 19 degrees of freedom:

$$d.f. = n - 1 = 20 - 1 = 19 \qquad \text{(degrees of freedom for } n = 20)$$

For a 90 percent confidence interval, we consult Appendix D and find $t_{\alpha/2} = t_{.05} = 1.729$:

	Confidence Level (1 − α)				
	0.80	*0.90*	*0.95*	*0.98*	*0.99*
	Upper Tail Area (α/2)				
d.f.	*0.10*	*0.05*	*0.025*	*0.01*	*0.005*
1	3.078	6.314	12.706	31.821	63.656
2	1.886	2.920	4.303	6.965	9.925
⋮	⋮	⋮	⋮	⋮	⋮
18	1.330	1.734	2.101	2.552	2.878
19	*1.328*	***1.729***	*2.093*	*2.539*	*2.861*
20	1.325	1.725	2.086	2.528	2.845

The 90 percent confidence interval is

$$\bar{x} \pm t_{\alpha/2}\frac{s}{\sqrt{n}} \quad \text{or} \quad 510 \pm (1.729)\frac{73.77}{\sqrt{20}} \quad \text{or} \quad 510 \pm 28.52$$

We are 90 percent confident that the true mean GMAT score is within the interval [481.48, 538.52] as shown in Figure 8.15. If we wanted a narrower interval with the same level of confidence, we would need a larger sample size to reduce the right-hand side of $\bar{x} \pm t_{\alpha/2}\frac{s}{\sqrt{n}}$.

EXAMPLE 8.4

Hospital Stays

Maternity

During a certain period of time, Balzac Hospital had 8,261 maternity cases. Hospital management needs to know the mean length of stay (LOS) so they can plan the maternity unit bed capacity and schedule the nursing staff. Each case is assigned a code called a DRG (which stands for "Diagnostic Related Group"). The most common DRG was 373 (simple delivery without complicating diagnoses), accounting for 4,409 cases during the study period. For DRG 373, a random sample of hospital records for $n = 25$ births, the mean length of stay was $\bar{x} = 39.144$ hours with a standard deviation of $s = 16.204$ hours. What is the 95 percent confidence interval for the true mean?

To justify using the Student's t distribution, we will assume that the population is normal (we will examine this assumption later). Since the population standard deviation is unknown, we use the Student's t for our confidence interval with 24 degrees of freedom:

$$d.f. = n - 1 = 25 - 1 = 24 \qquad \text{(degrees of freedom for } n = 25)$$

For a 95 percent confidence interval, we consult Appendix D and find $t_{\alpha/2} = t_{.025} = 2.064$:

	Confidence Level (1 − α)				
	0.80	*0.90*	*0.95*	*0.98*	*0.99*
	Upper Tail Area (α/2)				
d.f.	*0.10*	*0.05*	*0.025*	*0.01*	*0.005*
1	3.078	6.314	12.706	31.821	63.656
2	1.886	2.920	4.303	6.965	9.925
⋮	⋮	⋮	⋮	⋮	⋮
23	1.319	1.714	2.069	2.500	2.807
24	*1.318*	*1.711*	**2.064**	*2.492*	*2.797*
25	1.316	1.708	2.060	2.485	2.787

The 95 percent confidence interval is

$$\bar{x} \pm t_{\alpha/2}\frac{s}{\sqrt{n}} \quad \text{or} \quad 39.144 \pm (2.064)\frac{16.204}{\sqrt{25}} \quad \text{or} \quad 39.144 \pm 6.689$$

With 95 percent confidence, the true mean LOS is within the interval [32.455, 45.833] so our estimate is that a simple maternity stay averages between 32.5 hours and 45.8 hours. A dot plot of this sample and confidence interval are shown in Figure 8.16.

FIGURE 8.16 **Dot Plot and 95 Percent Confidence Interval (*n* = 25 Births)**
Maternity

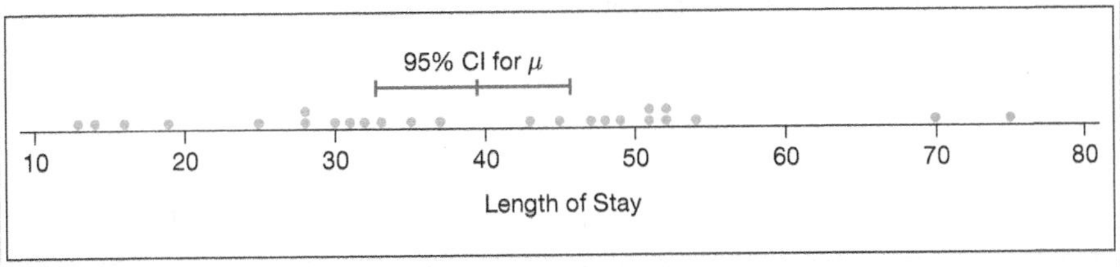

Our confidence interval width reflects the sample size, the confidence level, and the standard deviation. If we wanted a narrower interval (i.e., more precision), we could either increase the sample size or lower the confidence level (e.g., to 90 percent or even 80 percent). But we cannot do anything about the standard deviation because it is an aspect of the sample. In fact, some samples could have larger standard deviations than this one.

Outliers and Messy Data

Outliers and messy data are common. Managers often encounter large databases containing unruly data and they must decide how to treat atypical observations. What if we had a patient in our LOS example that stayed in the hospital for 254 hours? If a handful of maternity patients stay 10 days (240 hours) instead of 2 days (48 hours), real resources will be required to treat them. Would this be common or an outlier? Even if we decide that 10 days is unusual or an outlier, we cannot simply ignore it. We should investigate what might have happened to make this patient's stay longer than usual. It's possible that the diagnostic code DRG 373 (simple delivery without complicating diagnoses) was assigned incorrectly. We should ask if there are multiple outliers that might invalidate the assumption of normality. If the data are highly skewed, we might consider taking a sample larger than 25 so that the Central Limit Theorem is more applicable. Health care managers in hospitals, clinics, insurers, and state and federal agencies all spend significant time working with messy data just like this. In the

United States, health care spending is more than one-sixth of the GDP, suggesting that one job out of every six (perhaps yours) is tied directly or indirectly to health care, so examples like this are not unusual. You need to be ready to deal with messy data.

Must the Population Be Normal?

The t distribution assumes a normal population. While this assumption is often in doubt, simulation studies have shown that confidence intervals using Student's t are reliable as long as the population is not badly skewed and if the sample size is not too small (see Chapter 8 McGraw-Hill Connect® supplements for simulation demonstrations).

Using Appendix D

Beyond *d.f.* = 50, Appendix D shows *d.f.* in steps of 5 or 10. If Appendix D does not show the exact degrees of freedom that you want, use the t-value for the *next lower d.f.* For example, if *d.f.* = 54, you would use *d.f.* = 50. Using the next lower degrees of freedom is a conservative procedure because it overestimates the margin of error. Since t-values change very slowly as *d.f.* rises beyond *d.f.* = 50, rounding down will make little difference.

Can I Ever Use z Instead of t?

In large samples, z and t give similar results. But a conservative statistician always uses the t distribution for confidence intervals when σ is unknown because using z would underestimate the margin of error. Since t tables are easy to use (or we can get t-values from Excel), there isn't much justification for using z when σ is unknown.

Using Excel

If you have access to Excel, you don't need tables. Excel* 2010's function =T.INV.2T (probability,degrees of freedom) gives the value of $t_{\alpha/2}$, where probability is α. For example, for a 95 percent confidence interval with 60 degrees of freedom, the function =T.INV.2T(0.05,60) yields $t_{.025} = 2.000298$. So we would use 0.05 for 95 percent, 0.01 for 99 percent, etc. The output from Excel's Data Analysis > Descriptive Statistics does not give the confidence limits, but it does give the standard error and width of the confidence interval $t_{\alpha/2}s/\sqrt{n}$ (the oddly labeled last line in the table). Figure 8.17 shows Excel's results for sample 1 (maternity LOS).

FIGURE 8.17

Excel's Confidence Interval for μ

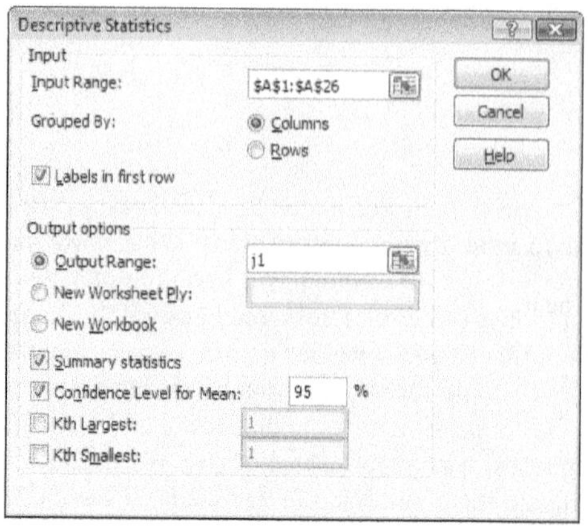

	Maternity
Mean	39.144
Standard Error	3.240769405
Median	37.37
Mode	#N/A
Standard Deviation	16.20384702
Sample Variance	262.5646583
Kurtosis	-0.28780002
Skewness	0.263313568
Range	61.92
Minimum	12.59
Maximum	74.51
Sum	978.6
Count	25
Confidence Level(95.0%)	6.688619266

*Note that previous versions of Excel used the function =TINV(probability, degrees of freedom) to calculate the value of $t_{\alpha/2}$. Please see Appendix J for a complete description of Excel functions from both 2010 and previous versions.

Using MegaStat

If you really want to make the calculations easy, MegaStat gives you a choice of z or t, and does all the calculations for you, as illustrated in Figure 8.18 for sample 1 (maternity LOS). Notice the Preview button. If you click OK you will also see the t-value and other details.

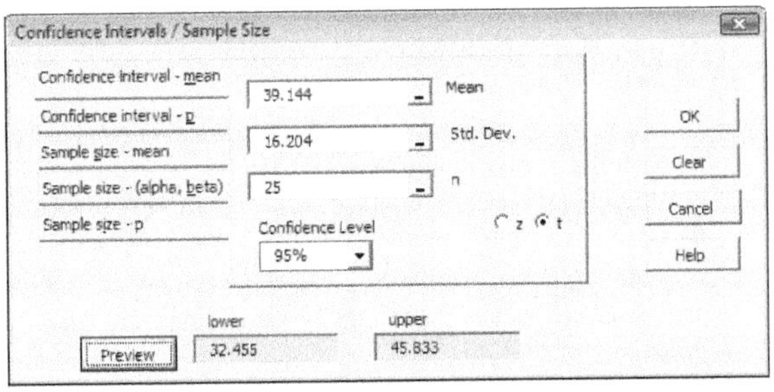

FIGURE 8.18

MegaStat's Confidence Interval for μ

Using MINITAB

Use MINITAB's Stat > Basic Statistics > Graphical Summary to get confidence intervals, as well as a histogram and box plot. MINITAB uses the Student's t for the confidence interval for the mean. It also gives confidence intervals for the median and standard deviation. Figure 8.19 shows the MINITAB Graphical Summary for sample 1 (maternity LOS).

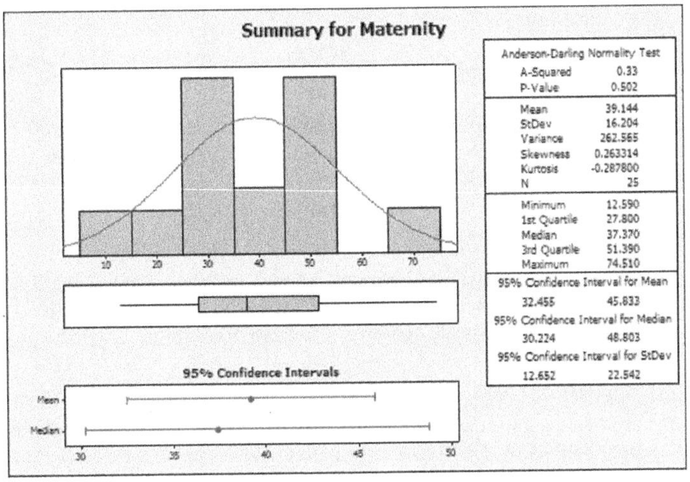

FIGURE 8.19

MINITAB's Confidence Interval and Graphical Summary

SECTION EXERCISES

connect

8.18 Find a confidence interval for μ assuming that each sample is from a normal population.

a. $\bar{x} = 24$, $s = 3$, $n = 7$, 90 percent confidence
b. $\bar{x} = 42$, $s = 6$, $n = 18$, 99 percent confidence
c. $\bar{x} = 119$, $s = 14$, $n = 28$, 95 percent confidence

8.19 For each value of *d.f.* (degrees of freedom), look up the value of Student's t in Appendix D for the stated level of confidence. Then use Excel to find the value of Student's t to four decimal places. Which method (Appendix D or Excel) do you prefer, and why?

a. *d.f.* = 9, 95 percent confidence
b. *d.f.* = 15, 98 percent confidence
c. *d.f.* = 47, 90 percent confidence

8.20 For each value of *d.f.* look up the value of Student's t in Appendix D for the stated level of confidence. How close is the t-value to the corresponding z-value (at the bottom of the column for $d.f. = \infty$)?

a. $d.f. = 40$, 95 percent confidence
b. $d.f. = 80$, 95 percent confidence
c. $d.f. = 100$, 95 percent confidence

8.21 A random sample of 10 items is drawn from a population whose standard deviation is unknown. The sample mean is $\bar{x} = 270$ and the sample standard deviation is $s = 20$. Use Appendix D to find the values of Student's t.

a. Construct an interval estimate for μ with 95 percent confidence.
b. Repeat part a assuming that $n = 20$.
c. Repeat part a assuming that $n = 40$.
d. Describe how the confidence interval changes as n increases.

8.22 A random sample of 25 items is drawn from a population whose standard deviation is unknown. The sample mean is $\bar{x} = 850$ and the sample standard deviation is $s = 15$. Use Appendix D to find the values of Student's t.

a. Construct an interval estimate of μ with 95 percent confidence.
b. Repeat part a assuming that $s = 30$.
c. Repeat part a assuming that $s = 60$.
d. Describe how the confidence interval changes as s increases.

8.23 A sample of 21 minivan electrical warranty repairs for "loose, not attached" wires (one of several electrical failure categories the dealership mechanic can select) showed a mean repair cost of \$45.66 with a standard deviation of \$27.79. (a) Construct a 95 percent confidence interval for the true mean repair cost. (b) How could the confidence interval be made narrower? (Data are from a project by MBA student Tim Polulak.)

8.24 A random sample of 16 pharmacy customers showed the waiting times below (in minutes). Find a 90 percent confidence interval for μ, assuming that the sample is from a normal population. **Pharmacy**

21	22	22	17	21	17	23	20
20	24	9	22	16	21	22	21

8.25 A random sample of monthly rent paid by 12 college seniors living off campus gave the results below (in dollars). Find a 99 percent confidence interval for μ, assuming that the sample is from a normal population. **Rent1**

900	810	770	860	850	790
810	800	890	720	910	640

8.26 A random sample of 10 shipments of stick-on labels showed the following order sizes. (a) Construct a 95 percent confidence interval for the true mean order size. (b) How could the confidence interval be made narrower? (Data are from a project by MBA student Henry Olthof Jr.) **OrderSize**

12,000	18,000	30,000	60,000	14,000	10,500	52,000	14,000	15,700	19,000

8.27 Prof. Green gave three exams last semester. Scores were normally distributed on each exam. Below are scores for 10 randomly chosen students on each exam. (a) Find the 95 percent confidence interval for the mean score on each exam. (b) Do the confidence intervals overlap? What inference might you draw by comparing the three confidence intervals? **Exams2**

Exam 1: 81, 79, 88, 90, 82, 86, 80, 92, 86, 86
Exam 2: 87, 76, 81, 83, 100, 95, 93, 82, 99, 90
Exam 3: 77, 79, 74, 75, 82, 69, 74, 80, 74, 76

8.6 CONFIDENCE INTERVAL FOR A PROPORTION (π)

LO 8-7

Construct a confidence interval for a population proportion.

The Central Limit Theorem (CLT) also applies to a sample proportion, since a proportion is just a mean of data whose only values are 0 or 1. For a proportion, the CLT says that the distribution of a sample proportion $p = x/n$ tends toward normality as n increases. The distribution is centered at the population proportion π. Its standard error σ_p will decrease as n increases just as in the case of the standard error for $\bar{X}$. We say that $p = x/n$ is a *consistent* estimator of π.

Central Limit Theorem for a Proportion

As sample size increases, the distribution of the sample proportion $p = x/n$ approaches a normal distribution with mean π and standard error $\sigma_p = \sqrt{\frac{\pi(1-\pi)}{n}}$.

Illustration: Internet Hotel Reservations Hotel

Management of the Pan-Asian Hotel System tracks the percent of hotel reservations made over the Internet to adjust its advertising and web reservation system. Such data are binary: either a reservation is made on the Internet (x) or not (o). Last week (2,000 reservations) the proportion of Internet reservations was 20 percent ($\pi = .20$) as you can verify if you have the time. We can visualize the week's data like this:

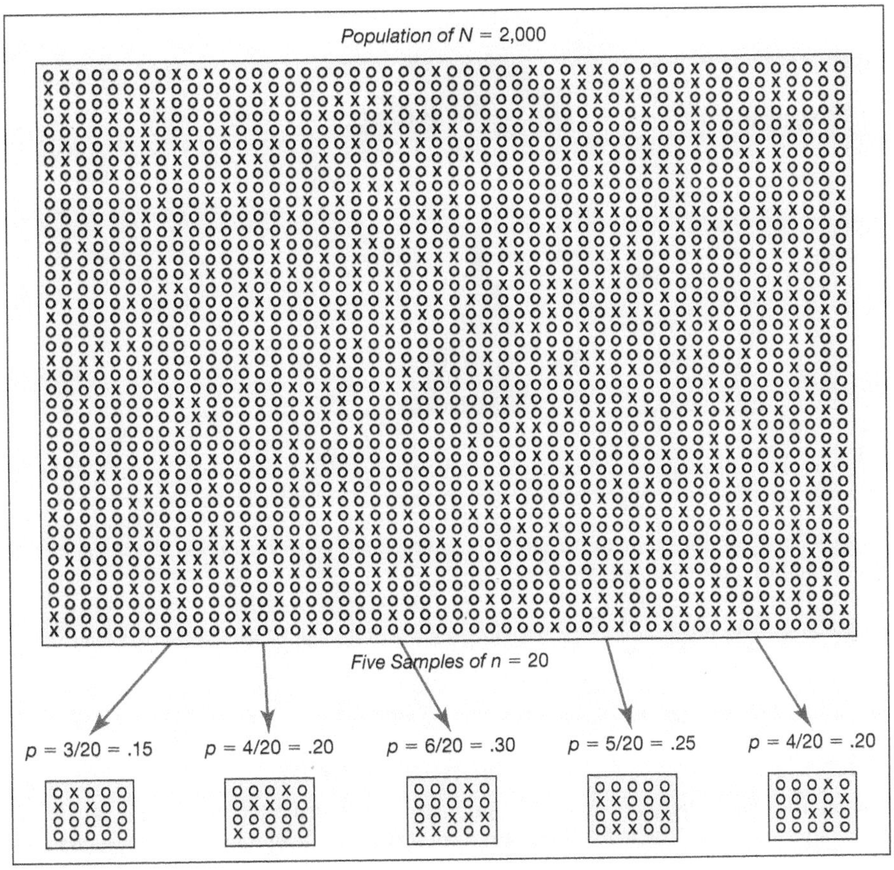

Five random samples of $n = 20$ hotel reservations are shown. Some sample proportions (p) are close to $\pi = .20$ while others are not, due to sampling variation. But each sample proportion p is a valid *point estimate* of the population proportion π:

$$p = \frac{x}{n} = \frac{\text{number of Internet reservations}}{\text{number of items in the sample}}$$

If we took many such samples, we could empirically study the *sampling distribution* of p. But even for a single sample, we can apply the CLT to *predict* the behavior of p. In Chapter 6, you learned that the binomial model describes the number of successes in a sample of n items from a population with constant probability of success π. A binomial distribution is symmetric if $\pi = .50$, and as n increases approaches symmetry even if $\pi \neq .50$. The same is true for the distribution of the sample proportion $p = x/n$. Figure 8.20 shows histograms of $p = x/n$ for 1,000 samples of various sizes with $\pi = .20$. For small n, the distribution is quite discrete. For example:

Sample Size	*Possible Values of $p = x/n$*
$n = 5$	0/5, 1/5, 2/5, 3/5, 4/5, 5/5
$n = 10$	0/10, 1/10, 2/10, 3/10, 4/10, 5/10, 6/10, 7/10, 8/10, 9/10, 10/10

As n increases, the statistic $p = x/n$ more closely resembles a continuous random variable and its distribution becomes more symmetric and bell-shaped.

FIGURE 8.20

Histograms of $p = x/n$ When $\pi = .20$ Hotel

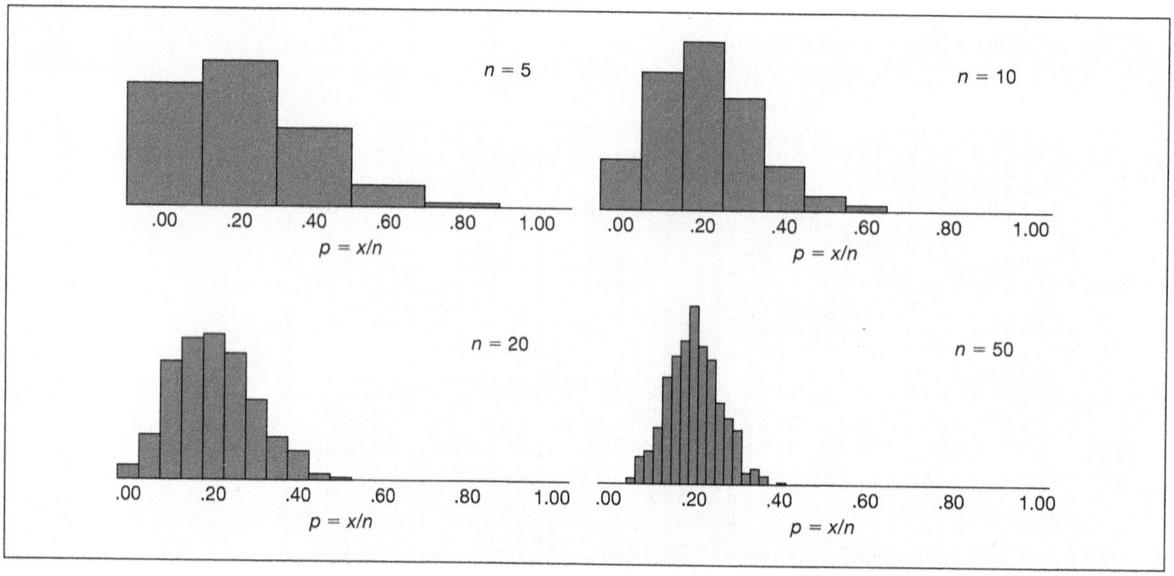

As n increases, the range of the sample proportion $p = x/n$ narrows because n appears in the denominator of the *standard error:*

$$\sigma_p = \sqrt{\frac{\pi(1-\pi)}{n}} \quad \text{(standard error of the sample proportion)} \tag{8.10}$$

Therefore, the sampling variation can be reduced by increasing the sample size. Larger samples also help justify the use of the normal distribution.

When Is It Safe to Assume Normality of p?

The statistic $p = x/n$ may be assumed normally distributed when the sample is "large." How large must n be? Table 8.8 illustrates a conservative rule of thumb that normality may be assumed whenever $n\pi \geq 10$ and $n(1 - \pi) \geq 10$. By this rule, a very large sample may be needed to assume normality of the sample proportion when π differs greatly from .50.*

Rule of Thumb

The sample proportion $p = x/n$ may be assumed normal if both $n\pi \geq 10$ and $n(1 - \pi) \geq 10$.

*A good alternative rule is to require $n > 9(1 - \pi)/\pi$ and $n > 9\pi/(1 - \pi)$. See Catherine Forbes, Merran Evans, Nicholas Hastings, and Brian Peacock, *Statistical Distributions,* 4th ed. (Wiley, 2011). Later on, we will discuss what to do when normality cannot be assumed.

TABLE 8.8

Minimum Sample Size to Assume Normality of $p = x/n$

π	n
.50	20
.40 or .60	25
.30 or .70	33
.20 or .80	50
.10 or .90	100
.05 or .95	200
.02 or .98	500
.01 or .99	1,000
.005 or .995	2,000
.002 or .998	5,000
.001 or .999	10,000

Standard Error of the Proportion

The **standard error of the proportion** is denoted σ_p. It depends on π, as well as on n, being largest when the population proportion is near $\pi = .50$ and becoming smaller when π is near 0 or 1. For example:

If $\pi = .50$, then for $n = 50$ $\quad \sigma_p = \sqrt{\dfrac{\pi(1-\pi)}{n}} = \sqrt{\dfrac{.50(1-.50)}{50}} = \sqrt{\dfrac{.25}{50}} = .0707$

for $n = 200$ $\quad \sigma_p = \sqrt{\dfrac{\pi(1-\pi)}{n}} = \sqrt{\dfrac{.50(1-.50)}{200}} = \sqrt{\dfrac{.25}{200}} = .0354$

If $\pi = .10$, then for $n = 50$ $\quad \sigma_p = \sqrt{\dfrac{\pi(1-\pi)}{n}} = \sqrt{\dfrac{.10(1-.10)}{50}} = \sqrt{\dfrac{.09}{50}} = .0424$

for $n = 200$ $\quad \sigma_p = \sqrt{\dfrac{\pi(1-\pi)}{n}} = \sqrt{\dfrac{.10(1-.10)}{200}} = \sqrt{\dfrac{.09}{200}} = .0212$

The formula is symmetric (i.e., $\pi = .10$ gives the same standard error as $\pi = .90$). Notice also that even if the sample size is quadrupled, the standard error is only halved. Figure 8.21 shows that as n increases, the standard error σ_p decreases, but at a slower rate.

Confidence Interval for π

By the Central Limit Theorem, we can state the probability that a sample proportion will fall within a given interval. For example, there is a 95 percent chance that p will fall within the interval $\pi \pm z_{.025}\sqrt{\frac{\pi(1-\pi)}{n}}$ where $z_{.025} = 1.96$ and similarly for other values of z. This is the

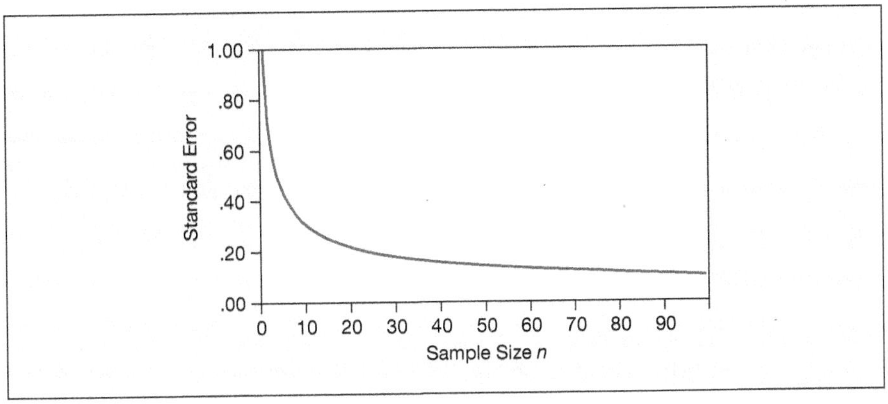

FIGURE 8.21

Effect of n on σ_p

basis for a confidence interval estimate of π. Replacing π with $p = x/n$ (since π is unknown) and assuming a large sample (to justify the assumption of normality) we obtain the formula for the confidence interval for π.

Confidence Interval for π

(8.11) $$p \pm z_{\alpha/2}\sqrt{\frac{p(1-p)}{n}}$$

Table 8.9 shows $z_{\alpha/2}$ values for common confidence levels.

TABLE 8.9

Common Confidence Levels and z-Values

Confidence level	$1-\alpha$	α	$\alpha/2$	$z_{\alpha/2}$
90%	.90	.10	.05	$z_{.05} = 1.645$
95%	.95	.05	.025	$z_{.025} = 1.960$
99%	.99	.01	.005	$z_{.005} = 2.576$

EXAMPLE 8.5

Auditing

A sample of 75 retail in-store purchases showed that 24 were paid in cash. We will construct a 95 percent confidence interval for the proportion of all retail in-store purchases that are paid in cash. The sample proportion is

$$p = x/n = 24/75 = .32 \qquad \text{(proportion of in-store cash transactions)}$$

We can assume that p is normally distributed* since np and $n(1-p)$ exceed 10. That is, $np = (75)(.32) = 24$ and $n(1-p) = (75)(.68) = 51$. The 95 percent confidence interval is

$$p \pm z_{\alpha/2}\sqrt{\frac{p(1-p)}{n}} \quad \text{or} \quad .32 \pm 1.960\sqrt{\frac{.32(1-.32)}{75}} \quad \text{or} \quad .32 \pm .106 \quad \text{or} \quad [.214, .426]$$

We cannot know with certainty whether or not the true proportion lies within the interval [.214, .426]. Either it does, or it does not. And it is true that different samples could yield different intervals. But we can say that, on average, 95 percent of the intervals constructed in this way would contain the true population proportion π. Therefore, we are 95 percent *confident* that the true proportion π is between .214 and .426.

Narrowing the Interval?

In this example, the confidence interval is fairly wide. The width of the confidence interval for π depends on

- Sample size
- Confidence level
- Sample proportion p

We cannot do anything about p because it is calculated from the sample. If we want a narrower interval (i.e., more precision), we could either increase the sample size or reduce the confidence level (e.g., from 95 percent to 90 percent). Once the confidence level is chosen, our only choice is to increase n. Of course, larger samples are more costly (or even impossible). The next example illustrates how the width of the interval becomes narrower when using a larger sample and a lower confidence level.

*When constructing a confidence interval, we use p instead of π in our rule of thumb to test whether n is large enough to assure normality because π is unknown. The test is therefore equivalent to asking if $x \geq 10$ and $n - x \geq 10$.

EXAMPLE 8.6

Display Ads

A random sample of 200 pages from the *Ameritech Pages Plus Yellow Pages* telephone directory revealed that 30 of the pages contained at least one multicolored display ad. What is the 90 percent confidence interval for the proportion of all pages with at least one multicolored display ad? The sample proportion is

$$p = x/n = 30/200 = .15 \qquad \text{(proportion of pages with at least one display ad)}$$

The normality test is easily met because $np = (200)(.15) = 30$ and $n(1 - p) = (200)(.85) = 170$. The 90 percent confidence interval requires $z = 1.645$:

$$p \pm z_{\alpha/2}\sqrt{\frac{p(1-p)}{n}} \quad \text{or} \quad .15 \pm 1.645\sqrt{\frac{.15(1-.15)}{200}} \quad \text{or} \quad .15 \pm .042 \quad \text{or} \quad [.108, .192].$$

We are 90 percent confident that between 10.8 percent and 19.2 percent of the pages have multicolor display ads. This confidence interval is narrower than the previous example because the sample size is larger, this sample proportion is farther from .5, and the confidence level is lower.

To illustrate the trade-off between *confidence* and *precision* (the interval half-width), here are some alternatives that could have been used in the display ad example:

Confidence Level	z	*Interval Width*
90%	$z = 1.645$	$.15 \pm .042$
95%	$z = 1.960$	$.15 \pm .049$
99%	$z = 2.576$	$.15 \pm .065$

Using Excel and MegaStat

Excel's Data Analysis does not offer a confidence interval for a proportion, presumably because the calculations are easy. For example:

=0.15–NORM.S.INV(.95)*SQRT(0.15*(1-0.15)/200) = .108 for the lower 90% confidence limit

=0.15+NORM.S.INV(.95)*SQRT(0.15*(1-0.15)/200) = .192 for the upper 90% confidence limit

MegaStat does offer a confidence interval for a proportion, as shown in Figure 8.22. You only need to enter p and n. A convenient feature is that, if you enter p larger than 1, MegaStat assumes that it is the x-value in $p = x/n$ so you don't even have to calculate p. Click the Preview button to see the confidence interval. This example verifies the Ameritech calculations shown previously (click OK for additional details). MegaStat always assumes normality, even when it is not justified, so you need to check this assumption for yourself.

Small Samples: MINITAB

If the sample is small (i.e., if we cannot meet the requirement that $n\pi \geq 10$ and $n(1 - \pi) \geq 10$), the distribution of p may not be well approximated by the normal. Instead of assuming

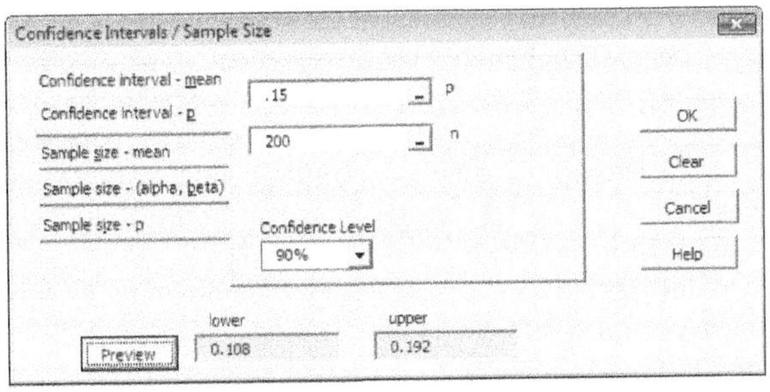

FIGURE 8.22

MegaStat's 90 Percent Confidence Interval for π

FIGURE 8.23

Minitab's 95 Percent Confidence Interval for π

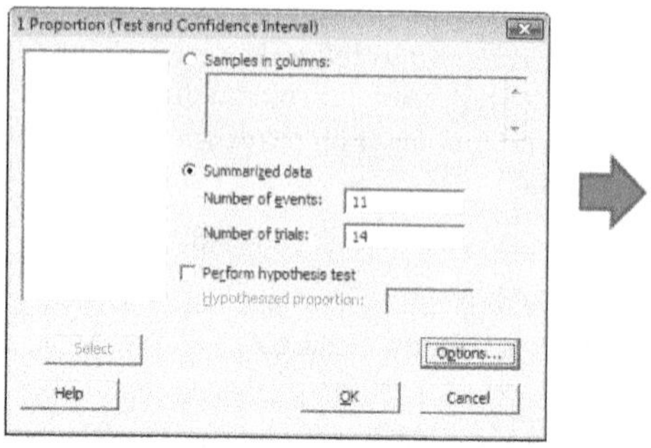

Test and CI for One Proportion

```
Sample   X   N  Sample p          95% CI
1       11  14  0.785714  (0.570776, 1.000000)

Using the normal approximation.
The normal approximation may be inaccurate for small samples.
```

Test and CI for One Proportion

```
Sample   X   N  Sample p          95% CI
1       11  14  0.785714  (0.492024, 0.953421)
```

a continuous normal model, confidence limits around p can be constructed by using the binomial distribution. MINITAB uses this method by default, since it works for any n (you have to press the Options button to assume normality). Although the underlying calculations are a bit complex, MINITAB does all the work and the resulting interval is correct for any n and p.

For example, in a sample of 14 purchasers of the 2011 movie *Thor* DVD, 11 watched only the film and never even looked at the "extras." The sample proportion is $p = 11/14$. What is the 95 percent confidence interval for the proportion of purchasers who never viewed the "extras"? We have $np = 11$, but $n(1 - p) = 3$, which is less than 10, so we should not assume normality. Figure 8.23 shows a sample of MINITAB's confidence interval using the binomial distribution with Stat > Basic Statistics > One Proportion. MINITAB's binomial confidence interval [.492, .953] is quite different from the normal confidence interval [.571, 1.000]. MINITAB includes a warning about the normal confidence interval.

Polls and Margin of Error

In polls and survey research, the margin of error is typically based on a 95 percent confidence level and the initial assumption that $\pi = .50$. This is a conservative assumption since σ_p is at its maximum when $\pi = .50$. Table 8.10 shows the margin of error for various sample sizes. The law of diminishing returns is apparent. Greater accuracy is possible, but each reduction in the margin of error requires a disproportionately larger sample size.

EXAMPLE 8.7

Election Polls

A hotly contested race for a Colorado senate seat took place in November 2010 between Michael Bennet and Ken Buck. A poll by Public Policy Polling on November 1, 2010, showed Buck leading Bennet 49 percent to 48 percent. The sample size was 1,059 likely adult voters, and the reported accuracy was ±3 percent. On the same day, a FOX News poll, conducted by Pulse Opinion Research, showed Buck leading Bennet 50 percent to 46 percent, based on 1,000 likely voters, with a reported accuracy of ±3 percent. These are typical sample sizes for opinion polls on major issues such as state and national elections, foreign policy, or a Supreme Court decision. Tracking polls do vary, but if several different independent polls show the same candidate ahead, and if the margin is stable over time, they usually get it right. In this case, the margins of error for both polls made the outcome too close to call before all votes were tallied. Bennet ended up winning with 48 percent of the vote while Buck garnered 47 percent of the vote.

The margin of error is sometimes referred to as the *sample accuracy*. Popular media sometimes use statistical terminology loosely, but the idea is the same. Statewide political polls, such as a gubernatorial race, typically have 800 respondents (margin of error ±3.5 percent) while a mayoral or local political poll might have 400 respondents (margin of error ±4.9 percent). Private market research or customer mail surveys may rely on even smaller samples, while Internet surveys can yield very large samples. In spite of the large samples possible from an Internet survey, it is important to consider *nonresponse bias* (see Chapter 2).

TABLE 8.10

Margin of Error for 95 Percent Confidence Interval Assuming $\pi = .50$

$n = 100$	$n = 200$	$n = 400$	$n = 800$	$n = 1{,}200$	$n = 1{,}600$
±9.8%	±6.9%	±4.9%	±3.5%	±2.8%	±2.5%

Rule of Three

A useful quick rule is the *Rule of Three*. If in n independent trials no events occur, the upper 95 percent confidence bound is approximately $3/n$. For example, if no medical complications arise in 17 prenatal fetal surgeries, the upper bound on such complications is roughly $3/17 = .18$, or about 18 percent. This rule is sometimes used by health care practitioners when limited data are available. This rule is especially useful because the formula for the standard error σ_p breaks down when $p = 0$. The rule of three is a conservative approach with an interesting history.*

Proportions Are Important in Business

Proportions are easy to work with, and they occur frequently in business (most often expressed as percents). In many ways, estimating π is simpler than estimating μ because you are just counting things. Using surveys, businesses study many aspects of their customers' satisfaction to determine where they are doing well and where they need to improve. Of particular importance is the proportion of customers who say they are extremely likely to recommend the company to a friend or colleague. The higher this percentage is, the larger the group of "promoters" a company has among its customers.

SECTION EXERCISES

connect

8.28 Calculate the standard error of the sample proportion.

a. $n = 30, \pi = .50$ b. $n = 50, \pi = .20$ c. $n = 100, \pi = .10$ d. $n = 500, \pi = .005$

8.29 Calculate the standard error of the sample proportion.

a. $n = 40, \pi = .30$ b. $n = 200, \pi = .10$ c. $n = 30, \pi = .40$ d. $n = 400, \pi = .03$

8.30 Should p be assumed normal?

a. $n = 200, \pi = .02$ b. $n = 100, \pi = .05$ c. $n = 50, \pi = .50$

8.31 Should p be assumed normal?

a. $n = 25, \pi = .50$ b. $n = 60, \pi = .20$ c. $n = 100, \pi = .08$

8.32 Find the margin of error for a poll, assuming that $\pi = .50$.

a. $n = 50$ b. $n = 200$ c. $n = 500$ d. $n = 2{,}000$

8.33 A car dealer is taking a customer satisfaction survey. Find the margin of error (i.e., assuming 95% confidence and $\pi = .50$) for (a) 250 respondents, (b) 125 respondents, and (c) 65 respondents.

8.34 In a sample of 500 new websites registered on the Internet, 24 were anonymous (i.e., they shielded their name and contact information). (a) Construct a 95 percent confidence interval for the proportion of all new websites that were anonymous. (b) May normality of p be assumed? Explain.

8.35 From a list of stock mutual funds, 52 funds were selected at random. Of the funds chosen, it was found that 19 required a minimum initial investment under $1,000. (a) Construct a 90 percent confidence interval for the true proportion requiring an initial investment under $1,000. (b) May normality of p be assumed? Explain.

8.36 Of 43 bank customers depositing a check, 18 received some cash back. (a) Construct a 90 percent confidence interval for the proportion of all depositors who ask for cash back. (b) Check the normality assumption of p.

8.37 A survey showed that 4.8 percent of the 250 Americans surveyed had suffered some kind of identity theft in the past 12 months. (a) Construct a 99 percent confidence interval for the true proportion of Americans who had suffered identity theft in the past 12 months. (b) May normality of p be assumed? Explain.

*For further details, see B. D. Jovanovic and P. S. Levy, "A Look at the Rule of Three," *The American Statistician* 51, no. 2 (May 1997), pp. 137–139.

Mini Case 8.1

Airline Water Quality

Is the water on your airline flight safe to drink? It isn't feasible to analyze the water on every flight, so sampling is necessary. In August and September 2004, the Environmental Protection Agency (EPA) found bacterial contamination in water samples from the lavatories and galley water taps on 20 of 158 randomly selected U.S. flights (12.7 percent of the flights). Alarmed by the data, the EPA ordered sanitation improvements and then tested water samples again in November and December 2004. In the second sample, bacterial contamination was found in 29 of 169 randomly sampled flights (17.2 percent of the flights).

Aug./Sep. sample: $p = 20/158 = .12658$, or 12.7% contaminated

Nov./Dec. sample: $p = 29/169 = .17160$, or 17.2% contaminated

Is the problem getting worse instead of better? From these samples, we can construct confidence intervals for the true proportion of flights with contaminated water. We begin with the 95 percent confidence interval for π based on the August/September water sample:

$$p \pm z_{\alpha/2}\sqrt{\frac{p(1-p)}{n}} \quad \text{or} \quad .12658 \pm 1.96\sqrt{\frac{.12658(1-.12658)}{158}}$$

$$\text{or } .12658 \pm .05185, \text{ or } 7.5\% \text{ to } 17.8\%$$

Next we determine the 95 percent confidence interval for π based on the November/December water sample:

$$p \pm z_{\alpha/2}\sqrt{\frac{p(1-p)}{n}} = .17160 \pm 1.96\sqrt{\frac{.17160(1-.17160)}{169}}$$

$$= .17160 \pm .05684, \text{ or } 11.5\% \text{ to } 22.8\%$$

Although the sample percentage (a point estimate of π) did rise, the margin of error is a little over 5 percent in each sample. Since the confidence intervals overlap, we cannot rule out the possibility that there has been no change in water contamination on airline flights; that is, the difference could be due to sampling variation. Nonetheless, the EPA is taking further steps to encourage airlines to improve water quality.

The Wall Street Journal, November 10, 2004, and January 20, 2005.

8.7 ESTIMATING FROM FINITE POPULATIONS

LO 8-8

Know how to modify confidence intervals when the population is finite.

In Chapter 2 we discussed infinite and finite populations and the implication of a finite population when sampling without replacement. If the sample size n is less than 5 percent of the population, and we are sampling without replacement, then we consider the size of the population to be effectively infinite. However, on occasion we will take samples without replacement where n is greater than 5 percent of the population. When this happens, our margin of error on the interval estimate is actually less than when the sample size is "small" relative to the population size. As we sample more of the population, we get more precise estimates. We need to account for the fact that we are sampling a larger percentage of the population.

The **finite population correction factor** (FPCF) $\sqrt{\frac{N-n}{N-1}}$ reduces the margin of error and provides a more precise interval estimate, shown in formulas 8.12–8.15 in the box below. The FPCF can be omitted when the population is infinite (e.g., sampling from an ongoing production process) or effectively infinite (population at least 20 times as large as the sample, i.e., $n/N < .05$). When $n/N < .05$, the FPCF is almost equal to 1, so it will have a negligible effect on the confidence interval. See Chapters 2 and 6 for further discussion of finite populations.

Confidence Intervals for Finite Populations

$$\bar{x} \pm z_{\alpha/2}\frac{\sigma}{\sqrt{n}}\sqrt{\frac{N-n}{N-1}} \quad \text{estimating } \mu \text{ with known } \sigma \qquad \textbf{(8.12)}$$

$$\bar{x} \pm t_{\alpha/2}\frac{s}{\sqrt{n}}\sqrt{\frac{N-n}{N-1}} \quad \text{estimating } \mu \text{ with unknown } \sigma \qquad \textbf{(8.13)}$$

$$p \pm z_{\alpha/2}\sqrt{\frac{p(1-p)}{n}}\sqrt{\frac{N-n}{N-1}} \quad \text{estimating } \pi \qquad \textbf{(8.14)}$$

where

$$\sqrt{\frac{N-n}{N-1}} \text{ is the finite population correction factor (FPCF)} \qquad \textbf{(8.15)}$$

Illustration Streeling Pharmaceutical has a staff of 1,000 employees. The human resources department sent a survey to a random sample of 75 employees to estimate the average number of hours per week its employees use the company's on-site exercise facility. The sample results showed $\bar{x} = 3.50$ hours and $s = 0.83$ hour. Because more than 5 percent of the population was sampled ($n/N = 75/1000 = 7.5\%$) a finite population correction is suggested. The FPCF would be:

$$\sqrt{\frac{N-n}{N-1}} = \sqrt{\frac{1{,}000-75}{1{,}000-1}} = \sqrt{.9259} = .9623$$

The 95 percent confidence interval estimate, with $t_{.025} = 1.993$ ($d.f. = 74$), would be

$$\bar{x} \pm t_{\alpha/2}\sqrt{\frac{N-n}{N-1}}\frac{s}{\sqrt{n}} \quad \text{or} \quad 3.50 \pm 1.993(.9623)\left(\frac{0.83}{\sqrt{75}}\right) \quad \text{or} \quad 3.50 \pm 0.184$$

If the FPCF had been omitted, the confidence interval would have been:

$$\bar{x} \pm t\frac{s}{\sqrt{n}} \quad \text{or} \quad 3.50 \pm 1.993\frac{0.83}{\sqrt{75}} \quad \text{or} \quad 3.50 \pm 0.191$$

In this example, the FPCF narrowed the confidence interval only slightly, by reducing the margin of error from ±.191 to ±.184.

SECTION EXERCISES

connect

8.38 Calculate the FPCF for each sample and population size. Can the population be considered effectively infinite in each case?

a. $N = 450$, $n = 10$
b. $N = 300$, $n = 25$
c. $N = 1800$, $n = 280$

8.39 Use the following information—$\bar{x} = 50$, $\sigma = 15$, $n = 90$, $N = 1{,}000$—to calculate confidence intervals for μ assuming the sample is from a normal population: (a) 90 percent confidence; (b) 95 percent confidence; (c) 99 percent confidence.

8.40 Use the following information—$\bar{x} = 3.7$, $s = 0.2$, $n = 1{,}200$, $N = 5{,}800$—to calculate confidence intervals for μ assuming the sample is from a normal population: (a) 90 percent confidence; (b) 95 percent confidence; (c) 99 percent confidence.

8.41 A random survey of 500 students was conducted from a population of 2,300 students to estimate the proportion who had part-time jobs. The sample showed that 245 had part-time jobs. Calculate the 90 percent confidence interval for the true proportion of students who had part-time jobs.

8.8 SAMPLE SIZE DETERMINATION FOR A MEAN

Sample Size to Estimate μ

LO 8-9

Calculate sample size to estimate a mean.

Suppose we wish to estimate a population mean with a maximum allowable margin of error of $\pm E$. What sample size is required? We start with the general form of the confidence interval:

General Form	*What We Want*
$\bar{x} \pm z\frac{\sigma}{\sqrt{n}}$	$\bar{x} \pm E$

In this confidence interval, we use z instead of t because we are going to solve for n, and degrees of freedom cannot be determined unless we know n. Equating the maximum error E to half of the confidence interval width and solving for n,

$$E = z\frac{\sigma}{\sqrt{n}} \quad \rightarrow \quad E^2 = z^2\frac{\sigma^2}{n} \quad \rightarrow \quad n = z^2\frac{\sigma^2}{E^2}$$

Thus, the formula for the sample size can be written:

(8.16) $$n = \left(\frac{z\sigma}{E}\right)^2 \quad \text{(sample size to estimate } \mu\text{)}$$

Always round n to the next higher integer to be conservative.

A Myth

Many people believe that when the population is large, you need a larger sample to obtain a given level of precision in the estimate. This is incorrect. For a given level of precision, it is only the sample size that matters, even if the population is a million or a billion. This is apparent from the confidence interval formula, which includes n but not N.

How to Estimate σ?

We can plug our desired precision E and the appropriate z for the desired confidence level into formula 8.11. However, σ poses a problem since it is usually unknown. Table 8.11

TABLE 8.11

Four Ways to Estimate σ

Method 1: Take a Preliminary Sample

Take a small preliminary sample and use the sample estimate s in place of σ. This method is the most common, though its logic is somewhat circular (i.e., take a sample to plan a sample).

Method 2: Assume Uniform Population

Estimate upper and lower limits a and b and set $\sigma = [(b - a)^2/12]^{1/2}$. For example, we might guess the weight of a light-duty truck to range from 1,500 pounds to 3,500 pounds, implying a standard deviation of $\sigma = [(3{,}500 - 1{,}500)^2/12]^{1/2} = 577$ pounds. Since a uniform distribution has no central tendency, the actual σ is probably smaller than our guess, so we get a larger n than necessary (a conservative result).

Method 3: Assume Normal Population

Estimate upper and lower bounds a and b, and set $\sigma = (b - a)/6$. This assumes normality with most of the data within $\mu + 3\sigma$ and $\mu - 3\sigma$ so the range is 6σ. For example, we might guess the weight of a light truck to range from 1,500 pounds to 3,500 pounds, implying $\sigma = (3{,}500 - 1{,}500)/6 = 333$ pounds. This estimate of σ is based on the Empirical Rule. Recent research suggests that this method may not be conservative enough (see Related Reading).

Method 4: Poisson Arrivals

In the special case when λ is a Poisson arrival rate, then $\sigma = \sqrt{\lambda}$. For example, if you think the arrival rate is about 20 customers per hour, then you would estimate $\sigma = \sqrt{20} = 4.47$.

shows several ways to approximate the value of σ. You can always try more than one method and see how much difference it makes. But until you take the sample, you will not know for sure if you have achieved your goal (i.e., the desired precision E).

EXAMPLE 8.8

Onion Weight

A produce manager wants to estimate the mean weight of Spanish onions being delivered by a supplier, with 95 percent confidence and an error of ±1 ounce. A preliminary sample of 12 onions shows a sample standard deviation of 3.60 ounces. For a 95 percent confidence interval, we will set $z = 1.96$. We use $s = 3.60$ in place of σ and set the desired error $E = 1$ to obtain the required sample size:

$$n = [(1.96)(3.60)/(1)]^2 = 49.79, \text{ or } 50 \text{ onions}$$

We would round to the next higher integer and take a sample of 50 Spanish onions. This should ensure an estimate of the true mean weight with an error not exceeding ±1 ounce.

A seemingly modest change in E can have a major effect on the sample size because E is squared. Suppose we reduce the maximum error to $E = 0.5$ ounce to obtain a more precise estimate. The required sample size would then be

$$n = [(1.96)(3.60)/(0.5)]^2 = 199.1, \text{ or } 200 \text{ onions}$$

Using MegaStat

There is also a sample size calculator in MegaStat, as illustrated in Figure 8.24. The Preview button lets you change the setup and see the result immediately.

Practical Advice

When estimating a mean, the maximum error E is expressed in the same units as X and σ. For example, E would be expressed in dollars when estimating the mean order size for mail-order customers (e.g., $E = \$2$) or in minutes to estimate the mean wait time for patients at a clinic (e.g., $E = 10$ minutes). To estimate last year's starting salaries for MBA graduates from a university, the maximum error could be large (e.g., $E = \$2{,}000$) because a \$2,000 error in estimating μ might still be a reasonably accurate estimate.

Using z in the sample size formula for a mean is necessary but not conservative. Because t always exceeds z for a given confidence level, your actual interval may be wider than $\pm E$ as intended. As long as the required sample size is large (say 30 or more), the difference will be acceptable.

The sample size formulas for a mean are not conservative, that is, they tend to underestimate the required sample size (see Kupper and Hafner article in the end-of-chapter references). Therefore, the sample size formulas for a mean should be regarded only as a minimum guideline. Whenever possible, samples should exceed this minimum.

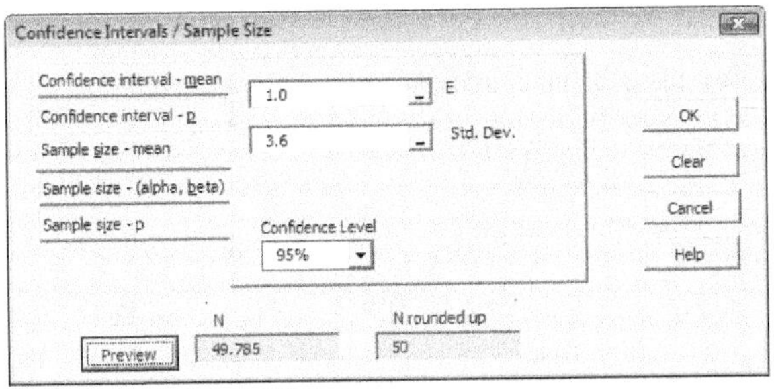

FIGURE 8.24

MegaStat's Sample Size for a Mean

If you are sampling a finite population without replacement and your required sample size (n) exceeds 5 percent of the population size (N), you can adjust the sample size by using $n' = \frac{nN}{n + (N-1)}$. This adjustment allows you to meet the desired confidence level with a smaller sample and will also guarantee that the sample size never exceeds the population size. See *LearningStats* for details.

SECTION EXERCISES

connect

8.42 For each level of precision, find the required sample size to estimate the mean starting salary for a new CPA with 95 percent confidence, assuming a population standard deviation of $7,500 (same as last year).

a. $E = \$2{,}000$ b. $E = \$1{,}000$ c. $E = \$500$

8.43 Last year, a study showed that the average ATM cash withdrawal took 65 seconds with a standard deviation of 10 seconds. The study is to be repeated this year. How large a sample would be needed to estimate this year's mean with 95 percent confidence and an error of ±4 seconds?

8.44 The EPA city/hwy mpg range for a Saturn Vue FWD automatic 5-speed transmission is 20 to 28 mpg. (a) Estimate σ using Method 3 from Table 8.11. (b) If you owned this vehicle, how large a sample (e.g., how many tanks of gas) would be required to estimate your mean mpg with an error of ±1 mpg and 90 percent confidence? (Source: www.fueleconomy.gov.).

8.45 Popcorn kernels are believed to take between 100 and 200 seconds to pop in a certain microwave. (a) Estimate σ using Method 3 from Table 8.11. (b) What sample size (number of kernels) would be needed to estimate the true mean seconds to pop with an error of ±5 seconds and 95 percent confidence?

8.46 Analysis showed that the mean arrival rate for vehicles at a certain Shell station on Friday afternoon last year was 4.5 vehicles per minute. How large a sample would be needed to estimate this year's mean arrival rate with 98 percent confidence and an error of ±0.5?

8.47 Noodles & Company wants to estimate the mean spending per customer at a certain restaurant with 95 percent confidence and an error of ±$0.25. What is the required sample size, assuming a standard deviation of $2.50 (based on similar restaurants elsewhere)?

8.48 In an intra-squad swim competition, men's freestyle 100 swim times at a certain university ranged from 43.89 seconds to 51.96 seconds. (a) Estimate the standard deviation using Method 3 (the Empirical Rule for a normal distribution). (b) What sample size is needed to estimate the mean for all swimmers with 95 percent confidence and an error of ±0.50 second?

8.49 The city fuel economy of a 2009 Toyota 4Runner 2WD 6 cylinder 4 L automatic 5-speed using regular gas is a normally distributed random variable with a range 16 MPG to 21 MPG. (a) Estimate the standard deviation using Method 3 (the Empirical Rule for a normal distribution). (b) What sample size is needed to estimate the mean with 90 percent confidence and an error of ±0.25 MPG? (Source: www.fueleconomy.gov.)

8.9 SAMPLE SIZE DETERMINATION FOR A PROPORTION

LO 8-10

Calculate sample size to estimate a proportion.

Suppose we wish to estimate a population proportion with a precision (maximum error) of ± E. What sample size is required? We start with the general form of the confidence interval:

General Form	*What We Want*
$p \pm z\sqrt{\frac{\pi(1-\pi)}{n}}$	$p \pm E$

We equate the maximum error E to half of the confidence interval width and solve for n:

$$E = z\sqrt{\frac{\pi(1-\pi)}{n}} \quad \rightarrow \quad E^2 = z^2\frac{\pi(1-\pi)}{n} \quad \rightarrow \quad n = z^2\frac{\pi(1-\pi)}{E^2}$$

Thus, the formula for the sample size for a proportion can be written:

(8.17) $$n = \left(\frac{z}{E}\right)^2\pi(1-\pi) \quad \text{(sample size to estimate } \pi\text{)}$$

Always round n to the next higher integer.

Because a proportion is a number between 0 and 1, the maximum error E is also between 0 and 1. For example, if we want an error of ± 7 percent, we would specify $E = 0.07$.

Because π is unknown (that's why we are taking the sample) we need to make an assumption about π to plan our sample size. If we have a prior estimate of π (e.g., from last year or a comparable application), we can plug p into the formula. Or we could take a small preliminary sample to obtain an initial value of p. Some experts recommend using $\pi = .50$ because the resulting sample size will guarantee the desired precision for any π. However, this conservative assumption may lead to a larger sample than necessary because π is not always equal to .5. Sampling costs money, so if a prior estimate of π is available, it might be advisable to use it, especially if you think that π differs greatly from .50. For example, in estimating the proportion of home equity loans that result in default, we would expect π to be much smaller than .50, while in estimating the proportion of motorists who use seat belts, we would hope that π would be much larger than .50. Table 8.12 details three ways to estimate π.

TABLE 8.12

Three Ways to Estimate π

Method 1: Assume That $\pi = .50$

This method is conservative and ensures the desired precision. It is therefore a sound choice and is often used. However, the sample may end up being larger than necessary.

Method 2: Take a Preliminary Sample

Take a small preliminary sample and insert p into the sample size formula in place of π. This method is appropriate if π is believed to differ greatly from .50, as is often the case, though its logic is somewhat circular (i.e., we must take a sample to plan our sample).

Method 3: Use a Prior Sample or Historical Data

A reasonable approach, but how often are such data available? And might π have changed enough to make it a questionable assumption?

EXAMPLE 8.9

ATM Withdrawals

A university credit union wants to know the proportion of cash withdrawals that exceed \$50 at its ATM located in the student union building. With an error of ± 2 percent and a confidence level of 95 percent, how large a sample is needed to estimate the proportion of withdrawals exceeding \$50? The z-value for 95 percent confidence is $z = 1.960$. Using $E = 0.02$ and assuming conservatively that $\pi = .50$, the required sample size is

$$n = \left(\frac{z}{E}\right)^2 \pi(1 - \pi) = \left(\frac{1.960}{0.02}\right)^2 (.50)(1 - .50) = 2{,}401$$

We would need to examine $n = 2{,}401$ withdrawals to estimate π within ± 2 percent and with 95 percent confidence. In this case, last year's proportion of ATM withdrawals over \$50 was 27 percent. If we had used this estimate in our calculation, the required sample size would be

$$n = \left(\frac{z}{E}\right)^2 p(1 - p) = \left(\frac{1.960}{0.02}\right)^2 (.27)(1 - .27) = 1{,}893 \quad \text{(rounded to next higher integer)}$$

We would need to examine $n = 1{,}893$ withdrawals to estimate π within ± 0.02. The required sample size is smaller than when we make the conservative assumption $\pi = .50$.

Alternatives

Suppose that our research budget will not permit a large sample. In the previous example, we could reduce the confidence interval level from 95 to 90 percent and increase the maximum error to ± 4 percent. Assuming $\pi = .50$, the required sample size is

$$n = \left(\frac{z}{E}\right)^2 \pi(1 - \pi) = \left(\frac{1.645}{0.04}\right)^2 (.50)(1 - .50) = 423 \qquad \text{(rounded to next higher integer)}$$

These seemingly modest changes make a huge difference in the sample size.

Practical Advice

Choosing a sample size is a common problem. Clients who take samples are constrained by time and money. Naturally, they prefer the highest possible confidence level and the lowest possible error. But when a statistical consultant shows them the required sample size, they may find it infeasible. A better way to look at it is that the formula for sample size provides a structure for a dialogue between statistician and client. A good consultant can propose several possible confidence levels and errors, and let the client choose the combination that best balances the need for accuracy against the available time and budget. The statistician can offer advice about these trade-offs, so the client's objectives are met. Other issues include nonresponse rates, dropout rates from ongoing studies, and possibly incorrect assumptions used in the calculation.

A common error is to insert $E = 2$ in the formula when you want an error of ± 2 percent. Because we are dealing with a *proportion*, a 2% error is $E = 0.02$. In other words, when estimating a proportion, E is always between 0 and 1.

SECTION EXERCISES

connect

8.50 What sample size would be required to estimate the true proportion of American female business executives who prefer the title "Ms.," with an error of ± 0.025 and 98 percent confidence?

8.51 What sample size would be needed to estimate the true proportion of American households that own more than one DVD player, with 90 percent confidence and an error of ± 0.02?

8.52 What sample size would be needed to estimate the true proportion of students at your college (if you are a student) who are wearing backpacks, with 95 percent confidence and an error of ± 0.04?

8.53 What sample size would be needed to estimate the true proportion of American adults who know their cholesterol level, using 95 percent confidence and an error of ± 0.02?

8.54 How large a sample size would be needed to estimate the percentage of wireless routers in San Francisco that use data encryption, with an error of ± 2 percent and 95 percent confidence?

8.55 Inspection of a random sample of 19 aircraft showed that 15 needed repairs to fix a wiring problem that might compromise safety. How large a sample would be needed to estimate the true proportion of jets with the wiring problem, with 90 percent confidence and an error of ± 6 percent?

8.10 CONFIDENCE INTERVAL FOR A POPULATION VARIANCE, σ^2 (OPTIONAL)

Chi-Square Distribution

LO 8-11

Construct a confidence interval for a variance (optional).

In our previous discussions of means and differences in means, we have indicated that many times we do not know the population variance, σ^2. A variance estimate can be useful information for many business applications. If the population is normal, we can construct a confidence interval for the population variance σ^2 using the **chi-square distribution** (the Greek letter χ is pronounced "kye") with degrees of freedom equal to $d.f. = n - 1$. Lower-tail and upper-tail percentiles for the chi-square distribution (denoted χ^2_L and χ^2_U, respectively) can be found in Appendix E. Alternatively, we can use the Excel functions =CHISQ.INV(α/2,df) and =CHISQ.INV.RT(α/2,df) to find χ^2_L and χ^2_U, respectively. Using the sample variance s^2, the confidence interval is

(8.18) $$\frac{(n-1)s^2}{\chi^2_U} \le \sigma^2 \le \frac{(n-1)s^2}{\chi^2_L}$$ (confidence interval for σ^2 from sample variance s^2)

EXAMPLE 8.10

Pizza Delivery

PIZZA

On a particular Friday night, the charges for 40 pizza delivery orders from Mama Frida's Pizza showed a mean of $\bar{x} = 24.76$ with a sample variance $s^2 = 12.77$.

29.51	21.09	29.98	29.95	21.07	29.52	21.07	24.95	21.07	24.95
24.98	29.95	24.95	21.07	25.30	25.30	29.95	29.99	29.95	24.95
24.95	21.07	24.98	21.09	21.07	24.98	21.07	25.30	29.95	25.30
25.30	24.98	16.86	25.30	25.30	16.86	24.95	24.98	25.30	21.07

The sample data were nearly symmetric (median \$24.98) with no outliers. Normality of the prices will be assumed. From Appendix E, using 39 degrees of freedom

($d.f. = n - 1 = 40 - 1 = 39$) we obtain bounds for the 95 percent middle area, as illustrated in Figures 8.25 and 8.26.

$\chi^2_L = 23.65$ (lower 2.5 percent) or χ^2_L =CHISQ.INV(.025,39)

$\chi^2_U = 58.12$ (upper 2.5 percent) or χ^2_U =CHISQ.INV.RT(.025,39)

The 95 percent confidence interval for the population variance σ^2 is

$$\text{Lower bound: } \frac{(n-1)s^2}{\chi^2_U} = \frac{(40-1)(12.77)}{58.12} = 8.569$$

$$\text{Upper bound: } \frac{(n-1)s^2}{\chi^2_L} = \frac{(40-1)(12.77)}{23.65} = 21.058$$

With 95 percent confidence, we believe that $8.569 \le \sigma^2 \le 21.058$.

FIGURE 8.25 **Chi-Square Values for 95 Percent Confidence with *d.f.* = 39**

Example for *d.f.* = 4

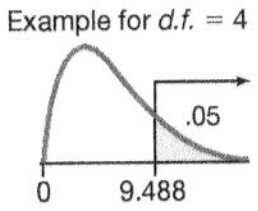

CHI-SQUARE CRITICAL VALUES

This table shows the critical values of chi-square for each desired tail area and degrees of freedom (d.f.).

	Area in Upper Tail									
d.f.	.995	.990	.975	.95	.90	.10	.05	.025	.01	.005
1	0.000	0.000	0.001	0.004	0.016	2.706	3.841	5.024	6.635	7.879
2	0.010	0.020	0.051	0.103	0.211	4.605	5.991	7.378	9.210	10.60
3	0.072	0.115	0.216	0.352	0.584	6.251	7.815	9.348	11.34	12.84
4	0.207	0.297	0.484	0.711	1.064	7.779	9.488	11.14	13.28	14.86
5	0.412	0.554	0.831	1.145	1.610	9.236	11.07	12.83	15.09	16.75
.	.	.	.	.	.	.	.	.	.	.
.	.	.	.	.	.	.	.	.	.	.
.	.	.	.	.	.	.	.	.	.	.
36	17.89	19.23	21.34	23.27	25.64	47.21	51.00	54.44	58.62	61.58
37	18.59	19.96	22.11	24.08	26.49	48.36	52.19	55.67	59.89	62.88
38	19.29	20.69	22.89	24.88	27.34	49.51	53.38	56.90	61.16	64.18
39	20.00	21.43	23.65	25.70	28.20	50.66	54.57	58.12	62.43	65.48
40	20.71	22.16	24.43	26.51	29.05	51.81	55.76	59.34	63.69	66.48
.	.	.	.	.	.	.	.	.	.	.
.	.	.	.	.	.	.	.	.	.	.
.	.	.	.	.	.	.	.	.	.	.
100	67.33	70.07	74.22	77.93	82.36	118.5	124.3	129.6	135.8	140.2

FIGURE 8.26 **Chi-Square Tail Values for *d.f.* = 39**

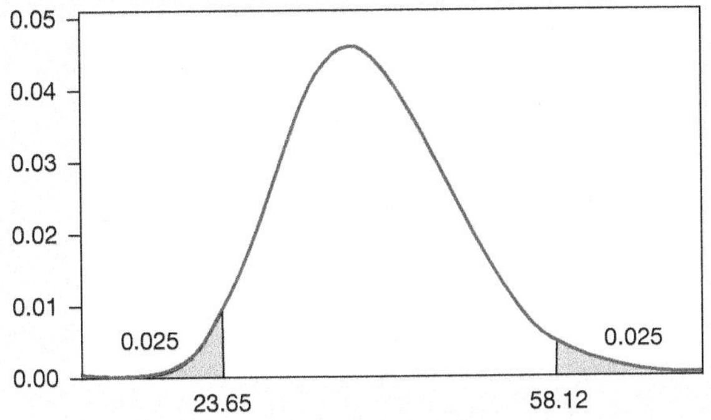

Confidence Interval for σ

If you want a confidence interval for the standard deviation, just take the square root of the interval bounds. In the pizza delivery example, we get $2.93 \le \sigma \le 4.59$. If you have raw data, MINITAB's Stat > Basic Statistics > Graphical Summary gives nice confidence intervals for the mean, median, and standard deviation for a column of raw data, as well as a histogram and box plot. MINITAB uses Student's t for the confidence interval for the mean and calculates the confidence interval for σ, as illustrated in Figure 8.27.

Caution: Assumption of Normality

The methods just described for confidence interval estimation of the variance and standard deviation are highly dependent on the population having a normal distribution. There is not a CLT that can be used for the statistic s^2. If the population does not have a normal distribution, then the confidence interval for the variance should not be considered accurate.

FIGURE 8.27

MINITAB's Confidence Intervals

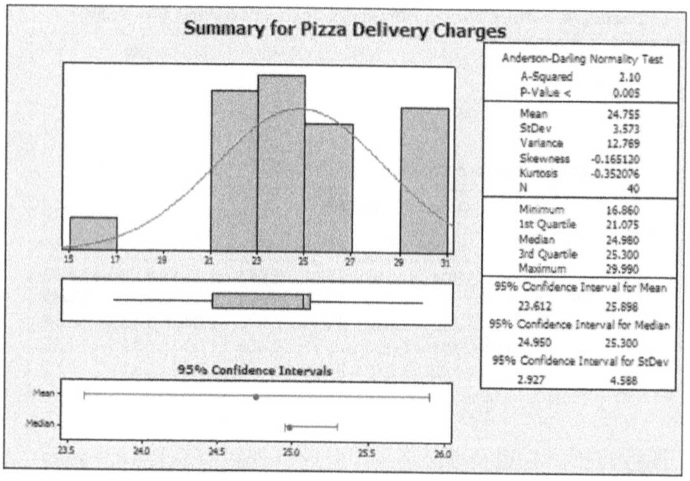

SECTION EXERCISES

connect

8.56 Find the 95 percent confidence interval for the population variance from these samples.

a. $n = 15$ commuters, $s = 10$ miles driven
b. $n = 18$ students, $s = 12$ study hours

8.57 The weights of 20 oranges (in ounces) are shown below. Construct a 95 percent confidence interval for the population standard deviation. *Note:* Scale was only accurate to the nearest ¼ ounce. (Data are from a project by statistics student Julie Gillman.) **Oranges**

5.50	6.25	6.25	6.50	6.50	7.00	7.00	7.00	7.50	7.50
7.75	8.00	8.00	8.50	8.50	9.00	9.00	9.25	10.00	10.50

8.58 A pediatrician's records showed the mean height of a random sample of 25 girls at age 12 months to be 29.530 inches with a standard deviation of 1.0953 inches. Construct a 95 percent confidence interval for the population variance. (Data are from a project by statistics students Lori Bossardet, Shannon Wegner, and Stephanie Rader.)

8.59 Find the 90 percent confidence interval for the standard deviation of gasoline mileage mpg for these 16 San Francisco commuters driving hybrid gas-electric vehicles. **Hybrid**

38.8	48.9	28.5	40.0	38.8	29.2	29.1	38.5
34.4	46.1	51.8	30.7	36.9	25.6	42.7	38.3

CHAPTER SUMMARY

An **estimator** is a sample statistic ($\bar{x}$, s, p) that is used to estimate an unknown population **parameter** (μ, σ, π). A desirable estimator is **unbiased** (correctly centered), **efficient** (minimum variance), and **consistent** (variance goes to zero as n increases). **Sampling error** (the difference between an estimator and its parameter) is inevitable, but a larger sample size yields estimates that are closer to the unknown parameter. The **Central Limit Theorem** (CLT) states that the sample mean $\bar{x}$ is centered at μ and follows a normal distribution if n is large, regardless of the population shape. A **confidence interval** for μ consists of lower and upper bounds that have a specified **confidence level** of enclosing μ. Any confidence level may be used, but 90, 95, and 99 percent are common. If the population variance is unknown, we replace z in the confidence interval formula for μ with **Student's *t*** using $n - 1$ degrees of freedom. The CLT also applies to the sample proportion (p) as an estimator of π, using a rule of thumb to decide if normality may be assumed. The **margin of error** is the half-width of the confidence interval. The **finite population correction factor** adjusts the margin of error to reflect better estimation precision when sample size is close to the population size. Formulas exist for the required **sample size** for a given level of precision in a confidence interval for μ or π, although they entail assumptions and are only approximate. Confidence intervals and sample sizes may be adjusted for finite populations, but often the adjustments are not material. Confidence intervals may be created for a variance using the **chi-square distribution**.

KEY TERMS

bias
Central Limit Theorem
chi-square distribution
confidence interval
confidence level
consistent estimator
degrees of freedom
efficiency (efficient estimator)
estimate
estimator
finite population correction factor
interval estimate
margin of error
minimum variance estimator
parameter
point estimate
sampling distribution
sampling error
sampling variation
standard error of the mean
standard error of the proportion
statistical estimation
Student's *t* distribution
unbiased estimator

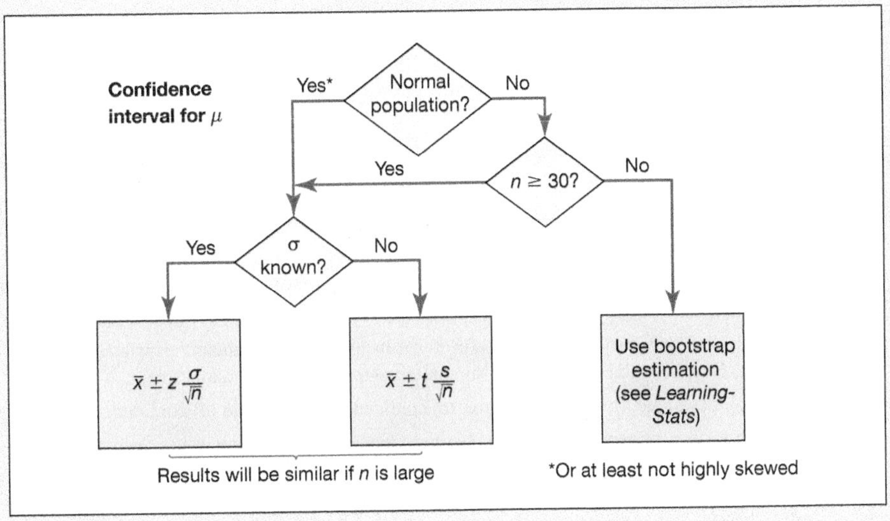

Commonly Used Formulas in Sampling Distributions and Estimation

Sample proportion: $p = \frac{x}{n}$

Standard error of the sample mean: $\sigma_{\bar{x}} = \frac{\sigma}{\sqrt{n}}$

Confidence interval for μ, known σ: $\bar{x} \pm z_{\alpha/2}\frac{\sigma}{\sqrt{n}}$

Confidence interval for μ, unknown σ: $\bar{x} \pm t_{\alpha/2}\frac{s}{\sqrt{n}}$ with $d.f. = n - 1$

Standard error of the sample proportion: $\sigma_p = \sqrt{\frac{\pi(1-\pi)}{n}}$

Confidence interval for π: $p \pm z_{\alpha/2}\sqrt{\frac{p(1-p)}{n}}$

Finite population correction factor (FPCF): $\sqrt{\frac{N-n}{N-1}}$

Confidence interval for μ, known σ, finite population: $\bar{x} \pm z_{\alpha/2}\frac{\sigma}{\sqrt{n}}\sqrt{\frac{N-n}{N-1}}$

Confidence interval for μ, unknown σ, finite population: $\bar{x} \pm t_{\alpha/2}\frac{s}{\sqrt{n}}\sqrt{\frac{N-n}{N-1}}$

Confidence interval for π, finite population: $p \pm z_{\alpha/2}\sqrt{\frac{p(1-p)}{n}}\sqrt{\frac{N-n}{N-1}}$

Sample size to estimate μ: $n = \left(\frac{z\sigma}{E}\right)^2$

Sample size to estimate π: $n = \left(\frac{z}{E}\right)^2\pi(1-\pi)$

CHAPTER REVIEW

1. Define (a) parameter, (b) estimator, (c) sampling error, and (d) sampling distribution.
2. Explain the difference between sampling error and bias. Can they be controlled?
3. Name three estimators. Which ones are unbiased?
4. Explain what it means to say an estimator is (a) unbiased, (b) efficient, and (c) consistent.
5. State the main points of the Central Limit Theorem for a mean.
6. Why is population shape of concern when estimating a mean? What does sample size have to do with it?
7. (a) Define the standard error of the mean. (b) What happens to the standard error as sample size increases? (c) How does the law of diminishing returns apply to the standard error?
8. Define (a) point estimate, (b) margin of error, (c) confidence interval, and (d) confidence level.
9. List some common confidence levels. What happens to the margin of error as you increase the confidence level, all other things being equal?
10. List differences and similarities between Student's t and the standard normal distribution.
11. Give an example to show that (a) for a given confidence level, the Student's t confidence interval for the mean is wider than if we use a z-value; and (b) it makes little difference in a large sample whether we use Student's t or z.
12. Why do outliers and skewed populations pose a problem for estimating a sample mean?
13. (a) State the Central Limit Theorem for a proportion. (b) When is it safe to assume normality for a sample proportion?
14. (a) Define the standard error of the proportion. (b) What happens to the standard error as sample size increases? (c) Why does a larger sample improve a confidence interval?
15. When would you use the FPCF and what does it do to the margin of error?

16. (a) Why does σ pose a problem for sample size calculation for a mean? (b) How can σ be approximated when it is unknown?
17. When calculating a sample size for a proportion, why is it conservative to assume that $\pi = .50$?
18. Why would we be interested in a confidence interval for a variance? Give an example.

CHAPTER EXERCISES

Note: Explain answers and show your work clearly. Problems marked * rely on optional material from this chapter.

8.60 A random sample of 30 lunch orders at Noodles and Company showed a mean bill of \$10.36 with a standard deviation of \$5.31. Find the 95 percent confidence interval for the mean bill of all lunch orders. NoodlesOrderSize

8.61 A random sample of 21 nickels measured with a very accurate micrometer showed a mean diameter of 0.834343 inch with a standard deviation of 0.001886 inch. (a) Why would nickel diameters vary? (b) Construct a 99 percent confidence interval for the true mean diameter of a nickel. (c) Discuss any assumptions that are needed. (d) What sample size would ensure an error of ±0.0005 inch with 99 percent confidence? (Data are from a project by MBA student Bob Tindall.)

8.62 A random sample of 10 miniature Tootsie Rolls was taken from a bag. Each piece was weighed on a very accurate scale. The results in grams were

3.087	3.131	3.241	3.241	3.270	3.353	3.400	3.411	3.437	3.477

(a) Construct a 90 percent confidence interval for the true mean weight. (b) What sample size would be necessary to estimate the true weight with an error of ±0.03 gram with 90 percent confidence? (Data are from a project by MBA student Henry Scussel.) Tootsie

8.63 Statistics students were asked to go home and fill a 1-cup measure with raisin bran, tap the cup lightly on the counter three times to settle the contents, if necessary add more raisin bran to bring the contents exactly up to the 1-cup line, spread the contents on a large plate, and count the raisins. For the 13 students who chose Kellogg's brand, the reported results were

23	33	44	36	29	42	31	33	61	36	34	23	24

Construct a 90 percent confidence interval for the mean number of raisins per cup. Show your work clearly. Raisins

8.64 A sample of 20 pages was taken without replacement from a Yellow Pages directory that has 1,591 pages. (a) Calculate the FPCF for this sample. (b) Should the population be considered effectively infinite?

8.65 Twenty-five blood samples were selected by taking every seventh blood sample from racks holding 187 blood samples from the morning draw at a medical center. (a) Calculate the FPCF for this sample. (b) Should the population be considered effectively infinite?

8.66 A sample of 20 pages was taken from a Yellow Pages directory. On each page, the mean area devoted to display ads was measured (a display ad is a large block of multicolored illustrations, maps, and text). The data (in square millimeters) are shown below:

0	260	356	403	536	0	268	369	428	536
268	396	469	536	162	338	403	536	536	130

(a) Construct a 95 percent confidence interval for the true mean. (b) What sample size would be needed to obtain an error of ±20 square millimeters with 95 percent confidence? (Data are based on a project by MBA student Daniel R. Dalach.) DisplayAds

8.67 Sixteen owners of 2010 Audi A4 sedans kept track of their average fuel economy for a month. The results are shown below. (a) Construct a 95 percent confidence interval for the mean. (b) What factor(s) limit the conclusions that can be drawn about the true mean? (Data are from www.fueleconomy.gov.) MPG

20.8	20.0	19.4	19.7	21.1	22.6	18.3	20.1
20.5	19.5	17.4	22.4	18.9	20.2	19.6	19.0

8.68 Twenty-five blood samples were selected by taking every seventh blood sample from racks holding 187 blood samples from the morning draw at a medical center. The white blood count (WBC) was measured using a Coulter Counter Model S. The mean WBC was 8.636 with a standard deviation of 3.9265. (a) Construct a 90 percent confidence interval for the true mean using the FPCF. (b) What sample size would be needed for an error of ±1.5 with 90 percent confidence? (Data are from a project by MBA student Wendy Blomquist.)

8.69 Twenty-one warranty repairs were selected from a population of 126 by selecting every sixth item. The population consisted of "loose, not attached" minivan electrical wires (one of several electrical failure categories the dealership mechanic can select). The mean repair cost was \$45.664 with a standard deviation of \$27.793. (a) Construct a 95 percent confidence interval for the true mean repair cost. (b) What sample size would be needed to obtain an error of ±\$5 with 95 percent confidence? *(c) Construct a 95 percent confidence interval for the true standard deviation. (Data are from a project by MBA student Tim Polulak.)

8.70 Dave the jogger runs the same route every day (about 2.2 miles). On 18 consecutive days, he recorded the number of steps using a pedometer. The results were

3,450	3,363	3,228	3,360	3,304	3,407	3,324	3,365	3,290
3,289	3,346	3,252	3,237	3,210	3,140	3,220	3,103	3,129

(a) Construct a 95 percent confidence interval for the true mean number of steps Dave takes on his run. (b) What sample size would be needed to obtain an error of ±20 steps with 95 percent confidence? (c) Using Excel, plot a line chart of the data. What do the data suggest about the pattern over time? **DaveSteps**

8.71 A pediatrician's records showed the mean height of a random sample of 25 girls at age 12 months to be 29.530 inches with a standard deviation of 1.0953 inches. (a) Construct a 95 percent confidence interval for the true mean height. (b) What sample size would be needed for 95 percent confidence and an error of ±.20 inch? (Data are from a project by statistics students Lori Bossardet, Shannon Wegner, and Stephanie Rader.)

***8.72** A random sample of 10 exam scores showed a standard deviation of 7.2 points. Find the 95 percent confidence interval for the population standard deviation. Use Appendix E to obtain the values of χ_L^2 and χ_U^2.

NOODLES & COMPANY

***8.73** A random sample of 30 lunch orders at Noodles and Company showed a standard deviation of \$5.31. Find the 90 percent confidence interval for the population standard deviation. Use Excel to obtain χ_L^2 =CHISQ.INV(α/2,*d.f.*) and χ_U^2 =CHISQ.INV.RT(α/2,*d.f.*)

8.74 During the Rose Bowl, the length (in seconds) of 12 randomly chosen commercial breaks during timeouts (following touchdown, turnover, field goal, or punt) were

65	75	85	95	80	100	90	80	85	85	60	65

Assuming a normal population, construct a 90 percent confidence interval for the mean length of a commercial break during the Rose Bowl. **TimeOuts**

8.75 A sample of 40 CDs from a student's collection showed a mean length of 52.74 minutes with a standard deviation of 13.21 minutes. (a) Construct a 95 percent confidence interval for the mean. (b) Why might the normality assumption be an issue here? (c) What sample size would be needed to estimate μ with 95 percent confidence and an error of ±3 minutes? (Data are from a project by statistics students Michael Evatz, Nancy Petack, and Jennifer Skladanowski.)

8.76 The Environmental Protection Agency (EPA) requires that cities monitor over 80 contaminants in their drinking water. Samples from the Lake Huron Water Treatment Plant gave the results shown here. Only the range is reported, not the mean. For each substance, estimate the *standard deviation* σ by using one of the methods shown in Table 8.11 in Section 8.8.

Substance	*MCLG Range Detected*	*Allowable MCLG*	*Origin of Substance*
Chromium	0.47 to 0.69	100	Discharge from steel and pulp mills, natural erosion
Barium	0.004 to 0.019	2	Discharge from drilling wastes, metal refineries, natural erosion
Fluoride	1.07 to 1.17	4.0	Natural erosion, water additive, discharge from fertilizer and aluminum factories

MCLG = Maximum contaminant level goal

8.77 In a sample of 100 Planter's Mixed Nuts, 19 were found to be almonds. (a) Construct a 90 percent confidence interval for the true proportion of almonds. (b) May normality be assumed? Explain. (c) What sample size would be needed for 90 percent confidence and an error of ± 0.03? (d) Why would a quality control manager at Planter's need to understand sampling?

8.78 A study showed that fourteen of 180 publicly traded business services companies failed a test for compliance with Sarbanes-Oxley requirements for financial records and fraud protection. Assuming that these are a random sample of all publicly traded companies, construct a 95 percent confidence interval for the overall noncompliance proportion.

8.79 How "decaffeinated" is decaffeinated coffee? If a researcher wants to estimate the mean caffeine content of a cup of Starbucks' decaffeinated espresso with 98 percent confidence and an error of ± 0.1 mg, what is the required number of cups that must be tested? Assume a standard deviation of 0.5 mg, based on a small preliminary sample of 12 cups.

8.80 Noodles & Company wants to estimate the percent of customers who order dessert, with 95 percent confidence and an error of $\pm 10\%$. What is the required sample size?

8.81 Junior Achievement and Deloitte commissioned a "teen ethics poll" of 787 students aged 13–18, finding that 29 percent felt inadequately prepared to make ethical judgments. (a) Assuming that this was a random sample, find the 95 percent confidence interval for the true proportion of U.S. teens who feel inadequately prepared to make ethical judgments. (b) Is the sample size large enough to assume normality? (See http://ja.org/.)

8.82 A random sample of 30 cans of Del Vino crushed tomatoes revealed a mean weight of 798.3 grams (excluding the juice). The can-filling process for Del Vino crushed tomatoes has a known standard deviation of 3.1 grams. Construct the 95 percent confidence interval for the mean weight of cans, assuming that the weight of cans is a normally distributed random variable.

8.83 A poll of 125 college students who watch *The Big Bang Theory* showed that 83 of them usually watch on a mobile device (e.g., laptop). (a) Assuming that this was a random sample, construct a 90 percent confidence interval for the proportion of all college students who usually watch this show on a mobile device. (b) Would a finite population correction be required? Explain.

8.84 A survey of 4,581 U.S. households that owned a mobile phone found that 58 percent are satisfied with the coverage of their cellular phone provider. Assuming that this was a random sample, construct a 90 percent confidence interval for the true proportion of satisfied U.S. mobile phone owners.

8.85 A "teen ethics poll" was commissioned by Junior Achievement and Deloitte. The survey by Harris Interactive surveyed 787 students aged 13–18. (a) Assuming that this was a random sample of all students in this age group, find the margin of error of the poll. (b) Would the margin of error be greater or smaller for the subgroup consisting only of male students? Explain. (See http://ja.org/.)

8.86 Biting an unpopped kernel of popcorn hurts! As an experiment, a self-confessed connoisseur of cheap popcorn carefully counted 773 kernels and put them in a popper. After popping, the unpopped kernels were counted. There were 86. (a) Construct a 90 percent confidence interval for the proportion of all kernels that would not pop. (b) Check the normality assumption for p.

8.87 A sample of 213 newspaper tire ads from several Sunday papers showed that 98 contained a low-price guarantee (offer to "meet or beat any price"). (a) Assuming that this was a random sample, construct a 95 percent confidence interval for the proportion of all Sunday newspaper tire ads that contain a low-price guarantee. (b) Is the criterion for normality of p met?

8.88 A physician's billing office conducted a random check of patient records and found that 36 of 50 patients had changed insurance plans within the past year. Construct a 90 percent confidence interval for the true proportion.

8.89 Of 250 college students taking a statistics class, 4 reported an allergy to peanuts. (a) Is the criterion for normality of p met? (b) Assuming that this was a random sample, use MINITAB to construct a 95 percent confidence interval for the proportion of all college statistics students with a peanut allergy.

8.90 (a) A poll of 2,277 likely voters was conducted on the president's performance. Approximately what margin of error would the approval rating estimate have? (b) The poll showed that 44 percent approved the president's performance. Construct a 90 percent confidence interval for the true proportion. (c) Would you say that the percentage of all voters who approve of the president's performance could be 50 percent?

8.91 To determine the proportion of taxpayers who prefer filing tax returns electronically, a survey of 600 taxpayers was conducted. Calculate the margin of error used to estimate this proportion. What assumptions are required to find the margin of error?

8.92 A sample of 40 CDs from a student's collection showed a mean length of 52.74 minutes with a standard deviation of 13.21 minutes. Construct a 95 percent confidence interval for the population standard deviation. (Data are from a project by statistics students Michael Evatz, Nancy Petack, and Jennifer Skladanowski.)

8.93 Vail Resorts would like to send a survey to their guests asking about their satisfaction with the new 2009 website design. They would like to have a margin of error of ±5 percent on responses with 95 percent confidence. (a) Using the conservative approach, what sample size is needed to ensure this level of confidence and margin of error? (b) If Vail Resorts wanted the margin of error to be only ±2.5 percent, what would happen to the required sample size?

MINI-PROJECTS

8.94 This is an exercise using Excel. (a) Use =RANDBETWEEN(0,99) to create 20 samples of size $n = 4$ by choosing two-digit random numbers between 00 and 99. (b) For each sample, calculate the mean. (c) Make a histogram of the 80 *individual X-values* using bins 10 units wide (i.e., 0, 10, 20, . . . , 100). Describe the shape of the histogram. (d) Make a histogram of your 20 *sample means* using bins 10 units wide. (e) Discuss the histogram shape. Does the Central Limit Theorem seem to be working? (f) Find the mean of your 20 sample means. Was it what you would expect? Explain. (g) Find the standard deviation of your 20 sample means. Was it what you would expect?

8.95 For 10 tanks of gas for your car, calculate the miles per gallon. (a) Construct a 95 percent confidence interval for the true mean mpg for your car. (b) How many tanks of gas would you need to obtain an error of ±0.2 mpg with 95 percent confidence? Use the value of s from your sample.

8.96 (a) Look at 50 vehicles in a parking lot near you. Count the number that are SUVs (state your definition of SUV). Use any sampling method you like (e.g., the first 50 you see). (b) Construct a 95 percent confidence interval for the true population proportion of SUVs. (c) What sample size would be needed to ensure an error of ±0.025 with 98 percent confidence? (d) Would the proportion be the same if this experiment were repeated in a university parking lot?

8.97 (a) From the New York Stock Exchange website, take a random sample of 30 companies that are on the IPO (Initial Public Offering) Showcase list for last year. (b) Calculate a 90 percent confidence interval for the average closing stock price on the day of the IPO.

RELATED READING

Boos, Dennis D.; and Jacqueline M. Hughes-Oliver. "How Large Does n Have to be for z and t Intervals?" *The American Statistician* 54, no. 2 (May 2000), pp. 121–28.

Browne, Richard H. "Using the Sample Range as a Basis for Calculating Sample Size in Power Calculations." *The American Statistician* 55, no. 4 (November 2001), pp. 293–98.

Kupper, Lawrence L.; and Kerry B. Hafner. "How Appropriate Are Popular Sample Size Formulas?" *The American Statistician* 43, no. 2 (May 1989), pp. 101–105.

Lenth, Russell V. "Some Practical Guidelines for Effective Sample Size Determination." *The American Statistician* 55, no. 3 (August 2001), pp. 187–93.

Parker, Robert A. "Sample Size: More Than Calculations." *The American Statistician* 57, no. 3 (August 2003), pp. 166–70.

van Belle, Gerald. *Statistical Rules of Thumb*. 2nd ed. Wiley, 2008.

CHAPTER 8 More Learning Resources

You can access these *LearningStats* demonstrations through McGraw-Hill's Connect® to help you understand sampling distributions and confidence intervals.

connect™

Topic	*LearningStats Demonstrations*
Central Limit Theorem	CLT Demonstration: Simulation CLT Demonstration: Finite Population
Sampling distributions	Sampling Distributions Critical Values (z, t, χ^2) Sample Proportion Demonstration
Confidence intervals	Confidence Interval: Means Confidence Interval: Proportions Confidence Interval: Variances Confidence Interval: Simulation Confidence Interval: Bootstrap Finite Populations Bootstrap Explained
Sample size	Sample Size Calculator
Tables	Appendix D—Student's t Appendix E—Chi-Square

Key: = Excel = Pdf

Chapter 9. One-Sample Hypothesis Tests

CHAPTER 9

One-Sample Hypothesis Tests

CHAPTER CONTENTS

CHAPTER LEARNING OBJECTIVES

LO

When you finish this chapter you should be able to

LO 9-1 Know the steps in testing hypotheses and define H_0 and H_1.

LO 9-2 Define Type I error, Type II error, and power.

LO 9-3 Formulate a null and alternative hypothesis for μ or π.

LO 9-4 Explain decision rules, critical values, and rejection regions.

LO 9-5 Perform a hypothesis test for a mean with known σ using z.

LO 9-6 Use tables or Excel to find the p-value in tests of μ.

LO 9-7 Perform a hypothesis test for a mean with unknown σ using t.

LO 9-8 Perform a hypothesis test for a proportion and find the p-value.

LO 9-9 Check whether normality may be assumed in testing a proportion.

LO 9-10 Interpret a power curve or OC curve (optional).

LO 9-11 Perform a hypothesis test for a variance (optional).

Data are used in business every day to support marketing claims, help managers make decisions, and measure business improvement. Whether the business is small or large, profit or nonprofit, the use of data allows businesses to find the best answers to their questions.

- Should Ball Corporation's aluminum can division change suppliers of metal?
- Did the proportion of defective products decrease after a new manufacturing process was introduced?
- Has the average service time at a Noodles & Company restaurant decreased since last year?
- Has a ski resort decreased its average response time to accidents?
- Did the proportion of satisfied car repair customers increase after providing more training for the employees?

Savvy businesspeople use data and many of the statistical tools that you've already learned to answer these types of questions. We will build on these tools in this chapter and learn about one of the most widely used statistical tools—**hypothesis testing**. Hypothesis testing is used in science and business to test assumptions and theories and guide managers when facing decisions. First we will explain the logic behind hypothesis testing and then show how *statistical hypothesis testing* helps businesses make decisions.

9.1 LOGIC OF HYPOTHESIS TESTING

LO 9-1

Know the steps in testing hypotheses and define H_0 and H_1.

The business analyst asks questions, makes assumptions, and proposes testable theories about the values of key parameters of the business operating environment. Each assumption is tested against observed data. If an assumption has not been disproved, in spite of rigorous efforts to do so, the business may operate under the belief that the statement is true. The analyst states the assumption, called a **hypothesis**, in a format that can be tested using well-known statistical procedures. The hypothesis is compared with sample data to determine if the data are consistent or inconsistent with the hypothesis. When the data are found to be inconsistent (i.e., in conflict) with the hypothesis, the hypothesis is either discarded or reformulated.

The process of hypothesis testing can be an iterative process, as illustrated in Figure 9.1. Not every hypothesis has to be retested continuously. Some questions are relevant only at a point in time, such as asking whether or not consumers under age 25 prefer a new Coke flavor to an existing flavor. If a carefully designed marketing study provides a clear-cut answer, no

FIGURE 9.1

Hypothesis Testing as an Ongoing Process

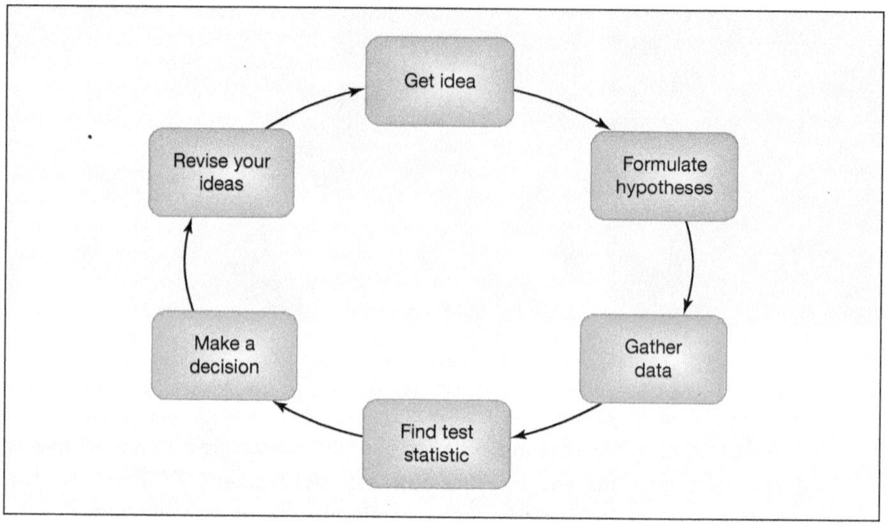

more testing is required. On the other hand, clinical testing of new drugs may go on for years, at different hospitals and with different types of patients. The efficacy and side effects of new drugs may involve subtle effects that only show up in very large samples and over longer periods of time, sometimes with profound financial implications for the company. Automobile safety testing is ongoing because of changes in car technology and driver habits. There is plenty of work for data analysts who continually look for changes in customer satisfaction, shifts in buying patterns, and trends in warranty claims.

Who Uses Hypothesis Testing?

The innovative vigor of our economy is largely based on technology: new materials, new manufacturing methods, new distribution systems, new information strategies. All business managers need at least a basic understanding of hypothesis testing because managers often interact with specialists, read technical reports, and then make recommendations on key financial or strategic decisions based on statistical evidence. A confidence interval sometimes gives enough information to make a decision. Knowing the 95 percent range of likely values for a key decision parameter (e.g., the proportion of repeat customers under age 30) may be all you need. This chapter extends the idea of confidence intervals by showing how to test a sample against a benchmark, and how to assess the risk of incorrect decisions.

Steps in Hypothesis Testing

Step 1: State the hypothesis to be tested.

Step 2: Specify what level of inconsistency with the data will lead to rejection of the hypothesis. This is called a *decision rule.*

Step 3: Collect data and calculate necessary statistics to test the hypothesis.

Step 4: Make a decision. Should the hypothesis be rejected or not?

Step 5: Take action based on the decision.

Step 1: State the Hypotheses Formulate a pair of mutually exclusive, collectively exhaustive statements about the world. One statement or the other must be true, but they cannot both be true.

H_0: Null Hypothesis

H_1: Alternative Hypothesis

The two statements are *hypotheses* because the truth is unknown. Efforts will be made to reject the **null hypothesis** (sometimes called the *maintained hypothesis* or the *research hypothesis*). H_0 must be stated in a precise way, so that it can be tested against empirical evidence from a sample. If H_0 happens to be an established theory, we might not really expect to reject it, but we try anyway. If we reject H_0, we tentatively conclude that the **alternative hypothesis** H_1 is the case. H_0 represents the *status quo* (e.g., the current state of affairs), while H_1 is sometimes called the *action alternative* because action may be required if we reject H_0 in favor of H_1. For example:

Criminal Trial In a criminal trial, the hypotheses are:

H_0: The defendant is innocent
H_1: The defendant is guilty

Our legal system assumes a defendant is innocent *unless the evidence gathered by the prosecutor is sufficient to reject this assumption.*

Drug Testing When an Olympic athlete is tested for performance-enhancing drugs ("doping"), the presumption is that the athlete is in compliance with the rules. The hypotheses are:

H_0: No banned substance was used
H_1: Banned substance was used

Samples of urine or blood are taken as evidence and *used only to disprove the null hypothesis, because we assume the athlete is free of banned substances.*

Biometric Security To identify authorized and unauthorized persons for computer access, ATM withdrawals, and entry into secure facilities, there is increasing interest in using the person's physical characteristics (e.g., fingerprints, facial structure, or iris patterns) instead of paper and plastic IDs, which can be forged. The hypotheses are:

H_0: User is legitimate
H_1: User is not legitimate

The system assumes the user is legitimate *unless the physical characteristic being presented is inconsistent with the biometric profile of that individual.*

Step 2: Specify the Decision Rule Before collecting data to compare against the hypothesis, the researcher must specify *how* the evidence will be used to reach a decision about the null hypothesis. In our legal system, the evidence presented by the prosecutor must convince a jury "beyond a reasonable doubt" that the defendant is not innocent. In steroid testing, the lab that analyzes the urine or blood sample must conduct tests to decide whether the sample exceeds the agreed-upon benchmark or threshhold. With biometric screening, the designer of the security system determines how many discrepancies on a fingerprint would indicate an unauthorized user.

Steps 3 and 4: Data Collection and Decision Making Much of the critical work in hypothesis testing takes place during steps 1 and 2. Once the hypotheses and decision rule have been clearly articulated, the process of data collection, while occasionally time-consuming, is straightforward. We compare the data with the hypothesis, using the decision rule, and decide to reject or not reject the null hypothesis.

Step 5: Take Action Based on Decision This last step—taking action—requires experience and expertise on the part of the decision maker. Suppose the evidence presented at a trial convinces a jury that the defendant is not innocent. What punishment should the judge impose? Or suppose the blood sample of an athlete shows steroid use. What fine should the athletic commission impose? Should the athlete be banned from competing? If the fingerprint presented for authentication has been rejected, should an alarm go off? Should a security breach be recorded in the system? Appropriate action for the decision should relate back to the purpose of conducting the hypothesis test in the first place.

Can a Null Hypothesis Be Proved?

No, we cannot prove a null hypothesis—we can only *fail to reject* it. A null hypothesis that survives repeated tests without rejection is "true" only in the limited sense that it has been thoroughly scrutinized and tested. Today's "true" hypothesis could be disproved tomorrow if new data are found. If we fail to reject H_0, the same hypothesis may be retested. That is how scientific inquiry works. Einstein's theories, for example, are over 100 years old but are still being subjected to rigorous tests. Few scientists really think that Einstein's theories are "wrong." Yet it's in the nature of science to keep trying to refute accepted theories, especially when a new test is possible or when new data become available. Similarly, the safety of commonly used prescription drugs is continually being studied. Sometimes, "safe" drugs are revealed to have serious side effects only after large-scale, long-term use by consumers (e.g., the Vioxx arthritis drug that was at first shown to be safe in clinical trials, but later showed a dangerous association with heart attack after years of use by millions of people).

9.2 TYPE I AND TYPE II ERROR

LO 9-2

Define Type I error, Type II error, and power.

Our ability to collect evidence can be limited by our tools and by time and financial resources. On occasion we will be making a decision about the null hypothesis that could be wrong. Consequently, our decision rule will be based on the levels of risk of making a wrong decision. We can allow more risk or less risk by changing the threshold of the decision rule.

It is possible to make an incorrect decision regarding the null hypothesis. As illustrated in the table below, either the null hypothesis is true or it is false. We have two possible choices concerning the null hypothesis. We either reject H_0 or fail to reject H_0.

	H_0 is true	***H_0 is false***
Reject H_0	Type I error	Correct decision
Fail to reject H_0	Correct decision	Type II error

The true situation determines whether our decision was correct. If the decision about the null hypothesis matches the true situation, the decision was correct. Rejecting the null hypothesis when it is true is a **Type I error** (also called a **false positive**). Failure to reject the null hypothesis when it is false is a **Type II error** (also called a **false negative**). In either case, an incorrect decision was made.

Because we rarely have perfect information about the true situation, we can't always know whether we have committed a Type I or Type II error. But by using statistics, we can calculate the *probability* of making an incorrect decision. We can minimize the chance of error by collecting as much sample evidence as our resources allow, and by choosing proper testing procedures.

Consequences of Type I and Type II Errors

The consequences of these two errors are quite different, and the costs are borne by different parties. Depending on the situation, decision makers may fear one error more than the other. It would be nice if both types of error could be avoided. Unfortunately, when making a decision based on a fixed body of sample evidence, reducing the risk of one type of error often increases the risk of the other.

H_0: Defendant is innocent
H_1: Defendant is guilty

Criminal Trial Type I error is convicting an innocent defendant, so the costs are borne by the defendant. Type II error is failing to convict a guilty defendant, so the costs are borne by society if the guilty person returns to the streets. Concern for the rights of the accused and stricter rules of evidence may suggest rules that would reduce the risk of Type I error. But concern over the social costs of crime and victims' rights could lead to rules that would reduce Type II error, presumably at the expense of Type I error. Both risks can be reduced only by devoting more effort to gathering evidence and strengthening the legal process (expediting trials, improving jury quality, increasing investigative work).

Drug Testing Type I error (a false positive) is unfairly disqualifying an athlete who is "clean." Type II error (a false negative) is letting the drug user get away with it and have an unfair competitive advantage. The costs of Type I error are hard feelings, unnecessary embarrassment, and possible loss of lifetime earnings for professional athletes. The costs of Type II error are tarnishing the Olympic image and rewarding those who break the rules. Over time, improved tests have reduced the risk of both types of error. However, for a given technology, the threshold can be set lower or higher, balancing Type I and Type II errors.

H_0: No illegal doping
H_1: Illegal doping

Biometric Security Type I error means denying a legitimate user access to a facility or funds. Type II error is letting an unauthorized user have access to facilities or a financial account. Technology has progressed to the point where Type II errors have become very rare, though Type I errors remain a problem. The error rates depend, among other things, on how much is spent on the equipment and software.

H_0: User is legitimate
H_1: User is not legitimate

Probability of Type I and Type II Errors

The *probability* of a Type I error (rejecting a true null hypothesis) is denoted α (the lowercase Greek letter "alpha"). Statisticians refer to α as the **level of significance**. The probability of a Type II error (not rejecting a false hypothesis) is denoted β (the lowercase Greek letter "beta"), as shown in Table 9.1.

TABLE 9.1
Key Terms in Hypothesis Testing

Key Term	*What Is It?*	*Symbol*	*Definition*	*Also Called*
Type I error	Reject a true hypothesis	α	$P(\text{reject } H_0 \mid H_0 \text{ is true})$	False positive
Type II error	Fail to reject a false hypothesis	β	$P(\text{fail to reject } H_0 \mid H_0 \text{ is false})$	False negative
Power	Correctly reject a false hypothesis	$1 - \beta$	$P(\text{reject } H_0 \mid H_0 \text{ is false})$	Sensitivity

The **power** of a test is the probability that a false hypothesis *will* be rejected (as it should be). Power equals $1 - \beta$ and is the complement of Type II error. Reducing β would correspondingly increase power (usually accomplished by increasing the sample size).

More powerful tests are more likely to detect false hypotheses. For example, if a new weight-loss drug actually is effective, we would want to reject the null hypothesis that the drug has no effect. We prefer the most powerful test possible. Larger samples lead to increased power, which is why clinical trials often involve thousands of people.

Relationship between α and β

We desire tests that avoid false negatives (small β) yet we also want to avoid false positives (small α). Given two equivalent tests, we will choose the more powerful test (smaller β). But for a given type of test and fixed sample size, there is a trade-off between α and β. The larger critical value needed to reduce α makes it harder to reject H_0, thereby increasing β. The proper balance between α and β can be elusive. Consider these examples:

- If your household carbon monoxide detector's sensitivity threshold is increased to reduce the risk of overlooking danger (reduced β), there will be more false alarms (increased α).
- A doctor who is conservative about admitting patients with symptoms of heart attack to the ICU (reduced β) will admit more patients with no heart attack (increased α).
- More sensitive airport weapons detectors (reduced β) will inconvenience more safe passengers (increased α).

Both α and β can be reduced simultaneously only by increasing the sample size (gathering more evidence), which is not always feasible or cost-effective.

Mini Case 9.1

BIOMETRIC SECURITY

If your ATM could recognize your physical characteristics (e.g., fingerprint, face, palm, iris), you wouldn't need an ATM card or a PIN. A reliable biometric ID system could also reduce the risk of ID theft, eliminate computer passwords, and speed airport security screening. The hypotheses are

H_0: User is legitimate

H_1: User is not legitimate

Fujitsu Laboratories has tested a palm ID system on 700 people, ranging from children to seniors. It achieved a false rejection rate of 1 percent and a false acceptance rate of 0.5 percent. Bank of Tokyo-Mitsubishi introduced palm-scanning at its ATM machines in 2004. DigitalPersona of Redwood City, California, has developed a fingerprint scanner (called *U.Are.U*) that is able to recognize fingerprints in 200 milliseconds with a 1 percent false rejection rate and a 0.002 percent false acceptance rate. In some high-end devices, false acceptance rates as low as 25 per million have been achieved. These low rates of false acceptance (Type II error) are encouraging, since they mean that others cannot easily impersonate you. Fingerprint scanning is popular (e.g., at the entrance gates of Disney World or Universal Studios) because it is cheaper and easier to implement, though some experts believe that iris scanning or several combined tests have better long-run potential to reduce both error rates. Any such system requires a stored database of biometric data.

PRODUCT SAFETY

Firms are increasingly wary of Type II error (failing to recall a product as soon as sample evidence begins to indicate potential problems):

H_0: Product is performing safely

H_1: Product is not performing safely

They may even order a precautionary product recall before the statistical evidence has become convincing (e.g., Verizon's 2004 recall of 50,000 cell phone batteries after one exploded and another caused a car fire) or even *before* anything bad happens (e.g., Intel's 2004 recall of its 915 G/P and 925X chip sets from OEMs (original equipment manufacturers), before the chips actually reached any consumers). Failure to act swiftly can generate liability and adverse publicity as with the spate of Ford Explorer rollover accidents and eventual recall of certain 15-inch Firestone radial tires. Ford and Firestone believed they had found an engineering work-around to make the tire design safe, until accumulating accident data, lawsuits, and NHTSA pressure forced recognition that there was a problem. In 2004, certain COX_2 inhibitor drugs that had previously been thought effective and safe, based on extensive clinical trials, were found to be associated with increased risk of heart attack. The makers' stock price plunged (e.g., Merck). The courts often must use statistical evidence to adjudicate product liability claims.

SECTION EXERCISES

connect

9.1 If you repeated a hypothesis test 1,000 times (in other words, 1,000 different samples from the same population), how many times would you expect to commit a Type I error, assuming the null hypothesis were true, if (a) $\alpha = .05$; (b) $\alpha = .01$; or (c) $\alpha = .001$?

9.2 Define Type I and Type II error for each scenario, and identify the cost(s) of each type of error.

a. A 25-year-old ER patient in Minneapolis complains of chest pain. Heart attacks in 25-year-olds are rare, and beds are scarce in the hospital. The null hypothesis is that there is no heart attack (perhaps muscle pain due to shoveling snow).

b. Approaching O'Hare for landing, a British Air flight from London has been in a holding pattern for 45 minutes due to bad weather. Landing is expected within 15 minutes. The flight crew could declare an emergency and land immediately, but an FAA investigation would be launched and other flights might be endangered. The null hypothesis is that there is enough fuel to stay aloft for 15 more minutes.

c. You are trying to finish a lengthy statistics report and print it for your evening class. Your color printer is very low on ink, and you just have time to get to Staples for a new cartridge. But it is snowing and you need every minute to finish the report. The null hypothesis is that you have enough ink.

9.3 A firm decides to test its employees for illegal drugs. (a) State the null and alternative hypotheses. (b) Define Type I and II errors. (c) What are the consequences of each type of error, and to whom?

9.4 A hotel installs smoke detectors with adjustable sensitivity in all public guest rooms. (a) State the null and alternative hypotheses. (b) Define Type I and II errors. (c) What are the consequences of each type of error, and to whom?

9.5 What is the consequence of a false negative in an inspection of your car's brakes? *Hint:* The null hypothesis is the status quo (things are OK).

9.6 What is the consequence of a false positive in a weekly inspection of a nuclear plant's cooling system? *Hint:* The null hypothesis is the status quo (things are OK).

9.3 DECISION RULES AND CRITICAL VALUES

LO 9-3 Formulate a null and alternative hypothesis for μ or π.

LO 9-4 Explain decision rules, critical values, and rejection regions.

A **statistical hypothesis** is a statement about the value of a population parameter that we are interested in. For example, the parameter could be a mean, a proportion, or a variance. A **hypothesis test** is a decision between two competing, mutually exclusive, and collectively exhaustive hypotheses about the value of the parameter.

The hypothesized value of the parameter is the center of interest. For example, if the true value of μ is 5, then the sample mean should not differ greatly from 5. We rely on our knowledge of the *sampling distribution* and the *standard error of the estimate* to decide if the sample estimate is far enough away from 5 to contradict the assumption that $\mu = 5$. We can calculate the likelihood of an observed sample outcome. If the sample outcome is very unlikely, we would reject the claimed mean $\mu = 5$.

The null hypothesis states a benchmark value that we denote with the subscript "0" as in μ_0 or π_0. The hypothesized value μ_0 or π_0 does not come from a sample but is based on past performance, an industry standard, a target, or a product specification.

Where Do We Get μ_0 (or π_0)?

For a mean (or proportion), the value of μ_0 (or π_0) that we are testing is a *benchmark* based on past experience, an industry standard, a target, or a product specification. The value of μ_0 (or π_0) does *not* come from a sample.

One-Tailed and Two-Tailed Tests

For a mean, the null hypothesis H_0 states the value(s) of μ_0 that we will try to reject. There are three possible alternative hypotheses:

Left-Tailed Test	*Two-Tailed Test*	*Right-Tailed Test*
H_0: $\mu \geq \mu_0$	H_0: $\mu = \mu_0$	H_0: $\mu \leq \mu_0$
H_1: $\mu < \mu_0$	H_1: $\mu \neq \mu_0$	H_1: $\mu > \mu_0$

The application will dictate which of the three alternatives is appropriate. The *direction of the test* is indicated by which way the inequality symbol points in H_1:

$<$ indicates a **left-tailed test**

$\neq$ indicates a **two-tailed test**

$>$ indicates a **right-tailed test**

EXAMPLE 9.1

Right-Tailed Test for μ

EPA guidelines for the maximum safe level of radon (a naturally occurring radioactive gas) in a home is 4.0 pCi/L (picocuries per liter of air). When a home is tested, a number of measurements are taken and averaged. A homeowner would be concerned if the average radon level is too high. In this case, the homeowner would choose a *right-tailed test*. The inequality in H_1 indicates the tail of the test.

H_0: $\mu \leq 4.0$ pCiL ⇐ Assume H_0 is true unless evidence says otherwise

H_1: $\mu > 4.0$ pCiL ⇐ The $>$ inequality in H_1 points right (right-tailed test)

The mean radon level is assumed safe (i.e., H_0 is assumed to be true) unless the sample mean indicates an average radon level too far *above* 4.0 to be due to chance variation.

EXAMPLE 9.2

Left-Tailed Test for μ

The Diehard Platinum automobile battery has a claimed CCA (cold cranking amperes) of 880 amps. A consumer testing agency chooses a sample of several batteries and finds the average CCA for the batteries tested. The consumer testing agency would only be concerned if the battery delivers less than the claimed CCA, so they would choose a *left-tailed test*. The inequality in H_1 indicates the tail of the test.

H_0: $\mu \geq 880$ CCA ⇐ Assume H_0 is true unless evidence says otherwise

H_1: $\mu < 880$ CCA ⇐ The $<$ inequality in H_1 points left (left-tailed test)

The CCA mean is assumed at or above 880 amps (i.e., H_0 is assumed to be true) unless the sample mean indicates that CCA is too far *below* 880 to be due to chance variation.

EXAMPLE 9.3

Two-Tailed Test for μ

The width of a sheet of standard size copier paper should be $\mu = 216$ mm (i.e., 8.5 inches). There is variation in paper width due to the nature of the production process, so the width of a sheet of paper is a random variable. Samples are taken from the production process and the mean width is calculated. If the paper is too narrow, the pages might not be well-centered in the sheet feeder. If the pages are too wide, sheets could jam in the feeder or paper trays. Either violation poses a quality problem, so the manufacturer might choose a *two-tailed test*.

H_0: $\mu = 216$ mm ⇐ Assume H_0 is true unless evidence says otherwise

H_1: $\mu \neq 216$ mm ⇐ The $\neq$ in H_1 points to both tails (two-tailed test)

If the null hypothesis is rejected, action is required to adjust the manufacturing process. The action depends on the severity of the departure from H_0.

Decision Rule

When performing a statistical hypothesis test, we compare a sample statistic to the hypothesized value of the population parameter stated in the null hypothesis. Extreme outcomes occurring in the left tail would cause us to reject the null hypothesis in a left-tailed test; extreme outcomes occurring in the right tail would cause us to reject the null hypothesis in a right-tailed test. Extreme values in *either* the left or right tail would cause us to reject the null hypothesis in a two-tailed test.

We specify our decision rule by defining an "extreme" outcome. We rely on our knowledge of the *sampling distribution* and the *standard error of the estimate* to decide if the sample statistic is far enough away from μ_0 to contradict the assumption that $\mu = \mu_0$. The area under the sampling distribution curve that defines an extreme outcome is called the

rejection region. You may visualize the level of significance (α) as an area in the tail(s) of a distribution (e.g., normal) far enough from the center that it represents an unlikely outcome if our null hypothesis is true. We will calculate a **test statistic** that measures the difference between the sample statistic and the hypothesized parameter. A test statistic that falls in the shaded region will cause rejection of H_0, as illustrated in Figure 9.2. The area of the nonrejection region (white area) is $1 - \alpha$.

FIGURE 9.2

Tests for H_0: $\mu = \mu_0$

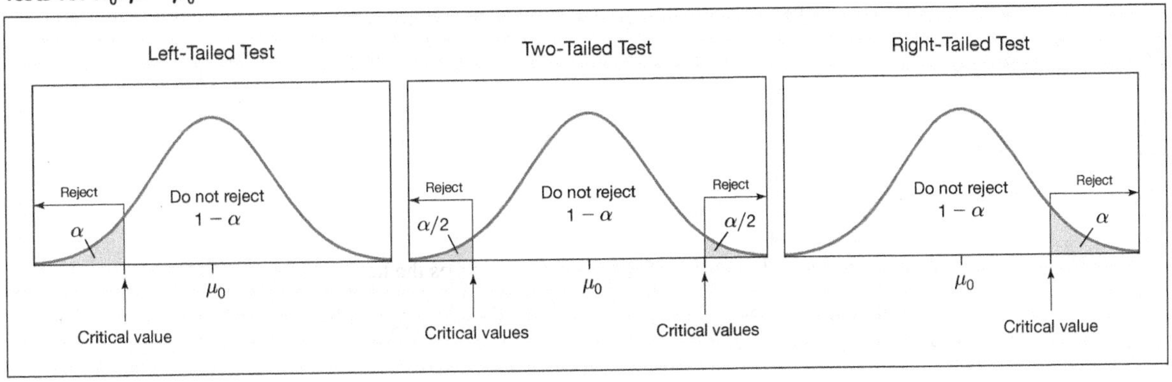

Critical Value

The **critical value** is the boundary between the two regions (reject H_0, do not reject H_0). The **decision rule** states what the critical value of the test statistic would have to be in order to reject H_0 at the chosen level of significance (α). For example, if we are dealing with a normal sampling distribution for a mean, we might reject H_0 if the sample mean $\bar{x}$ differs from μ_0 by more than 1.96 times the standard error of the mean (outside the 95 percent confidence interval for μ).

The decision maker specifies the value of α for the test (common choices for α are .10, .05, or .01). The level of significance is usually expressed as a percent (e.g., 10 percent, 5 percent, or 1 percent). A small value of α is desirable, to ensure a low probability of Type I error. For example, if we specify a decision rule based on $\alpha = .05$, we would expect to commit a Type I error about 5 times in 100 samples. In a two-tailed test, the risk is split with $\alpha/2$ in each tail, since there are two ways to reject H_0. For example, in a two-tailed test using $\alpha = .10$ we would put $\alpha/2 = .05$ in each tail. We can look up the critical value from a table or from Excel (e.g., z or t).

By choosing a small α (say $\alpha = .01$), the decision maker can make it harder to reject the null hypothesis. By choosing a larger α (say $\alpha = .05$), it is easier to reject the null hypothesis. This raises the possibility of manipulating the decision. For this reason, the choice of α should precede the calculation of the test statistic, thereby minimizing the temptation to select α so as to favor one conclusion over the other.

In a left-tailed or right-tailed test, the inequality in H_0 comprises an *infinite* number of hypotheses. We can only test *one* value of the hypothesized parameter at a time, so we test the null hypothesis (H_0: $\mu \leq \mu_0$ or H_0: $\mu \geq \mu_0$) *only* at the point of equality $\mu = \mu_0$. If we reject $\mu = \mu_0$ in favor of the alternative, we implicitly reject the *entire class* of H_0 possibilities. For example, suppose the sample mean in the radon test is far enough above 4.0 to cause us to reject the null hypothesis H_0: $\mu = 4.0$ in favor of the alternative hypothesis H_1: $\mu > 4.0$. The same sample would also permit rejection of any value of μ *less than* $\mu = 4.0$, so we actually can reject H_0: $\mu \leq 4.0$.

In quality control, any deviation from specifications indicates that something may be wrong, so a two-tailed test is common. If the decision maker has no *a priori* reason to expect rejection in one direction, it is reasonable to use a two-tailed test. Rejection in a two-tailed test guarantees rejection in a one-tailed test, other things being equal.

When the consequences of rejecting H_0 are asymmetric, or where one tail is of special importance to the researcher, we might perform a one-tailed test. For example, suppose that a machine is supposed to bore holes with a 3.5-mm diameter in a piece of sheet metal. Although any deviation from 3.5 mm is a violation of the specification, the consequences of rejecting H_0 may be different. Suppose an attachment pin is to be inserted into the hole. If the hole is too small, the pin cannot be inserted, but the metal piece might be reworked to enlarge the hole so the pin does fit. On the other hand, if the hole is too large, the pin will fit too loosely and may fall out. The piece may have to be discarded since an oversized hole cannot be made smaller. This is illustrated in Figure 9.3.

FIGURE 9.3

Asymmetric Effects of Nonconformance

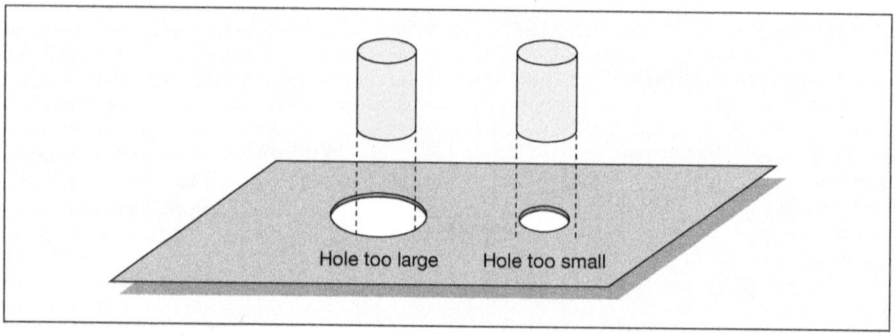

SECTION EXERCISES

connect

9.7 A manufacturer claims that its compact fluorescent bulbs contain an average of 2.5 mg of mercury. Write the hypotheses for a two-tailed test, using the manufacturer's claim about the mean as the null hypothesis.

9.8 Noodles & Company is interested in testing whether their new menu design helps reduce the average order time for their customers. Suppose that the average order time prior to the introduction of their new menu was 1.2 minutes. Write the hypotheses for a left-tailed test, using their previous average order time as the claim about the mean for the null hypothesis.

9.9 The Scottsdale fire department aims to respond to fire calls in 4 minutes or less, on average. State the hypotheses you would use if you had reason to believe that the fire department's claim is not being met. *Hint:* Remember that sample data are used as evidence *against* the null, not to prove the null is true.

9.10 The average age of a part-time seasonal employee at a Vail Resorts ski mountain has historically been 37 years. State the hypotheses one would use to test if this average has decreased since the last season.

9.11 Sketch a diagram of the decision rule for each pair of hypotheses.

a. H_0: $\mu \geq 80$ versus H_1: $\mu < 80$

b. H_0: $\mu = 80$ versus H_1: $\mu \neq 80$

c. H_0: $\mu \leq 80$ versus H_1: $\mu > 80$

9.12 The Ball Corporation's aluminum can manufacturing facility in Ft. Atkinson, Wisconsin, wants to use a sample to perform a two-tailed test to see whether the mean incoming metal thickness is at the target of 0.2731 mm. A deviation in either direction would pose a quality concern. State the hypotheses they should test.

LO 9-5

Perform a hypothesis test for a mean with known σ using z.

LO 9-6

Use tables or Excel to find the p-value in tests of μ.

9.4 TESTING A MEAN: KNOWN POPULATION VARIANCE

We will first explain how to test a population mean, μ. The sample statistic used to estimate μ is the random variable $\bar{X}$. The sampling distribution for $\bar{X}$ depends on whether or not the population variance σ^2 is known. We begin with the case of known σ^2. We learned in Chapter 8 that the sampling distribution of $\bar{X}$ will be a normal distribution provided that we have a normal population (or, by the Central Limit Theorem, if the sample size is large). In Section 9.4 we will turn to the more common case when σ^2 is unknown.

Test Statistic

A *test statistic* measures the difference between a given sample mean $\bar{x}$ and a benchmark μ_0 in terms of the standard error of the mean. The test statistic is the "standardized score" of the sample statistic. When testing μ with a known σ, the test statistic is a z score. Once we have collected our sample, we calculate a value of the test statistic using the sample mean and then compare it against the critical value of z. We will refer to the calculated value of the test statistic as z_{calc}.

Test Statistic for a Mean: Known σ

Sample mean → $\bar{x}$; Hypothesized mean → μ_0; Standard error of the sample mean → $\sigma_{\bar{x}}$

$$z_{\text{calc}} = \frac{\bar{x} - \mu_0}{\sigma_{\bar{x}}} = \frac{\bar{x} - \mu_0}{\dfrac{\sigma}{\sqrt{n}}} \quad \textbf{(9.1)}$$

If the true mean of the population is μ_0, then the value of a particular sample mean $\bar{x}$ calculated from our sample should be near μ_0 and therefore the test statistic should be near zero.

Critical Value

The test statistic is compared with a *critical value* from a table. The critical value is the boundary between two regions (reject H_0, do not reject H_0) in the decision rule. For a two-tailed test (but *not* for a one-tailed test), the hypothesis test is equivalent to asking whether the confidence interval for μ includes zero. In a two-tailed test, half the risk of Type I error (i.e., $\alpha/2$) goes in each tail, as shown in Table 9.2, so the z-values are the same as for a confidence interval. You can verify these z-values from Excel.

TABLE 9.2

Some Common z-Values

Level of Significance (α)	Left-Tailed Test	Two-Tailed Test	Right-Tailed Test
	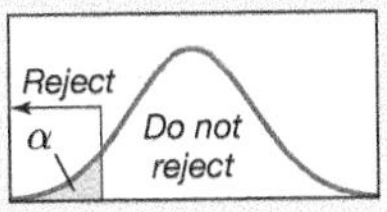	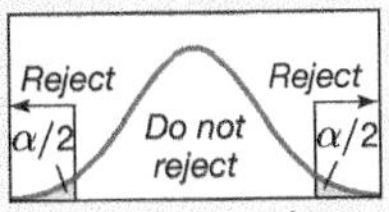	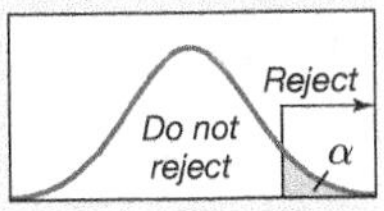
.10	$z_{.10} = -1.282$	$z_{.05} = \pm 1.645$	$z_{.10} = +1.282$
.05	$z_{.05} = -1.645$	$z_{.025} = \pm 1.960$	$z_{.05} = +1.645$
.01	$z_{.01} = -2.326$	$z_{.005} = \pm 2.576$	$z_{.01} = +2.326$

EXAMPLE 9.4

Paper Manufacturing

The Hammermill Company produces paper for laser printers. Standard paper width is 216 mm, or 8.5 inches. Suppose that the actual width is a random variable that is normally distributed with a known standard deviation of .0230 based on the manufacturing technology currently in use. Variation arises during manufacturing because of slight differences in the paper stock, vibration in the rollers and cutting tools, and wear and tear on the equipment. The cutters can be adjusted if the paper width drifts from the correct mean. Suppose that a quality control inspector chooses 50 sheets at random and measures them with a precise instrument, obtaining a mean width of 216.0070 mm. Using a 5 percent level of significance ($\alpha = .05$), does this sample show that the product mean exceeds the specification? **Paper**

Step 1: State the Hypotheses The question indicates a right-tailed test, so the hypotheses would be

H_0: $\mu \leq 216$ mm (product mean does not exceed the specification)

H_1: $\mu > 216$ mm (product mean has risen above the specification)

From the null hypothesis we see that $\mu_0 = 216$ mm, which is the product specification.

Step 2: Specify the Decision Rule We use the *level of significance* to find the *critical value* of the z statistic that determines the threshold for rejecting the null hypothesis to be $\alpha = .05$. The critical value of z that accomplishes this is $z_{.05} = 1.645$. As illustrated in Figure 9.4, the decision rule is

Reject H_0 if $z_{\text{calc}} > 1.645$

Otherwise do not reject H_0

FIGURE 9.4

Right-Tailed *z* Test for $\alpha = .05$

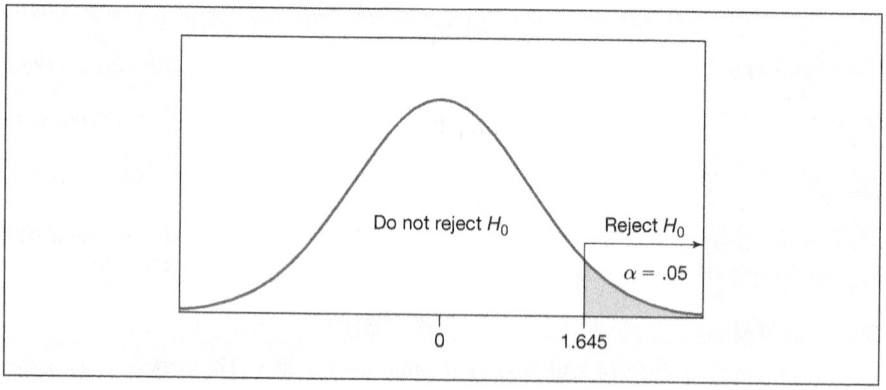

Step 3: Collect Sample Data and Calculate the Test Statistic If H_0 is true, then the test statistic should be near 0 because $\bar{x}$ should be near μ_0. The value of the test statistic is

$$z_{\text{calc}} = \frac{\bar{x} - \mu_0}{\frac{\sigma}{\sqrt{n}}} = \frac{216.0070 - 216.0000}{\frac{.0230}{\sqrt{50}}} = \frac{0.0070}{0.00325269} = 2.152$$

Step 4: Make the Decision The test statistic falls in the right rejection region, so we reject the null hypothesis H_0: $\mu \leq 216$ and conclude the alternative hypothesis H_1: $\mu > 216$ at the 5 percent level of significance. Although the difference is slight, it is statistically significant.

Step 5: Take Action Now that we have concluded that the process is producing paper with an average width *greater* than the specification, it is time to adjust the manufacturing process to bring the average width back to specification. Our course of action could be to readjust the machine settings or it could be time to resharpen the cutting tools. At this point it is the responsibility of the process engineers to determine the best course of action.

p-Value Method

The critical value method described above requires that you specify your rejection criterion in terms of the test statistic before you take a sample. The ***p*-value method** is a more flexible approach that is often preferred by statisticians over the critical value method. It requires that you express the strength of your evidence (i.e., your sample) against the null hypothesis in terms of a probability. The *p*-value is a direct measure of the likelihood of the observed sample under H_0. The *p*-value answers the following question: If the null hypothesis is true, what is the probability that we would observe our particular sample mean (or one even farther away from μ_0)? The p-value gives us more information than a test using one particular value of α because the observer can choose any α that is appropriate for the problem.

We compare the p-value with the level of significance. If the p-value is smaller than α, the sample contradicts the null hypothesis, and so we reject H_0. For a right-tailed test, the decision rule using the p-value approach is stated as:

Reject H_0 if $P(Z > z_{\text{calc}}) < \alpha$, otherwise fail to reject H_0.

Whether we use the critical value approach or the p-value approach, our decision about the null hypothesis will be the same.

What Is a *p*-Value?

A sample statistic is a random variable that may differ from the hypothesized value merely by chance, so we do not expect the sample to agree *exactly* with H_0. The p-value is the probability of obtaining a test statistic as extreme as the one observed, assuming that the null hypothesis is true. A large p-value (near 1.00) tends to support H_0, while a small p-value (near 0.00) tends to contradict H_0. If the p-value is less than the chosen level of significance (α), then we conclude that the null hypothesis is false.

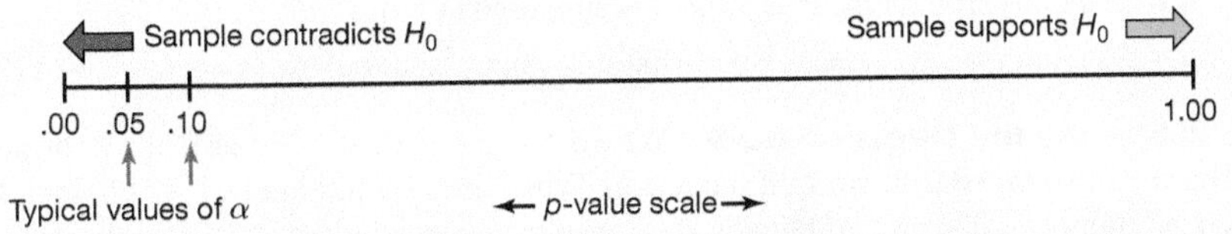

In order to calculate the p-value, we first need to calculate the test statistic z_{calc}. In this example, $z_{\text{calc}} = 2.152$, so the p-value for a right-tailed test is $P(Z > 2.152)$. The direction of the inequality in the p-value is the same as in the alternative hypothesis: H_1: $\mu > 216$ mm.

To find the p-value, we can use Excel's function =NORM.S.DIST(2.152,1) to obtain the left-tail area for the cumulative Z distribution (see Figure 9.5). Since $P(Z < 2.152) = .9843$, the right-tail area is $P(Z > 2.152) = 1 - .9843 = .0157$. This is the p-value for the right-tailed test, as illustrated in Figure 9.5. The p-value diagram does not show α. The p-value of .0157 indicates that in a right-tailed test, a test statistic of $z_{\text{calc}} = 2.152$ (or a more extreme test statistic) would happen by chance about 1.57 percent of the time if the null hypothesis were true.

FIGURE 9.5

***p*-Value for a Right-Tailed Test with $z_{\text{calc}} = 2.152$, Using Excel**

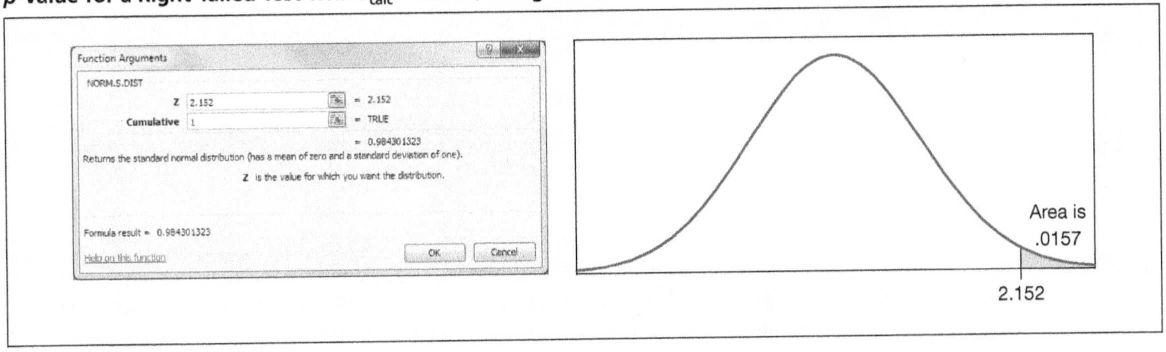

We could also obtain the p-value from Appendix C-2, which shows cumulative standard normal areas less than z, as illustrated in Table 9.3. The cumulative area is not exactly the same as Excel because Appendix C-2 requires that we round the test statistic to two decimals ($z = 2.15$).

TABLE 9.3

Finding the p-Value for $z = 2.15$ in Appendix C-2

z	.00	.01	.02	.03	.04	.05	.06	.07	.08	.09
−3.7	.00011	.00010	.00010	.00010	.00009	.00009	.00008	.00008	.00008	.00008
−3.6	.00016	.00015	.00015	.00014	.00014	.00013	.00013	.00012	.00012	.00011
−3.5	.00023	.00022	.00022	.00021	.00020	.00019	.00019	.00018	.00017	.00017
⋮	⋮	⋮	⋮	⋮	⋮	⋮	⋮	⋮	⋮	⋮
2.0	.97725	.97778	.97831	.97882	.97932	.97982	.98030	.98077	.98124	.98169
2.1	.98214	.98257	.98300	.98341	.98382	***.98422***	.98461	.98500	.98537	.98574
2.2	.98610	.98645	.98679	.98713	.98745	.98778	.98809	.98840	.98870	.98899

Two-Tailed Test

In this case, the manufacturer decided that a two-tailed test would be more appropriate, since the objective is to detect a deviation from the desired mean in *either* direction.

Step 1: State the Hypotheses For a two-tailed test, the hypotheses are

H_0: $\mu = 216$ mm (product mean is what it is supposed to be)

H_1: $\mu \neq 216$ mm (product mean is not what it is supposed to be)

Step 2: Specify the Decision Rule We will use the same $\alpha = .05$ as in the right-tailed test. But for a two-tailed test, we split the risk of Type I error by putting $\alpha/2 = .05/2 = .025$ in each tail. For $\alpha = .05$ in a two-tailed test, the critical value is $z_{.025} = \pm 1.96$ so the decision rule is

Reject H_0 if $z_{\text{calc}} > +1.96$ or if $z_{\text{calc}} < -1.96$

Otherwise do not reject H_0

The decision rule is illustrated in Figure 9.6.

FIGURE 9.6

Two-Tailed z Test for $\alpha = .05$

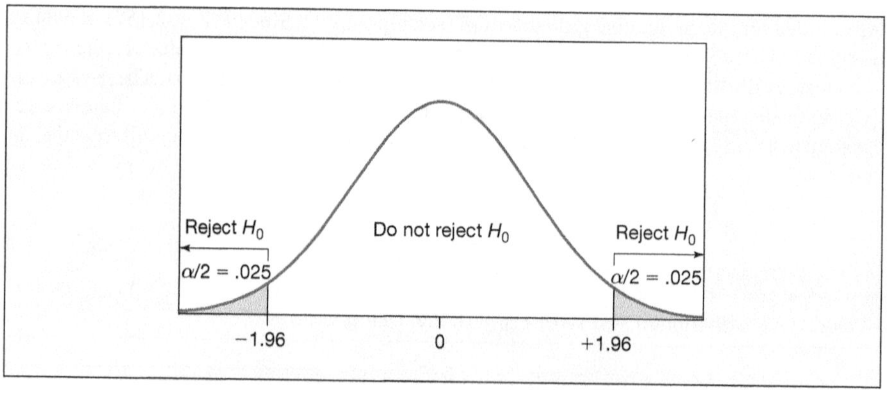

Step 3: Calculate the Test Statistic The test statistic is *unaffected by the hypotheses or the level of significance.* The value of the test statistic is the same as for the one-tailed test:

$$z_{\text{calc}} = \frac{\bar{x} - \mu_0}{\dfrac{\sigma}{\sqrt{n}}} = \frac{216.0070 - 216.0000}{\dfrac{.0230}{\sqrt{50}}} = \frac{.0070}{.00325269} = 2.152$$

Step 4: Make the Decision Since the test statistic falls in the right tail of the rejection region, we reject the null hypothesis H_0: $\mu = 216$ and conclude H_1: $\mu \neq 216$ at the 5 percent level of significance. Another way to say this is that the sample mean *differs significantly* from the desired specification at $\alpha = .05$ in a two-tailed test. Note that this decision is rather a close one, since the test statistic just barely falls into the rejection region.

Step 5: Take Action An adjustment is needed, such as changing the cutting tool settings. Now it is up to the process engineers to choose the best course of action.

Using the *p*-Value Approach

In a two-tailed test, the decision rule using the *p*-value is the same as in a one-tailed test.

Reject H_0 if *p*-value $< \alpha$. Otherwise, do not reject H_0.

The difference between a one-tailed and a two-tailed test is how we obtain the *p*-value. Because we allow rejection in either the left or the right tail in a two-tailed test, the level of significance, α, is divided equally between the two tails to establish the rejection region. In order to fairly evaluate the *p*-value against α, we must now double the tail area. The *p*-value in this two-tailed test is $2 \times P(z_{calc} > 2.152) = 2 \times .0157 = .0314$. See Figure 9.7. This says that in a two-tailed test a result as extreme as 2.152 would arise about 3.14 percent of the time by chance alone *if the null hypothesis were true.*

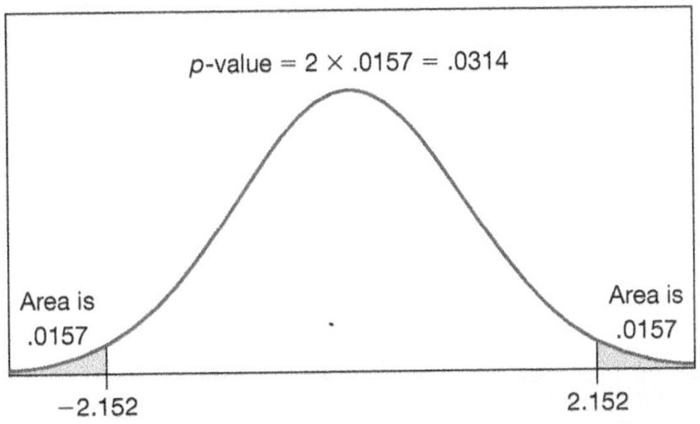

FIGURE 9.7

Two-Tailed *p*-Value for $z = 2.152$

Interpretation Although the sample mean 216.007 might seem very close to 216, it is more than two standard deviations from the desired mean. This example shows that even a small difference can be significant. It all depends on σ and n, that is, on the standard error of the mean in the denominator of the test statistic. In this case, there is a high degree of precision in the manufacturing process ($\sigma = .023$ is very small) so the standard error (and hence the allowable variation) is extremely small. Such a tiny difference in means would not be noticeable to consumers, but stringent quality control standards are applied to ensure that no shipment goes out with any noticeable nonconformance.

Our statistical tests show that there is a statistically *significant* departure from the desired mean for paper width at $\alpha = .05$. But is the difference *important*? Is 216.007 so close to 216 that nobody could tell the difference? The question of whether to adjust the process is up to the engineers or business managers, not statisticians.

Analogy to Confidence Intervals

A two-tailed hypothesis test at the 5 percent level of significance ($\alpha = .05$) is exactly equivalent to asking whether the 95 percent confidence interval for the mean includes the hypothesized mean. If the confidence interval includes the hypothesized mean H_0: $\mu = 216$, then we cannot reject the null hypothesis. In this case the 95 percent confidence interval would be

$$\bar{x} \pm z_{\alpha/2}\frac{\sigma}{\sqrt{n}} \quad \text{or} \quad 216.0070 \pm 1.960\frac{.0230}{\sqrt{50}} \quad \text{or} \quad [216.001, 216.013]$$

Because this confidence interval does not include 216, we reject the null hypothesis H_0: $\mu = 216$. However, the decision is rather a close one as it was with the two-tailed hypothesis test, as the lower limit of the confidence interval almost includes 216.

Statistical Significance versus Practical Importance

Suppose that a redesigned engine could improve a truck's mpg rating by 0.5 mpg, but requires spending $1.2 billion on new plant and equipment. Is it worth doing? Such a decision requires understanding not only statistical **significance**, but also the **importance** of the potential improvement: the magnitude of the effect and its implications for product durability, customer satisfaction, budgets, cash flow, and staffing.

Because the standard error of most sample estimators approaches zero as sample size increases (if they are consistent estimators), even a small difference between the sample statistic and the hypothesized parameter may be significant if the sample size is large enough. Researchers who deal with large samples must expect "significant" effects, even when an effect is too slight to have practical importance. Is an improvement of 0.2 mpg in fuel economy *important* to Toyota buyers? Is a 0.2 percent loss of market share *important* to Hertz? Is a 15-minute increase in laptop battery life *important* to Dell customers?

Such questions require a cost/benefit calculation. Because resources are always scarce, a dollar spent on a quality improvement always has an opportunity cost (the forgone alternative). If we spend money to make a certain product improvement, then some other project may have to be shelved. We can't do everything, so we must ask whether a proposed product improvement is the best use of our scarce resources. These are questions that must be answered by experts in medicine, marketing, product safety, or engineering, rather than by statisticians.

SECTION EXERCISES

connect

9.13 Find the z_{calc} test statistic for each hypothesis test.

a. $\bar{x} = 242$, $\mu_0 = 230$, $\sigma = 18$, $n = 20$
b. $\bar{x} = 3.44$, $\mu_0 = 3.50$, $\sigma = 0.24$, $n = 40$
c. $\bar{x} = 21.02$, $\mu_0 = 20.00$, $\sigma = 2.52$, $n = 30$

9.14 Use Excel to find the critical value of z for each hypothesis test.

a. 10 percent level of significance, two-tailed test
b. 1 percent level of significance, right-tailed test
c. 5 percent level of significance, left-tailed test

9.15 Use Excel to find the critical value of z for each hypothesis test.

a. $\alpha = .05$, two-tailed test
b. $\alpha = .10$, right-tailed test
c. $\alpha = .01$, left-tailed test

9.16 Find the z_{calc} test statistic for each hypothesis test.

a. $\bar{x} = 423$, $\mu_0 = 420$, $\sigma = 6$, $n = 9$
b. $\bar{x} = 8330$, $\mu_0 = 8{,}344$, $\sigma = 48$, $n = 36$
c. $\bar{x} = 3.102$, $\mu_0 = 3.110$, $\sigma = .250$, $n = 25$

9.17 GreenBeam Ltd. claims that its compact fluorescent bulbs average no more than 3.50 mg of mercury. A sample of 25 bulbs shows a mean of 3.59 mg of mercury. (a) Write the hypotheses for a right-tailed test, using GreenBeam's claim as the null hypothesis about the mean. (b) Assuming a known standard deviation of 0.18 mg, calculate the z test statistic to test the manufacturer's claim. (c) At the 1 percent level of significance ($\alpha = .01$) does the sample exceed the manufacturer's claim? (d) Find the p-value.

9.18 The mean potassium content of a popular sports drink is listed as 140 mg in a 32-oz bottle. Analysis of 20 bottles indicates a sample mean of 139.4 mg. (a) Write the hypotheses for a two-tailed test of the claimed potassium content. (b) Assuming a known standard deviation of 2.00 mg, calculate the z test statistic to test the manufacturer's claim. (c) At the 10 percent level of significance ($\alpha = .10$), does the sample contradict the manufacturer's claim? (d) Find the p-value.

9.19 Calculate the test statistic and p-value for each sample.

a. H_0: $\mu = 60$ versus H_1: $\mu \neq 60$, $\alpha = .025$, $\bar{x} = 63$, $\sigma = 8$, $n = 16$
b. H_0: $\mu \geq 60$ versus H_1: $\mu < 60$, $\alpha = .05$, $\bar{x} = 58$, $\sigma = 5$, $n = 25$
c. H_0: $\mu \leq 60$ versus H_1: $\mu > 60$, $\alpha = .05$, $\bar{x} = 65$, $\sigma = 8$, $n = 36$

9.20 Determine the p-value for each test statistic.

a. Right-tailed test, $z = +1.34$
b. Left-tailed test, $z = -2.07$
c. Two-tailed test, $z = -1.69$

9.21 Procyon Mfg. produces tennis balls. Weights are supposed to be normally distributed with a mean of 2.035 ounces and a standard deviation of 0.002 ounce. A sample of 25 tennis balls shows a mean weight of 2.036 ounces. At $\alpha = .025$ in a right-tailed test, is the mean weight heavier than it is supposed to be?

9.22 The mean arrival rate of flights at O'Hare Airport in marginal weather is 195 flights per hour with a historical standard deviation of 13 flights. To increase arrivals, a new air traffic control procedure is implemented. In the next 30 days of marginal weather, the mean arrival rate is 200 flights per hour. (a) Set up a right-tailed decision rule at $\alpha = .025$ to decide whether there has been a significant increase in the mean number of arrivals per hour. (b) Carry out the test and make the decision. Is it close? Would the decision be different if you used $\alpha = .01$? (c) What assumptions are you making, if any? **Flights**

210	215	200	189	200	213	202	181	197	199
193	209	215	192	179	196	225	199	196	210
199	188	174	176	202	195	195	208	222	221

9.23 An airline serves bottles of Galena Spring Water that are supposed to contain an average of 10 ounces. The filling process follows a normal distribution with process standard deviation 0.07 ounce. Twelve randomly chosen bottles had the weights shown below (in ounces). (a) Set up a two-tailed decision rule to detect quality control violations using the 5 percent level of significance. (b) Carry out the test. (c) What assumptions are you making, if any? **BottleFill**

10.02	9.95	10.11	10.10	10.08	10.04	10.06	10.03	9.98	10.01	9.92	9.89

9.24 The Scottsdale fire department aims to respond to fire calls in 4 minutes or less, on average. Response times are normally distributed with a standard deviation of 1 minute. Would a sample of 18 fire calls with a mean response time of 4 minutes 30 seconds provide sufficient evidence to show that the goal is not being met at $\alpha = .01$? What is the p-value? (See *Arizona Republic*, November 23, 2006, p. A10.)

9.25 The lifespan of xenon metal halide arc-discharge bulbs for aircraft landing lights is normally distributed with a mean of 3,000 hours and a standard deviation of 500 hours. If a new ballast system shows a mean life of 3,515 hours in a test on a sample of 10 prototype new bulbs, would you conclude that the new lamp's mean life exceeds the current mean life at $\alpha = .01$? What is the p-value? (For more information, see www.xevision.com.)

9.26 Discuss the issues of *statistical significance* and *practical importance* in each scenario.

a. A process for producing I-beams of oriented strand board used as main support beams in new houses has a mean breaking strength of 2,000 lbs./ft. A sample of boards from a new process has a mean breaking strength of 2,150 lbs./ft. The improvement is statistically significant, but the per-unit cost is higher.
b. Under continuous use, the mean battery life in a certain cell phone is 45 hours. In tests of a new type of battery, the sample mean battery life is 46 hours. The improvement is statistically significant, but the new battery costs more to produce.
c. For a wide-screen HDTV LCD unit, the mean half-life (i.e., to lose 50 percent of its brightness) is 32,000 hours. A new process is developed. In tests of the new display, the sample mean half-life is 35,000 hours. The improvement is statistically significant, though the new process is more costly.

9.27 The target activation force of the buttons on a keyless entry clicker is 1.967 newtons. Variation exists in activation force due to the nature of the manufacturing process. A sample of 9 clickers showed a mean activation force of 1.88 newtons. The standard deviation is known to be 0.145 newton. Too much force makes the keys hard to click, while too little force means the keys might be clicked accidentally. Therefore, the manufacturer's quality control engineers use a two-tailed hypothesis test for samples taken from each production batch, to detect excessive deviations in either direction. At $\alpha = .05$, does the sample indicate a significant deviation from the target?

9.5 TESTING A MEAN: UNKNOWN POPULATION VARIANCE

LO 9-7

Perform a hypothesis test for a mean with unknown σ using *t*.

If the population variance σ^2 must be estimated from the sample, the hypothesis testing procedure is modified. There is a loss of information when s replaces σ in the formulas, and it is no longer appropriate to use the normal distribution. However, the basic hypothesis testing steps are the same.

Using Student's *t*

When the population standard deviation σ is unknown (as it usually is) and the population may be assumed normal (or generally symmetric with no outliers), the test statistic follows the Student's t distribution with $n - 1$ degrees of freedom. Since σ is rarely known, we generally expect to use Student's t instead of z, as you saw for confidence intervals in the previous chapter.

Test Statistic for a Mean: σ Unknown

Sample mean → $\bar{x}$; Hypothesized mean → μ_0; Sample st. dev. → s

$$t_{calc} = \frac{\bar{x} - \mu_0}{\frac{s}{\sqrt{n}}} \quad \text{if } \sigma \text{ is unknown} \qquad \textbf{(9.2)}$$

EXAMPLE 9.5

Hot Chocolate

In addition to its core business of bagels and coffee, Bruegger's Bagels also sells hot chocolate for the noncoffee crowd. Customer research shows that the ideal temperature for hot chocolate is 142°F ("hot" but not "too hot"). A random sample of 24 cups of hot chocolate is taken at various times, and the temperature of each cup is measured using an ordinary kitchen thermometer that is accurate to the nearest whole degree. HotChoc

140	140	141	145	143	144	142	140
145	143	140	140	141	141	137	142
143	141	142	142	143	141	138	139

The sample mean is 141.375 with a sample standard deviation of 1.99592. At $\alpha = .10$, does this sample evidence show that the true mean differs from 142?

Step 1: State the Hypotheses

We use a two-tailed test. The null hypothesis is in conformance with the desired standard.

H_0: $\mu = 142$ (mean temperature is correct)

H_1: $\mu \neq 142$ (mean temperature is incorrect)

Step 2: Specify the Decision Rule

For $\alpha = .10$, using the Excel function =T.INV.2T(α, *d.f.*) =T.INV.2T(0.10,23) = 1.714 gives the two-tailed critical value for $d.f. = n - 1 = 24 - 1 = 23$ degrees of freedom. The same value can be obtained from Appendix D, shown here in abbreviated form:

	Upper Tail Area				
d.f.	*.10*	*.05*	*.025*	*.01*	*.005*
1	3.078	6.314	12.706	31.821	63.657
2	1.886	2.920	4.303	6.965	9.925
3	1.638	2.353	3.182	4.541	5.841
⋮	⋮	⋮	⋮	⋮	⋮
21	1.323	1.721	2.080	2.518	2.831
22	1.321	1.717	2.074	2.508	2.819
23	1.319	*1.714*	2.069	2.500	2.807
24	1.318	1.711	2.064	2.492	2.797
25	1.316	1.708	2.060	2.485	2.787

We will reject H_0 if $t_{calc} > 1.714$ or if $t_{calc} < -1.714$, as illustrated in Figure 9.8.

FIGURE 9.8 **Two-Tailed Test for a Mean Using *t* for *d.f.* = 23**

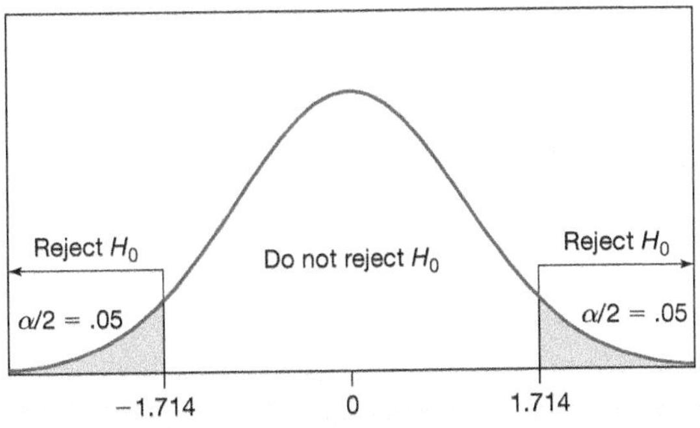

Step 3: Calculate the Test Statistic
Inserting the sample information, the test statistic is

$$t_{calc} = \frac{\bar{x} - \mu_0}{\frac{s}{\sqrt{n}}} = \frac{141.375 - 142}{\frac{1.99592}{\sqrt{24}}} = \frac{-.6250}{.40742} = -1.534$$

Step 4: Make the Decision
Since the test statistic lies within the range of chance variation, we cannot reject the null hypothesis H_0: $\mu = 142$.

Sensitivity to α How sensitive is our conclusion to the choice of level of significance? Table 9.4 shows several critical values of Student's *t*. At $\alpha = .20$ we could reject H_0, but not at the other α values shown. This table is not to suggest that experimenting with various α values is desirable, but merely to illustrate that our decision is affected by our choice of α.

TABLE 9.4 **Effect of α on the Decision (Two-Tailed *t* Test with *d.f.* = 23)**

	$\alpha = .20$	$\alpha = .10$	$\alpha = .05$	$\alpha = .01$
Critical value	$t_{.10} = \pm 1.319$	$t_{.05} = \pm 1.714$	$t_{.025} = \pm 2.069$	$t_{.005} = \pm 2.807$
Decision	Reject H_0	Don't reject H_0	Don't reject H_0	Don't reject H_0

Using the *p*-Value

A more general approach favored by researchers is to find the *p*-value. After the *p*-value is calculated, different analysts can compare it to the level of significance (α) that is appropriate for the task. We want to determine the tail area less than $t = -1.534$ or greater than $t = +1.534$. However, from Appendix D we can only get a range for the *p*-value. From Appendix D, we see that the two-tail *p*-value must lie between .20 and .10 (it's a two-tailed test, so we double the right-tail area). It is easier and more precise to use Excel's function =T.DIST.2T(t test statistic, degrees of freedom) = T.DIST.2T(1.534,23) to get the two-tailed *p*-value of .13867. The area of each tail is half that, or .06934, as shown in Figure 9.9. A sample mean as extreme in either tail would occur by chance about 139 times in 1,000 two-tailed tests if H_0 were true. Since the *p*-value $> \alpha$, we cannot reject H_0.

FIGURE 9.9

Two-Tailed *p*-Value for $t = 1.534$

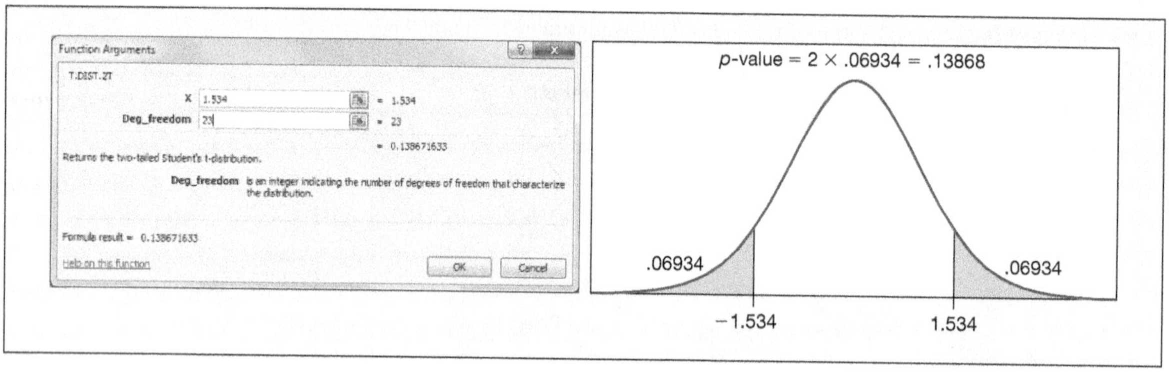

Interpretation

It is doubtful whether a consumer could tell the difference in hot chocolate temperature within a few degrees of 142°F, so a tiny difference in means might lack *practical importance* even if it were *statistically significant*. Importance must be judged by management, not by the statistician.

In the hot chocolate example, there are no outliers and something of a bell-shape, as shown in the dot plot below. The *t* test is reasonably robust to mild non-normality. However, outliers or extreme skewness can affect the test, just as when we construct confidence intervals.

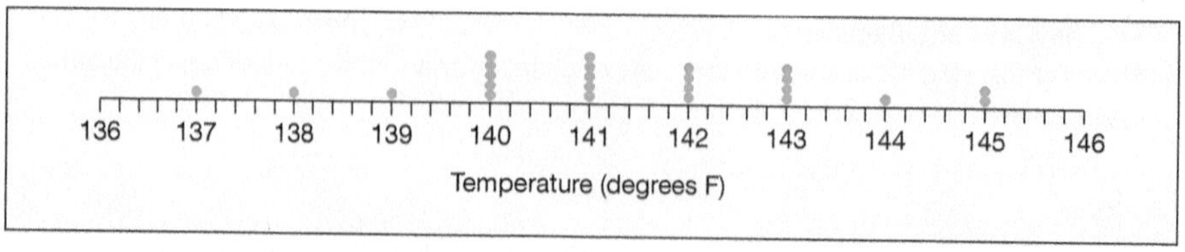

Who Uses *p*-Values?

"Executives at Noodles & Company may not perform a statistical analysis themselves, but they do understand the *p*-value associated with the results of an analysis. The *p*-value allows us to objectively consider the data and statistical results when we make an important strategic decision."

Dave Boennighausen, Chief Financial Officer at Noodles & Company

Confidence Interval versus Hypothesis Test

The two-tailed test at the 10 percent level of significance is equivalent to a two-tailed 90 percent confidence interval. If the confidence interval does not contain μ_0, we reject H_0. For the hot chocolate, the sample mean is 141.375 with a sample standard deviation of 1.99592. Using Appendix D we find $t_{.05} = 1.714$ so the 90 percent confidence interval for μ is

$$\bar{x} \pm t_{\alpha/2}\frac{s}{\sqrt{n}} \quad \text{or} \quad 141.375 \pm (1.714)\frac{1.99592}{\sqrt{24}} \quad \text{or} \quad 141.375 \pm .6983$$

Since $\mu = 142$ lies within the 90 percent confidence interval [140.677, 142.073], we cannot reject the hypothesis H_0: $\mu = 142$ at $\alpha = .10$ in a two-tailed test. Many decisions can be handled either as hypothesis tests or using confidence intervals. The confidence interval has the appeal of providing a graphic feeling for the location of the hypothesized mean within the confidence interval, as shown in Figure 9.10. We can see that 142 is near the upper end of the confidence interval, nearly leading to a rejection of H_0: $\mu = 142$.

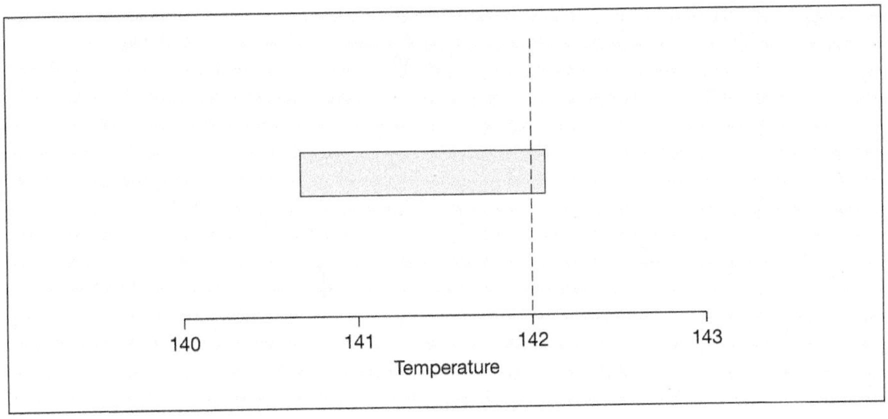

FIGURE 9.10

90 Percent Confidence Interval for μ

Using MegaStat

Excel does not offer a one-sample *t*-test, but you can get tests for one mean, including a confidence interval, using MegaStat. Figure 9.11 shows its setup screen and output for the test of one mean for the hot chocolate data. You enter the data range and everything else is automatic. You have a choice of *z* or *t*, but to use *z* you must know σ.

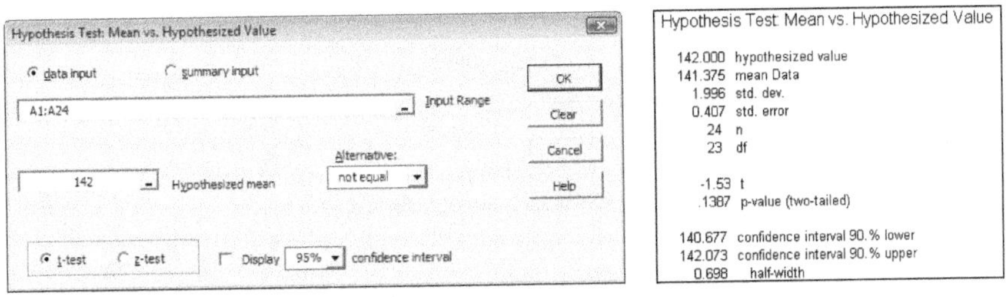

FIGURE 9.11

MegaStat Test for One Mean

Large Samples

From Appendix D you can verify that when *n* is large, there is little difference between critical values of *t* and *z* (the last line in Appendix D, for *d.f.* = ∞). For this reason, it is unlikely that harm will result if you use *z* instead of *t*, as long as the sample size is not small. The test statistic is

$$z_{calc} = \frac{\bar{x} - \mu_0}{\frac{s}{\sqrt{n}}} \quad \text{(large sample, unknown } \sigma) \qquad \textbf{(9.3)}$$

However, using z instead of t is not conservative because it will increase Type I error somewhat. Therefore, statisticians recommend that we always apply t when σ is unknown. We then can use Excel or Appendix D to get the critical value.

How's Your Intuition?

A laptop manufacturer claims an average battery life of 6 hours (360 minutes). Four laptops are operated until the battery is exhausted. Which samples in the illustration below would make you doubt that $\mu = 360$? Sample 1's mean agrees perfectly with H_0: $\mu = 360$, and its p-value is 1.000, so the sample gives no evidence to contradict H_0. The other four samples give progressively stronger evidence against H_0. If you choose $\alpha = .05$, then samples 4 and 5 would lead to rejection of H_0: $\mu = 360$, while sample 3 would be near the borderline.

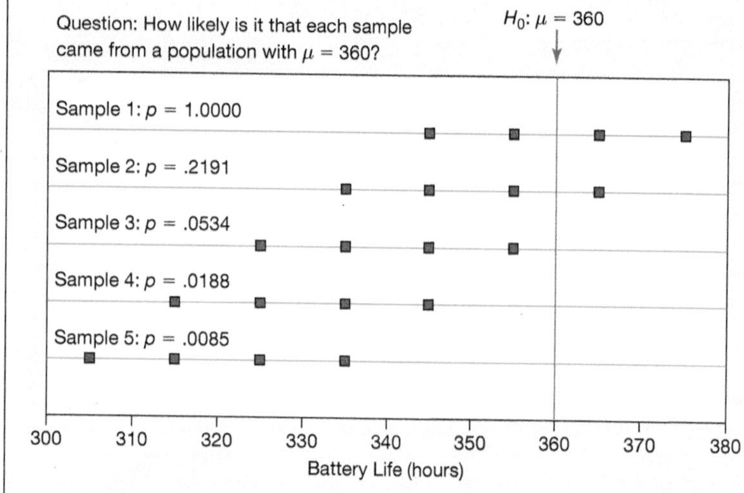

Sample	$\bar{x}$	s	n	t_{calc}	p-value
1	360	12.91	4	0.000	1.000
2	350	12.91	4	−1.549	0.219
3	340	12.91	4	−3.098	0.053
4	330	12.91	4	−4.648	0.019
5	320	12.91	4	−6.197	0.009

SECTION EXERCISES

connect

9.28 Find the t_{calc} test statistic for each hypothesis test.

a. $\bar{x} = 14.7$, $\mu_0 = 13.0$, $s = 1.8$, $n = 12$
b. $\bar{x} = 241$, $\mu_0 = 250$, $s = 12$, $n = 8$
c. $\bar{x} = 2{,}102$, $\mu_0 = 2{,}000$, $s = 242$, $n = 17$

9.29 Find the critical value of Student's t for each hypothesis test.

a. 10 percent level of significance, two-tailed test, $n = 21$
b. 1 percent level of significance, right-tailed test, $n = 9$
c. 5 percent level of significance, left-tailed test, $n = 28$

9.30 Find the critical value of Student's t for each hypothesis test.

a. Two-tailed test, $n = 18$, $a = .05$
b. Right-tailed test, $n = 15$, $a = .10$
c. Left-tailed test, $n = 31$, $a = .01$

9.31 Find the t_{calc} test statistic for each hypothesis test.

a. $\bar{x} = 347$, $\mu_0 = 349$, $s = 1.8$, $n = 9$
b. $\bar{x} = 45$, $\mu_0 = 50$, $s = 12$, $n = 16$
c. $\bar{x} = 4.103$, $\mu_0 = 4.004$, $s = 0.245$, $n = 25$

9.32 Estimate the p-value *as a range* using Appendix D (*not* Excel):

a. $t = 1.457$, $d.f. = 14$, right-tailed test
b. $t = 2.601$, $d.f. = 8$, two-tailed test
c. $t = -1.847$, $d.f. = 22$, left-tailed test

9.33 Find the p-value using Excel (*not* Appendix D):

a. $t = 1.457$, $d.f. = 14$, right-tailed test
b. $t = 2.601$, $d.f. = 8$, two-tailed test
c. $t = -1.847$, $d.f. = 22$, left-tailed test

9.34 Use Excel to find the p-value for each test statistic.

a. Right-tailed test, $t = +1.677$, $n = 13$
b. Left-tailed test, $t = -2.107$, $n = 5$
c. Two-tailed test, $t = -1.865$, $n = 34$

9.35 Calculate the test statistic and p-value for each sample. State the conclusion for the specified α.

a. H_0: $\mu = 200$ versus H_1: $\mu \neq 200$, $\alpha = .025$, $\bar{x} = 203$, $s = 8$, $n = 16$
b. H_0: $\mu \geq 200$ versus H_1: $\mu < 200$, $\alpha = .05$, $\bar{x} = 198$, $s = 5$, $n = 25$
c. H_0: $\mu \leq 200$ versus H_1: $\mu > 200$, $\alpha = .05$, $\bar{x} = 205$, $s = 8$, $n = 36$

9.36 The manufacturer of an airport baggage scanning machine claims it can handle an average of 530 bags per hour. At $\alpha = .05$ in a left-tailed test, would a sample of 16 randomly chosen hours with a mean of 510 and a standard deviation of 50 indicate that the manufacturer's claim is overstated?

9.37 The manufacturer of Glo-More flat white interior latex paint claims one-coat coverage of 400 square feet per gallon on interior walls. A painter keeps careful track of 6 gallons and finds coverage (in square feet) of 360, 410, 380, 360, 390, 400. (a) At $\alpha = .10$ does this evidence contradict the claim? State your hypotheses and decision rule. (b) Is this conclusion sensitive to the choice of α? (c) Use Excel to find the p-value. Interpret it. (d) Discuss the distinction between importance and significance in this example. **Paint**

9.38 The average weight of a package of rolled oats is supposed to be at least 18 ounces. A sample of 18 packages shows a mean of 17.78 ounces with a standard deviation of 0.41 ounce. (a) At the 5 percent level of significance, is the true mean smaller than the specification? Clearly state your hypotheses and decision rule. (b) Is this conclusion sensitive to the choice of α? (c) Use Excel to find the p-value. Interpret it.

9.39 According to J.D. Power & Associates, the mean purchase price of a smartphone device (such as an iPhone or Blackberry) in 2008 was \$216. In 2009, a random sample of 20 business managers who owned a smartphone device showed a mean purchase price of \$209 with a sample standard deviation of \$13. (a) At $\alpha = .05$, has the mean purchase price decreased? State the hypotheses and decision rule clearly. (b) Use Excel to find the p-value and interpret it.

9.40 The average age of a part-time seasonal employee at a Vail Resorts ski mountain has historically been 37 years. A random sample of 50 part-time seasonal employees in 2010 had a sample mean age of 38.5 years with a sample standard deviation equal to 16 years. At the 10 percent level of significance, does this sample show that the average age was different in 2010?

9.41 The number of entrees purchased in a single order at a Noodles & Company restaurant has had an historical average of 1.60 entrees per order. On a particular Saturday afternoon, a random sample of 40 Noodles orders had a mean number of entrees equal to 1.80 with a standard deviation equal to 1.11. At the 5 percent level of significance, does this sample show that the average number of entrees per order was greater than expected?

9.42 In 2008, a small dealership leased 21 Suburu Outbacks on 2-year leases. When the cars were returned in 2010, the mileage was recorded (see below). Is the dealer's mean significantly greater than the national average of 30,000 miles for 2-year leased vehicles, using the 10 percent level of significance? **Mileage**

40,060	24,960	14,310	17,370	44,740	44,550	20,250
33,380	24,270	41,740	58,630	35,830	25,750	28,910
25,090	43,380	23,940	43,510	53,680	31,810	36,780

9.43 At Oxnard University, a sample of 18 senior accounting majors showed a mean cumulative GPA of 3.35 with a standard deviation of 0.25. (a) At $\alpha = .05$ in a two-tailed test, does this differ significantly from 3.25 (the mean GPA for all business school seniors at the university)? (b) Use the sample to construct a 95 percent confidence interval for the mean. Does the confidence interval include 3.25? (c) Explain how the hypothesis test and confidence interval are equivalent.

Mini Case 9.2

Beauty Products and Small Business

Lisa has been working at a beauty counter in a department store for 5 years. In her spare time she's also been creating lotions and fragrances using all natural products. After receiving positive feedback from her friends and family about her beauty products, Lisa decides to open her own store. Lisa knows that convincing a bank to help fund her new business will require more than a few positive testimonials from family. Based on her experience working at the department store, Lisa believes women in her area spend more than the national average on fragrance products. This fact could help make her business successful.

Lisa would like to be able to support her belief with data to include in a business plan proposal that she would then use to obtain a small business loan. Lisa took a business statistics course while in college and decides to use the hypothesis testing tool she learned. After conducting research she learns that the national average spending by women on fragrance products is \$59 every 3 months.

The hypothesis test is based on this survey result:

H_0: $\mu \leq \$59$
H_1: $\mu > \$59$

In other words, she will assume the average spending in her town is the same as the national average *unless she has strong evidence that says otherwise*. Lisa takes a random sample of 25 women and finds that the sample mean $\bar{x}$ is \$68 and the sample standard deviation s is \$15. Lisa uses a t statistic because she doesn't know the population standard deviation. Her calculated t statistic is

$$t_{\text{calc}} = \frac{68 - 59}{\frac{15}{\sqrt{25}}} = 3.00 \quad \text{with 24 degrees of freedom}$$

Using the Excel formula =T.DIST.RT(3,24), Lisa finds that the right-tail p-value is .003103. This p-value is quite small and she can safely reject her null hypothesis. Lisa now has strong evidence to conclude that over a 3-month period women in her area spend more than \$59 on average.

Lisa would also like to include an estimate for the average amount women in her area *do* spend. Calculating a confidence interval would be her next step. Lisa chooses a 95 percent confidence level and finds the t value to use in her calculations by using the Excel formula =T.INV(0.05,24). The result is $t_{.025} = 2.0639$. Her 95 percent confidence interval for μ is

$$\bar{x} \pm t_{\alpha/2}\frac{s}{\sqrt{n}} \quad \text{or} \quad \$68 \pm 2.0639\frac{15}{\sqrt{25}} \quad \text{or} \quad \$68 \pm \$6.19 \quad \text{or} \quad [61.81, 74.19].$$

Lisa's business plan proposal can confidently claim that women in her town spend more than the national average on fragrance products and that she estimates the average spending is between \$62 and \$74 every 3 months. Hopefully the bank will see not only that Lisa creates excellent beauty products, but she also is a smart businessperson!

LO 9-8

Perform a hypothesis test for a proportion and find the p-value.

LO 9-9

Check whether normality may be assumed in testing a proportion.

9.6 TESTING A PROPORTION

Proportions are used frequently in business situations and collecting proportion data is straightforward. It is easier for customers to say whether they like or dislike this year's new automobile color than it is for customers to quantify their degree of satisfaction with the new color. Also, many business performance indicators such as market share, employee retention rates, and employee accident rates are expressed as proportions.

EXAMPLE 9.6

Testing a Proportion

In 2006, U.S. airlines mishandled 6 out of every 1,000 bags checked for air travel. One airline, FlyFast, found that 54 percent of their mishandled bag incidents were related to transferring baggage to a connecting flight. FlyFast recently installed an RFID (Radio Frequency Identification) system with the goal of decreasing the proportion of mistakes caused during transfer and ultimately reducing the overall proportion of lost bags. After operating their new system for several months, FlyFast would like to know if the wireless system has been effective. FlyFast could use a hypothesis test to answer this question. The benchmark for the null hypothesis is their proportion of transfer mistakes using their old system ($\pi_0 = .54$.) The possible set of statistical hypotheses would be:

Left-Tailed Test	*Two-Tailed Test*	*Right-Tailed Test*
H_0: $\pi \geq .54$	H_0: $\pi = .54$	H_0: $\pi \leq .54$
H_1: $\pi < .54$	H_1: $\pi \neq .54$	H_1: $\pi > .54$

Which set of hypotheses would be most logical for FlyFast to use? Since FlyFast believes the RFID system will reduce the proportion of transfer errors, they might use a left-tailed test. They would assume there has been no improvement, unless their evidence shows otherwise. If they can reject H_0 in favor of H_1 in a left-tailed test FlyFast would be able to say that their data provide evidence that the proportion of transfer errors has decreased since the RFID tagging system was implemented.

The steps we follow for testing a hypothesis about a population proportion, π, are the same as the ones we follow for testing a mean. The difference is that we now calculate a sample proportion, p, to calculate the test statistic. We know from Chapter 8 that for a sufficiently large sample the sample proportion can be assumed to follow a normal distribution. Our rule is to assume normality if $n\pi_0 \geq 10$ and $n(1 - \pi_0) \geq 10$. If we can assume a normal sampling distribution, then the test statistic would be the z-score. Recall that the sample proportion is

$$p = \frac{x}{n} = \frac{\text{number of successes}}{\text{sample size}} \quad \textbf{(9.4)}$$

The test statistic, calculated from sample data, is the difference between the sample proportion p and the hypothesized proportion π_0 divided by the *standard error of the proportion* (sometimes denoted σ_p):

Test Statistic for a Proportion

$$z_{\text{calc}} = \frac{p - \pi_0}{\sigma_p} = \frac{p - \pi_0}{\sqrt{\dfrac{\pi_0(1 - \pi_0)}{n}}} \quad \textbf{(9.5)}$$

The value of π_0 we are testing is a **benchmark**, such as past performance, an industry standard, or a product specification. The value of π_0 does *not* come from a sample.

EXAMPLE 9.7

Return Policy

Retailers such as Guess, Staples, Sports Authority, and Limited Brands are employing new technology to crack down on "serial exchangers"—customers who abuse their return and exchange policies (*The Wall Street Journal,* November 29, 2004). For example, some customers buy an outfit, wear it once or twice, and then return it. Software called *Verify-1,* a product of a California-based company Return Exchange, tracks a shopper's record of bringing back items. The historical return rate for merchandise at department stores is 13.0 percent. At one department store, after implementing the new software, there were 22 returns in a sample of 250 purchases. At $\alpha = .05$, does this sample indicate that the true return rate has fallen?

Step 1: State the Hypotheses
The hypotheses are

H_0: $\pi \geq .13$ (return rate is the same or greater than the historical rate)
H_1: $\pi < .13$ (return rate has fallen below the historical rate)

Step 2: Specify the Decision Rule
For $\alpha = .05$ in a left-tailed test, the critical value is $z_{.05} = -1.645$, so the decision rule is

Reject H_0 if $z_{\text{calc}} < -1.645$
Otherwise do not reject H_0

This decision rule is illustrated in Figure 9.12.

FIGURE 9.12 **Left-Tailed z Test Using $\alpha = .05$**

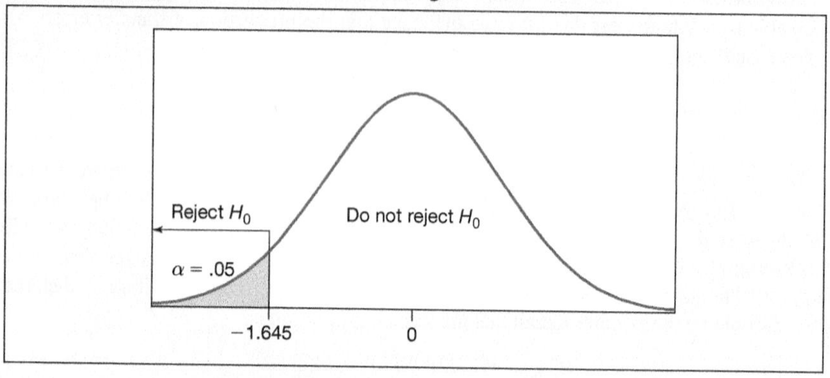

Before using z we should check the normality assumption. To assume normality we require that $n\pi_0 \geq 10$ and $n(1 - \pi_0) \geq 10$. Note that we use the hypothesized proportion π_0 (not p) to check normality because we are assuming H_0 to be the truth about the population. Inserting $\pi_0 = .13$ and $n = 250$, we see that these conditions are easily met: $(250)(.13) = 32.5$ and $(250)(1 - .13) = 217.5$.

Step 3: Calculate the Test Statistic
Since $p = x/n = 22/250 = .088$, the sample seems to favor H_1. But we will assume that H_0 is true and see if the test statistic contradicts this assumption. We test the hypothesis at $\pi = .13$. If we can reject $\pi = .13$ in favor of $\pi < .13$, then we implicitly reject the class of hypotheses $\pi \geq .13$. The test statistic is the difference between the sample proportion $p = x/n$ and the hypothesized parameter π_0 divided by the standard error of p:

$$z_{\text{calc}} = \frac{p - \pi_0}{\sqrt{\frac{\pi_0(1 - \pi_0)}{n}}} = \frac{.088 - .13}{\sqrt{\frac{.13(1 - .13)}{250}}} = \frac{-.042}{.02127} = -1.975$$

Step 4: Make the Decision
Because the test statistic falls in the left-tail rejection region, we reject H_0. We conclude that the return rate is less than .13 after implementing the new software.

Step 5: Take Action
The rate of returns seems to be reduced, so the store might want to try using the software at its other locations.

Calculating the *p*-Value

For our test statistic $z_{calc} = -1.975$, the *p*-value (.02413) can be obtained from Excel's cumulative standard normal =NORM.S.DIST(−1.975). Alternatively, if we round the test statistic to two decimals, we can use the cumulative normal table in Appendix C-2. Depending on how we round the test statistic, we might obtain two possible *p*-values, as shown in Table 9.5. Using the *p*-value, we reject H_0 at $\alpha = .05$, but the decision would be very close if we had used $\alpha = .025$. Figure 9.13 illustrates the *p*-value.

TABLE 9.5 Finding the *p*-Value for *z* = 1.975 in Appendix C-2

z	*.00*	*.01*	*.02*	*.03*	*.04*	*.05*	*.06*	*.07*	*.08*	*.09*
−3.7	.00011	.00010	.00010	.00010	.00009	.00009	.00008	.00008	.00008	.00008
−3.6	.00016	.00015	.00015	.00014	.00014	.00013	.00013	.00012	.00012	.00011
−3.5	.00023	.00022	.00022	.00021	.00020	.00019	.00019	.00018	.00017	.00017
⋮	⋮	⋮	⋮	⋮	⋮	⋮	⋮	⋮	⋮	⋮
−2.0	.02275	.02222	.02169	.02118	.02068	.02018	.01970	.01923	.01876	.01831
−1.9	.02872	.02807	.02743	.02680	.02619	.02559	.02500	***.02442***	***.02385***	.02330
−1.8	.03593	.03515	.03438	.03362	.03288	.03216	.03144	.03074	.03005	.02938

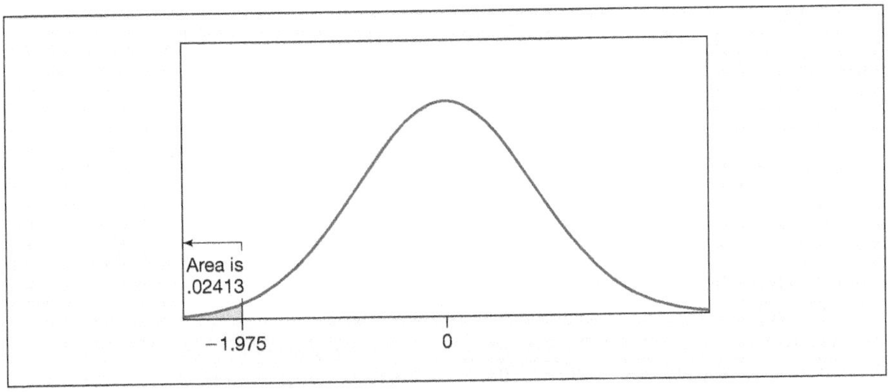

FIGURE 9.13
***p*-Value for a Left-Tailed Test with $z_{calc} = -1.975$**

The *smaller* the *p*-value, the more we are inclined to *reject* H_0. Does this seem backward? You might think a large *p*-value would be "more significant" than a small one. But the *p*-value is the likelihood of the sample if H_0 is true, so a small *p*-value makes us doubt H_0. The *p*-value is a direct measure of the level of significance at which we could reject H_0, so *a smaller p-value is more convincing*. For the left-tailed test, the *p*-value tells us that there is a .02413 probability of getting a sample proportion of .088 or less if the true proportion is .13; that is, such a sample would arise by chance only about 24 times in 1,000 tests if the null hypothesis is true. In our left-tailed test, we would reject H_0 because the *p*-value (.02413) is smaller than α (.05). In fact, we could reject H_0 at *any* α greater than .02413.

Two-Tailed Test

What if we used a two-tailed test? This might be appropriate if the objective is to detect a change in the return rate in *either* direction. In fact, two-tailed tests are used more often, because rejection in a two-tailed test always implies rejection in a one-tailed test, other things being equal. The same sample can be used for either a one-tailed or two-tailed test. The type of hypothesis test is up to the statistician.

Step 1: State the Hypotheses The hypotheses are

H_0: $\pi = .13$ (return rate is the same as the historical rate)

H_1: $\pi \neq .13$ (return rate is different from the historical rate)

Step 2: Specify the Decision Rule For a two-tailed test, we split the risk of Type I error by putting $\alpha/2 = .05/2 = .025$ in each tail (as we would for a confidence interval). For $\alpha = .05$ in a two-tailed test, the critical value is $z_{.025} = 1.96$, so the decision rule is

Reject H_0 if $z_{calc} > +1.96$ or if $z_{calc} < -1.96$
Otherwise do not reject H_0

The decision rule is illustrated in Figure 9.14.

FIGURE 9.14

Two-Tailed *z* Test for $\alpha = .05$

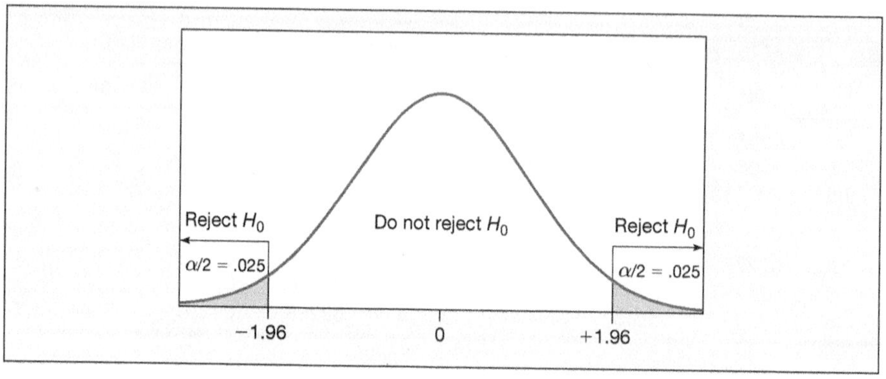

Step 3: Calculate the Test Statistic The test statistic is *unaffected by the hypotheses or the level of significance*. The value of the test statistic is the same as for the one-tailed test:

$$z_{calc} = \frac{p - \pi_0}{\sqrt{\dfrac{\pi_0(1-\pi_0)}{n}}} = \frac{.088 - .13}{\sqrt{\dfrac{.13(1-.13)}{250}}} = \frac{-.042}{.02127} = -1.975$$

Step 4: Make the Decision Because the test statistic falls in the left tail of the rejection region, we reject the null hypothesis H_0: $\pi = .13$ and conclude H_1: $\pi \neq .13$ at the 5 percent level of significance. Another way to say this is that the sample proportion *differs significantly* from the historical return rate at $\alpha = .05$ in a two-tailed test. Note that this decision is rather a close one, since the test statistic just barely falls into the rejection region.

The rejection was stronger in a one-tailed test, that is, the test statistic is farther from the critical value. *Holding α constant, rejection in a two-tailed test always implies rejection in a one-tailed test.* This reinforces the logic of choosing a two-tailed test unless there is a specific reason to prefer a one-tailed test.

Calculating a *p*-Value for a Two-Tailed Test

In a two-tailed test, we divide the risk into equal tails, one on the left and one on the right, to allow for the possibility that we will reject H_0 whenever the sample statistic is very small or very large. With the *p*-value approach in a two-tailed test, we find the tail area associated with our sample test statistic, multiply this by two, and then compare that probability to α. Our z statistic was calculated to be -1.975. The *p*-value would then be

$$2 \times P(Z < -1.975) = 2 \times .02413 = .04826$$

We would reject the null hypothesis because the *p*-value .04826 is less than α (.05).

Effect of α

Would the decision be the same if we had used a different level of significance? While the test statistic $z_{calc} = -1.975$ is the same regardless of our choice of α, our choice of α *does* affect the decision. Referring to Table 9.6 we see that we can reject the null hypothesis at $\alpha = .10$ ($z_{crit} = \pm 1.645$) or $\alpha = .05$ ($z_{crit} = \pm 1.960$), but we cannot reject at $\alpha = .01$ ($z_{crit} = \pm 2.576$).

TABLE 9.6

Effect of Varying α

α	*Test Statistic*	*Two-Tailed Critical Values*	*Decision*
.10	$z_{calc} = -1.975$	$z_{.05} = \pm 1.645$	Reject H_0
.05	$z_{calc} = -1.975$	$z_{.025} = \pm 1.960$	Reject H_0
.01	$z_{calc} = -1.975$	$z_{.005} = \pm 2.576$	Don't reject H_0

Which level of significance is the "right" one? They all are. It depends on how much Type I error we are willing to allow. Before concluding that $\alpha = .01$ is "better" than the others because it allows less Type I error, you should remember that smaller Type I error leads to increased Type II error. In this case, Type I error would imply that there has been a change in return rates when in reality nothing has changed, while Type II error implies that the software had no effect on the return rate, when in reality the software did decrease the return rate.

EXAMPLE 9.8

Length of Hospital Stay

A hospital is comparing its performance against an industry benchmark that no more than 50 percent of normal births should result in a hospital stay exceeding 2 days (48 hours). Thirty-one births in a sample of 50 normal births had a length of stay (LOS) greater than 48 hours. At $\alpha = .025$, does this sample prove that the hospital exceeds the benchmark? This question requires a right-tailed test.

Step 1: State the Hypotheses
The hypotheses are

H_0: $\pi \le .50$ (the hospital is compliant with the benchmark)

H_1: $\pi > .50$ (the hospital is exceeding the benchmark)

Step 2: Specify the Decision Rule
For $\alpha = .025$ in a right-tailed test, the critical value is $z_{.025} = 1.96$, so the decision rule is

Reject H_0 if $z > 1.960$

Otherwise do not reject H_0

This decision rule is illustrated in Figure 9.15.

FIGURE 9.15 **Right-Tailed z Test Using $\alpha = .025$**

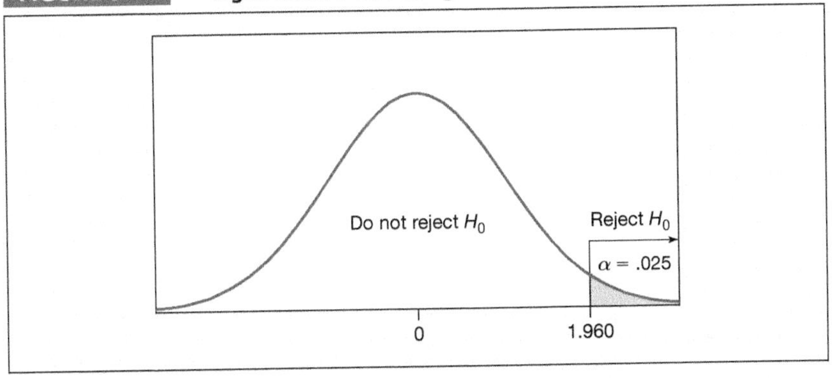

To assume normality of the sample proportion p, we require that $n\pi_0 \ge 10$ and $n(1 - \pi_0) \ge 10$. Inserting $\pi_0 = .50$ and $n = 50$, we see that the normality conditions are easily met: $(50)(.50) = 25$ and $(50)(1 - .50) = 25$.

Step 3: Calculate the Test Statistic
Since $p = x/n = 31/50 = .62$, the sample seems to favor H_1. But we will assume that H_0 is true and see if the test statistic contradicts this assumption. We test the hypothesis

at $\pi = .50$. If we can reject $\pi = .50$ in favor of $\pi > .50$, then we can reject the class of hypotheses $\pi \le .50$. The test statistic is the difference between the sample proportion $p = x/n$ and the hypothesized parameter π_0 divided by the standard error of p:

$$z_{calc} = \frac{p - \pi_0}{\sqrt{\frac{\pi_0(1-\pi_0)}{n}}} = \frac{.62 - .50}{\sqrt{\frac{.50(1-.50)}{50}}} = \frac{.12}{.07071068} = 1.697$$

Step 4: Make the Decision
The test statistic does not fall in the right-tail rejection region, so we cannot reject the hypothesis that $\pi \le .50$ at the 2.5 percent level of significance. In other words, the test statistic is within the realm of chance at $\alpha = .025$.

Step 5: Take Action
The hospital appears compliant with the benchmark, so no action is required at this time.

Calculating the *p*-Value

In this case, the *p*-value can be obtained from Excel's cumulative standard normal function =1−NORM.S.DIST(1.697, 1) = .04485 or from Appendix C-2 (using $z = 1.70$ we get $p = 1 - .9554 = .0446$). Excel's accuracy is greater because $z = 1.697$ is not rounded to $z = 1.70$. Since we want a right-tail area, we must subtract the cumulative distribution function from 1. The *p*-value is greater than .025 so we fail to reject the null hypothesis in a right-tailed test. We could (barely) reject at $\alpha = .05$. This demonstrates that the level of significance can affect our decision. The advantage of the *p*-value is that it tells you exactly the point of indifference between rejecting or not rejecting H_0. The *p*-value is illustrated in Figure 9.16.

FIGURE 9.16

***p*-Value for a Right-Tailed Test with $z_{calc} = 1.697$**

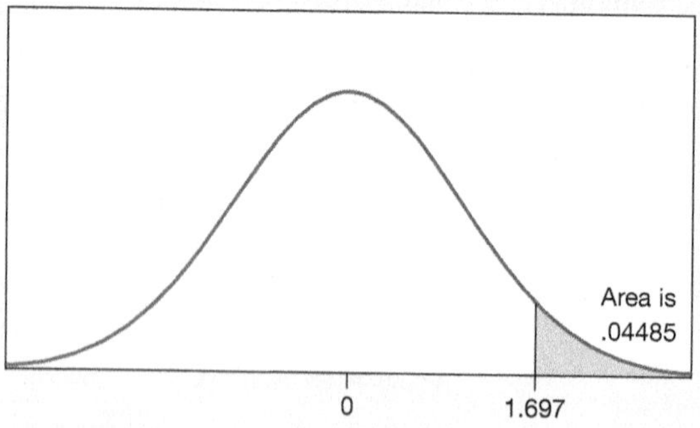

SECTION EXERCISES

connect

9.44 Interpret each *p*-value in your own words:

a. *p*-value = .387, H_0: $\pi \ge .20$, H_1: $\pi < .20$, $\alpha = .10$
b. *p*-value = .043, H_0: $\pi \le .90$, H_1: $\pi > .90$, $\alpha = .05$
c. *p*-value = .0012, H_0: $\pi = .50$, H_1: $\pi \ne .50$, $\alpha = .01$

9.45 Calculate the test statistic and *p*-value for each sample.

a. H_0: $\pi = .20$ versus H_1: $\pi \ne .20$, $\alpha = .025$, $p = .28$, $n = 100$
b. H_0: $\pi \le .50$ versus H_1: $\pi > .50$, $\alpha = .025$, $p = .60$, $n = 90$
c. H_0: $\pi \le .75$ versus H_1: $\pi > .75$, $\alpha = .10$, $p = .82$, $n = 50$

9.46 Calculate the test statistic and p-value for each sample.

a. H_0: $\pi \leq .60$ versus H_1: $\pi > .60$, $\alpha = .05$, $x = 56$, $n = 80$
b. H_0: $\pi = .30$ versus H_1: $\pi \neq .30$, $\alpha = .05$, $x = 18$, $n = 40$
c. H_0: $\pi \geq .10$ versus H_1: $\pi < .10$, $\alpha = .01$, $x = 3$, $n = 100$

9.47 May normality of the sample proportion p be assumed? Show your work.

a. H_0: $\pi = .30$ versus H_1: $\pi \neq .30$, $n = 20$
b. H_0: $\pi = .05$ versus H_1: $\pi \neq .05$, $n = 50$
c. H_0: $\pi = .10$ versus H_1: $\pi \neq .10$, $n = 400$

9.48 In a recent survey, 10 percent of the participants rated Pepsi as being "concerned with my health." PepsiCo's response included a new "Smart Spot" symbol on its products that meet certain nutrition criteria, to help consumers who seek more healthful eating options. At $\alpha = .05$, would a follow-up survey showing that 18 of 100 persons now rate Pepsi as being "concerned with my health" provide sufficient evidence that the percentage has increased?

9.49 In a hospital's shipment of 3,500 insulin syringes, 14 were unusable due to defects. (a) At $\alpha = .05$, is this sufficient evidence to reject future shipments from this supplier if the hospital's quality standard requires 99.7 percent of the syringes to be acceptable? State the hypotheses and decision rule. (b) May normality of the sample proportion p be assumed? (c) Explain the effects of Type I error and Type II error. (d) Find the p-value.

9.50 To combat antibiotic resistance, the Quality Improvement Consortium recommends a throat swab to confirm strep throat before a physician prescribes antibiotics to children under age 5. In a random sample of 60 children who received antibiotics for throat infections, 18 did not have a throat swab. (a) At $\alpha = .05$, is this a statistically significant reduction over last year's national rate of 40 percent? (b) Is it safe to assume normality of the sample proportion p? Explain.

9.51 To encourage telephone efficiency, a catalog call center issues a guideline that at least half of all telephone orders should be completed within 2 minutes. Subsequently, a random sample of 64 telephone calls showed that only 24 calls lasted 2 minutes or less. (a) At $\alpha = .05$ is this a significant departure from the guideline in a left-tailed test? State your hypotheses and decision rule. (b) Find the p-value. (c) Is the difference important (as opposed to significant)?

9.52 The recent default rate on all student loans is 5.2 percent. In a recent random sample of 300 loans at private universities, there were 9 defaults. (a) Does this sample show sufficient evidence that the private university loan default rate is below the rate for all universities, using a left-tailed test at $\alpha = .01$? (b) Calculate the p-value. (c) Verify that the assumption of normality of the sample proportion p is justified.

9.53 A poll of 702 frequent and occasional fliers found that 442 respondents favored a ban on cell phones in flight, even if technology permits it. At $\alpha = .05$, can we conclude that more than half the sampled population supports a ban?

Small Samples and Non-Normality

In random tests by the FAA, 12.5 percent of all passenger flights failed the agency's test for bacterial count in water served to passengers (*The Wall Street Journal,* November 10, 2004, p. D1). Airlines now are trying to improve their compliance with water quality standards. Random inspection of 16 recent flights showed that only 1 flight failed the water quality test. Has overall compliance improved?

H_0: $\pi \geq .125$ (failure rate has not improved)
H_1: $\pi < .125$ (failure rate has declined)

The sample is clearly too small to assume normality since $n\pi_0 = (16)(.125) = 2$. Instead, we use MINITAB to test the hypotheses by finding the exact binomial left-tail probability of a sample proportion $p = 1/16 = .0625$ under the assumption that $\pi = .125$, as shown in Figure 9.17.

The p-value of .388 does not permit rejection of H_0 at any of the usual levels of significance (e.g., 5 percent). The binomial test is easy and is always correct since no assumption of normality is required. Lacking MINITAB, you could do the same thing by using Excel to calculate the cumulative binomial probability of the observed sample result under the null hypothesis as $P(X \leq 1 \mid n = 16, \pi = .125)$ =BINOM.DIST(1,16,.125,1) = .38793.

FIGURE 9.17

MINITAB Small-Sample Test of a Proportion

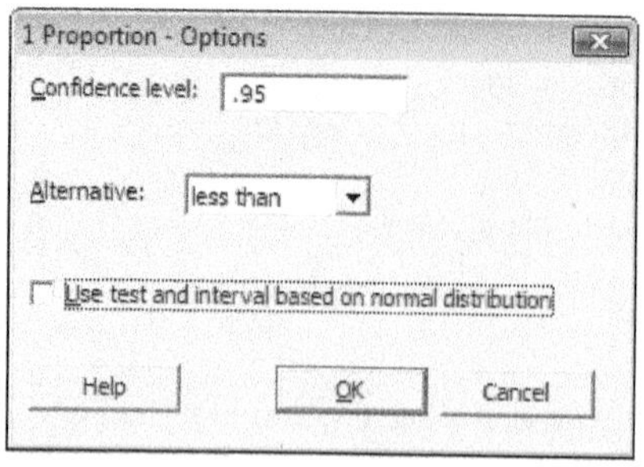

Test and CI for One Proportion

```
Test of p = 0.125 vs p < 0.125

                                   95%
                                 Upper      Exact
Sample  X   N  Sample p          Bound    P-Value
1       1  16  0.062500       0.263957      0.388
```

Mini Case 9.3

Every Minute Counts

As more company business is transacted by telephone or Internet, there is a considerable premium to reduce customer time spent with human operators. Verizon recently installed a new speech recognition system for its repair calls. In the old system, the user had to press keys on the numeric keypad to answer questions, which led many callers to opt to talk to an operator instead. Under the old system, 94 percent of the customers had to talk to an operator to get their needs met. Suppose that, using the new system, a sample of 150 calls showed that 120 required an operator. The hypotheses are

H_0: $\pi \geq .94$ (the new system is no better than the old system)

H_1: $\pi < .94$ (the new system has reduced the proportion of operator calls)

These hypotheses call for a left-tailed test. Using $\alpha = .01$, the left-tail critical value is $z_{.01} = -2.326$, as illustrated in Figure 9.18.

FIGURE 9.18 **Decision Rule for Left-Tailed Test**

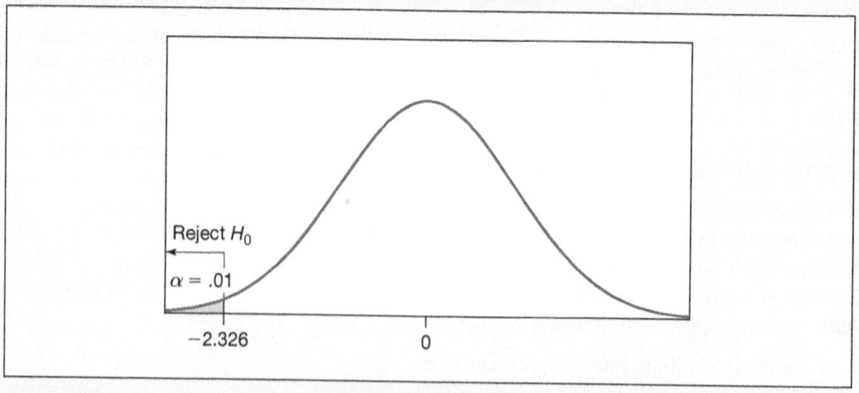

For normality of the sample proportion p, we want $n\pi_0 \geq 10$ and $n(1 - \pi_0) \geq 10$. The condition for normality is not quite met, since $(150)(.94) = 141$ but $(150)(.06) = 9$. We will proceed, bearing in mind this possible concern. The sample proportion is $p = 120/150 = .80$, so the test statistic is

$$z_{\text{calc}} = \frac{p - \pi_0}{\sqrt{\frac{\pi_0(1-\pi_0)}{n}}} = \frac{.80 - .94}{\sqrt{\frac{.94(1-.94)}{150}}} = \frac{-.14}{.01939} = -7.22$$

The test statistic is far below the critical value, so we conclude that the percentage of customers who require an operator has declined. MINITAB verifies this calculation and also gives the p-value (.000) as shown in Figure 9.19.

Besides being significant, such savings are important. For example, Boston Financial Data Services, a company that provides record-keeping services for mutual funds, shaved a minute off the mean time to process a customer request. Its call centers process 1.7 million calls a year, so the savings are very large. See *The Wall Street Journal,* July 26, 2004.

FIGURE 9.19

MINITAB Results for One-Sample Proportion

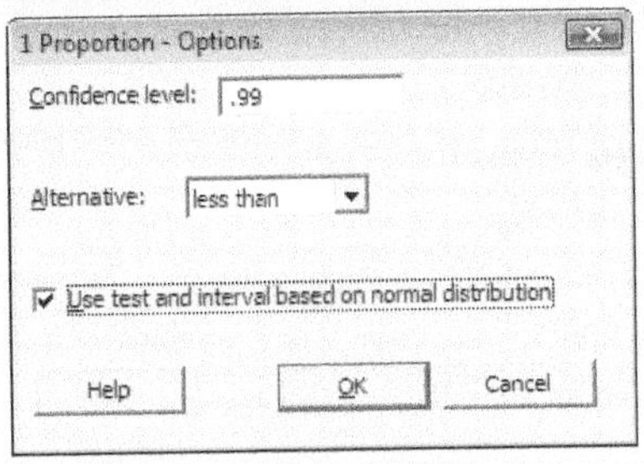


```
Test and CI for One Proportion

Test of p = 0.94 vs p < 0.94
99%
                                    Upper
Sample    X    N  Sample p          Bound  Z-Value  P-Value
1       120  150  0.800000       0.875978    -7.22    0.000
```

SECTION EXERCISES

9.54 A coin was flipped 12 times and came up heads 10 times. (a) Would we be justified in assuming that the sample proportion p is normally distributed? Explain. (b) Calculate a p-value for the observed sample outcome, using the normal distribution. At the .05 level of significance in a right-tailed test, is the coin biased toward heads? (c) Use Excel to calculate the binomial probability $P(X \geq 10 \mid n = 12, \pi = .50) = 1 - P(X \leq 9 \mid n = 12, \pi = .50)$.

9.55 BriteScreen, a manufacturer of 19-inch LCD computer screens, requires that on average 99.9 percent of all LCDs conform to its quality standard. In a day's production of 2,000 units, 4 are defective. (a) Assuming this is a random sample, is the standard being met, using the 10 percent level of significance? *Hint:* Use Excel to find the binomial probability $P(X \geq 4 \mid n = 2000, \pi = .001) = 1 - P(X \leq 3 \mid n = 2000, \pi = .001)$. Alternatively, use MINITAB. (b) Show that normality of the sample proportion p should not be assumed.

9.56 Perfect pitch is the ability to identify musical notes correctly without hearing another note as a reference. The probability that a randomly chosen person has perfect pitch is .0005. (a) If 20 students at Julliard School of Music are tested, and 2 are found to have perfect pitch, would you conclude at the .01 level of significance that Julliard students are more likely than the general population to have perfect pitch? *Hint:* Use Excel to find the right-tailed binomial probability $P(X \geq 2 \mid n = 20, \pi = .0005)$. Alternatively, use MINITAB. (b) Show that normality of the sample proportion p should not be assumed.

9.7 POWER CURVES AND OC CURVES (OPTIONAL)

LO 9-10

Interpret a power curve or OC curve (optional).

Recall that *power* is the probability of correctly rejecting a false null hypothesis. While we cannot always attain the power we desire in a statistical test, we can at least calculate what the power would be in various possible situations. We will show step by step how to calculate power for tests of a mean or proportion, and how to draw *power curves* that show how power depends on the true value of the parameter we are estimating.

Power Curve for a Mean: An Example

Power depends on how far the true value of the parameter is from the null hypothesis value. The further away the true population value is from the assumed value, the easier it is for your hypothesis test to detect and the more power it has. To illustrate the calculation of β risk and power, consider a utility that is installing underground PVC pipe as a cable conduit. The specifications call for a mean strength of 12,000 psi (pounds per square inch). A sample of 25 pieces of pipe is tested under laboratory conditions to ascertain the compressive pressure that causes the pipe to collapse. The standard deviation is known from past experience to be $\sigma = 500$ psi. If the pipe proves stronger than the specification, there is no problem, so the utility requires a left-tailed test:

H_0: $\mu \geq 12{,}000$

H_1: $\mu < 12{,}000$

If the true mean strength is 11,900 psi, what is the probability that the utility will fail to reject the null hypothesis and mistakenly conclude that $\mu = 12{,}000$? At $\alpha = .05$, what is the power of the test? Recall that β is the risk of Type II error, the probability of incorrectly accepting a false hypothesis. Type II error is bad, so we want β to be small.

(9.6) $$\beta = P(\text{accept } H_0 \mid H_0 \text{ is false})$$

In this example, $\beta = P(\text{conclude } \mu = 12{,}000 \mid \mu = 11{,}900)$.

Conversely, power is the probability that we correctly reject a false hypothesis. More power is better, so we want power to be as close to 1 as possible:

(9.7) $$\text{Power} = P(\text{reject } H_0 \mid H_0 \text{ is false}) = 1 - \beta$$

The values of β and power will vary, depending on the difference between the true mean μ and the hypothesized mean μ_0, the standard deviation σ, the sample size n, and the level of significance α.

(9.8) $$\text{Power} = f(\mu - \mu_0, \sigma, n, \alpha) \quad \text{(determinants of power for a mean)}$$

Table 9.7 summarizes their effects. While we cannot change μ and σ, the sample size and level of significance often are under our control. We can get more power by increasing α, but would we really want to increase Type I error in order to reduce Type II error? Probably not, so the way we usually increase power is by choosing a larger sample size. We will discuss each of these effects in turn.

TABLE 9.7

Determinants of Power in Testing One Mean

Parameter	*If . . .*	*then . . .*
True mean (μ)	$\lvert\mu - \mu_0\rvert \uparrow$	Power ↑
True standard deviation (σ)	$\sigma \uparrow$	Power ↓
Sample size (n)	$n \uparrow$	Power ↑
Level of significance (α)	$\alpha \uparrow$	Power ↑

Calculating Power

To calculate β and power, we follow a simple sequence of steps for any given values of μ, σ, n, and α. We assume a normal population (or a large sample) so that the sample mean $\bar{X}$ may be assumed normally distributed.

Step 1 Find the left-tail *critical value* for the sample mean. At $\alpha = .05$ in a left-tailed test, we know that $z_{.05} = -1.645$. Using the formula for a z-score,

$$z_{\text{critical}} = \frac{\bar{x}_{\text{critical}} - \mu_0}{\frac{\sigma}{\sqrt{n}}}$$

we can solve algebraically for $\bar{x}_{\text{critical}}$:

$$\bar{x}_{\text{critical}} = \mu_0 + z_{\text{critical}}\frac{\sigma}{\sqrt{n}} = 12{,}000 - 1.645\left(\frac{500}{\sqrt{25}}\right) = 11{,}835.5$$

In terms of the data units of measurement (pounds per square·inch), the decision rule is

Reject H_0: $\mu \geq 12{,}000$ if $\bar{X} < 11{,}835.5$ psi

Otherwise do not reject H_0

Now suppose that the true mean is $\mu = 11{,}900$. Then the sampling distribution of $\bar{X}$ would be centered at 11,900 instead of 12,000 as we hypothesized. The probability of β error is the area to the right of the critical value $\bar{x}_{\text{critical}} = 11{,}835.5$ (the nonrejection region) representing $P(\bar{X} > \bar{x}_{\text{critical}} \mid \mu = 11{,}900)$. Figure 9.20 illustrates this situation.

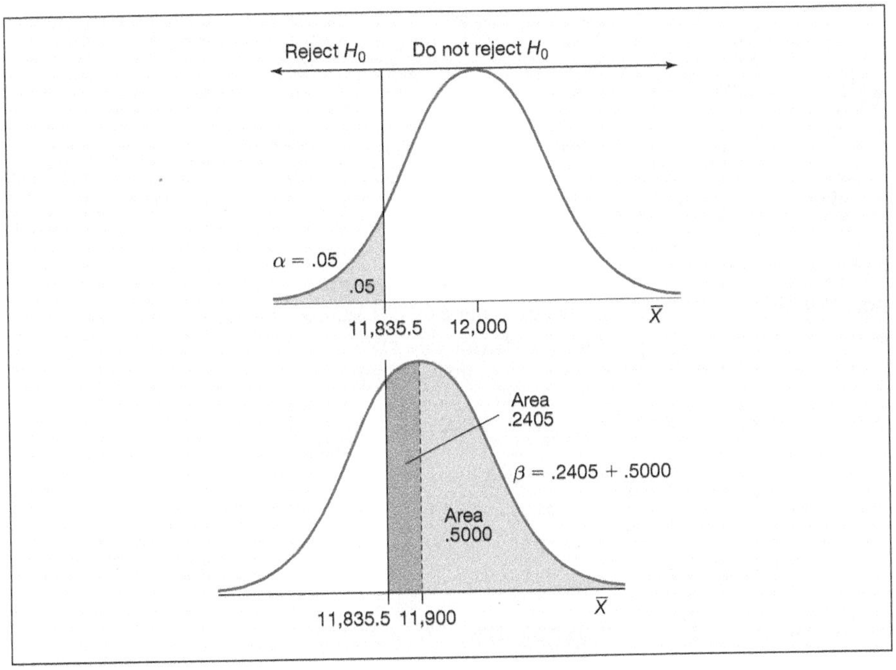

FIGURE 9.20

Finding β When $\mu = 11{,}900$

Step 2 Express the difference between the critical value $\bar{x}_{\text{critical}}$ and the true mean μ as a z-value:

$$z = \frac{\bar{x}_{\text{critical}} - \mu}{\frac{\sigma}{\sqrt{n}}} = \frac{11{,}835.5 - 11{,}900}{\frac{500}{\sqrt{25}}} = -0.645$$

Step 3 Find the β risk and power as areas under the normal curve, using Appendix C-2 or Excel:

Calculation of β	*Calculation of Power*
$\beta = P(\bar{X} > \bar{x}_{\text{critical}} \mid \mu = 11{,}900)$	Power $= P(\bar{X} < \bar{x}_{\text{critical}} \mid \mu = 11{,}900)$
$= P(Z > -0.645)$	$= 1 - \beta$
$= 0.2405 + 0.5000$	$= 1 - 0.7405$
$= 0.7405$, or 74.1%	$= 0.2595$, or 26.0%

This calculation shows that if the true mean is $\mu = 11{,}900$, then there is a 74.05 percent chance that we will commit β error by failing to reject $\mu = 12{,}000$. Since 11,900 is not very far from 12,000 in terms of the standard error, our test has relatively low power. Although our test may not be sensitive enough to reject the null hypothesis reliably if μ is only *slightly* less than 12,000, we would expect that if μ is *far* below 12,000 our test would be more likely to lead to rejection of H_0. Although we cannot know the true mean, we *can* repeat our power calculation for as many values of μ and n as we wish. These calculations may appear tedious, but they are straightforward in a spreadsheet. Table 9.8 shows β and power for samples of $n = 25$, 50, and 100 over a range of μ values from 12,000 down to 11,600.

Notice that β drops toward 0 and power approaches 1 when the true value μ is far from the hypothesized mean $\mu_0 = 12{,}000$. When $\mu = 12{,}000$ there can be no β error, since β error can only occur if H_0 is false. Power is then equal to $\alpha = .05$, the lowest power possible.

TABLE 9.8

β and Power for $\mu_0 = 12{,}000$

	$n = 25$			$n = 50$			$n = 100$		
True μ	**z**	**β**	**Power**	**z**	**β**	**Power**	**z**	**β**	**Power**
12000	−1.645	.9500	.0500	−1.645	.9500	.0500	−1.645	.9500	.0500
11950	−1.145	.8739	.1261	−0.938	.8258	.1742	−0.645	.7405	.2595
11900	−0.645	.7405	.2595	−0.231	.5912	.4088	0.355	.3612	.6388
11850	−0.145	.5576	.4424	0.476	.3169	.6831	1.355	.0877	.9123
11800	0.355	.3612	.6388	1.184	.1183	.8817	2.355	.0093	.9907
11750	0.855	.1962	.8038	1.891	.0293	.9707	3.355	.0004	.9996
11700	1.355	.0877	.9123	2.598	.0047	.9953	4.355	.0000	1.0000
11650	1.855	.0318	.9682	3.305	.0005	.9995	5.355	.0000	1.0000
11600	2.355	.0093	.9907	4.012	.0000	1.0000	6.355	.0000	1.0000

Effect of Sample Size

Table 9.8 also shows that, other things being equal, if sample size were to increase, β risk would decline and power would increase because the critical value $\bar{x}_{\text{critical}}$ would be closer to the hypothesized mean μ. For example, if the sample size were increased to $n = 50$, then

$$\bar{x}_{\text{critical}} = \mu_0 + z_{\text{critical}}\frac{\sigma}{\sqrt{n}} = 12{,}000 - 1.645\left(\frac{500}{\sqrt{50}}\right) = 11{,}883.68$$

$$z = \frac{\bar{x}_{\text{critical}} - \mu}{\dfrac{\sigma}{\sqrt{n}}} = \frac{11{,}883.68 - 11{,}900}{\dfrac{500}{\sqrt{25}}} = -0.231$$

$$\text{Power} = P(\bar{X} < \bar{x}_{\text{critical}} \mid \mu = 11{,}900) = P(Z < -.231) = .4088, \text{ or } 40.9\%$$

Relationship of the Power and OC Curves

Power is much easier to understand when it is made into a graph. A **power curve** is a graph whose Y-axis shows the power of the test $(1 - \beta)$ and whose X-axis shows the various possible true values of the parameter while holding the sample size constant. Figure 9.21 shows the power curve for this example, using three different sample sizes. You can see that power increases as the departure of μ from 12,000 becomes greater and that each larger sample size creates a higher power curve. In other words, larger samples have more power. Since the power curve approaches $\alpha = .05$ as the true mean approaches the hypothesized mean of 12,000, we can see that α also affects the power curve. If we increase α, the power curve will shift up. Although it is not illustrated here, power also rises if the standard deviation is smaller because a small σ gives the test more precision.

FIGURE 9.21

Power Curves for H_0: $\mu \geq 12{,}000$ H_1: $\mu < 12{,}000$

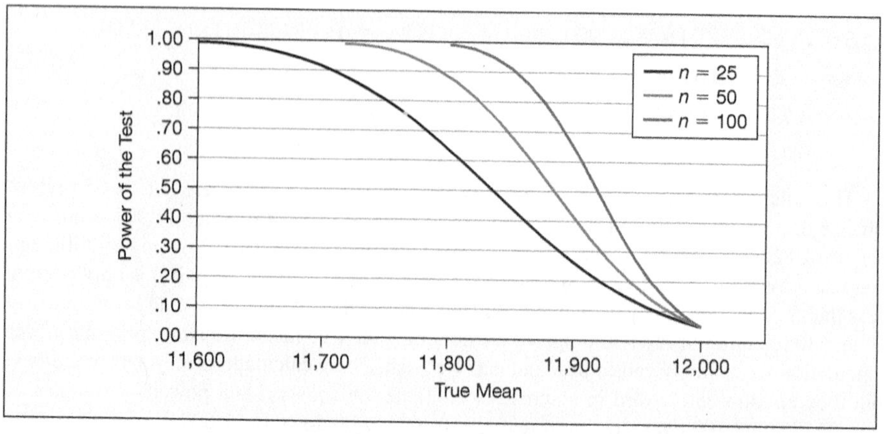

The graph of β risk against this same X-axis is called the operating characteristic or **OC curve**. Figure 9.22 shows the OC curve for this example. It is simply the converse of the power curve, so it is redundant if you already have the power curve.

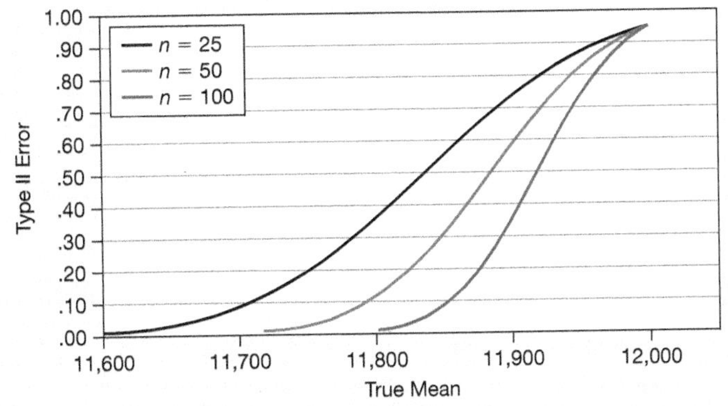

FIGURE 9.22

OC Curves for
H_0: $\mu \geq 12,000$
H_1: $\mu < 12,000$

Power Curve for Tests of a Proportion

For tests of a proportion, power depends on the true proportion π, the hypothesized proportion π_0, the sample size n, and the level of significance α. Table 9.9 summarizes their effects on power. As with a mean, enlarging the sample size is the most common method of increasing power, unless we are willing to raise the level of significance (that is, trade off Type I error against Type II error).

TABLE 9.9

Determinants of Power in Testing a Proportion

Parameter	*If . . .*	*then . . .*
True proportion π	$\lvert\pi - \pi_0\rvert \uparrow$	Power $\uparrow$
Sample size n	$n \uparrow$	Power $\uparrow$
Level of significance α	$\alpha \uparrow$	Power $\uparrow$

EXAMPLE 9.9

Length of Hospital Stay: Power Curve

A sample is taken of 50 births in a major hospital. We are interested in knowing whether at least half of all mothers have a length of stay (LOS) less than 48 hours. We will do a right-tailed test using $\alpha = .10$. The hypotheses are

H_0: $\pi \leq .50$
H_1: $\pi > .50$

To find the power curve, we follow the same procedure as for a mean—actually, it is easier than a mean because we don't have to worry about σ. For example, what would be the power of the test if the true proportion were $\pi = .60$ and the sample size were $n = 50$?

Step 1
Find the right-tail *critical value* for the sample proportion. At $\alpha = .10$ in a right-tailed test, we would use $z_{.10} = 1.282$ (actually, $z_{.10} = 1.28155$ if we use Excel) so

$$p_{\text{critical}} = \pi_0 + 1.28155\sqrt{\frac{\pi_0(1-\pi_0)}{n}} = .50 + 1.28155\sqrt{\frac{(.50)(1-.50)}{50}} = .590619$$

Step 2
Express the difference between the critical value p_{critical} and the true proportion π as a z-value:

$$z = \frac{p_{\text{critical}} - \pi}{\sqrt{\frac{\pi(1-\pi)}{n}}} = \frac{.590619 - .600000}{\sqrt{\frac{(.60)(1-.60)}{50}}} = -0.1354$$

Step 3

Find the β risk and power as areas under the normal curve:

Calculation of β

$$\beta = P(p < p_{\text{critical}} \mid \pi = .60)$$
$$= P(Z < -0.1354)$$
$$= .4461, \text{ or } 44.61\%$$

Calculation of Power

$$\text{Power} = P(p > p_{\text{critical}} \mid \pi = .60)$$
$$= 1 - \beta$$
$$= 1 - 0.4461$$
$$= .5539, \text{ or } 55.39\%$$

We can repeat these calculations for any values of π and n. Table 9.10 illustrates power for values of π ranging from .50 to .70, at which point power is near its maximum, and for sample sizes of $n = 50$, 100, and 200. As expected, power increases sharply as sample size increases, and as π differs more from $\pi_0 = .50$.

TABLE 9.10 β and Power for $\pi_0 = .50$

	$n = 50$			$n = 100$			$n = 200$		
π	z	β	Power	z	β	Power	z	β	Power
.50	1.282	.9000	.1000	1.282	.9000	.1000	1.282	.9000	.1000
.52	1.000	.8412	.1588	0.882	.8112	.1888	0.716	.7631	.2369
.54	0.718	.7637	.2363	0.483	.6855	.3145	0.151	.5599	.4401
.56	0.436	.6686	.3314	0.082	.5327	.4673	−0.419	.3378	.6622
.58	0.152	.5605	.4395	−0.323	.3735	.6265	−0.994	.1601	.8399
.60	−0.135	.4461	.5539	−0.733	.2317	.7683	−1.579	.0572	.9428
.62	−0.428	.3343	.6657	−1.152	.1246	.8754	−2.176	.0148	.9852
.64	−0.727	.2335	.7665	−1.582	.0569	.9431	−2.790	.0026	.9974
.66	−1.036	.1502	.8498	−2.025	.0214	.9786	−3.424	.0003	.9997
.68	−1.355	.0877	.9123	−2.485	.0065	.9935	−4.083	.0000	1.0000
.70	−1.688	.0457	.9543	−2.966	.0015	.9985	−4.774	.0000	1.0000

Interpretation Figure 9.23 presents the results for our LOS example visually. As would be expected, the power curves for the larger sample sizes are higher, and the power of each curve is lowest when π is near the hypothesized value of $\pi_0 = .50$. The lowest point on the curve has power equal to $\alpha = .10$. Thus, if we increase α, the power curve would shift up. In other words, we can decrease β (and thereby raise power) by increasing the chance of Type I error, a trade-off we might not wish to make.

FIGURE 9.23

Power Curve Families for
H_0: $\pi \le .50$
H_1: $\pi > .50$

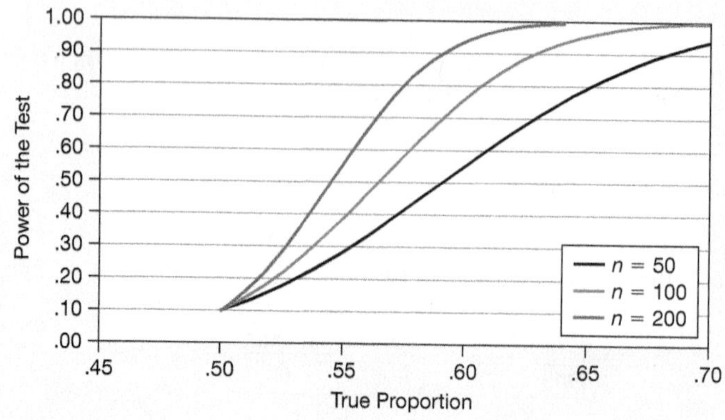

Two-Tailed Power Curves and OC Curves

Both previous examples used one-tailed tests. But if we choose a two-tailed hypothesis test, we will see both sides of the power curve and/or OC curve. Figure 9.24 shows the two-tailed power and OC curves for the previous two examples (H_0: $\mu = 12{,}000$ and H_0: $\pi = .50$). Each power curve resembles an inverted normal curve, reaching its minimum value when $\mu = \mu_0$ (for a mean) or at $\pi = \pi_0$ (for a proportion). The minimum power is equal to the value of α that we select. In our examples, we chose $\alpha = .05$ for testing μ and $\alpha = .10$ for testing π. If we change α, we will raise or lower the entire power curve. You can download power curve spreadsheet demonstrations for μ and π (see McGraw-Hill Connect® resources at the end of this chapter) if you want to try your own experiments with power curves (with automatic calculations).

FIGURE 9.24

Two-Tailed Power and OC Curves

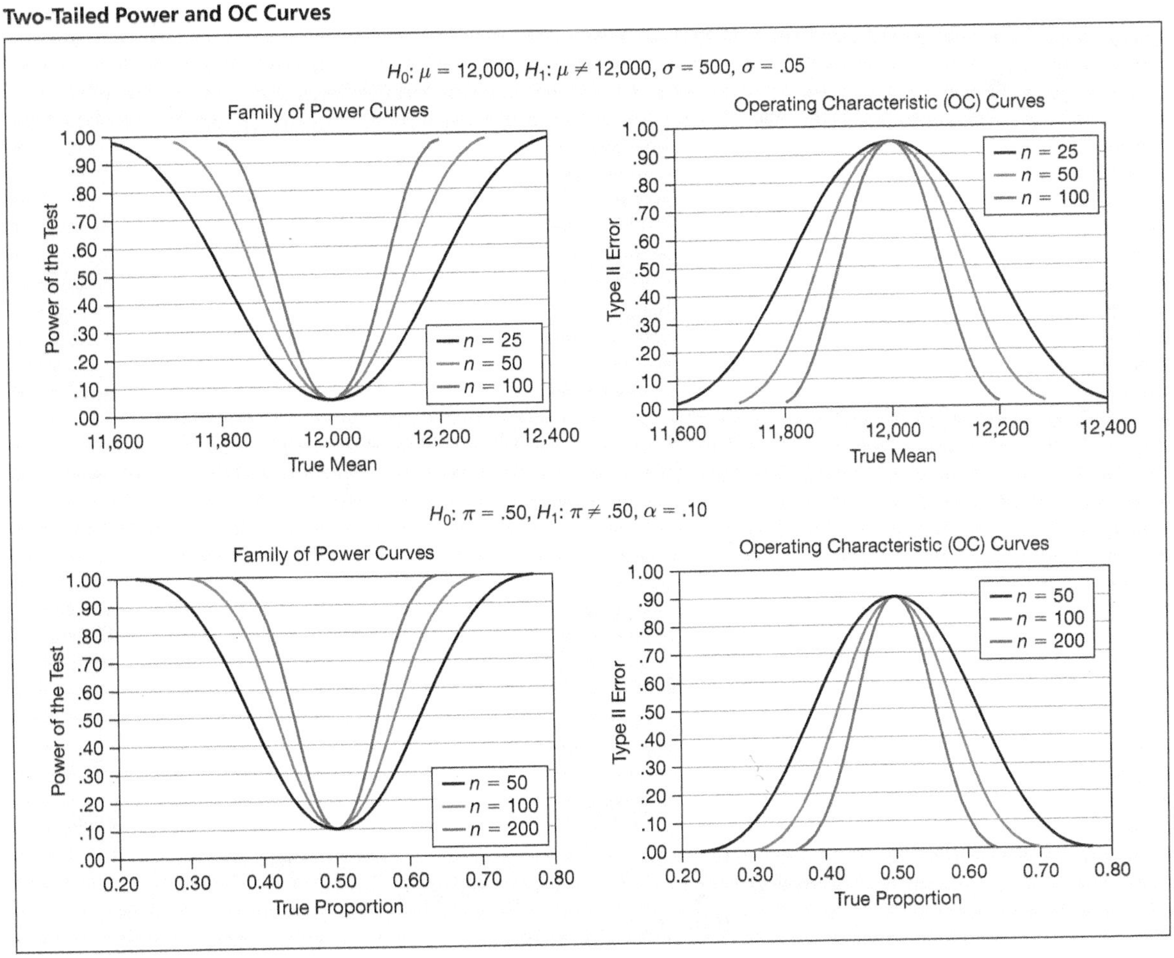

SECTION EXERCISES

connect

Hint: Check your answers using *LearningStats* (from the McGraw-Hill Connect® downloads at the end of this chapter).

9.57 A quality expert inspects 400 items to test whether the population proportion of defectives exceeds .03, using a right-tailed test at $\alpha = .10$. (a) What is the power of this test if the true proportion of defectives is $\pi = .04$? (b) If the true proportion is $\pi = .05$? (c) If the true proportion of defectives is $\pi = .06$?

9.58 Repeat the previous exercise, using $\alpha = .05$. For each true value of π, is the power higher or lower?

9.59 For a certain wine, the mean pH (a measure of acidity) is supposed to be 3.50 with a known standard deviation of $\sigma = .10$. The quality inspector examines 25 bottles at random to test whether the pH is too low, using a left-tailed test at $\alpha = .01$. (a) What is the power of this test if the true mean is $\mu = 3.48$? (b) If the true mean is $\mu = 3.46$? (c) If the true mean is $\mu = 3.44$?

9.60 Repeat the previous exercise, using $\alpha = .05$. For each true value of μ, is the power higher or lower?

9.8 TESTS FOR ONE VARIANCE (OPTIONAL)

LO 9-11

Perform a hypothesis test for a variance (optional).

Not all business hypothesis tests involve proportions or means. In quality control, for example, it is important to compare the variance of a process with a historical benchmark, σ_0^2, to see whether variance reduction has been achieved, or to compare a process standard deviation with an engineering specification.

EXAMPLE 9.10

Attachment Times

Historical statistics show that the standard deviation of attachment times for an instrument panel in an automotive assembly line is $\sigma = 7$ seconds. Observations on 20 randomly chosen attachment times are shown in Table 9.11. At $\alpha = .05$, does the variance in attachment times differ from the historical variance ($\sigma^2 = 7^2 = 49$)?

TABLE 9.11 Panel Attachment Times (seconds) Attachment

120	143	136	126	122
140	133	133	131	131
129	128	131	123	119
135	137	134	115	122

The sample mean is $\bar{x} = 129.400$ with a standard deviation of $s = 7.44382$. We ignore the sample mean since it is irrelevant to this test. For a two-tailed test, the hypotheses are

H_0: $\sigma^2 = 49$

H_1: $\sigma^2 \neq 49$

For a test of one variance, assuming a normal population, the test statistic follows the **chi-square distribution** with degrees of freedom equal to $d.f. = n - 1 = 20 - 1 = 19$. Denoting the hypothesized variance as σ_0^2, the test statistic is

(9.9) $$\chi^2_{calc} = \frac{(n-1)s^2}{\sigma_0^2} \quad \text{(test for one variance)}$$

For a two-tailed test, the decision rule based on the upper and lower critical values of chi-square is

Reject H_0 if $\chi^2_{calc} < \chi^2_{lower}$ or if $\chi^2_{calc} > \chi^2_{upper}$
Otherwise do not reject H_0

We can use the Excel function =CHISQ.INV to get the critical values:

$$\chi^2_{lower} = \text{CHISQ.INV}(\alpha/2, d.f.) = \text{CHISQ.INV}(0.025,19) = 8.907$$

$$\chi^2_{upper} = \text{CHISQ.INV}(1-\alpha/2, d.f.) = \text{CHISQ.INV}(0.975,19) = 32.852$$

The decision rule is illustrated in Figure 9.25. The value of the test statistic is

$$\chi^2_{calc} = \frac{(n-1)s^2}{\sigma^2} = \frac{(20-1)(7.44382)^2}{7^2} = 21.49$$

FIGURE 9.25 Decision Rule for Chi-Square Test

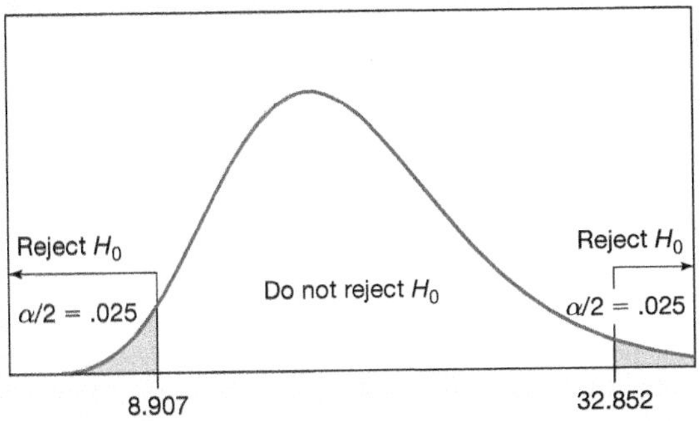

Because the test statistic is within the middle range, we conclude that the population variance does not differ significantly from 49; that is, the assembly process variance is unchanged.

If Excel is unavailable, we can obtain upper and lower critical values of chi-square to define the rejection region from Appendix E, as illustrated in Figure 9.26.

FIGURE 9.26 Two-Tail Chi-Square Values for *d.f.* = 19 and σ = .05

CHI-SQUARE CRITICAL VALUES

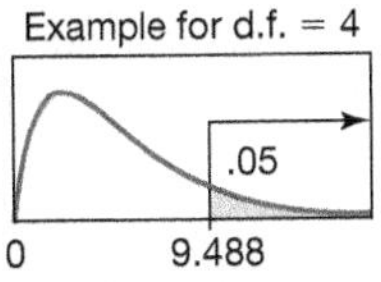

This table shows the critical value of chi-square for each desired tail area and degrees of freedom (d.f.).

	Area in Upper Tail									
d.f.	.995	.990	.975	.95	.90	.10	.05	.025	.01	.005
1	0.000	0.000	0.001	0.004	0.016	2.706	3.841	5.024	6.635	7.879
2	0.010	0.020	0.051	0.103	0.211	4.605	5.991	7.378	9.210	10.60
3	0.072	0.115	0.216	0.352	0.584	6.251	7.815	9.348	11.34	12.84
4	0.207	0.297	0.484	0.711	1.064	7.779	9.488	11.14	13.28	14.86
5	0.412	0.554	0.831	1.145	1.610	9.236	11.07	12.83	15.09	16.75
⋮	⋮	⋮	⋮	⋮	⋮	⋮	⋮	⋮	⋮	⋮
16	5.142	5.812	6.908	7.962	9.312	23.54	26.30	28.85	32.00	34.27
17	5.697	6.408	7.564	8.672	10.09	24.77	27.59	30.19	33.41	35.72
18	6.265	7.015	8.231	9.390	10.86	25.99	28.87	31.53	34.81	37.16
19	6.844	7.633	8.907	10.12	11.65	27.20	30.14	32.85	36.19	38.58
20	7.434	8.260	9.591	10.85	12.44	28.41	31.41	34.17	37.57	40.00
⋮	⋮	⋮	⋮	⋮	⋮	⋮	⋮	⋮	⋮	⋮
100	67.33	70.06	74.22	77.93	82.36	118.5	124.3	129.6	135.8	140.2

Using MegaStat

Excel has no test for a variance, but you can use Minitab or MegaStat. Figure 9.27 shows MegaStat's setup screen and output for the variance test, including a confidence interval for σ^2.

FIGURE 9.27

MegaStat Test for One Variance

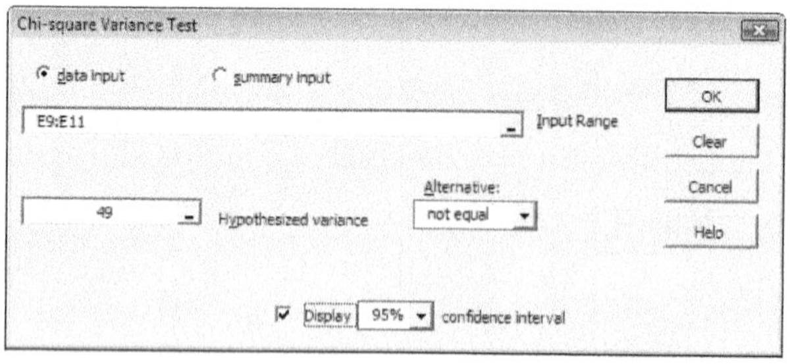

Chi-square Variance Test

49.000000	hypothesized variance
55.410456	observed variance of Blood Pressure
20	n
19	df
21.49	chi-square
.6212	p-value (two-tailed)
32.046386	confidence interval 95% lower
118.205464	confidence interval 95% upper

When to Use Tests for One Variance

In general, we would be interested in a test of variances when it is not the *center* of the distribution, but rather the *variability* of the process, that matters. More variation implies a more erratic data-generating process. For example, variance tests are important in manufacturing processes because increased variation around the mean can be a sign of wear and tear on equipment or other problems that would require attention.

Caution The chi-square test for a variance is not robust to non-normality of the population. If normality cannot be assumed (e.g., if the data set has outliers or severe skewness), you might need to use a bootstrap method (see *LearningStats* Unit 08) to test the hypothesis, using specialized software. In such a situation, it is best to consult a statistician.

Mini Case 9.4

Ball Corporation Metal Thickness

Ball Corporation is the largest supplier of beverage cans in the world. Metal beverage containers are lightweight, fully recyclable, quickly chilled, and easy to store. For these reasons, the metal beverage container is the package of choice in homes, vending machines, and coolers around the world. Ball's many manufacturing sites throughout the world turn out more than 100 million cans each day.

At its Ft. Atkinson, Wisconsin, manufacturing facility, Ball's quality group must evaluate the metal of potential new suppliers. Because of the large quantity of cans produced each day, Ball has established very precise specifications on the metal characteristics. One characteristic that is critical to production is the variation in metal thickness. Inconsistent thickness across a sheet of metal can create serious problems for Ball's manufacturing process. Ball's current supplier has a known thickness standard deviation $\sigma = 0.000959$ mm. To qualify a potential new metal supplier, Ball conducted a two-tailed hypothesis test to determine if the potential supplier's thickness variance was consistent with that of the current supplier. The null and alternative hypotheses are

$$H_0: \sigma^2 = (0.000959)^2$$
$$H_1: \sigma^2 \neq (0.000959)^2$$

Ball received a sample of 168 sheets of metal from the potential supplier. Therefore, the degrees of freedom for the chi-square test statistic are 167. Using $\alpha = .10$, the decision rule states:

If $\chi^2_{\text{calc}} < 138.1$ or $\chi^2_{\text{calc}} > 198.2$, reject H_0

The sample standard deviation was calculated to be $s = 0.00106$ mm. The calculated test statistic was then found to be

$$\chi^2_{\text{calc}} = \frac{(n-1)s^2}{\sigma^2} = \frac{(168-1)(0.00106)^2}{(0.000959)^2} = 204.03$$

Because $\chi^2_{\text{calc}} > 198.2$, the decision was to reject H_0. Ball concluded that the variation in metal thickness for the potential supplier was not equivalent to that of their primary supplier. The potential supplier was not a candidate for supplying metal to Ball.

SECTION EXERCISES

connect

9.61 A sample of size $n = 15$ has variance $s^2 = 35$. At $\alpha = .01$ in a left-tailed test, does this sample contradict the hypothesis that $\sigma^2 = 50$?

9.62 A sample of size $n = 10$ has variance $s^2 = 16$. At $\alpha = .10$ in a two-tailed test, does this sample contradict the hypothesis that $\sigma^2 = 24$?

9.63 A sample of size $n = 19$ has variance $s^2 = 1.96$. At $\alpha = .05$ in a right-tailed test, does this sample contradict the hypothesis that $\sigma^2 = 1.21$?

9.64 pH is a measure of acidity that winemakers must watch. A "healthy wine" should have a pH in the range 3.1 to 3.7. The target standard deviation is $\sigma = 0.10$ (i.e., $\sigma^2 = 0.01$). The pH measurements for a sample of 16 bottles of wine are shown below. At $\alpha = .05$ in a two-tailed test, is the sample variance either too high or too low? Show all steps, including the hypotheses and critical values from Appendix E. Hint: Ignore the mean. (See www.winemakermag.com.) WinePH

3.49	3.54	3.58	3.57	3.54	3.34	3.48	3.60
3.48	3.27	3.46	3.32	3.51	3.43	3.56	3.39

9.65 In U.S. hospitals, the average length of stay (LOS) for a diagnosis of pneumonia is 137 hours with a standard deviation of 25 hours. The LOS (in hours) for a sample of 12 pneumonia patients at Santa Theresa Memorial Hospital is shown below. In a two-tailed test at $\alpha = .05$, is this sample variance consistent with the national norms? Show all steps, including the hypotheses and critical values from Appendix E. *Hint:* Ignore the mean. (See National Center for Health Statistics, *Advance Data from Vital and Health Statistics,* no. 332 [April 9, 2003], p. 13.) Pneumonia

132	143	143	120	124	116
130	165	100	83	115	141

CHAPTER SUMMARY

The **null hypothesis (H_0)** represents the status quo or a benchmark. We try to reject H_0 in favor of the **alternative hypothesis (H_1)** on the basis of the sample evidence. The alternative hypothesis points to the tail of the test (< for a left-tailed test, > for a right-tailed test, ≠ for a two-tailed test). Rejecting a true H_0 is **Type I error,** while failing to reject a false H_0 is **Type II error.** The **power** of the test is the probability of correctly rejecting a false H_0. The probability of Type I error is denoted α (often called **the level of significance**) and can be set by the researcher. The probability of Type II error is denoted β and is dependent on the true parameter value, sample size, and α. In general, lowering α increases β, and vice versa. The **test statistic** compares the sample statistic with the hypothesized parameter. For a mean, the **decision rule** tells us whether to reject H_0 by comparing the test statistic with the **critical value** of z (known σ) or t (unknown σ) from a table or from Excel. Tests of a proportion are based on the normal distribution (if the sample is large enough, according to a rule of thumb), although in small samples the binomial is required. In any hypothesis test, the ***p*-value** shows the probability that the test statistic (or one more extreme) would be observed by chance, assuming that H_0 is true. If the p-value is smaller than α, we reject H_0 (i.e., a small p-value indicates a **significant** departure from H_0). A two-tailed test is analogous to a confidence interval seen in the last chapter. Power is greater when the true parameter is farther from the null hypothesis value. A **power curve** is a graph that plots the power of the test $(1 - \beta)$ against possible values of the true parameter, while the **OC curve** is a plot of the probability of a false negative (β). Tests of a variance use the **chi-square distribution** and suffer if the data are badly skewed.

KEY TERMS

alternative hypothesis
benchmark
chi-square distribution
critical value
decision rule
false positive
false negative
hypothesis
hypothesis test
hypothesis testing
importance
left-tailed test
level of significance
null hypothesis
OC curve
power
power curve
p-value method
rejection region
right-tailed test
significance
statistical hypothesis
test statistic
two-tailed test
Type I error
Type II error

Commonly Used Formulas in One-Sample Hypothesis Tests

Type I error: $\alpha = P(\text{reject } H_0 \mid H_0 \text{ is true})$

Type II error: $\beta = P(\text{fail to reject } H_0 \mid H_0 \text{ is false})$

Power: $1 - \beta = P(\text{reject } H_0 \mid H_0 \text{ is false})$

Test statistic for sample mean, σ known: $$z_{calc} = \frac{\bar{x} - \mu_0}{\frac{\sigma}{\sqrt{n}}}$$

Test statistic for sample mean, σ unknown: $$t_{calc} = \frac{\bar{x} - \mu_0}{\frac{s}{\sqrt{n}}} \quad \text{with } d.f. = n - 1$$

Test statistic for sample proportion: $$z_{calc} = \frac{p - \pi_0}{\sqrt{\frac{\pi_0(1 - \pi_0)}{n}}}$$

Test statistic for sample variance: $$\chi^2_{calc} = \frac{(n-1)s^2}{\sigma_0^2} \quad \text{with } d.f. = n - 1$$

CHAPTER REVIEW

Note: Questions labeled * are based on optional material from this chapter.

1. (a) List the steps in testing a hypothesis. (b) Why can't a hypothesis ever be proven?
2. (a) Explain the difference between the null hypothesis and the alternative hypothesis. (b) How is the null hypothesis chosen (why is it "null")?
3. (a) Why do we say "fail to reject H_0" instead of "accept H_0"? (b) What does it mean to "provisionally accept a hypothesis"?
4. (a) Define Type I error and Type II error. (b) Give an example to illustrate.
5. (a) Explain the difference between a left-tailed test, two-tailed test, and right-tailed test. (b) When would we choose a two-tailed test? (c) How can we tell the direction of the test by looking at a pair of hypotheses?
6. (a) What is a test statistic? (b) Explain the meaning of the rejection region in a decision rule. (c) Why do we need to know the sampling distribution of a statistic before we can do a hypothesis test?
7. (a) Define level of significance. (b) Define power.
8. (a) Why do we prefer low values for α and β? (b) For a given sample size, why is there a trade-off between α and β? (c) How could we decrease both α and β?
9. (a) Why is a "statistically significant difference" not necessarily a "practically important difference"? Give an illustration. (b) Why do statisticians play only a limited role in deciding whether a significant difference requires action?

10. (a) In a hypothesis test for a proportion, when can normality be assumed? *Optional* (b) If the sample is too small to assume normality, what can we do?
11. (a) In a hypothesis test of one mean, when do we use t instead of z? (b) When is the difference between z and t small?
12. (a) Explain what a p-value means. Give an example and interpret it. (b) Why is the p-value method an attractive alternative to specifying α in advance?
13. Why is a confidence interval similar to a two-tailed test?

*14. (a) What does a power curve show? (b) What factors affect power for a test of a mean? (c) What factors affect power for a proportion? (d) What is the most commonly used method of increasing power?

*15. (a) In testing a hypothesis about a variance, what distribution do we use? (b) When would a test of a variance be needed? (c) If the population is not normal, what can we do?

CHAPTER EXERCISES

connect

Note: Explain answers and show your work clearly. Problems marked * rely on optional material from this chapter.

HYPOTHESIS FORMULATION AND TYPE I AND II ERROR

9.66 Suppose you always reject the null hypothesis, regardless of any sample evidence. (a) What is the probability of Type II error? (b) Why is this a bad policy?

9.67 Suppose the judge decides to acquit all defendants, regardless of the evidence. (a) What is the probability of Type I error? (b) Why is this a bad policy?

9.68 High blood pressure, if untreated, can lead to increased risk of stroke and heart attack. A common definition of hypertension is diastolic blood pressure of 90 or more. (a) State the null and alternative hypotheses for a physician who checks your blood pressure. (b) Define Type I and II errors. What are the consequences of each?

9.69 A nuclear power plant replaces its ID card facility access system cards with a biometric security system that scans the iris pattern of the employee and compares it with a data bank. Users are classified as authorized or unauthorized. (a) State the null and alternative hypotheses. (b) Define Type I and II errors. What are the consequences of each?

9.70 A test-preparation company advertises that its training program raises SAT scores by an average of at least 30 points. A random sample of test-takers who had completed the training showed a mean increase smaller than 30 points. (a) Write the hypotheses for a left-tailed test of the mean. (b) Explain the consequences of a Type I error in this context.

9.71 Telemarketers use a predictive dialing system to decide whether a person actually answers a call (as opposed to an answering machine). If so, the call is routed to a telemarketer. If no telemarketer is free, the software must automatically hang up the phone within two seconds, to comply with FAA regulations against tying up the line. The SmartWay company says that its new system is smart enough to hang up on no more than 2 percent of the answered calls. Write the hypotheses for a right-tailed test, using SmartWay's claim about the proportion as the null hypothesis.

9.72 If the true mean is 50 and we reject the hypothesis that $\mu = 50$, what is the probability of Type II error? *Hint:* This is a trick question.

9.73 If we fail to reject the null hypothesis that $\pi = .50$ even though the true proportion is .60, what is the probability of Type I error? *Hint:* This is a trick question.

9.74 Pap smears are a test for abnormal cancerous and precancerous cells taken from the cervix. (a) State a pair of hypotheses and then explain the meaning of a false negative and a false positive. (b) Why is the null hypothesis "null"? (c) Who bears the cost of each type of error?

9.75 In a commercially available fingerprint scanner (e.g., for your home or office PC), false acceptances are 1 in 25 million, with false rejection rates of 3 percent. (a) Define Type I and II errors. (b) Why do you suppose the false rejection rate is so high compared with the false acceptance rate?

9.76 When told that over a 10-year period a mammogram test has a false positive rate of 50 percent, Bob said, "That means that about half the women tested actually have no cancer." Correct Bob's mistaken interpretation.

TESTS OF MEANS AND PROPORTIONS

9.77 Malcheon Health Clinic claims that the average waiting time for a patient is 20 minutes or less. A random sample of 15 patients shows a mean wait time of 24.77 minutes with a standard deviation of 7.26 minutes. (a) Write the hypotheses for a right-tailed test, using the clinic's claim as the null hypothesis. (b) Calculate the t test statistic to test the claim. (c) At the 5 percent level of significance ($\alpha = .05$), does the sample contradict the clinic's claim? (d) Use Excel to find the p-value and compare it to the level of significance. Did you come to the same conclusion as you did in part (c)?

9.78 The sodium content of a popular sports drink is listed as 220 mg in a 32-oz bottle. Analysis of 10 bottles indicates a sample mean of 228.2 mg with a sample standard deviation of 18.2 mg. (a) Write the hypotheses for a two-tailed test of the claimed sodium content. (b) Calculate the t test statistic to test the manufacturer's claim. (c) At the 5 percent level of significance ($\alpha = .05$), does the sample contradict the manufacturer's claim? (d) Use Excel to find the p-value and compare it to the level of significance. Did you come to the same conclusion as you did in part (c)?

9.79 A can of peeled whole tomatoes is supposed to contain an average of 19 ounces of tomatoes (excluding the juice). The actual weight is a normally distributed random variable whose standard deviation is known to be 0.25 ounce. (a) In quality control, would a one-tailed or two-tailed test be used? Why? (b) Explain the consequences of departure from the mean in either direction. (c) Which sampling distribution would you use if samples of four cans are weighed? Why? (d) Set up a two-tailed decision rule for $\alpha = .01$.

9.80 At Ajax Spring Water, a half-liter bottle of soft drink is supposed to contain a mean of 520 ml. The filling process follows a normal distribution with a known process standard deviation of 4 ml. (a) Which sampling distribution would you use if random samples of 10 bottles are to be weighed? Why? (b) Set up hypotheses and a two-tailed decision rule for the correct mean using the 5 percent level of significance. (c) If a sample of 16 bottles shows a mean fill of 515 ml, does this contradict the hypothesis that the true mean is 520 ml?

9.81 On eight Friday quizzes, Bob received scores of 80, 85, 95, 92, 89, 84, 90, 92. He tells Prof. Hardtack that he is really a 90+ performer, but this sample just happened to fall below his true performance level. (a) State an appropriate pair of hypotheses. (b) State the formula for the test statistic and show your decision rule using the 1 percent level of significance. (c) Carry out the test. Show your work. (d) What assumptions are required? (e) Use Excel to find the p-value and interpret it. **BobQuiz**

9.82 Faced with rising fax costs, a firm issued a guideline that transmissions of 10 pages or more should be sent by 2-day mail instead. Exceptions are allowed, but they want the average to be 10 or below. The firm examined 35 randomly chosen fax transmissions during the next year, yielding a sample mean of 14.44 with a standard deviation of 4.45 pages. (a) At the .01 level of significance, is the true mean greater than 10? (b) Use Excel to find the right-tail p-value.

9.83 A U.S. dime weighs 2.268 grams when minted. A random sample of 15 circulated dimes showed a mean weight of 2.256 grams with a standard deviation of .026 gram. (a) Using $\alpha = .05$, is the mean weight of all circulated dimes lower than the mint weight? State your hypotheses and decision rule. (b) Why might circulated dimes weigh less than the mint specification?

9.84 A coin was flipped 60 times and came up heads 38 times. (a) At the .10 level of significance, is the coin biased toward heads? Show your decision rule and calculations. (b) Calculate a p-value and interpret it.

9.85 A sample of 100 one-dollar bills from the Subway cash register revealed that 16 had something written on them besides the normal printing (e.g., "Bob ♥ Mary"). (a) At $\alpha = .05$, is this sample evidence consistent with the hypothesis that 10 percent or fewer of all dollar bills have anything written on them besides the normal printing? Include a sketch of your decision rule and show all calculations. (b) Is your decision sensitive to the choice of α? (c) Find the p-value.

9.86 A sample of 100 mortgages approved during the current year showed that 31 were issued to a single-earner family or individual. The historical percentage is 25 percent. (a) At the .05 level of significance in a right-tailed test, has the percentage of single-earner or individual mortgages risen? Include a sketch of your decision rule and show all work. (b) Is this a close decision? (c) State any assumptions that are required.

9.87 A quality control standard requires that no more than 5 percent of bags of Halloween candy be underweight. A random sample of 200 bags showed that 16 were underweight. (a) At $\alpha = .025$, is the standard being violated? Use a right-tailed test and show your work. (b) Find the p-value.

9.88 Ages for the 2009 Boston Red Sox pitchers are shown below. (a) Assuming this is a random sample of major league pitchers, at the 5 percent level of significance does this sample show that the true mean age of all American League pitchers is over 30 years? State your hypotheses and decision rule and show all work. (b) If there is a difference, is it important? (c) Find the *p*-value and interpret it. (Data are from http://boston.redsox.mlb.com.) **RedSox**

Ages of Boston Red Sox Pitchers, May 2009

Bard	24	Lester	25	Okajima	34	Ramirez	28
Beckett	29	Masterson	24	Papelbon	29	Saito	39
Delcarmen	27	Matsuzaka	29	Penny	31	Wakefield	43

9.89 The EPA is concerned about the quality of drinking water served on airline flights. A sample of 112 flights found unacceptable bacterial contamination on 14 flights. (a) At $\alpha = .05$, does this sample show that more than 10 percent of all flights have contaminated water? (b) Find the *p*-value.

9.90 A web-based company has a goal of processing 95 percent of its orders on the same day they are received. If 485 out of the next 500 orders are processed on the same day, would this prove that they are exceeding their goal, using $\alpha = .025$?

9.91 In a major football conference, a sample showed that only 267 out of 584 freshmen players graduated within 6 years. (a) At $\alpha = .05$, does this sample contradict the claim that at least half graduate within 6 years? State your hypotheses and decision rule. (b) Calculate the *p*-value and interpret it. (c) Do you think the difference is important, as opposed to significant?

9.92 An auditor reviewed 25 oral surgery insurance claims from a particular surgical office, determining that the mean out-of-pocket patient billing above the reimbursed amount was $275.66 with a standard deviation of $78.11. (a) At the 5 percent level of significance, does this sample prove a violation of the guideline that the average patient should pay no more than $250 out-of-pocket? State your hypotheses and decision rule. (b) Is this a close decision?

9.93 The average service time at a Noodles & Company restaurant was 3.5 minutes in the previous year. Noodles implemented some time-saving measures and would like to know if they have been effective. They sample 20 service times and find the sample average is 3.2 minutes with a sample standard deviation of .4 minute. Using $\alpha = .05$, were the measures effective?

9.94 A digital camcorder repair service has set a goal not to exceed an average of 5 working days from the time the unit is brought in to the time repairs are completed. A random sample of 12 repair records showed the following repair times (in days): 9, 2, 5, 1, 5, 4, 7, 5, 11, 3, 7, 2. At $\alpha = .05$, is the goal being met? **Repair**

9.95 A recent study by the Government Accountability Office found that consumers got correct answers about Medicare only 67 percent of the time when they called 1-800-MEDICARE. (a) At $\alpha = .05$, would a subsequent audit of 50 randomly chosen calls with 40 correct answers suffice to show that the percentage had risen? What is the *p*-value? (b) Is the normality criterion for the sample proportion met?

9.96 Beer shelf life is a problem for brewers and distributors because when beer is stored at room temperature, its flavor deteriorates. When the average furfuryl ether content reaches 6 μg per liter, a typical consumer begins to taste an unpleasant chemical flavor. (a) At $\alpha = .05$, would the following sample of 12 randomly chosen bottles stored for a month convince you that the mean furfuryl ether content exceeds the taste threshhold? (b) What is the *p*-value? **BeerTaste**

6.53, 5.68, 8.10, 7.50, 6.32, 8.75, 5.98, 7.50, 5.01, 5.95, 6.40, 7.02

9.97 (a) A statistical study reported that a drug was effective with a *p*-value of .042. Explain in words what this tells you. (b) How would that compare to a drug that had a *p*-value of .087?

9.98 Bob said, "Why is a small *p*-value significant, when a large one isn't? That seems backwards." Try to explain it to Bob, giving an example to make your point.

9.99 Sarpedon Corp. claims that its car batteries average at least 880 CCA (cold-cranking amps). Tests on a sample of 9 batteries yield a mean of 871 CCA with a standard deviation of 15.6 CCA. (a) State the hypotheses to test Sarpedon's claim against this sample evidence. (b) What is the critical value at the 5 percent level of significance? (c) Should we reject Sarpedon's claim?

9.100 Thetis Mfg. says that its outboard watercraft engine's noise level at 75 percent throttle averages 100 decibels or less from the operator's seating position. A random sample of 8 noise level measurements showed a mean of 106 decibels with a standard deviation of 7.2 decibels. At the 5 percent level of significance, should we reject Thetis's claim?

PROPORTIONS: SMALL SAMPLES

9.101 An automaker states that its cars equipped with electronic fuel injection and computerized engine controls will start on the first try (hot or cold) 99 percent of the time. A survey of 100 new car owners revealed that 3 had not started on the first try during a recent cold snap. (a) At $\alpha = .025$, does this demonstrate that the automaker's claim is incorrect? (b) Calculate the *p*-value and interpret it. *Hint:* Use MINITAB, or use Excel to calculate the cumulative binomial probability $P(X \geq 3 \mid n = 100, \pi = .01) = 1 - P(X \leq 2 \mid n = 100, \pi = .01)$.

9.102 A quality standard says that no more than 2 percent of the eggs sold in a store may be cracked (not broken, just cracked). In 3 cartons (12 eggs each carton), 2 eggs are cracked. (a) At the .10 level of significance, does this prove that the standard is exceeded? (b) Calculate a *p*-value for the observed sample result. *Hint:* Use Excel to calculate the binomial probability $P(X \geq 2 \mid n = 36, \pi = .02) = 1 - P(X \leq 1 \mid n = 36, \pi = .02)$.

9.103 An experimental medication is administered to 16 people who suffer from migraines. After an hour, 10 say they feel better. Is the medication effective (i.e., is the percent who feel better greater than 50 percent)? Use $\alpha = .10$, explain fully, and show all steps.

9.104 The historical on-time percentage for Amtrak's Sunset Limited is 10 percent. In July, the train was on time 0 times in 31 runs. At the .10 level of significance, has the on-time percentage fallen? Explain clearly. *Hint:* Use Excel to calculate the cumulative binomial probability $P(X \leq 0 \mid n = 31, \pi = .10)$.

9.105 After 7 months, none of 238 angioplasty patients who received a drug-coated stent to keep their arteries open had experienced restenosis (re-blocking of the arteries). (a) Use MINITAB to construct a 95 percent binomial confidence interval for the proportion of all angioplasty patients who experience restenosis. (b) Why is it necessary to use a binomial in this case? (c) If the goal is to reduce the occurrence of restenosis to 5 percent or less, does this sample show that the goal is being achieved?

POWER

Hint: In the power problems, use *LearningStats* (from the McGraw-Hill Connect® downloads) to check your answers.

9.106 A certain brand of flat white interior latex paint claims one-coat coverage of 400 square feet per gallon. The standard deviation is known to be 20. A sample of 16 gallons is tested. (a) At $\alpha = .05$ in a left-tailed test, find the β risk and power assuming that the true mean is really 380 square feet per gallon. (b) Construct a left-tailed power curve, using increments of 5 square feet (400, 395, 390, 385, 380).

9.107 A process is normally distributed with standard deviation 12. Samples of size 4 are taken. Suppose that you wish to test the hypothesis that $\mu = 500$ at $\alpha = .05$ in a left-tailed test. (a) What is the β risk if the true mean is 495? If the true mean is 490? If the true mean is 485? If the true mean is 480? (b) Calculate the power for each of the preceding values of μ and sketch a power curve. (c) Repeat the previous exercises using $n = 16$.

TESTS OF VARIANCES

Hint: Use MegaStat or a similar software tool to check your work.

9.108 Is this sample of 25 exam scores inconsistent with the hypothesis that the true variance is 64 (i.e., $\sigma = 8$)? Use the 5 percent level of significance in a two-tailed test. Show all steps, including the hypotheses and critical values from Appendix E. **Exams**

80	79	69	71	74
73	77	75	65	52
81	84	84	79	70
78	62	77	68	77
88	70	75	85	84

9.109 Hammermill Premium Inkjet 24 lb. paper has a specified brightness of 106. (a) At $\alpha = .005$, does this sample of 24 randomly chosen test sheets from a day's production run show that the mean brightness exceeds the specification? (b) Does the sample show that $\sigma^2 < 0.0025$? State the hypotheses and critical value for the left-tailed test from Appendix E. **Brightness**

106.98	107.02	106.99	106.98	107.06	107.05	107.03	107.04
107.01	107.00	107.02	107.04	107.00	106.98	106.91	106.93
107.01	106.98	106.97	106.99	106.94	106.98	107.03	106.98

RELATED READING

Vickers, Andrew J. *What Is a p-Value Anyway? 34 Stories to Help You Actually Understand Statistics.* Addison-Wesley, 2010.

CHAPTER 9 More Learning Resources

connect™

You can access these *LearningStats* demonstrations through McGraw-Hill's Connect® to help you understand one-sample hypothesis tests.

Topic	*LearningStats Demonstrations*
Common hypothesis tests	Overview of Hypothesis Tests Do-It-Yourself Simulation Sampling Distribution Examples
Type I error and power	Type I Error *p*-Value Illustration Power Curves: Examples Power Curves: Do-It-Yourself Power Curve Families Finite Populations Useful Formulas
Tables	Appendix C—Normal Appendix D—Student's *t* Appendix E—Chi-Square

Key: = Excel = Powerpoint = PDF

Chapter 12. Simple Regression

CHAPTER 12 Simple Regression

CHAPTER CONTENTS

CHAPTER LEARNING OBJECTIVES

LO

When you finish this chapter you should be able to

LO 12-1 Calculate and test a correlation coefficient for significance.

LO 12-2 Interpret a regression equation and use it to make predictions.

LO 12-3 Explain the form and assumptions of a simple regression model.

LO 12-4 Explain the least squares method, apply formulas for coefficients, and interpret R^2.

LO 12-5 Construct confidence intervals and test hypotheses for the slope and intercept.

LO 12-6 Interpret the ANOVA table and use it to calculate F, R^2, and standard error.

LO 12-7 Distinguish between confidence and prediction intervals for Y.

LO 12-8 Calculate residuals and perform tests of regression assumptions.

LO 12-9 Identify unusual residuals and tell when they are outliers.

LO 12-10 Define leverage and identify high-leverage observations.

LO 12-11 Improve data conditioning and use transformations if needed (optional).

12.1 VISUAL DISPLAYS AND CORRELATION ANALYSIS

LO 12-1

Calculate and test a correlation coefficient for significance.

Up to this point, our study of the discipline of statistical analysis has primarily focused on learning how to describe and make inferences about single variables. It is now time to learn how to describe and summarize relationships *between* variables. Businesses of all types can be quite complex. Understanding how different variables in our business processes are related to each other helps us predict and, hopefully, improve our business performance.

Examples of quantitative variables that might be related to each other include: spending on advertising and sales revenue, produce delivery time and percentage of spoiled produce, premium and regular gas prices, preventive maintenance spending and manufacturing productivity rates. It may be that with some of these pairs there is one variable that we would like to be able to *predict* such as sales revenue, percentage of spoiled produce, and productivity rates. But first we must learn how to *visualize, describe,* and *quantify* the relationships between variables such as these.

Visual Displays

Analysis of **bivariate data** (i.e., two variables) typically begins with a **scatter plot** that displays each observed data pair (x_i, y_i) as a dot on an X-Y grid. This diagram provides a visual indication of the strength of the relationship or association between the two random variables. This simple display requires no assumptions or computation. A scatter plot is typically the precursor to more complex analytical techniques. Figure 12.1 shows a scatter plot comparing the average price per gallon of regular unleaded gasoline to the average price per gallon of premium gasoline for all 50 states.

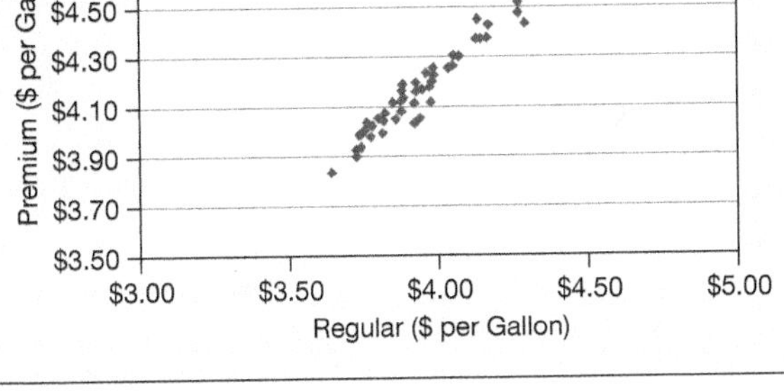

FIGURE 12.1

Fuel Prices (n = 50 states)

FuelPrices

Source: AAA Fuel Gauge Report, May 8, 2011, www.fuelgaugereport.aaa.com

We look at scatter plots to get an initial idea of the relationship between two random variables. Is there an evident pattern to the data? Is the pattern linear or nonlinear? Are there data points that are not part of the overall pattern? We would characterize the fuel price relationship as linear (although not perfectly linear) and positive (as premium prices increase, so do regular unleaded prices). We see one pair of values set slightly apart from the rest, above and to the right. This happens to be the state of Hawaii.

In contrast to the positive relationship seen in Figure 12.1, Figure 12.2 shows a negative relationship. This scatter plot compares the incidence of infectious disease to average IQ scores for 184 different countries. We would characterize this relationship as fairly linear and negative (as the incidence of infectious disease decreases, the average IQ score increases). We see one pair of unusual values near the bottom of the scatter plot, which is the country of Saint Lucia, in the Caribbean.

FIGURE 12.2

IQ Scores (n = 184 countries)

IQScores

Source: Christopher Eppig, Corey L. Fincher, and Randy Thornhill, "Parasite Prevalence and the Worldwide Distribution of Cognitive Ability," *Proceedings of the Royal Society of Biological Sciences* (published online June 30, 2010).

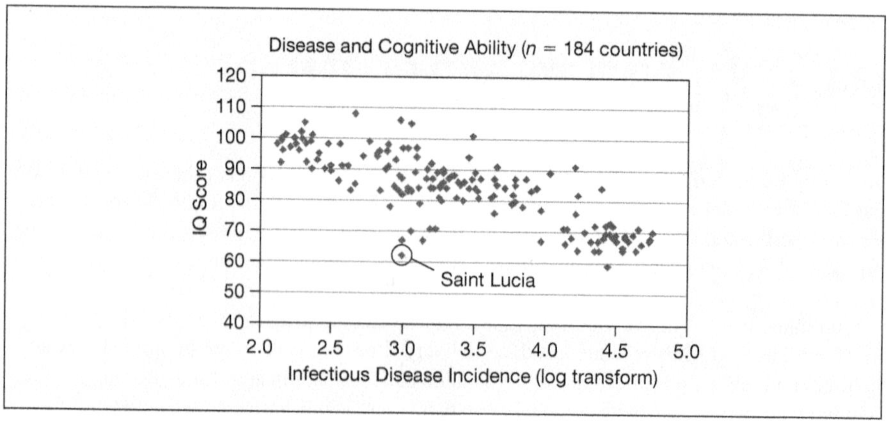

Correlation Coefficient

A visual display is a good first step in analysis, but we would also like to quantify the strength of the association between two variables. Therefore, accompanying the scatter plot is the **sample correlation coefficient** (also called the Pearson correlation coefficient.) This statistic measures the degree of linearity in the relationship between two random variables X and Y and is denoted r. Its value will fall in the interval $[-1, 1]$.

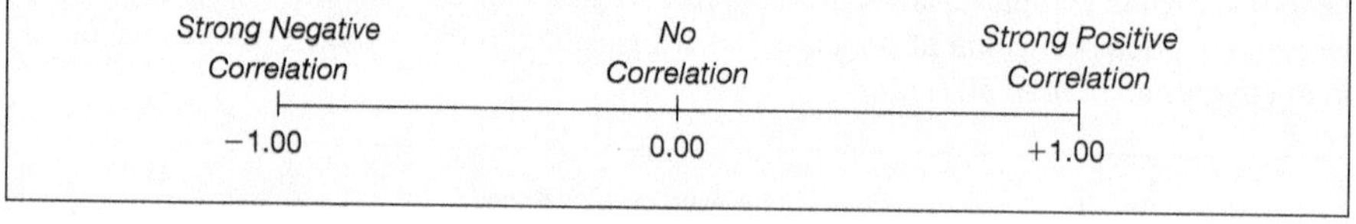

When r is near 0 there is little or no linear relationship between X and Y. An r-value near $+1$ indicates a strong positive relationship, while an r-value near -1 indicates a strong negative relationship.

(12.1)
$$r = \frac{\sum_{i=1}^{n}(x_i - \bar{x})(y_i - \bar{y})}{\sqrt{\sum_{i=1}^{n}(x_i - \bar{x})^2}\sqrt{\sum_{i=1}^{n}(y_i - \bar{y})^2}} \quad \text{(sample correlation coefficient)}$$

The product will be negative, that is, a negative correlation, when x_i tends to be *above* its mean while the associated y_i is *below* its mean. Conversely, the correlation coefficient will be positive when x_i and the associated y_i tend to be above their means at the same time or below their means at the same time. To simplify the notation here and elsewhere in this chapter, we define three terms called **sums of squares**:

$$SS_{xx} = \sum_{i=1}^{n}(x_i - \bar{x})^2 \qquad SS_{yy} = \sum_{i=1}^{n}(y_i - \bar{y})^2 \qquad SS_{xy} = \sum_{i=1}^{n}(x_i - \bar{x})(y_i - \bar{y}) \tag{12.2}$$

Using this notation, the formula for the sample correlation coefficient can be written

$$r = \frac{SS_{xy}}{\sqrt{SS_{xx}}\sqrt{SS_{yy}}} \quad \text{(sample correlation coefficient)} \tag{12.3}$$

Excel Tip

To calculate a sample correlation coefficient, use Excel's function =CORREL(array1,array2) where array1 is the range for X and array2 is the range for Y. Data may be in rows or columns. Arrays must be the same length.

The correlation coefficient for the variables shown in Figure 12.1 is $r = .970$, which is not surprising. We would expect to see a strong linear positive relationship between state regular unleaded gasoline prices and premium gasoline prices. The correlation coefficient for the variables shown in Figure 12.2 is $r = -.822$. We observed a fairly linear negative relationship between infectious disease incidence and average IQ scores. Figure 12.3 shows prototype scatter plots. We see that a correlation of .500 implies a great deal of random variation, and even a correlation of .900 is far from "perfect" linearity. The last scatter plot shows $r = .00$ despite an obvious *curvilinear* relationship between X and Y. This illustrates the fact that a correlation coefficient only measures the degree of *linear* relationship between X and Y.

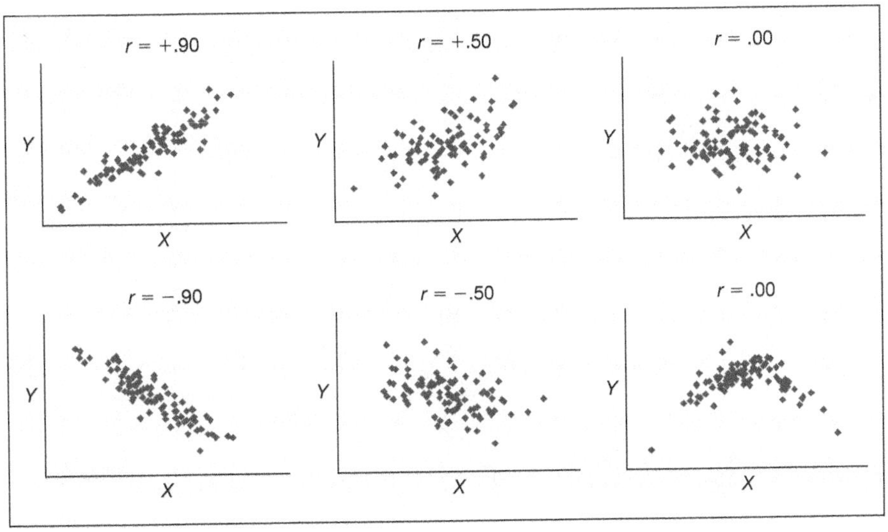

FIGURE 12.3
Scatter Plots Showing Various Correlation Coefficient Values ($n = 100$)

Correlation analysis has many business applications. For example:

- Financial planners study correlations between asset classes over time, in order to help their clients diversify their portfolios.
- Marketing analysts study correlations between customer online purchases in order to develop new web advertising strategies.
- Human resources experts study correlations between measures of employee performance in order to devise new job-training programs.

Tests for Significant Correlation Using Student's *t*

The sample correlation coefficient r is an estimate of the **population correlation coefficient** ρ (the Greek letter *rho*). There is no flat rule for a "high" correlation because sample size must be taken into consideration. To test the hypothesis H_0: $\rho = 0$, the test statistic is

$$t_{\text{calc}} = r\sqrt{\frac{n-2}{1-r^2}} \quad \text{(test for zero correlation)} \tag{12.4}$$

We compare this t test statistic with a critical value of t for a one-tailed or two-tailed test from Appendix D using $d.f. = n - 2$ degrees of freedom and any desired α. Recall that we lose a degree of freedom for each parameter that we estimate when we calculate a statistic. Because both $\bar{x}$ and $\bar{y}$ are used to calculate r, we lose 2 degrees of freedom and so $d.f. = n - 2$. After calculating the **t statistic**, we can find its p-value by using Excel's function =T.DIST.2T(t,deg_freedom). MINITAB directly calculates the p-value for a two-tailed test without displaying the t statistic.

EXAMPLE 12.1

MBA Applicants

MBA

In its admission decision process, a university's MBA program examines an applicant's score on the GMAT (Graduate Management Aptitude Test), which has both verbal and quantitative components. Figure 12.4 shows the scatter plot with the sample correlation coefficient for 30 MBA applicants randomly chosen from 1,961 MBA applicant records at a public university in the Midwest. Is the correlation ($r = .4356$) between verbal and quantitative GMAT scores statistically significant? It is not clear from the scatter plot shown in Figure 12.4 that there is a statistically significant linear relationship.

FIGURE 12.4 **Scatter Plot for 30 MBA Applicants** MBA

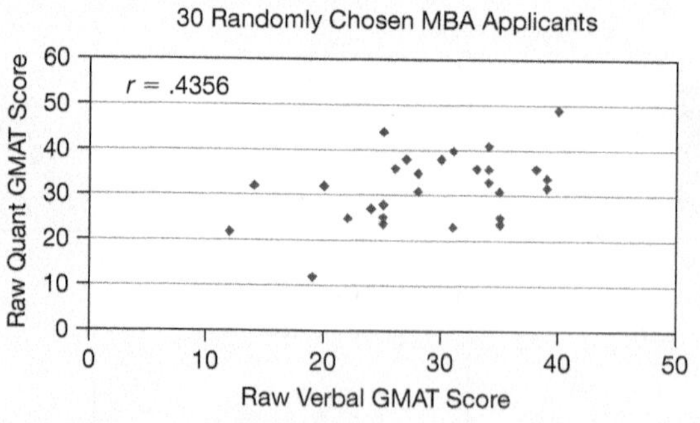

Step 1: State the Hypotheses

We will use a two-tailed test for significance at $\alpha = .05$. The hypotheses are

H_0: $\rho = 0$

H_0: $\rho \neq 0$

Step 2: Specify the Decision Rule

For a two-tailed test using $d.f. = n - 2 = 30 - 2 = 28$ degrees of freedom, Appendix D gives $t_{.025} = 2.048$. The decision rule is

Reject H_0 if $t_{\text{calc}} > 2.048$ or if $t_{\text{calc}} < -2.048$.

Step 3: Calculate the Test Statistic
To calculate the test statistic, we first need to calculate the value for r. Using Excel's function =CORREL(array1,array2), we find $r = .4356$ for the variables *Quant GMAT* and *Verbal GMAT*. We must then calculate t_{calc}.

$$t_{\text{calc}} = r\sqrt{\frac{n-2}{1-r^2}} = .4356\sqrt{\frac{30-2}{1-(.4356)^2}} = 2.561$$

Step 4: Make a Decision
The test statistic value ($t_{\text{calc}} = 2.561$) exceeds the critical value $t_{.025} = 2.048$, so we reject the hypothesis of zero correlation at $\alpha = .05$. We can also find the p-value using the Excel function =T.DIST.2T(t,deg_freedom). The two-tailed p-value for GMAT score is =T.DIST.2T(2.561,28) = .0161. We would reject $\rho = 0$ since the p-value $< .05$.

Step 5: Take Action
The admissions officers recognize that these scores tend to vary together for applicants.

Critical Value for Correlation Coefficient

An equivalent approach is to calculate a critical value for the correlation coefficient. First, look up the critical value of t from Appendix D with $d.f. = n - 2$ degrees of freedom for either a one-tailed or two-tailed test, with the α you choose. Then, the critical value of the correlation coefficient, r_{critical}, is

$$r_{\text{critical}} = \frac{t}{\sqrt{t^2 + n - 2}} \quad \text{(critical value for a correlation coefficient)} \quad \textbf{(12.5)}$$

An advantage of this method is that you get a benchmark for the correlation coefficient. Its disadvantage is that there is no p-value and it is inflexible if you change your mind about α. MegaStat uses this method, giving two-tail critical values for $\alpha = .05$ and $\alpha = .01$.

Table 12.1 shows that, as sample size increases, the critical value of r becomes smaller. Thus, in very large samples, even very small correlations could be "significant." In a larger sample, smaller values of the sample correlation coefficient can be considered "significant." While a larger sample does give a better estimate of the true value of ρ, a larger sample does *not* mean that the correlation is stronger nor does its increased *significance* imply increased *importance*.

TABLE 12.1

Values for r_{critical} for Different Sample Sizes

Sample Size	$r_{.05}$	$r_{.01}$
$n = 25$	.395	.504
$n = 50$	.279	.361
$n = 100$	.197	.256
$n = 200$	.139	.182

Significance versus Importance

In large samples, small correlations may be significant, even if the scatter plot shows little evidence of linearity. Thus, a *significant* correlation may lack practical *importance*.

SECTION EXERCISES

connect

12.1 For each sample, do a test for zero correlation. (a) Use Appendix D to find the critical value of t_α. (b) State the hypotheses about ρ. (c) Perform the t test and report your decision.

a. $r = +.45, n = 20, \alpha = .05$, two-tailed test
b. $r = -.35, n = 30, \alpha = .10$, two-tailed test
c. $r = +.60, n = 7, \alpha = .05$, right-tailed test
d. $r = -.30, n = 61, \alpha = .01$, left-tailed test

Instructions for exercises 12.2 and 12.3: (a) Make an Excel scatter plot. What does it suggest about the population correlation between X and Y? (b) Make an Excel worksheet to calculate SS_{xx}, SS_{yy}, and SS_{xy}. Use these sums to calculate the sample correlation coefficient. Check your work by using Excel's function =CORREL(array1,array2). (c) Use Appendix D to find $t_{.025}$ for a two-tailed test for zero correlation at α =.05. (d) Calculate the t test statistic. Can you reject $\rho = 0$? (e) Use Excel's function =T.DIST.2T(t,deg_freedom) to calculate the two-tail p-value.

12.2 College Student Weekly Earnings in Dollars (n = 5) WeekPay

Hours Worked (X)	Weekly Pay (Y)
10	93
15	171
20	204
20	156
35	261

12.3 Phone Hold Time for Concert Tickets in Seconds (n = 5) CallWait

Operators (X)	Wait Time (Y)
4	385
5	335
6	383
7	344
8	288

Instructions for exercises 12.4–12.6: (a) Make a scatter plot of the data. What does it suggest about the correlation between X and Y? (b) Use Excel, MegaStat, or MINITAB to calculate the correlation coefficient. (c) Use Excel or Appendix D to find $t_{.025}$ for a two-tailed test at α =.05. (d) Calculate the t test statistic. (e) Can you reject $\rho = 0$?

12.4 Moviegoer Snack Spending (n = 10) Movies

Age (X)	Spent (Y)	Age (X)	Spent (Y)
30	6.85	33	10.75
50	10.50	36	7.60
34	5.50	26	10.10
12	10.35	18	12.35
37	10.20	46	8.35

12.5 Annual Percent Return on Mutual Funds (n = 17) Portfolio

Last Year (X)	This Year (Y)
11.9	15.4
19.5	26.7
11.2	18.2
14.1	16.7
14.2	13.2
5.2	16.4
20.7	21.1
11.3	12.0
−1.1	12.1
3.9	7.4
12.9	11.5
12.4	23.0
12.5	12.7
2.7	15.1
8.8	18.7
7.2	9.9
5.9	18.9

12.6 Order Size and Shipping Cost (n = 12) ShipCost

Orders (X)	Ship Cost (Y)
1,068	4,489
1,026	5,611
767	3,290
885	4,113
1,156	4,883
1,146	5,425
892	4,414
938	5,506
769	3,346
677	3,673
1,174	6,542
1,009	5,088

Mini Case 12.1

Do Loyalty Cards Promote Sales Growth?

A business can achieve sales growth by increasing the number of new customers. Another way is by increasing business from existing customers. Loyal customers visit more often, thus contributing to sales growth. Loyalty cards are used by many companies to foster positive relationships with their customers. Customers carry a card that records the number of purchases or visits they make. They are rewarded with a free item or discount after so many visits. But do these loyalty cards provide incentive to repeat customers to visit more often? Surprisingly, Noodles & Company found out that this wasn't happening in some markets. After several years of running a loyalty card program without truly measuring its impact on the business, in 2005, Noodles performed a correlation analysis on the variables "Sales Growth Percentage" and "Loyalty Card Sales Percentage." The results showed that in some markets there was no significant correlation, meaning the loyalty cards weren't associated with increased sales revenue. However, in other markets there was actually *a statistically significant negative correlation.* In other words, loyalty cards were associated with a decrease in sales growth. Why? Ultimately, the free visits that customers had earned were replacing visits that they would have otherwise paid full price for. Moreover, the resources the company was devoting to the program were taking away from more proven sales-building techniques, such as holding nonprofit fundraisers or tastings for local businesses. Based on this analysis, Noodles & Company made the decision to discontinue their loyalty card program and focused on other approaches to building loyal customers. See Chapter Exercise 12.64.

12.2 SIMPLE REGRESSION

What Is Simple Regression?

LO 12-2

Interpret a regression equation and use it to make predictions.

Correlation coefficients and scatter plots provide clues about relationships among variables and may suffice for some purposes. But often, the analyst would like to mathematically model the relationship for prediction purposes. For example, a business might hypothesize that

- Advertising expenditures predict quarterly sales revenue.
- Number of dependents predicts employee prescription drug expenses.
- Apartment size predicts monthly rent.
- Engine horsepower predicts miles per gallon.

The hypothesized relationship may be linear, quadratic, or some other form. For now we will focus on the simple linear model in slope-intercept form: $Y = \text{slope} \times X + y\text{-intercept}$. In statistics this straight-line model is often referred to as a **simple regression equation**. The slope and intercept of the simple regression equation are used to describe the relationship between the two variables.

We define the Y variable as the **response variable** (the *dependent variable*) and the X variable as the **predictor variable** (the *independent variable*). If the relationship can be estimated, a business can explore policy questions such as

- How much extra sales will be generated, on average, by a $1 million increase in advertising expenditures? What would expected sales be with no advertising?
- How much do prescription drug costs per employee rise, on average, with each extra dependent? What would be the expected cost if the employee had no dependents?
- How much extra rent, on average, is paid per extra square foot?
- How much fuel efficiency, on average, is lost when the engine horsepower is increased?

Response or Predictor?

The *response* variable is the *dependent* variable. This is the *Y* variable. The *predictor* variable is the *independent* variable. This is the *X* variable. Only the dependent variable (not the independent variable) is treated as a random variable.

Interpreting an Estimated Regression Equation

The intercept and slope of an estimated regression can provide useful information. For example:

Sales = 268 + 7.37 *Ads*	Each extra $1 million of advertising will generate $7.37 million of sales on average. The firm would average $268 million of sales with zero advertising. However, the intercept may not be meaningful because *Ads* = 0 may be outside the range of observed data.
DrugCost = 410 + 550 *Dependents*	Each extra dependent raises the mean annual prescription drug cost by $550. An employee with zero dependents averages $410 in prescription drugs.
Rent = 150 + 1.05 *SqFt*	Each extra square foot adds $1.05 to monthly apartment rent. The intercept is not meaningful because no apartment can have *SqFt* = 0.
MPG = 49.22 − 0.079 *Horsepower*	Each unit increase in engine horsepower decreases the fuel efficiency by 0.079 mile per gallon. The intercept is not meaningful because a zero horsepower engine does not exist.

Cause and Effect?

When we propose a regression model, we might have a causal mechanism in mind, but cause and effect is not proven by a simple regression. We cannot assume that the explanatory variable is "causing" the variation we see in the response variable.

Prediction Using Regression

One of the main uses of regression is to make predictions. Once we have a fitted regression equation that shows the estimated relationship between *X* (the independent variable) and *Y* (the dependent variable), we can plug in any value of *X* to obtain the prediction for *Y*. For example:

Sales = 268 + 7.37 *Ads*	If the firm spends $10 million on advertising, its predicted sales would be $341.7 million, that is, *Sales* = 268 + 7.37 (10) = 341.7.
DrugCost = 410 + 550 *Dependents*	If an employee has four dependents, the predicted annual drug cost would be $2,610, that is, *DrugCost* = 410 + 550(4) = 2,610.
Rent = 150 + 1.05 *SqFt*	The predicted rent on an 800-square-foot apartment is $990, that is, *Rent* = 150 + 1.05 (800) = 990.
MPG = 49.22 − 0.079 *Horsepower*	If an engine has 200 horsepower, the predicted fuel efficiency is 33.42 mpg, that is, *MPG* = 49.22 − 0.079(200) = 33.42.

Extrapolation Outside the Range of X

Predictions from our fitted regression model are stronger within the range of our sample *x* values. The relationship seen in the scatter plot may not be true for values far outside our observed *x* range. *Extrapolation* outside the observed range of *x* is always tempting but should be approached with caution.

SECTION EXERCISES

12.7 (a) Interpret the slope of the fitted regression *HomePrice* = 125,000 + 150 *SquareFeet*. (b) What is the prediction for *HomePrice* if *SquareFeet* = 2,000? (c) Would the intercept be meaningful if this regression applies to home sales in a certain subdivision?

12.8 (a) Interpret the slope of the fitted regression *Sales* = 842 − 37.5 *Price*. (b) If *Price* = 20, what is the prediction for *Sales*? (c) Would the intercept be meaningful if this regression represents DVD sales at Blockbuster?

12.9 (a) Interpret the slope of the fitted regression *CarTheft* = 1,667 − 35.3 *MedianAge*, where *CarTheft* is the number of car thefts per 100,000 people by state, and *MedianAge* is the median age of the population. (b) What is the prediction for *CarTheft* if *MedianAge* is 40? (c) Would the intercept be meaningful if this regression applies to car thefts per 100,000 people by state?

12.10 (a) Interpret the slope of the fitted regression *Computer power dissipation* = 15.73 + 0.032 *Microprocessor speed*, where *Power dissipation* is measured in watts and *Microprocessor speed* is measured in MHz. (b) What is the prediction for *Power dissipation* if *Microprocessor speed* is 3,000 MHz? (c) Is this intercept meaningful?

12.11 (a) Interpret the slope of the fitted regression *Number of International Franchises* = −47.5 + 1.75 *PowerDistanceIndex*. The *PowerDistanceIndex* is a measure on a scale of 0–100 of the wealth gap between the richest and poorest in a country. (b) What is the prediction for number of international franchises in a country that has a *PowerDistanceIndex* of 85? (c) Is this intercept meaningful?

12.3 REGRESSION MODELS

Model and Parameters

LO 12-3

Explain the form and assumptions of a simple regression model.

The regression model's *unknown population parameters* are denoted by Greek letters β_0 (the **intercept**) and β_1 (the **slope**). The *population model* for a linear relationship is

$$y = \beta_0 + \beta_1 x + \varepsilon \qquad \text{(population regression model)} \qquad \textbf{(12.6)}$$

This relationship is assumed to be true for all (x_i, y_i) pairs in the population. Inclusion of a random error ε is necessary because other unspecified variables also may affect *Y* and because there may be measurement error in *Y*.

Each value of *X* may be paired with many different values of *Y* (e.g., there are many 800-square-foot apartments near a university, but each may rent for a different amount). The regression model without the error term represents the *expected value* of *Y* for a given *x* value. This is called the *simple regression equation*:

$$E(Y \mid x) = \beta_0 + \beta_1 x \qquad \text{(simple regression equation)} \qquad \textbf{(12.7)}$$

Even though the error term ε is not observable, we assume that the error is a normally distributed random variable with mean 0 and standard deviation σ. We also assume that σ is the same for each *x* and that the errors are independent of each other. These are called the **regression assumptions**. Figure 12.5 illustrates the regression assumptions.

- Assumption 1: The errors are normally distributed.
- Assumption 2: The errors have constant variance, σ^2.
- Assumption 3: The errors are independent of each other.

FIGURE 12.5

Regression Parameters and Error Assumptions

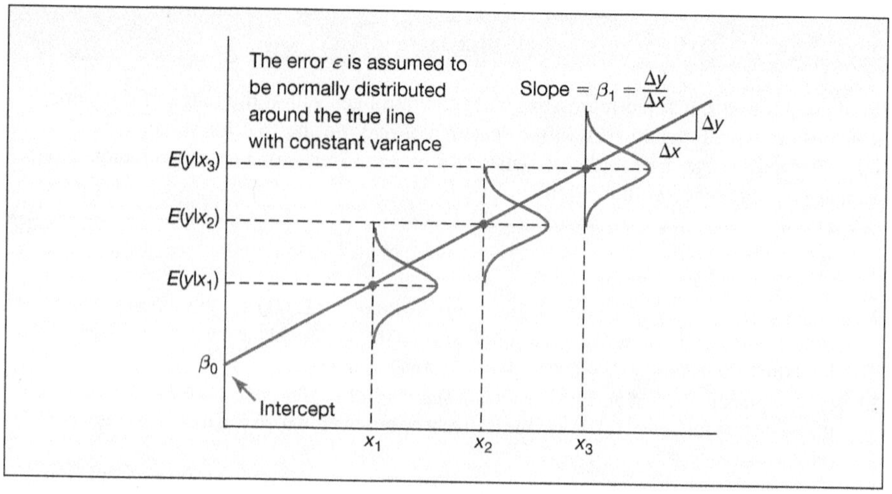

From the sample, we estimate the regression equation and use it to *predict* the expected value of Y for a given value of X:

(12.8) $\hat{y} = b_0 + b_1 x$ (estimated regression equation)

Roman letters denote the *coefficients* b_0 (the estimated intercept) and b_1 (the estimated slope). For a given value x_i, the estimated value of the dependent variable is $\hat{y}_i$. (You can read this as "y-hat.") The difference between the observed value y_i and its estimated value $\hat{y}_i$ is called a **residual** and is denoted e_i. The residual is the vertical distance between each y_i and the estimated regression line on a scatter plot of (x_i, y_i) values.

What Is a Residual?

A residual is calculated as the observed value of y minus the estimated value of y:

(12.9) $e_i = y_i - \hat{y}_i$ (residual)

The n residuals $e_1, e_2, \ldots, e_n$ are used to estimate σ, the standard deviation of the errors.

Fitting a Regression on a Scatter Plot

From a scatter plot, we could visually estimate the slope and intercept. Although this method is inexact, experiments suggest that people are pretty good at "eyeball" line fitting. We instinctively try to adjust the line to ensure that the line passes through the "center" of the scatter of data points, to match the data as closely as possible. In other words, we try to minimize the vertical distances between the *fitted* line and the observed y values.

A more precise method is to let Excel calculate the estimates. We enter observations on the independent variable $x_1, x_2, \ldots, x_n$ and the dependent variable $y_1, y_2, \ldots, y_n$ into separate columns, and let Excel fit the regression equation, as illustrated in Figure 12.6.* Excel will choose the regression coefficients so as to produce a good fit.

Follow these steps to use Excel to fit a regression line to the scatter plot. Figure 12.7 illustrates steps 4 and 5.

- Step 1: Highlight the data columns.
- Step 2: Click on Insert and choose Scatter to create a graph.
- Step 3: Click on the scatter plot points to select the data.

*Excel calls its regression equation a "trendline," although actually that would refer to a time-series trend.

FIGURE 12.6

Excel's Trendline

HP	*MPG*
151	41.0
220	35.0
198	28.0
134	36.6
347	16.4
213	31.8
353	31.9
121	42.8
247	26.6
162	36.9
239	27.4
140	40.6
253	23.9
237	27.8
248	35.4

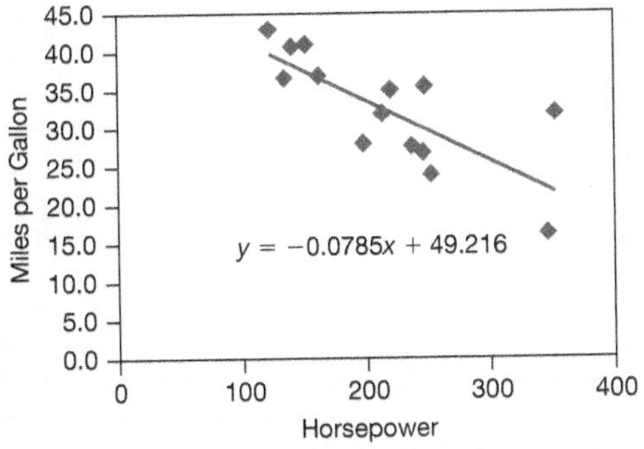

FIGURE 12.7

Excel's Trendline Menus

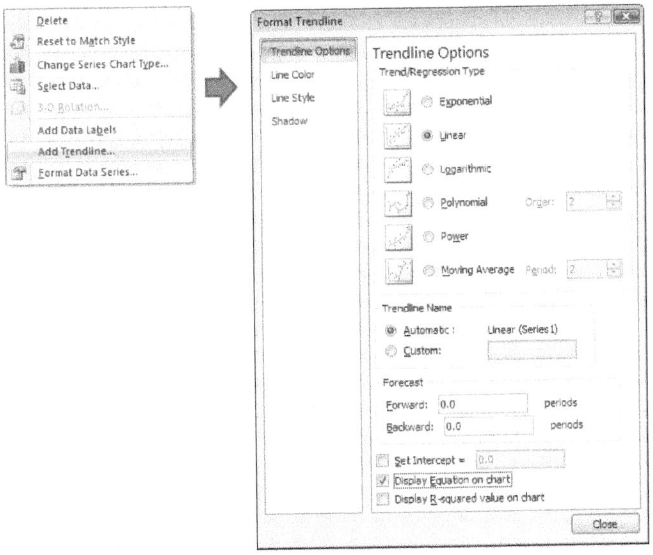

- Step 4: Right-click and choose Add Trendline.
- Step 5: Choose Options and check Display equation on chart.

Illustration: Miles per Gallon and Horsepower

Figure 12.6 shows a sample of miles per gallon and horsepower for 15 engines. The Excel graph and its fitted regression equation are also shown.

Slope Interpretation The fitted regression is $\hat{y} = 49.216 - 0.0785x$. The slope ($b_1 = -0.0785$) says that for each additional unit of engine horsepower, the miles per gallon decreases by 0.0785 mile. This estimated slope is a *statistic* because a different sample might yield a different estimate of the slope.

Intercept Interpretation The intercept ($b_0 = 49.216$) suggests that when the engine has no horsepower ($x = 0$), the fuel efficiency would be quite high. However, the intercept has little meaning in this case, not only because zero horsepower makes no logical sense, but also because extrapolating to $x = 0$ is beyond the range of the observed data.

Regression Caveats

- The "fit" of the regression does *not* depend on the sign of its slope. The sign of the fitted slope merely tells whether *X* has a positive or negative association with *Y*.
- View the intercept with skepticism unless $x = 0$ is logically possible and is within the observed range of *X*.
- Regression does not demonstrate cause and effect between *X* and *Y*. A good fit only shows that *X* and *Y* vary together. Both could be affected by another variable or by the way the data are defined.

SECTION EXERCISES

connect

12.12 The regression equation *NetIncome* = 2,277 + .0307 *Revenue* was estimated from a sample of 100 leading world companies (variables are in millions of dollars). (a) Interpret the slope. (b) Is the intercept meaningful? Explain. (c) Make a prediction of *NetIncome* when *Revenue* = 20,000. **Global100**

12.13 The regression equation *HomePrice* = 51.3 + 2.61 *Income* was estimated from a sample of 34 cities in the eastern United States. Both variables are in thousands of dollars. *HomePrice* is the median selling price of homes in the city, and *Income* is median family income for the city. (a) Interpret the slope. (b) Is the intercept meaningful? Explain. (c) Make a prediction of *HomePrice* when *Income* = 50 and also when *Income* = 100. **HomePrice1**

12.14 The regression equation *Credits* = 15.4 −.07 *Work* was estimated from a sample of 21 statistics students. *Credits* is the number of college credits taken and *Work* is the number of hours worked per week at an outside job. (a) Interpret the slope. (b) Is the intercept meaningful? Explain. (c) Make a prediction of *Credits* when *Work* = 0 and when *Work* = 40. What do these predictions tell you? **Credits**

12.15 Below are fitted regressions for *Y* = asking price of a used vehicle and *X* = the age of the vehicle. The observed range of *X* was 1 to 8 years. The sample consisted of all vehicles listed for sale in a particular week. (a) Interpret the slope of each fitted regression. (b) Interpret the intercept of each fitted regression. Does the intercept have meaning? (c) Predict the price of a 5-year-old Chevy Blazer. (d) Predict the price of a 5-year-old Chevy Silverado. **CarPrices**

Chevy Blazer: *Price* = 16,189 − 1,050 *Age* (n = 21 vehicles, observed *X* range was 1 to 8 years).

Chevy Silverado: *Price* = 22,591 − 1,339 *Age* (n = 24 vehicles, observed *X* range was 1 to 10 years).

12.16 Refer back to the regression equation in exercise 12.12: *NetIncome* = 2,277 + .0307 *Revenue*. Recall that the variables are both in millions of dollars. (a) Calculate the residual for the *x*, *y* pair ($41,078, $8,301). Did the regression equation underestimate or overestimate the net income? (b) Calculate the residual for the *x*, *y* pair ($61,768, $893). Did the regression equation underestimate or overestimate the net income?

12.17 Refer back to the regression equation in exercise 12.14: *Credits* = 15.4 − .07 *Work*. (a) Calculate the residual for the *x*, *y* pair (14, 18). Did the regression equation underestimate or overestimate the credits? (b) Calculate the residual for the *x*, *y* pair (30, 6). Did the regression equation underestimate or overestimate the credits?

12.4 ORDINARY LEAST SQUARES FORMULAS

LO 12-4

Explain the least squares method, apply formulas for coefficients, and interpret R^2.

Slope and Intercept

The **ordinary least squares** method (or **OLS** method for short) is used to estimate a regression so as to ensure the best fit. "Best" fit in this case means that we have selected the slope and intercept so that our residuals are as small as possible. Recall that a residual $e_i = y_i - \hat{y}_i$ is the difference between the observed *y* and the estimated *y*. Residuals can be either positive or negative. It is a characteristic of the OLS estimation method that the residuals around the regression line always sum to zero. That is, the positive residuals exactly cancel the negative ones:

$$\sum_{i=1}^{n} e_i = \sum_{i=1}^{n}(y_i - \hat{y}_i) = 0 \qquad \text{(OLS residuals always sum to zero)} \qquad \textbf{(12.10)}$$

Therefore to work with an equation that has a nonzero sum, we square the residuals, just as we squared the deviations from the mean when we developed the equation for variance back in Chapter 4. The fitted coefficients b_0 and b_1 are chosen so that the fitted linear model $\hat{y} = b_0 + b_1x$ has the smallest possible sum of squared residuals (SSE):

$$SSE = \sum_{i=1}^{n} e_i^2 = \sum_{i=1}^{n}(y_i - \hat{y}_i)^2 = \sum_{i=1}^{n}(y_i - b_0 - b_1x_i)^2 \qquad \text{(sum to be minimized)} \qquad \textbf{(12.11)}$$

This is an optimization problem that can be solved for b_0 and b_1 by using Excel's Solver Add-In. However, we can also use calculus to solve for b_0 and b_1.

$$b_1 = \frac{\sum_{i=1}^{n}(x_i - \bar{x})(y_i - \bar{y})}{\sum_{i=1}^{n}(x_i - \bar{x})^2} \qquad \text{(OLS estimator for slope)} \qquad \textbf{(12.12)}$$

$$b_0 = \bar{y} - b_1\bar{x} \qquad \text{(OLS estimator for intercept)} \qquad \textbf{(12.13)}$$

If we use the notation for sums of squares (see formula 12.2), then the OLS formula for the slope can be written

$$b_1 = \frac{SS_{xy}}{SS_{xx}} \qquad \text{(OLS estimator for slope)} \qquad \textbf{(12.14)}$$

These formulas require only a few spreadsheet operations to find the means, deviations around the means, and their products and sums. They are built into Excel and many calculators. Their Excel formulas are

b_0 =INTERCEPT(YData, XData)

b_1 =SLOPE(YData, XData)

The OLS formulas give unbiased and consistent estimates* of β_0 and β_1. *The OLS regression line always passes through the point* $(\bar{x}, \bar{y})$ *for any data, as illustrated in Figure 12.8.*

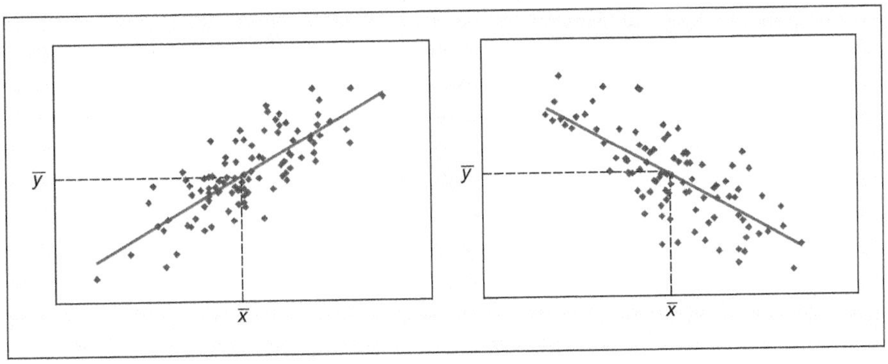

FIGURE 12.8

OLS Regression Line Always Passes Through $(\bar{x}, \bar{y})$.

*Recall from Chapter 8 that an unbiased estimator's expected value is the true parameter and that a consistent estimator approaches ever closer to the true parameter as the sample size increases.

Illustration: Exam Scores and Study Time

What is the relationship between the number of hours a student studies and his or her exam score? We can estimate the regression line for these two variables using a sample of 10 students. The worksheet in Table 12.2 shows the calculations of the sums needed for the slope and intercept. Figure 12.9 shows a fitted regression line. The vertical line segments in the scatter plot show the differences between the actual and fitted exam scores (i.e., residuals). The OLS residuals always sum to zero. We have:

$$b_1 = \frac{SS_{xy}}{SS_{xx}} = \frac{519.50}{264.50} = 1.9641 \qquad \text{(fitted slope)}$$

$$b_0 = \bar{y} - b_1\bar{x} = 70.1 - (1.9641)(10.5) = 49.477 \qquad \text{(fitted intercept)}$$

The fitted regression *Score* = 49.477 + 1.9641 *Study* says that, on average, each additional hour of study yields a little less than 2 additional exam points (the slope). A student who did not study (*Study* = 0) would expect a score of about 49 (the intercept). In this example, the intercept is meaningful because zero study time not only is possible (though hopefully uncommon) but also was almost within the range of observed data. The scatter plot shows an imperfect fit, since not all of the variation in exam scores can be explained by study time. The remaining *unexplained* variation in exam scores reflects other factors (e.g., previous night's sleep, class attendance, test anxiety). We can use the fitted regression equation $\hat{y} = 1.9641x + 49.477$ to

TABLE 12.2

Worksheet for Slope and Intercept Calculations

ExamScores

Student	Hours x_i	Score y_i	$x_i - \bar{x}$	$y_i - \bar{y}$	$(x_i - \bar{x})(y_i - \bar{y})$	$(x_i - \bar{x})^2$
Tom	1	53	−9.5	−17.1	162.45	90.25
Mary	5	74	−5.5	3.9	−21.45	30.25
Sarah	7	59	−3.5	−11.1	38.85	12.25
Oscar	8	43	−2.5	−27.1	67.75	6.25
Cullyn	10	56	−0.5	−14.1	7.05	0.25
Jaime	11	84	0.5	13.9	6.95	0.25
Theresa	14	96	3.5	25.9	90.65	12.25
Knut	15	69	4.5	−1.1	−4.95	20.25
Jin-Mae	15	84	4.5	13.9	62.55	20.25
Courtney	19	83	8.5	12.9	109.65	72.25
Sum	105	701	0	0	SS_{xy} = 519.50	SS_{xx} = 264.50
Mean	$\bar{x}$ = 10.5	$\bar{y}$ = 70.1				

FIGURE 12.9

Scatter Plot with Fitted Line and Residuals Shown as Vertical Line Segments

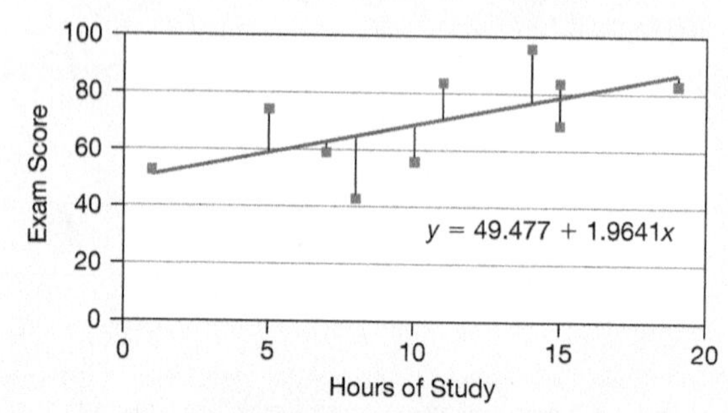

find each student's *expected* exam score. Each prediction is a *conditional mean,* given the student's study hours. For example:

Student and Study Time	*Expected Exam Score*
Oscar, $x = 8$ hours	$\hat{y} = 49.48 + 1.964(8) = 65.19$ (65 to nearest integer)
Theresa, $x = 14$ hours	$\hat{y} = 49.48 + 1.964(14) = 76.98$ (77 to nearest integer)
Courtney, $x = 19$ hours	$\hat{y} = 49.48 + 1.964(19) = 86.79$ (87 to nearest integer)

Oscar's actual exam score was only 43, so he did worse than his predicted score of 65. Theresa scored 96, far above her predicted score of 77. Courtney, who studied the longest (19 hours), scored 83, fairly close to her predicted score of 87. These examples show that study time is not a perfect predictor of exam scores.

Sources of Variation in *Y*

In a regression, we seek to explain the variation in the dependent variable around its mean. We express the *total variation* as a sum of squares (denoted *SST*):

$$SST = \sum_{i=1}^{n} (y_i - \bar{y})^2 \quad \text{(total sum of squares)} \qquad \textbf{(12.15)}$$

We can split the total variation into two parts:

SST	=	*SSR*	+	*SSE*
(*total* variation around the mean)		(variation explained by the *regression*)		(unexplained or *error* variation)

The *explained variation* in *Y* (denoted *SSR*) is the sum of the squared differences between the conditional mean $\hat{y}_i$ (conditioned on a given value x_i) and the unconditional mean $\bar{y}$ (same for all x_i):

$$SSR = \sum_{i=1}^{n} (\hat{y}_i - \bar{y})^2 \quad \text{(\textit{regression} sum of squares, explained)} \qquad \textbf{(12.16)}$$

The *unexplained variation* in *Y* (denoted *SSE*) is the sum of *squared* residuals, sometimes referred to as the **error sum of squares.***

$$SSE = \sum_{i=1}^{n} (y_i - \hat{y}_i)^2 \quad \text{(\textit{error} sum of squares, unexplained)} \qquad \textbf{(12.17)}$$

If the fit is good, *SSE* will be relatively small compared to *SST*. If each observed data value y_i is exactly the same as its estimate $\hat{y}_i$ (i.e., a perfect fit), then *SSE* will be zero. There is no upper limit on *SSE*. Table 12.3 shows the calculation of *SSE* for the exam scores.

TABLE 12.3 **Calculations of Sums of Squares** ExamScores

Student	Hours x_i	Score y_i	Estimated Score $\hat{y}_i = 1.9641x_i + 49.477$	Residual $y_i - \hat{y}_i$	$(y_i - \hat{y}_i)^2$	$(\hat{y}_i - \bar{y})^2$	$(y_i - \bar{y})^2$
Tom	1	53	51.441	1.559	2.43	348.15	292.41
Mary	5	74	59.298	14.702	216.15	116.68	15.21
Sarah	7	59	63.226	−4.226	17.86	47.25	123.21
Oscar	8	43	65.190	−22.190	492.40	24.11	734.41
Cullyn	10	56	69.118	−13.118	172.08	0.96	198.81
Jaime	11	84	71.082	12.918	166.87	0.96	193.21
Theresa	14	96	76.974	19.026	361.99	47.25	670.81
Knut	15	69	78.939	−9.939	98.78	78.13	1.21
Jin-Mae	15	84	78.939	5.061	25.61	78.13	193.21
Courtney	19	83	86.795	−3.795	14.40	278.72	166.41
					SSE = 1,568.57	*SSR* = 1,020.34	*SST* = 2,588.90

*But bear in mind that the residual e_i (observable) is not the same as the true error ε_i (unobservable).

Assessing Fit: Coefficient of Determination

Because the magnitude of *SSE* is dependent on sample size and on the units of measurement (e.g., dollars, kilograms, ounces), we want a *unit-free* benchmark to assess the fit of the regression equation. We can obtain a measure of *relative fit* by comparing *SST* to *SSR*. Recall that total variation in *Y* can be expressed as

$$SST = SSR + SSE$$

By dividing both sides by *SST* we now have the sum of two proportions on the right-hand side.

$$\frac{SST}{SST} = \frac{SSR}{SST} + \frac{SSE}{SST} \quad \text{or} \quad 1 = \frac{SSR}{SST} + \frac{SSE}{SST}$$

The first proportion SSR/SST has a special name: **coefficient of determination** or R^2. You can calculate this statistic in two ways.

(12.18)
$$R^2 = \frac{SSR}{SST} \quad \text{or} \quad R^2 = 1 - \frac{SSE}{SST}$$

The range of the coefficient of determination is $0 \le R^2 \le 1$. The highest possible R^2 is 1 because, if the regression gives a perfect fit, then $SSE = 0$:

$$R^2 = 1 - \frac{SSE}{SST} = 1 - \frac{0}{SST} = 1 - 0 = 1 \quad \text{if } SSE = 0 \text{ (perfect fit)}$$

The lowest possible R^2 is 0 because, if knowing the value of *X* does not help predict the value of *Y*, then $SSE = SST$:

$$R^2 = 1 - \frac{SSE}{SST} = 1 - \frac{SST}{SST} = 1 - 1 = 0 \quad \text{if } SSE = SST \text{ (worst fit)}$$

For the exam scores, the coefficient of determination is

$$R^2 = 1 - \frac{SSE}{SST} = 1 - \frac{1{,}568.57}{2{,}588.90} = 1 - .6059 = .3941$$

Because a coefficient of determination always lies in the range $0 \le R^2 \le 1$, it is often expressed as a *percent of variation explained*. Since the exam score regression yields $R^2 = .3941$, we could say that *X* (hours of study) "explains" 39.41 percent of the variation in *Y* (exam scores). On the other hand, 60.59 percent of the variation in exam scores is *not* explained by study time. The *unexplained variation* reflects factors not included in our model (e.g., reading skills, hours of sleep, hours of work at a job, physical health, etc.) or just plain random variation. Although the word "explained" does not necessarily imply causation, in this case we have *a priori* reason to believe that causation exists, that is, that increased study time improves exam scores.

R^2 and *r*

In a bivariate regression, R^2 is the square of the correlation coefficient *r*. Thus, if $r = .50$, then $R^2 = .25$. For this reason, MegaStat (and some textbooks) denotes the coefficient of determination as r^2 instead of R^2. In this textbook, the uppercase notation R^2 is used to indicate the difference in their definitions. It is tempting to think that a low R^2 indicates that the model is not useful. Yet in some applications (e.g., predicting crude oil future prices) even a slight improvement in predictive power can translate into millions of dollars.

SECTION EXERCISES

connect

Instructions for exercises 12.18 and 12.19: (a) Make an Excel worksheet to calculate SS_{xx}, SS_{yy}, and SS_{xy} (the same worksheet you used in exercises 12.2 and 12.3). (b) Use the formulas to calculate the slope and intercept. (c) Use your estimated slope and intercept to make a worksheet to calculate *SSE*, *SSR*, and *SST*. (d) Use these sums to calculate the R^2. (e) To check your answers, make an Excel scatter plot of *X* and *Y*, select the data points, right-click, select Add Trendline, select the Options tab, and choose Display equation on chart and Display R-squared value on chart.

12.18 College Student Weekly Earnings in Dollars (n = 5) WeekPay

Hours Worked (X)	Weekly Pay (Y)
10	93
15	171
20	204
20	156
35	261

12.19 Phone Hold Time for Concert Tickets in Seconds (n = 5) CallWait

Operators (X)	Wait Time (Y)
4	385
5	335
6	383
7	344
8	288

Instructions for exercises 12.20–12.22: (a) Use Excel to make a scatter plot of the data. (b) Select the data points, right-click, select Add Trendline, select the Options tab, and choose Display equation on chart and Display R-squared value on chart. (c) Interpret the fitted slope. (d) Is the intercept meaningful? Explain. (e) Interpret the R^2.

12.20 Moviegoer Snack Spending (n = 10) Movies

Age (X)	Spent (Y)
30	6.85
50	10.50
34	5.50
12	10.35
37	10.20
33	10.75
36	7.60
26	10.10
18	12.35
46	8.35

12.21 Annual Percent Return on Mutual Funds (n = 17) Portfolio

Last Year (X)	This Year (Y)
11.9	15.4
19.5	26.7
11.2	18.2
14.1	16.7
14.2	13.2
5.2	16.4
20.7	21.1
11.3	12.0
−1.1	12.1
3.9	7.4
12.9	11.5
12.4	23.0
12.5	12.7
2.7	15.1
8.8	18.7
7.2	9.9
5.9	18.9

12.22 Order Size and Shipping Cost (n = 12) ShipCost

Orders (X)	Ship Cost (Y)
1,068	4,489
1,026	5,611
767	3,290
885	4,113
1,156	4,883
1,146	5,425
892	4,414
938	5,506
769	3,346
677	3,673
1,174	6,542
1,009	5,088

12.5 TESTS FOR SIGNIFICANCE

Standard Error of Regression

LO 12-5

Construct confidence intervals and test hypotheses for the slope and intercept.

A measure of overall fit is the **standard error** of the estimate, denoted s_e:

$$s_e = \sqrt{\frac{SSE}{n-2}} \quad \text{(standard error)} \tag{12.19}$$

If the fitted model's predictions are perfect ($SSE = 0$), the standard error s_e will be zero. In general, a smaller value of s_e indicates a better fit. For the exam scores, we can use SSE from Table 12.3 to find s_e:

$$s_e = \sqrt{\frac{SSE}{n-2}} = \sqrt{\frac{1{,}568.57}{10-2}} = \sqrt{\frac{1{,}568.57}{8}} = 14.002$$

The standard error s_e is an estimate of σ (the standard deviation of the unobservable errors). Because it measures overall fit, the standard error s_e serves somewhat the same function as the coefficient of determination. However, unlike R^2, the magnitude of s_e depends on the units of measurement of the dependent variable (e.g., dollars, kilograms, ounces) and on the data magnitude. For this reason, R^2 is often the preferred measure of overall fit because its scale is always 0 to 1. The main use of the standard error s_e is to construct confidence intervals.

Confidence Intervals for Slope and Intercept

Once we have the standard error s_e, we construct confidence intervals for the coefficients from the formulas shown below. Excel, MegaStat, and MINITAB find them automatically.

(12.20) $$s_{b_1} = \frac{s_e}{\sqrt{\sum_{i=1}^{n}(x_i - \bar{x})^2}} \quad \text{(standard error of slope)}$$

(12.21) $$s_{b_0} = s_e\sqrt{\frac{1}{n} + \frac{\bar{x}^2}{\sum_{i=1}^{n}(x_i - \bar{x})^2}} \quad \text{(standard error of intercept)}$$

For the exam score data, plugging in the sums from Table 12.2, we get

$$s_{b_1} = \frac{s_e}{\sqrt{\sum_{i=1}^{n}(x_i - \bar{x})^2}} = \frac{14.002}{\sqrt{264.50}} = 0.86095$$

$$s_{b_0} = s_e\sqrt{\frac{1}{n} + \frac{\bar{x}^2}{\sum_{i=1}^{n}(x_i - \bar{x})^2}} = 14.002\sqrt{\frac{1}{10} + \frac{(10.5)^2}{264.50}} = 10.066$$

These standard errors are used to construct confidence intervals for the true slope and intercept, using Student's t with $d.f. = n - 2$ degrees of freedom and any desired confidence level. Some software packages (e.g., Excel and MegaStat) provide confidence intervals automatically, while others do not (e.g., MINITAB).

(12.22) $$b_1 - t_{\alpha/2}s_{b_1} \le \beta_1 \le b_1 + t_{\alpha/2}s_{b_1} \quad \text{(CI for true slope)}$$

(12.23) $$b_0 - t_{\alpha/2}s_{b_0} \le \beta_0 \le b_0 + t_{\alpha/2}s_{b_0} \quad \text{(CI for true intercept)}$$

For the exam scores, degrees of freedom are $n - 2 = 10 - 2 = 8$, so from Appendix D we get $t_{.025} = 2.306$ for 95 percent confidence. The 95 percent confidence intervals for the coefficients are

Slope

$$b_1 - t_{.025}s_{b_1} \le \beta_1 \le b_1 + t_{.025}s_{b_1}$$
$$1.9641 - (2.306)(0.86101) \le \beta_1 \le 1.9641 + (2.306)(0.86101)$$
$$-0.0213 \le \beta_1 \le 3.9495$$

Intercept

$$b_0 - t_{\alpha/2}s_{b_0} \le \beta_0 \le b_0 + t_{\alpha/2}s_{b_0}$$
$$49.477 - (2.306)(10.066) \le \beta_0 \le 49.477 + (2.306)(10.066)$$
$$26.26 \le \beta_0 \le 72.69$$

These confidence intervals are fairly wide. The width of any confidence interval can be reduced by obtaining a larger sample, partly because the t-value would shrink (toward the normal z-value) but mainly because the standard errors shrink as n increases. For the exam scores, the confidence interval for the slope includes zero, suggesting that the true slope could be zero.

Hypothesis Tests

Is the true slope different from zero? This is an important question because if $\beta_1 = 0$, then X does not influence Y and the regression model collapses to a constant β_0 plus a random error term:

Initial Model	*If $\beta_1 = 0$*	*Then*
$y = \beta_0 + \beta_1 x + \varepsilon$	$y = \beta_0 + (0)x + \varepsilon$	$y = \beta_0 + \varepsilon$

We could also test for a zero intercept. For either coefficient, we use a t test with $d.f. = n - 2$ degrees of freedom. The hypotheses and their test statistics are:

Coefficient	*Hypotheses*	*Test Statistic*	
Slope	$H_0: \beta_1 = 0$ $H_1: \beta_1 \neq 0$	$t_{calc} = \dfrac{\text{estimated slope} - \text{hypothesized slope}}{\text{standard error of the slope}} = \dfrac{b_1 - 0}{s_{b1}}$	**(12.24)**
Intercept	$H_0: \beta_0 = 0$ $H_1: \beta_0 \neq 0$	$t_{calc} = \dfrac{\text{estimated intercept} - \text{hypothesized intercept}}{\text{standard error of the intercept}} = \dfrac{b_0 - 0}{s_{b0}}$	**(12.25)**

Usually we are interested in testing whether the parameter is equal to zero as shown here, but you may substitute another value in place of 0 if you wish. The critical value of t is obtained from Appendix D or from Excel's function =T.INV.2T(α, d.f.). Often, the researcher uses a two-tailed test as the starting point because rejection in a two-tailed test always implies rejection in a one-tailed test (but not vice versa).

Slope versus Correlation

The test for zero slope is the same as the test for zero correlation. That is, the t test for zero slope (formula 12.24) will always yield *exactly* the same t_{calc} as the t test for zero correlation (formula 12.4).

Test for Zero Slope: Exam Scores ExamScores

For the exam scores, we would anticipate a positive slope (i.e., more study hours should improve exam scores) so we will use a right-tailed test.

Step 1: State the Hypotheses

$$H_0: \beta_1 = 0$$
$$H_1: \beta_1 > 0$$

Step 2: Specify the Decision Rule For a right-tailed test with $\alpha = .05$ and $d.f. = 10 - 2 = 8$, $t_{.05} = 1.860$. Our decision rule states:

$$\text{Reject } H_0 \text{ if } t_{calc} > 1.860$$

Step 3: Calculate the Test Statistic To calculate the test statistic, we use the slope estimate ($b_1 = 1.9641$) and the standard error ($s_{b_1} = 0.86095$) we calculated previously:

$$t_{calc} = \frac{b_1 - 0}{s_{b1}} = \frac{1.9641 - 0}{0.86095} = 2.281$$

Step 4: Make a Decision Because $t_{calc} > t_{.05}$ ($2.281 > 1.860$), we can reject the hypothesis of a zero slope in a right-tailed test. (We would be unable to do so in a two-tailed test because the critical value of our t statistic would be 2.306.) Once we calculate the test statistic for the slope or intercept, we can find the p-value by using Excel's function =T.DIST.RT(2.281, 8) = .025995. Because .02995 < .05, we would reject H_0. We conclude the slope is positive.

Using Excel: Exam Scores ExamScores

These calculations are normally done by computer (we have demonstrated the calculations only to illustrate the formulas). The Excel menu to accomplish these tasks is shown in Figure 12.10. The resulting output, shown in Figure 12.11, can be used to verify our calculations. Excel always does two-tailed tests, so you must halve the p-value if you need a one-tailed test. You may specify the confidence level, but Excel's default is 95 percent confidence.

FIGURE 12.10

Excel's Regression Menus

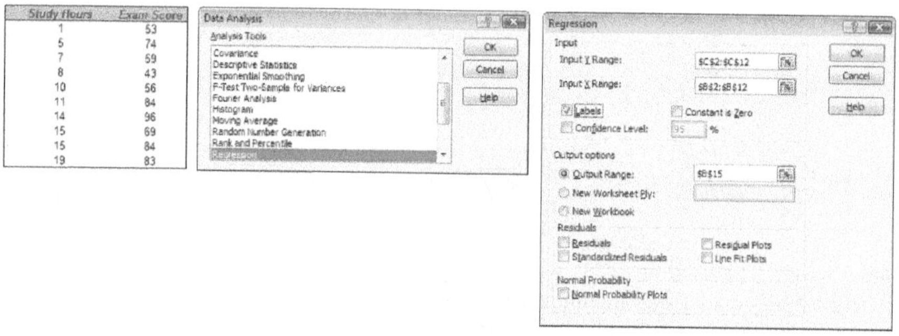

FIGURE 12.11

Excel's Regression Output

SUMMARY OUTPUT

Regression Statistics	
Multiple R	0.627790986
R Square	0.394121523
Adjusted R Square	0.318386713
Standard Error	14.00249438
Observations	10

ANOVA

	df	SS	MS	F	Significance F
Regression	1	1020.34121	1020.34121	5.203967954	0.051972204
Residual	8	1568.55879	196.0698488		
Total	9	2588.9			

	Coefficients	Standard Error	t Stat	P-value	Lower 95%	Upper 95%
Intercept	49.47712665	10.06646125	4.915046652	0.001171307	26.26382541	72.6904279
Study Hours	1.964083176	0.86097902	2.281220716	0.051972204	-0.021338002	3.949504354

Constant Is Zero?

Avoid checking the Constant is Zero box in Excel's menu. This would force the intercept through the origin, changing the model drastically. Leave this option to the experts.

Using MegaStat: Exam Scores ExamScores

Figure 12.12 shows MegaStat's menu. The output format is similar to Excel's, except that MegaStat highlights coefficients that differ significantly from zero at $\alpha = .05$ in a two-tailed test.

Using MINITAB: Exam Scores ExamScores

Figure 12.13 shows MINITAB's regression menus. MINITAB gives you the same general output as Excel, but with strongly rounded results.*

*You may have noticed that both Excel and MINITAB calculated something called "adjusted R-Square." For a bivariate regression, this statistic is of little interest, but in the next chapter it becomes important.

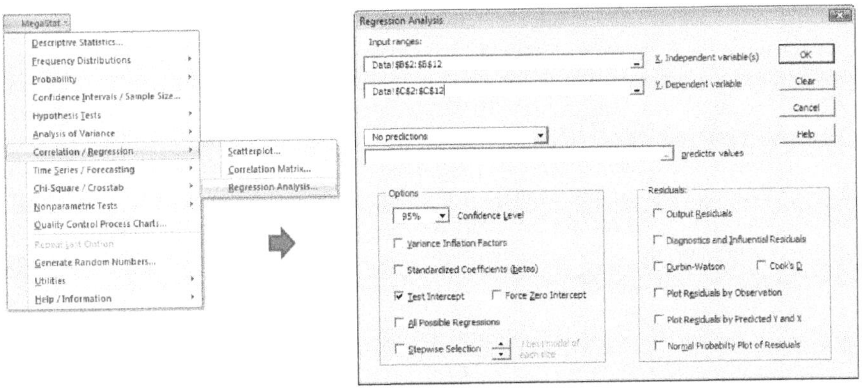

FIGURE 12.12

MegaStat's Regression Menus

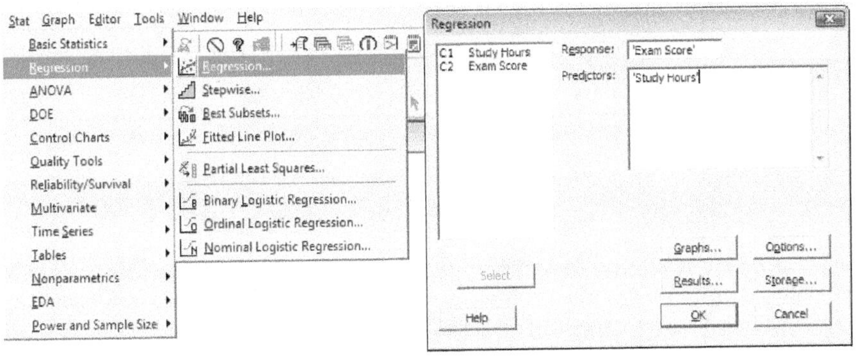

FIGURE 12.13

MINITAB's Regression Menus

Application: Retail Sales RetailSales

Is there a positive association between gross leasable area (X) and retail sales (Y) in shopping malls? We will assume a linear relationship between X and Y:

$$Sales = \beta_0 + \beta_1 Area + \varepsilon$$

We anticipate a positive slope (more leasable area permits more retail sales) and an intercept near zero (zero leasable space would imply no retail sales). Since retail sales do not depend solely on leasable area, the random error term will reflect all other factors that influence retail sales as well as possible measurement error. The regression line is estimated using a sample of $n = 24$ shopping malls randomly chosen from 24 different U.S. states.

Based on the scatter plot and Excel's fitted linear regression, displayed in Figure 12.14, the linear model seems justified. The very high R^2 says that *Area* "explains" about 98 percent of the variation in *Sales*. Although it is reasonable to assume causation between *Area* and *Sales* in this model, the high R^2 alone does not prove cause and effect.

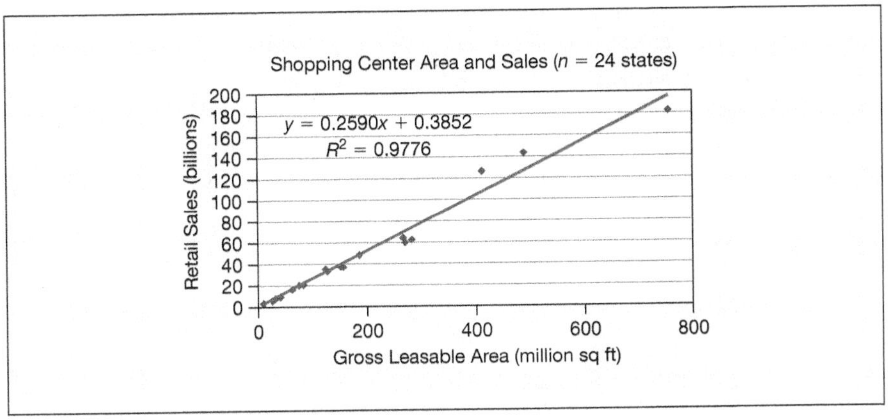

FIGURE 12.14

Leasable Area and Retail Sales RetailSales

Using MegaStat For a more detailed look, we examine MegaStat's regression output for these data, shown in Figure 12.15. On average, each extra million square feet of leasable space yields an extra $259.4 billion in retail sales ($b_1 = .2590$). The slope is nonzero in MegaStat's two-tail test ($t = 30.972$) as indicated by its tiny p-value (1.22×10^{-19}). MegaStat's yellow highlight indicates that the slope differs significantly from zero at $\alpha = .01$, and the narrow confidence interval for the slope [0.2417 to 0.2764] does not enclose zero. We conclude that this sample result (nonzero slope) did not arise by chance—rarely will you see such small p-values (except perhaps in time series data). But the intercept ($b_0 = 0.3852$) does not differ significantly from zero (p-value = .8479, t = 0.194) and the confidence interval for the intercept [−3.7320, 4.5023] includes zero. These conclusions are in line with our prior expectations.

FIGURE 12.15

MegaStat Regression Results for Retail Sales RetailSales

Regression Output					Confidence Interval	
Variables	*Coefficients*	*Std. Error*	*t (df = 26)*	*p-value*	*95% lower*	*95% upper*
Intercept	0.3852	1.9853	0.194	.8479	−3.7320	4.5023
Area	0.2590	0.0084	30.972	1.22E-19	0.2417	0.2764

Tip

The test for zero slope always yields a t statistic that is identical to the test for zero correlation coefficient. Therefore, it is not necessary to do both tests. Since regression output always includes a t test for the slope, that is the test we usually use.

Mini Case 12.2

Does Per Person Spending Predict Weekly Sales? NoodlesRevenue

Can Noodles & Company predict their average weekly sales at a restaurant from the average amount a person spends when visiting their restaurant? A random sample of data from 74 restaurants was used to answer this question. The scatter plot in Figure 12.16 below shows the relationship between *average spending per person* and *average weekly sales*.

FIGURE 12.16 **Noodles Weekly Sales**

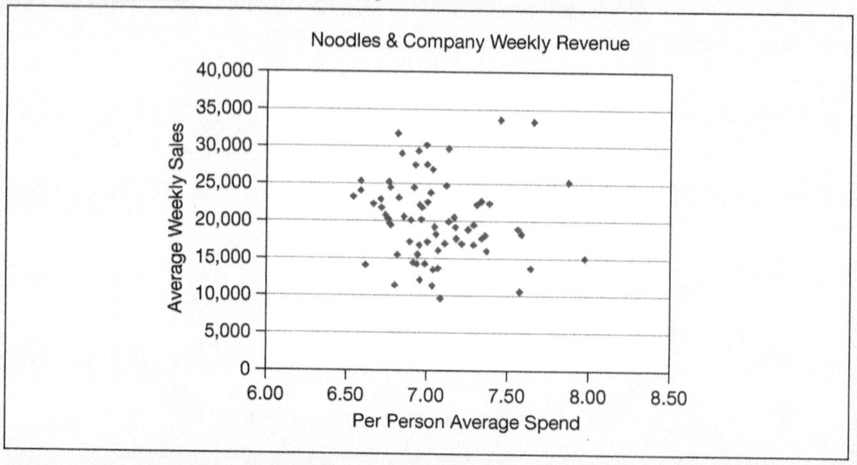

Regression Output					Confidence Interval	
Variables	*Coefficients*	*Std. Error*	*t(d.f. = 72)*	*p-value*	*95% lower*	*95% upper*
Intercept	32,710.5607	14,987.2764	2.183	.0323	2,833.9717	62,587.1497
Per Person Spend	−1,751.4472	2,125.6830	−0.824	.4127	−5,988.9187	2,486.0243

FIGURE 12.17

MegaStat Regression Results for Weekly Sales

The scatter plot shows almost no relationship between the two variables. This observation is also supported by the regression results shown in Figure 12.17.

The regression results show that b_1, the estimate for the slope β_1, is −\$1,751.45. It would appear that on average for each additional dollar an individual spends in a restaurant, weekly sales would decrease by \$1,751.45—seemingly a large number. But notice that the confidence interval for the slope [−\$5,988.92, \$2,486.02] contains zero and the standard error (\$2,125.68) is larger than the estimated coefficient. When we perform a two-tailed test for zero slope with H_0: $\beta_1 = 0$ and H_1: $\beta_1 \neq 0$, the p-value for this test is .4127. Because this p-value is much greater than any value of α we might choose, we *fail to reject* the null hypothesis of zero slope. Both the hypothesis for zero slope and the confidence interval show that the slope is not significantly different from zero. Our conclusion is that average weekly sales *should not be* predicted by per person average spending. Based on the information we have here, our best prediction of average weekly sales at a Noodles & Company restaurant is simply the mean ($\bar{y}$ = \$20,373).

SECTION EXERCISES

connect

Instructions for exercises 12.23 and 12.24: (a) Perform a regression using MegaStat or Excel. (b) State the null and alternative hypotheses for a two-tailed test for a zero slope. (c) Report the p-value and the 95 percent confidence interval for the slope shown in the regression results. (d) Is the slope significantly different from zero? Explain your conclusion.

12.23 College Student Weekly Earnings in Dollars (n = 5) WeekPay

Hours Worked (X)	*Weekly Pay (Y)*
10	93
15	171
20	204
20	156
35	261

12.24 Phone Hold Time for Concert Tickets in Seconds (n = 5) CallWait

Operators (X)	*Wait Time (Y)*
4	385
5	335
6	383
7	344
8	288

12.25 A regression was performed using data on 32 NFL teams. The variables were Y = current value of team (millions of dollars) and X = total debt held by the team owners (millions of dollars). (a) Write the fitted regression equation. (b) Construct a 95 percent confidence interval for the slope. (c) Perform a right-tailed t test for zero slope at α = .05. State the hypotheses clearly. (d) Use Excel to find the p-value for the t statistic for the slope. **NFL**

variables	*coefficients*	*std. error*
Intercept	557.4511	25.3385
Debt	3.0047	0.8820

12.26 A regression was performed using data on 16 randomly selected charities. The variables were Y = expenses (millions of dollars) and X = revenue (millions of dollars). (a) Write the fitted regression equation. (b) Construct a 95 percent confidence interval for the slope. (c) Perform a right-tailed t test for zero slope at $\alpha = .05$. State the hypotheses clearly. (d) Use Excel to find the p-value for the t statistic for the slope. **Charities**

variables	*coefficients*	*std. error*
Intercept	7.6425	10.0403
Revenue	0.9467	0.0936

12.6 ANALYSIS OF VARIANCE: OVERALL FIT

Decomposition of Variance

LO 12-6

Interpret the ANOVA table and use it to calculate F, R^2, and standard error.

A regression seeks to explain variation in the dependent variable around its mean. A simple way to see this is to express the deviation of y_i from its mean $\bar{y}$ as the sum of the deviation of y_i from the regression estimate $\hat{y}_i$ plus the deviation of the regression estimate $\hat{y}_i$ from the mean $\bar{y}$:

(12.26) $$y_i - \bar{y} = (y_i - \hat{y}_i) + (\hat{y}_i - \bar{y}) \quad \text{(adding and subtracting } \hat{y}_i\text{)}$$

It can be shown that this same decomposition also holds for the *sums of squares:*

(12.27) $$\sum_{i=1}^{n}(y_i - \bar{y})^2 = \sum_{i=1}^{n}(y_i - \hat{y}_i)^2 + \sum_{i=1}^{n}(\hat{y}_i - \bar{y})^2 \quad \text{(sums of squares)}$$

As we have already seen, this *decomposition of variance* may be written as

SST	=	*SSE*	+	*SSR*
(*total* variation around the mean)		(unexplained or *error* variation)		(variation explained by the *regression*)

F Statistic for Overall Fit

To test a regression for overall significance, we use an F test to compare the explained (SSR) and unexplained (SSE) sums of squares. We divide each sum by its respective degrees of freedom to obtain *mean squares* (MSR and MSE). The *F statistic* is the ratio of these two mean squares. Calculations of the F statistic are arranged in a table called the *analysis of variance* or ANOVA table (see Table 12.4).

TABLE 12.4

ANOVA Table for a Simple Regression

Source of Variation	*Sum of Squares*	*df*	*Mean Square*	*F*	*Excel p-value*
Regression (explained)	$SSR = \sum_{i=1}^{n}(\hat{y}_i - \bar{y})^2$	1	$MSR = \frac{SSR}{1}$	$F_{calc} = \frac{MSR}{MSE}$	=F.DIST(F_{calc},1, n−2)
Residual (unexplained)	$SSE = \sum_{i=1}^{n}(y_i - \hat{y}_i)^2$	$n - 2$	$MSE = \frac{SSE}{n-2}$		
Total	$SST = \sum_{i=1}^{n}(y_i - \bar{y})^2$	$n - 1$			

The ANOVA table also contains the sums required to calculate $R^2 = SSR/SST$. An ANOVA table is provided automatically by any regression software (e.g., Excel, MegaStat). The formula for the F test statistic is:

$$F_{\text{calc}} = \frac{MSR}{MSE} = \frac{SSR/1}{SSE/(n-2)} = (n-2)\frac{SSR}{SSE} \quad (F \text{ statistic for simple regression}) \quad \textbf{(12.28)}$$

The F statistic reflects both the sample size and the ratio of SSR to SSE. For a given sample size, a larger F statistic indicates a better fit (larger SSR relative to SSE), while F close to zero indicates a poor fit (small SSR relative to SSE). The F statistic must be compared with a critical value $F_{1,n-2}$ from Appendix F for whatever level of significance is desired, and we can find the p-value by using Excel's function =F.DIST(F_{calc},1,n−2). Software packages provide the p-value automatically.

EXAMPLE 12.2

Exam Scores: F Statistic

ExamScores

Figure 12.18 shows an ANOVA table for the exam scores. The F statistic is

$$F_{\text{calc}} = \frac{MSR}{MSE} = \frac{1020.3412}{196.0698} = 5.20$$

From Appendix F the critical value of $F_{1,8}$ at the 5 percent level of significance would be 5.32, so the exam score regression is not quite significant at $\alpha = .05$. The p-value of .052 says a sample such as ours would be expected about 52 times in 1,000 samples if X and Y were unrelated. In other words, if we reject the hypothesis of no relationship between X and Y, we face a Type I error risk of 5.2 percent. This p-value might be called *marginally significant*.

FIGURE 12.18 **ANOVA Table for Exam Data**

ANOVA table

Source	*SS*	*df*	*MS*	*F*	*p-value*
Regression	1,020.3412	1	1,020.3412	5.20	.0520
Residual	1,568.5588	8	196.0698		
Total	2,588.9000	9			

From the ANOVA table, we can calculate the standard error from the mean square for the residuals:

$$s_e = \sqrt{MSE} = \sqrt{196.0698} = 14.002 \quad \text{(standard error for exam scores)}$$

F Test *p*-Value and *t* Test *p*-Value

In a simple regression, the F test always yields the same p-value as a two-tailed t test for zero slope, which in turn always gives the same p-value as a two-tailed test for zero correlation. The relationship between the test statistics is $F_{\text{calc}} = t^2_{\text{calc}}$.

SECTION EXERCISES

connect

12.27 Below is a regression using X = home price (000), Y = annual taxes (000), n = 20 homes. (a) Write the fitted regression equation. (b) Write the formula for each t statistic and verify the t statistics shown below. (c) State the degrees of freedom for the t tests and find the two-tail critical value for t by using Appendix D. (d) Use Excel's function =T.DIST.2T(t, *d.f.*) to verify the p-value shown for each t statistic (slope, intercept). (e) Verify that $F = t^2$ for the slope. (f) In your own words, describe the fit of this regression.

R^2	0.452
Std. Error	0.454
n	12

ANOVA table

Source	*SS*	*df*	*MS*	*F*	*p-value*
Regression	1.6941	1	1.6941	8.23	.0167
Residual	2.0578	10	0.2058		
Total	3.7519	11			

Regression output

variables	*coefficients*	*std. error*	*t (df = 10)*	*p-value*	*confidence interval 95% lower*	*95% upper*
Intercept	1.8064	0.6116	2.954	.0144	0.4438	3.1691
Slope	0.0039	0.0014	2.869	.0167	0.0009	0.0070

12.28 Below is a regression using X = average price, Y = units sold, n = 20 stores. (a) Write the fitted regression equation. (b) Write the formula for each t statistic and verify the t statistics shown below. (c) State the degrees of freedom for the t tests and find the two-tail critical value for t by using Appendix D. (d) Use Excel's function =T.DIST.2T(t, *d.f.*) to verify the p-value shown for each t statistic (slope, intercept). (e) Verify that $F = t^2$ for the slope. (f) In your own words, describe the fit of this regression.

R^2	0.200
Std. Error	26.128
n	20

ANOVA table

Source	*SS*	*df*	*MS*	*F*	*p-value*
Regression	3,080.89	1	3,080.89	4.51	.0478
Residual	12,288.31	18	682.68		
Total	15,369.20	19			

Regression output

variables	*coefficients*	*std. error*	*t (df = 18)*	*p-value*	*confidence interval 95% lower*	*95% upper*
Intercept	614.9300	51.2343	12.002	.0000	507.2908	722.5692
Slope	−109.1120	51.3623	−2.124	.0478	−217.0202	−1.2038

Instructions for exercises 12.29–12.31: (a) Use Excel's Data Analysis > Regression (or MegaStat or MINITAB) to obtain regression estimates. (b) Interpret the 95 percent confidence interval for the slope. Does it contain zero? (c) Interpret the t test for the slope and its p-value. (d) Interpret the F statistic. (e) Verify that the p-value for F is the same as for the slope's t statistic, and show that $t^2 = F$. (f) Describe the fit of the regression.

12.29 Moviegoer Snack Spending (n = 10) Movies

Age (X)	*Spent (Y)*	*Age (X)*	*Spent (Y)*
30	6.85	33	10.75
50	10.50	36	7.60
34	5.50	26	10.10
12	10.35	18	12.35
37	10.20	46	8.35

12.30 Annual Percent Return on Mutual Funds (n = 17) Portfolio

Last Year (X)	This Year (Y)
11.9	15.4
19.5	26.7
11.2	18.2
14.1	16.7
14.2	13.2
5.2	16.4
20.7	21.1
11.3	12.0
−1.1	12.1
3.9	7.4
12.9	11.5
12.4	23.0
12.5	12.7
2.7	15.1
8.8	18.7
7.2	9.9
5.9	18.9

12.31 Order Size and Shipping Cost (n = 12) ShipCost

Orders (X)	Ship Cost (Y)
1,068	4,489
1,026	5,611
767	3,290
885	4,113
1,156	4,883
1,146	5,425
892	4,414
938	5,506
769	3,346
677	3,673
1,174	6,542
1,009	5,088

Mini Case 12.3

Airplane Cockpit Noise Cockpit

Career airline pilots face the risk of progressive hearing loss, due to the noisy cockpits of most jet aircraft. Much of the noise comes not from engines but from air roar, which increases at high speeds. To assess this workplace hazard, a pilot measured cockpit noise at randomly selected points during the flight by using a handheld meter. Noise level (in decibels) was measured in seven different aircraft at the first officer's left ear position using a handheld meter. For reference, 60 dB is a normal conversation, 75 is a typical vacuum cleaner, 85 is city traffic, 90 is a typical hair dryer, and 110 is a chain saw. Figure 12.19 shows 61 observations on cockpit noise (decibels) and airspeed (knots indicated air speed, KIAS) for a Boeing 727, an older type of aircraft lacking design improvements in newer planes.

The scatter plot in Figure 12.19 suggests that a linear model provides a reasonable description of the data. The fitted regression shows that each additional knot of airspeed increases the noise level by 0.0765 dB. Thus, a 100-knot increase in airspeed would add about 7.65 dB of noise. The intercept of 64.229 suggests that if the plane were not flying ($KIAS = 0$), the noise level would be only slightly greater than a normal conversation.

FIGURE 12.19 **Scatter Plot of Cockpit Noise Data** Cockpit

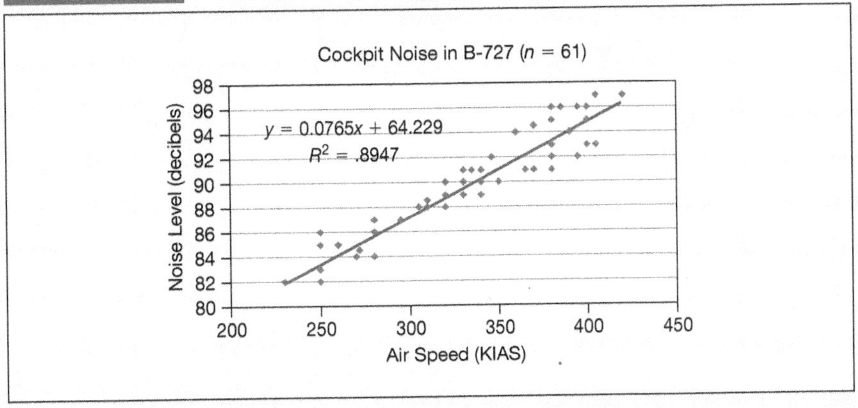

The regression results in Figure 12.20 show that the fit is very good ($R^2 = .895$) and that the regression is highly significant ($F = 501.16$, p-value $< .001$). Both the slope and intercept have p-values below .001, indicating that the true parameters are nonzero. Thus, the regression is significant, as well as having practical value.

FIGURE 12.20 **Regression Results of Cockpit Noise**

Regression Analysis

r²	0.895	n	61
r	0.946	k	1
Std. Error	1.292	Dep. Var.	Noise

ANOVA table

Source	*SS*	*df*	*MS*	*F*	*p-value*
Regression	836.9817	1	836.9817	501.16	1.60E-30
Residual	98.5347	59	1.6701		
Total	935.5164	60			

Regression output

variables	*coefficients*	*std. error*	*t (df = 59)*	*p-value*	*confidence interval* *95% lower*	*95% upper*
Intercept	64.2294	1.1489	55.907	8.29E-53	61.9306	66.5283
Speed	0.0765	0.0034	22.387	1.60E-30	0.0697	0.0834

12.7 CONFIDENCE AND PREDICTION INTERVALS FOR *Y*

How to Construct an Interval Estimate for *Y*

LO 12-7

Distinguish between confidence and prediction intervals for *Y*.

The regression line is an estimate of the *conditional mean* of Y, that is, the expected value of Y for a given value of X, *denoted* $E(Y|x_i)$. But the estimate may be too high or too low. To make this *point estimate* more useful, we need an *interval estimate* to show a range of likely values. To do this, we insert the x_i value into the fitted regression equation, calculate the estimated $\hat{y}_i$, and use the formulas shown below. The first formula gives a **confidence interval** for the conditional mean of Y, while the second is a **prediction interval** for individual values of Y. The formulas are similar, except that prediction intervals are wider because *individual* Y values vary more than the *mean* of Y.

$$\hat{y}_i \pm t_{\alpha/2} s_e \sqrt{\frac{1}{n} + \frac{(x_i - \bar{x})^2}{\sum_{i=1}^{n}(x_i - \bar{x})^2}} \quad \text{(confidence interval for mean of } Y\text{)} \qquad \textbf{(12.29)}$$

$$\hat{y}_i \pm t_{\alpha/2} s_e \sqrt{1 + \frac{1}{n} + \frac{(x_i - \bar{x})^2}{\sum_{i=1}^{n}(x_i - \bar{x})^2}} \quad \text{(prediction interval for individual } Y\text{)} \qquad \textbf{(12.30)}$$

Let's use formula 12.30 to predict the exam score for a student who studies 4 hours, using the regression model developed in Section 12.4. What is the 95 percent prediction interval? The student's predicted exam score (see Table 12.4) would be $\hat{y} = 1.9641(4) + 49.477 = 57.333$.

For 95 percent confidence with $d.f. = n - 2 = 10 - 2 = 8$, we use $t_{.025} = 2.306$. Using the sums from Table 12.3, the 95 percent prediction interval is:

$$57.333 \pm (2.306)(14.002)\sqrt{1 + \frac{1}{10} + \frac{(4 - 10.5)^2}{264.5}} \quad \text{or} \quad 57.33 \pm 36.24$$

This very wide interval says that we cannot make precise predictions of the exam score for a student who studies 4 hours. This is not surprising since the fit for the exam score data ($R^2 = .3941$) was not very high. Prediction intervals are more precise when R^2 is high.

Interval width varies with the value of x_i, being narrowest when x_i is near its mean (note that when $x_i = \bar{x}$, the last term under the square root disappears completely). For some data sets, the degree of narrowing near $\bar{x}$ is almost indiscernible, while for other data sets it is quite pronounced. These calculations are usually done by computer (see Figure 12.21). Both MegaStat and MINITAB, for example, will let you type in the x_i values and will give both confidence and prediction intervals *only* for that x_i value, but you must make your own graphs.

FIGURE 12.21

MegaStat's Confidence and Prediction Intervals

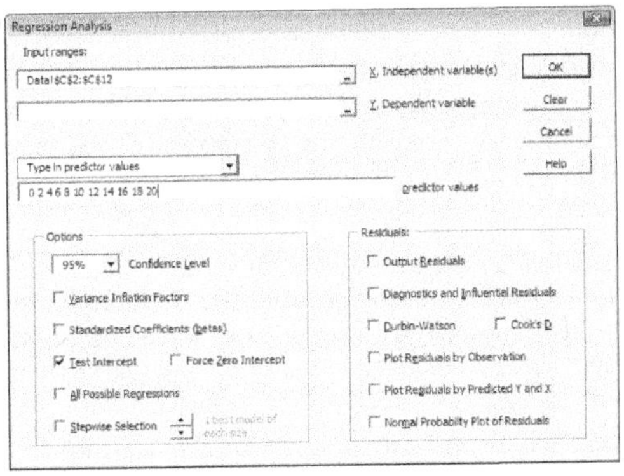

Predicted values for Exam Score

		95% Confidence Intervals		95% Prediction Intervals	
Study Hours	Predicted	lower	upper	lower	upper
0	49.477	26.264	72.690	9.709	89.245
2	53.405	33.681	73.130	15.568	91.243
4	57.333	40.877	73.790	21.092	93.575
6	61.262	47.694	74.829	26.237	96.286
8	65.190	53.836	76.543	30.962	99.417
10	69.118	58.859	79.377	35.238	102.998
12	73.046	62.410	83.682	39.050	107.043
14	76.974	64.623	89.325	42.403	111.546
16	80.902	65.952	95.853	45.320	116.485
18	84.831	66.775	102.886	47.836	121.826
20	88.759	67.311	110.207	49.995	127.523

Two Illustrations: Exam Scores and Retail Sales

ExamScores **RetailSales**

Since there will be a different interval for every X value, it is helpful to see confidence and prediction intervals over the entire range of X. Figure 12.22 shows confidence and prediction intervals for exam scores and retail sales. The contrast between the two graphs is striking. Confidence and prediction intervals for exam scores are wide and clearly narrower for X values near the mean. The prediction bands for exam scores for large X values (e.g., $x = 20$ hours of study) even extend above 100 points (presumably the upper limit for an exam score). In contrast, the intervals for retail sales appear narrow and only slightly wider for X values

FIGURE 12.22

Confidence and Prediction Intervals Illustrated

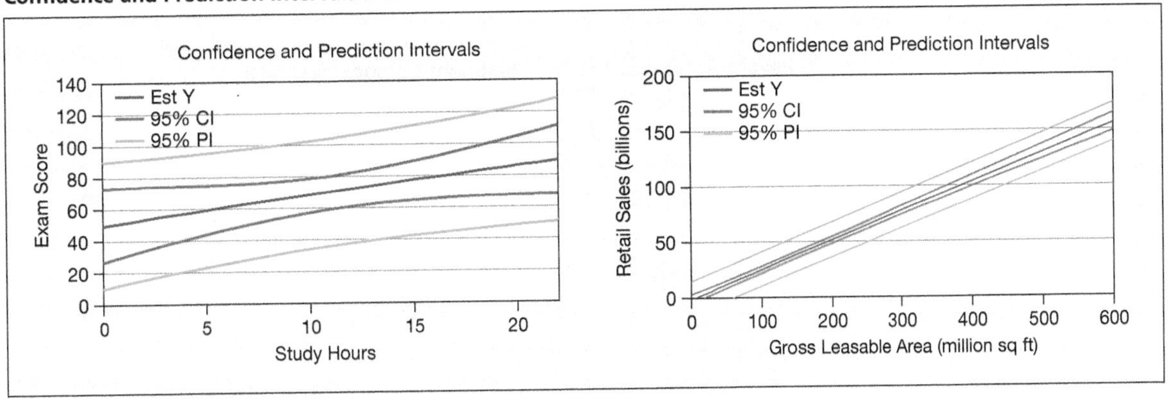

below or above the mean. While the prediction bands for retail sales seem narrow, they still represent billions of dollars (e.g., for $x = 500$, the retail sales prediction interval has a width of about \$33 billion). This shows that a high R^2 does not guarantee precise predictions.

Quick Rules for Confidence and Prediction Intervals

Because the confidence interval formulas are complex enough to discourage their use, we are motivated to consider approximations. When x_i is not too far from $\bar{x}$, the last term under the square root is small and might be ignored. As a further simplification, we might ignore $1/n$ in the individual Y formula (if n is large, then $1/n$ will be small). These simplifications yield the quick confidence and prediction intervals shown below. If you want a *really* quick 95 percent interval, you can plug in $t = 2$ (since most 95 percent t-values are not far from 2).

(12.31) $$\hat{y}_i \pm t_{\alpha/2}\frac{s_e}{\sqrt{n}}$$ (quick confidence interval for mean of Y)

(12.32) $$\hat{y}_i \pm t_{\alpha/2}s_e$$ (quick prediction interval for individual Y)

These quick rules lead to constant width intervals and are *not* conservative (i.e., the resulting intervals will be somewhat too narrow). They work best for large samples and when X is near its mean. They are questionable when X is near either extreme of its range. Yet they often are close enough to convey a general idea of the accuracy of your predictions. Their purpose is to give a quick answer without getting lost in unwieldy formulas.

SECTION EXERCISES

connect

12.32 Refer to the Weekly Earnings data set below. (a) Use MegaStat or MINITAB to find confidence and prediction intervals for Y using the following set of x values: 12, 17, 21, 25, and 30. (b) Report the 95 percent confidence interval and prediction interval for $x = 17$. (c) Calculate the 95 percent confidence interval for μ_y using the appropriate method from Chapter 8. (d) Compare the result from part (c) to the confidence interval you reported in part (b). How are they different?

College Student Weekly Earnings ($n = 5$) WeekPay

Hours Worked (X)	*Weekly Pay (Y)*
10	93
15	171
20	204
20	156
35	261

12.33 Refer to the Revenue and Profit data set below. Data are in billions of dollars. (a) Use MegaStat or MINITAB to find confidence and prediction intervals for Y using the following set of x values: 1.8, 15, and 30. (b) Report the 95 percent confidence interval and prediction interval for $x = 15$. (c) Calculate the 95 percent confidence interval for μ_y using the appropriate method from Chapter 8. (d) Compare the result from part (c) to the confidence interval you reported in part (b). How are they different?

Revenue and Profit of Entertainment Companies ($n = 9$) Entertainment

Revenue (X)	*Profit (Y)*
1.792	−0.020
8.931	1.146
2.446	−0.978
1.883	−0.162
2.490	0.185
43.877	2.639
1.311	0.155
26.585	1.417
27.061	1.267

12.8 RESIDUAL TESTS

Three Important Assumptions

LO 12-8

Calculate residuals and perform tests of regression assumptions.

Recall that the dependent variable is a random variable that has an error component, ε. In Section 12.3 we discussed three assumptions that the OLS method makes about the random error term ε. The regression assumptions are restated here:

- Assumption 1: The errors are *normally* distributed.
- Assumption 2: The errors have *constant* variance.
- Assumption 3: The errors are *independent.*

Because we cannot observe the error ε, we must rely on the residuals $e_1, e_2, \ldots, e_n$ from the estimated regression for clues about possible violations of these assumptions. While formal tests exist for identifying assumption violations, many analysts rely on simple visual tools to help them determine when an assumption has not been met and how serious the violation is.

In this chapter we will discuss the consequences of violating each assumption and explain the visual tools used for examining the residuals. In Chapter 13 we will discuss in more detail how to remedy an assumption violation and demonstrate a more formal method for examining assumption 3.

Violation of Assumption 1: Non-normal Errors

The main consequence of non-normality of errors is that confidence intervals for the parameters may be untrustworthy because the normality assumption is used to justify using Student's t to construct confidence intervals. However, if the sample size is large (say, $n > 30$), the confidence intervals should be OK. An exception would be if outliers exist, posing a serious problem that may be cured by large sample size. Non-normality of errors is usually considered a mild violation because the regression parameter estimates b_0 and b_1 and their variances remain unbiased and consistent. The hypotheses are

H_0: Errors are normally distributed

H_1: Errors are not normally distributed

A simple way to check for non-normality is to make a histogram of the residuals. You can use either plain residuals or **standardized residuals**. A *standardized residual* is obtained by dividing each residual by its standard error. Histogram shapes will be the same, but standardized residuals offer the advantage of a predictable scale (between -3 and $+3$ unless there are outliers). A simple "eyeball test" can usually reveal outliers or serious asymmetry. Figure 12.23 shows a standardized residual histogram for Mini Case 12.3 (cockpit noise). There are no outliers and the histogram is roughly symmetric, albeit possibly platykurtic (i.e., flatter than normal).

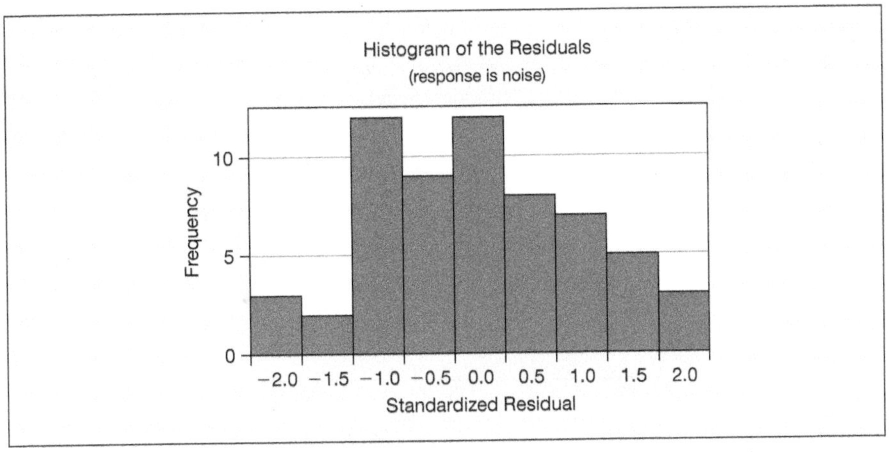

FIGURE 12.23

Cockpit Noise Residuals (Histogram) Cockpit

Another visual test for normality is the **normal probability plot**. It is produced as an option by all three software packages we've discussed. If the null hypothesis is true, the residual normal probability plot should be linear. For example, in Figure 12.24 we see slight deviations from linearity at the lower and upper ends of the residual probability plot for Mini Case 12.3 (cockpit noise). The residuals seem to be consistent with the null hypothesis of normality. There are more precise tests for normality, but the histogram and normal probability plot suffice for most purposes.

FIGURE 12.24

Cockpit Noise Residuals (Normal Probability Plot)

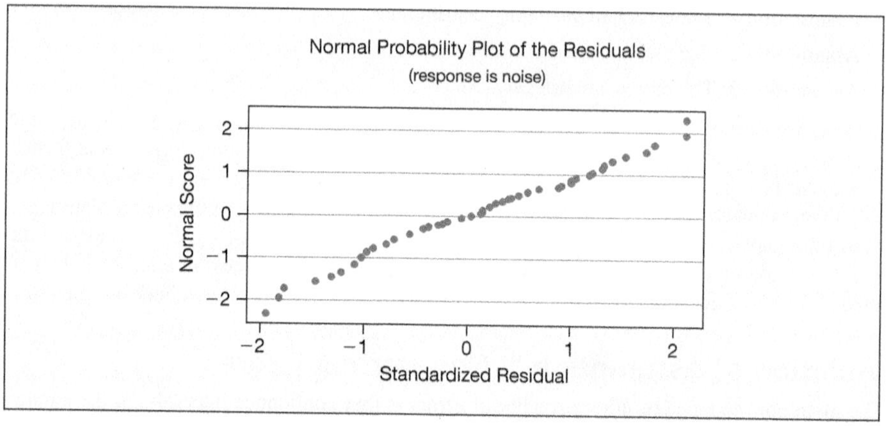

Normality Assumption Violation

Non-normality is not considered a major violation because the parameter estimates remain unbiased and consistent. Don't worry too much about it *unless* you have major outliers.

Violation of Assumption 2: Nonconstant Variance

The regression should fit equally well for all values of X. If the error magnitude is constant for all X, the errors are **homoscedastic** (the ideal condition). If the error magnitudes increase or decrease as X changes, they are **heteroscedastic**. Although the OLS regression parameter estimates b_0 and b_1 are still unbiased and consistent, their estimated variances are biased and are neither efficient nor asymptotically efficient. In the most common form of heteroscedasticity, the variances of the estimators are likely to be understated, resulting in overstated t statistics and artificially narrow confidence intervals. Your regression estimates may thus seem more significant than is warranted.

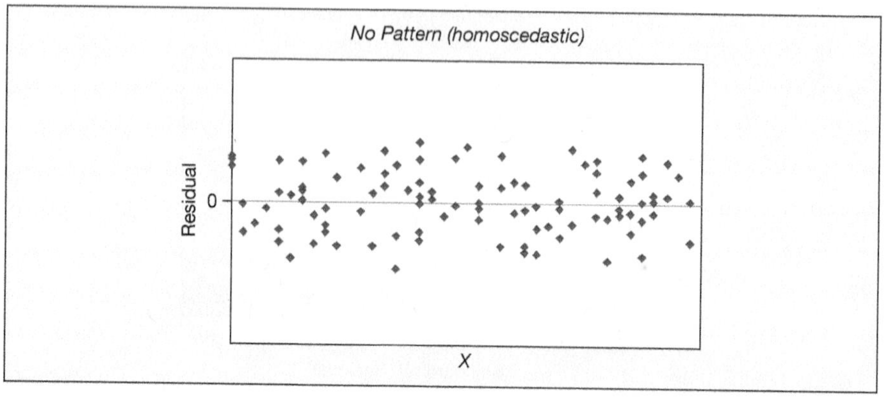

For a simple regression, you can see heteroscedasticity on the *XY* scatter plot, but a more general visual test is to plot the residuals against *X* or against $\hat{Y}$. Ideally, there is no pattern in the residuals as we move from left to right, as shown in the illustration below. Notice that residuals *always* have a mean of zero.

Although many patterns of nonconstant variance might exist, the "fan-out" pattern (increasing residual variance) is most common. Less frequently we might see a "funnel-in" pattern, which shows decreasing residual variance.

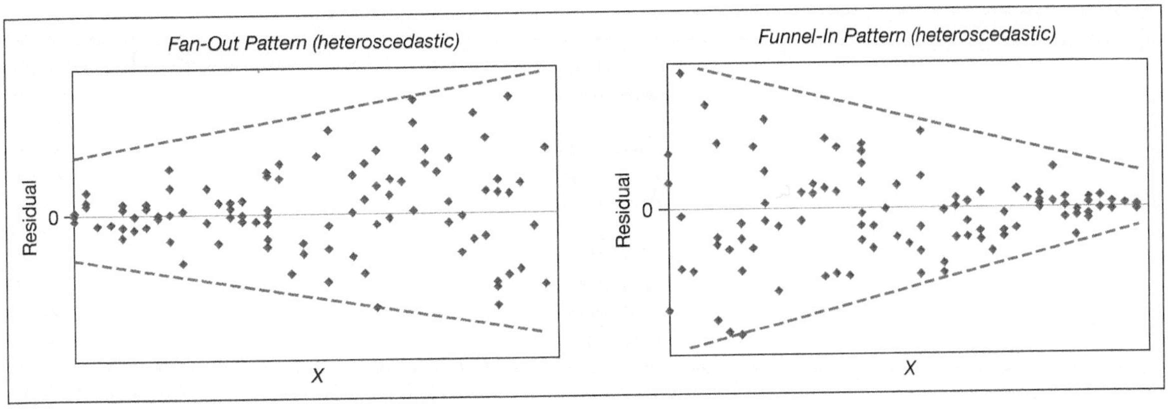

Residual plots provide a fairly sensitive "eyeball test" for heteroscedasticity. The residual plot is therefore considered an important tool in the statistician's diagnostic kit. The hypotheses are

H_0: Errors have constant variance (homoscedastic)

H_1: Errors have nonconstant variance (heteroscedastic)

Figure 12.25 shows a residual plot for Mini Case 12.3 (cockpit noise). In this residual plot, the magnitude of the residuals does not increase or decrease as we look from left to right. A pattern like this is consistent with the null hypothesis of homoscedasticity (constant variance). When using visual tools, we are looking for *obvious* departures from the assumptions of normality and constant variance. Consider the overall shape of the plot and don't focus on one or two residuals that might be considered outliers.

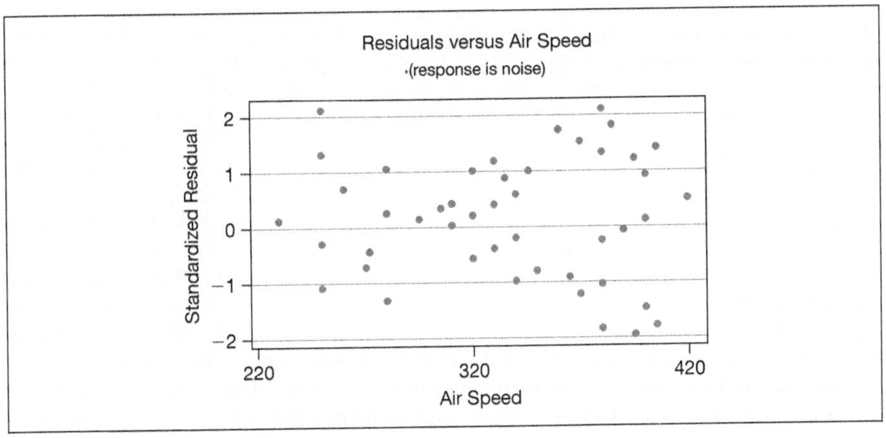

FIGURE 12.25

Cockpit Noise Residual Plot (Homoscedastic)

Figure 12.26 shows a heteroscedastic residual plot from a regression of home prices versus square feet. The magnitude of the residuals increases as the home size increases. A pattern like this is consistent with heteroscedasticity (nonconstant variance). In Chapter 13 you will learn how we might remedy the violation of constant error variance.

FIGURE 12.26

Home Price Residual Plot (Heteroscedastic)

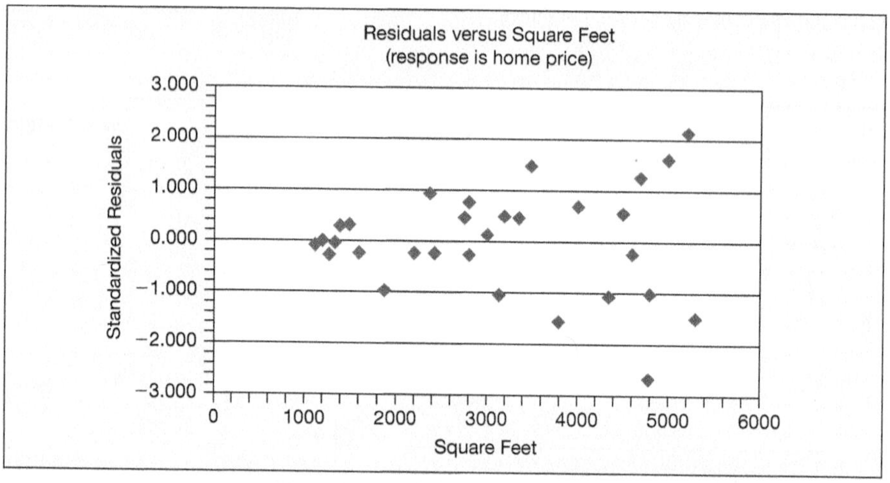

Homoscedastic Errors Assumption Violation

Although it can widen the confidence intervals for the coefficients, heteroscedasticity does not bias the estimates. At this stage of your training, it is sufficient just to recognize its existence.

Violation of Assumption 3: Autocorrelated Errors

Autocorrelation is a pattern of nonindependent errors, mainly found in time-series data. When variable observations are collected in a specific order such as in a time series, it is possible that the errors $e_1, e_2, \ldots, e_n$ are related to each other. In a regression, each residual e_t should be independent of its predecessors $e_{t-1}, e_{t-2}, \ldots, e_1$. Violations of this assumption can show up in different ways. In the simple model of *first-order autocorrelation,* we would find that e_t is correlated with the prior residual e_{t-1}. The OLS estimators b_0 and b_1 are still unbiased and consistent, but their estimated variances are biased in a way that typically leads to confidence intervals that are too narrow and t statistics that are too large. Thus, the model's fit may be overstated.

Positive autocorrelation is indicated by runs of residuals with the *same* sign, while *negative autocorrelation* is indicated by runs of residuals with *alternating* signs. Such patterns can sometimes be seen in a plot of the residuals against the order of data entry. In the *runs test,* we count the number of sign reversals (i.e., how often does the residual plot cross the zero centerline?). If the pattern is random, the number of sign changes should be approximately $n/2$. Fewer than $n/2$ centerline crossings would suggest positive autocorrelation, while more than $n/2$ centerline crossings would suggest negative autocorrelation. For example, if $n = 50$, we would expect about 25 centerline crossings. In the first illustration, there are only 11 crossings (positive autocorrelation), while in the second illustration there are 36 crossings (negative autocorrelation). Positive autocorrelation is common in economic time-series regressions due to the cyclical nature of the economy. It is harder to envision logical reasons for negative autocorrelation, and in fact it is rarely observed.

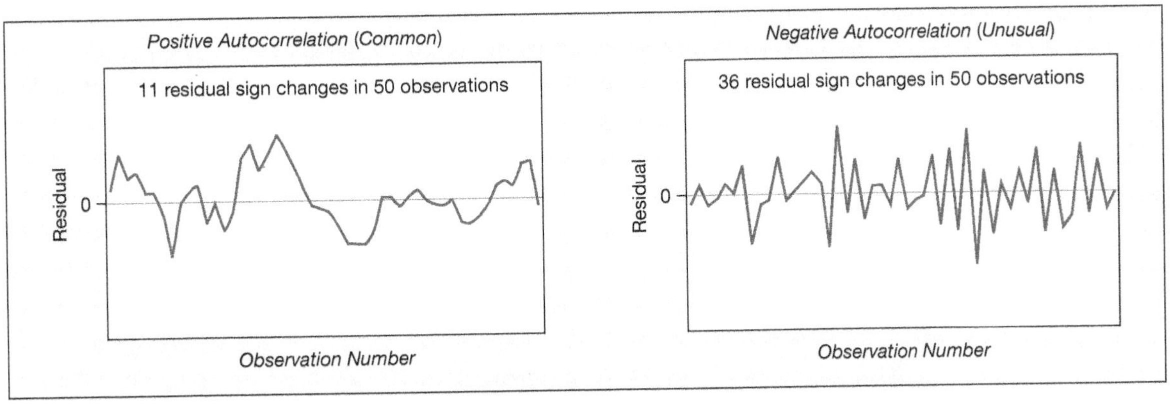

Independent Errors Assumption Violation

Autocorrelation is a concern with time-series data. Although it can widen the confidence intervals for the coefficients, autocorrelation does not bias the estimates. At this stage of your training, it is sufficient just to recognize when you have autocorrelation.

Mini Case 12.4

Exports and Imports **Exports**

We often see headlines about the persistent imbalance in U.S. foreign trade (e.g., "U.S. Trade Deficit Sets Record," *International Herald Tribune,* March 14, 2007). But when U.S. imports increase, other nations acquire dollar balances that economists predict will lead to increased purchases of U.S. goods and services, thereby increasing U.S. exports (i.e., trade imbalances are supposed to be self-correcting). Figure 12.27 shows a regression based on U.S. exports and imports for 1959–2005. To reduce autocorrelation (these are time-series data), the model regresses the *change* in exports (denoted $\triangle Exports$) against the *change* in imports (denoted $\triangle Imports$) for each period. The fitted model is $\triangle Exports = 5.2849 + 0.5193\ \triangle Imports$. As expected, the slope is positive and significant ($t = 10.277$, p-value $< .0001$) and the fit is fairly good ($R^2 = .7059$) despite the first-differences data transformation. But the slope ($b_1 = 0.5193$) indicates that the change in exports is only about half the change in imports, so the trade imbalance remains a puzzle. An economist would perhaps want to examine the role of exchange rate inflexibility, vis-à-vis China or other factors, in constructing a more complex model.

FIGURE 12.27 **Excel Scatter Plot and Regression**

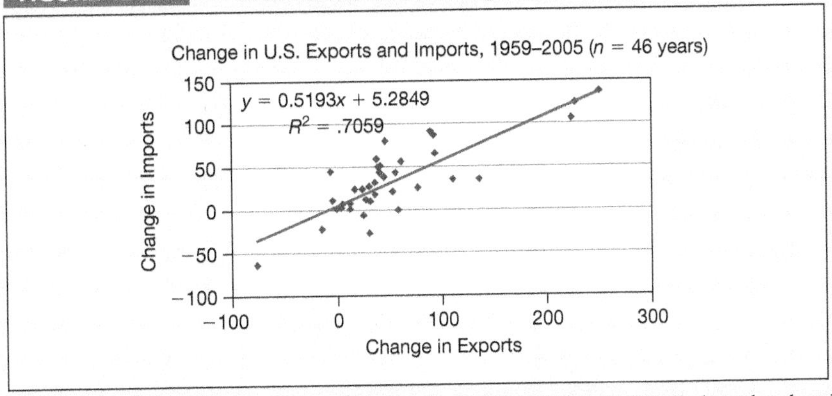

Figure 12.28 shows that the residuals appear normal (the histogram is bell-shaped and probability plot is roughly linear with no obvious outliers) and homoscedastic (no pattern in the

plot of residuals against predicted Y). But autocorrelation still appears to be a problem with 9 centerline crossings in the residual plot over time, which suggests positive autocorrelation.

FIGURE 12.28

Four Residual Tests

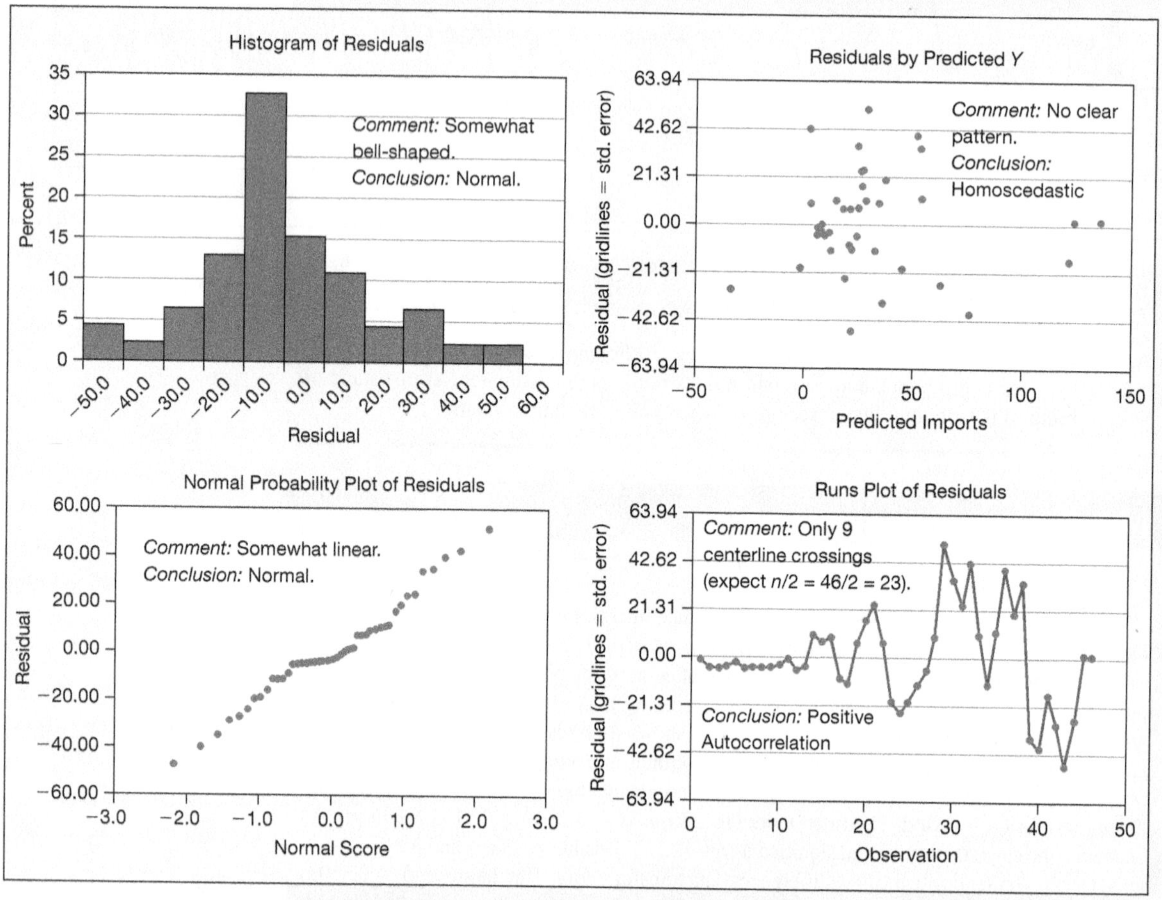

SECTION EXERCISES

connect

12.34 Review the two residual plots below. Do either of these show evidence that the regression error assumptions of normality and constant variation have been violated? Explain.

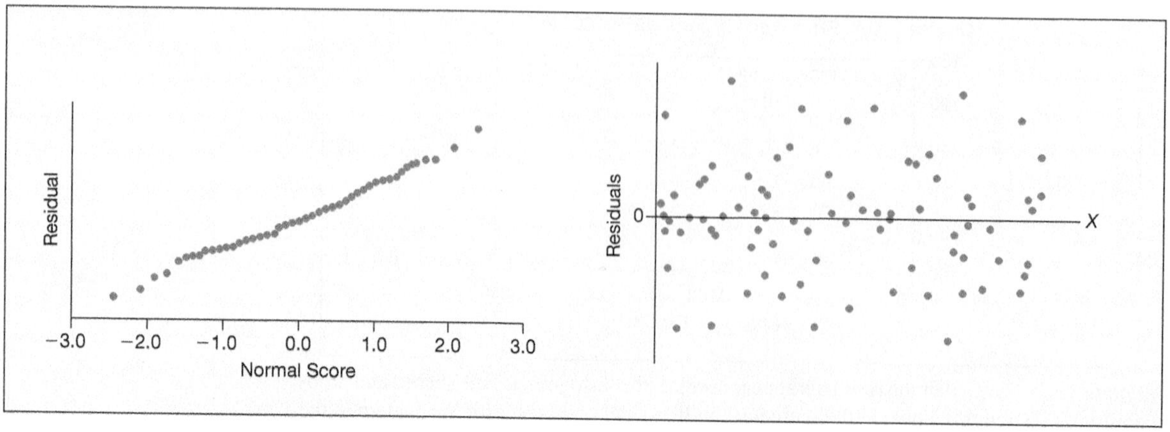

12.35 Review the two residual plots below. Do either of these show evidence that the regression error assumptions of normality and constant variation have been violated? Explain.

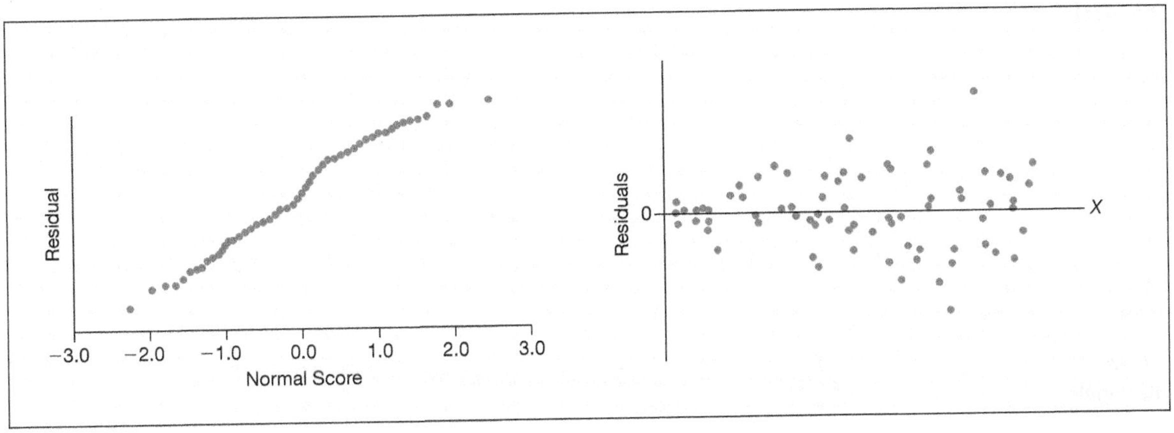

12.9 UNUSUAL OBSERVATIONS

LO 12-9

Identify unusual residuals and tell when they are outliers.

LO 12-10

Define leverage and identify high-leverage observations.

In a regression, we look for observations that are unusual. An observation could be unusual because its *Y*-value is poorly predicted by the regression model (*unusual residual*) or because its unusual *X*-value greatly affects the regression line (*high leverage*). Tests for unusual residuals and high leverage are important diagnostic tools in evaluating the fitted regression.

Unusual Residuals

Because every regression may have different *Y* units (e.g., stock price in dollars, shipping time in days), it is helpful to *standardize* the residuals by dividing each residual, e_i, by its individual standard error, s_{e_i}.

(12.33) $$e_i^* = \frac{e_i}{s_{e_i}} \quad \text{(standardized residual for observation } i\text{)}$$

where

$$s_{e_i} = s_e\sqrt{1-h_i} \quad \text{and} \quad h_i = \frac{1}{n} + \frac{(x_i-\bar{x})^2}{\sum(x_i-\bar{x})^2}$$

Notice that this calculation requires a unique adjustment for each residual based on the observation's distance from the mean. We will refer to this value e_i^* as a *standardized residual*. An equivalent name for this value is **studentized residual**, which is used by many software packages.

Using the Empirical Rule as a rule of thumb, any standardized residual whose absolute value is 2 or more is unusual, and any residual whose absolute value is 3 or more would be considered an outlier. There are subtle differences in the way Excel, MegaStat, and MINITAB calculate and display standardized residuals.

Excel's Data Analysis > Regression provides residuals as an option, as shown in Figure 12.29. Excel calculates its "standardized residuals" by dividing each residual by the standard deviation of the column of residuals. This procedure is not quite correct, but generally suffices to identify unusual residuals. Using the Empirical Rule, there are no unusual residuals in Figure 12.29.

MINITAB gives the same general output as Excel, but with rounded results and more detailed residual information. Its menus are shown in Figure 12.30. MINITAB reports standardized residuals, which usually are close in value to Excel's "standardized" residuals.

FIGURE 12.29

Excel's Exam Score Residuals

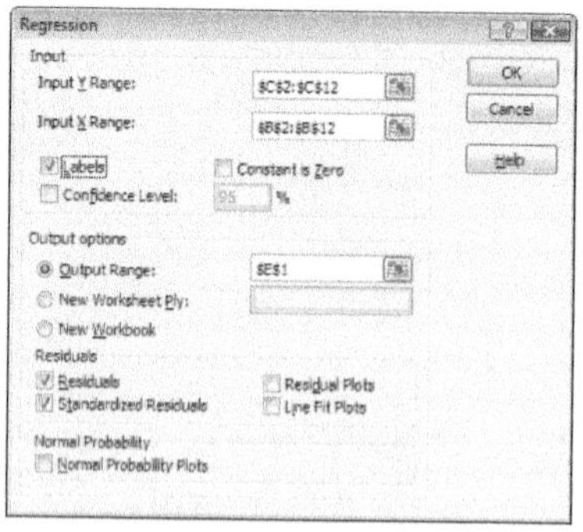

RESIDUAL OUTPUT

Observation	Predicted Exam Score	Residuals	Standard Residuals
1	51.44120983	1.55879017	0.118075152
2	59.29754253	14.70245747	1.113680937
3	63.22570888	-4.225708885	-0.320088764
4	65.18979206	-22.18979206	-1.680831145
5	69.11795841	-13.11795841	-0.99365839
6	71.08204159	12.91795841	0.978508801
7	76.97429112	19.02570888	1.441158347
8	78.93837429	-9.938374291	-0.752811428
9	78.93837429	5.061625709	0.383407745
10	86.79470699	-3.794706994	-0.287441256

FIGURE 12.30

MINITAB's Exam Score Residuals

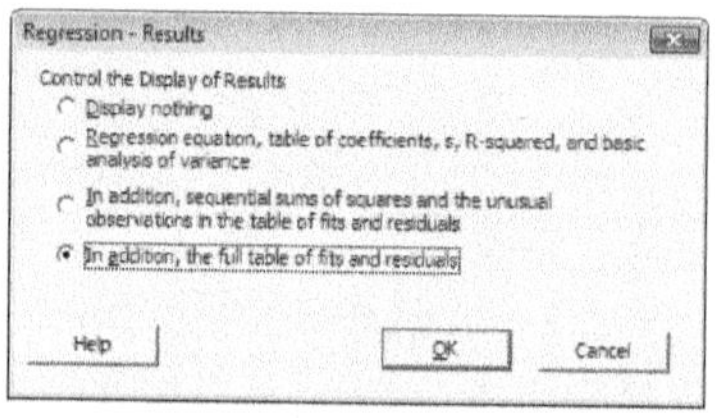

Obs	Hours	Score	Fit	SE Fit	Residual	St Resid
1	1.0	53.00	51.44	9.30	1.56	0.15
2	5.0	74.00	59.30	6.48	14.70	1.18
3	7.0	59.00	63.23	5.36	-4.23	-0.33
4	8.0	43.00	65.19	4.92	-22.19	-1.69
5	10.0	56.00	69.12	4.45	-13.12	-0.99
6	11.0	84.00	71.08	4.45	12.92	0.97
7	14.0	96.00	76.97	5.36	19.03	1.47
8	15.0	69.00	78.94	5.88	-9.94	-0.78
9	15.0	84.00	78.94	5.88	5.06	0.40
10	19.0	83.00	86.79	8.55	-3.79	-0.34

MINITAB's results confirm that there are no unusual residuals in the exam score regression. An attractive feature of MINITAB is that the actual and fitted Y-values are displayed (Excel shows only the fitted Y-values). MINITAB also gives the standard error for the mean of Y (the column labeled SE Fit), which you can multiply by $t_{\alpha/2}$ to get the confidence interval width.

MegaStat gives the same general output as Excel and MINITAB. Its regression menu is shown in Figure 12.31. Like MINITAB, it offers studentized residuals, but MegaStat also shows *studentized deleted residuals*. This is yet another way to identify unusual residuals. The calculation is equivalent to rerunning the regression n times, with each observation omitted in turn, and recalculating the studentized residuals. Further calculation details are reserved for an advanced statistics class, but interpretation is simple. A studentized deleted residual whose absolute value is 2 or more is unusual and one whose absolute value is 3 or more is typically considered an outlier. To make the output more readable, MegaStat rounds off the values (like MINITAB) and highlights unusual and outlier standardized residuals.

FIGURE 12.31

MegaStat's Exam Score Residuals

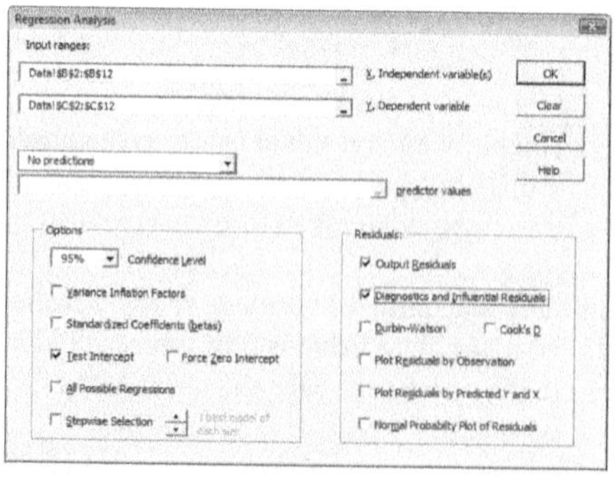

Observation	Exam Score	Predicted	Residual	Leverage	Studentized Residual	Studentized Deleted Residual
1	53.0	51.4	1.6	0.441	0.149	0.139
2	74.0	59.3	14.7	0.214	1.185	1.220
3	59.0	63.2	-4.2	0.146	-0.327	-0.308
4	43.0	65.2	-22.2	0.124	-1.693	-1.977
5	56.0	69.1	-13.1	0.101	-0.988	-0.986
6	84.0	71.1	12.9	0.101	0.973	0.969
7	96.0	77.0	19.0	0.146	1.471	1.610
8	69.0	78.9	-9.9	0.177	-0.782	-0.761
9	84.0	78.9	5.1	0.177	0.398	0.376
10	83.0	86.8	-3.8	0.373	-0.342	-0.323

High Leverage

A high **leverage** statistic indicates that the observation is far from the mean of X. Such observations have great influence on the regression estimates because they are at the "end of the lever." Figure 12.32 illustrates this concept. One individual worked 65 hours, while the others worked between 12 and 42 hours. This individual will have a big effect on the slope estimate because he is so far above the mean of X.

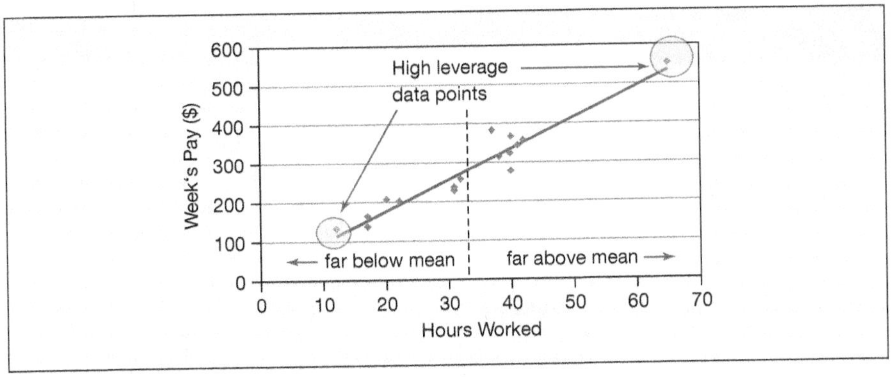

FIGURE 12.32 Illustration of High Leverage Leverage

The leverage for observation i is denoted h_i and is calculated as

$$h_i = \frac{1}{n} + \frac{(x_i - \bar{x})^2}{\sum_{i=1}^{n}(x_i - \bar{x})^2} \tag{12.34}$$

High Leverage

As a rule of thumb for a simple regression, a leverage statistic that exceeds $4/n$ is unusual (if $x_i = \bar{x}$, the leverage statistic h_i is $1/n$ so the rule of thumb is just four times this value).

EXAMPLE 12.3 *Exam Scores: Leverage and Influence* ExamScores

We see from Figure 12.33 that two data points (Tom and Courtney) are likely to have high leverage because Tom studied for only 1 hour (far below the mean) while Courtney studied for 19 hours (far above the mean). Using the sums from Table 12.3, we can calculate their leverages:

$$h_{\text{Tom}} = \frac{1}{10} + \frac{(1 - 10.5)^2}{264.50} = .441 \quad \text{(Tom's leverage)}$$

$$h_{\text{Courtney}} = \frac{1}{10} + \frac{(19 - 10.5)^2}{264.50} = .373 \quad \text{(Courtney's leverage)}$$

FIGURE 12.33 Scatter Plot for Exam Data ExamScores

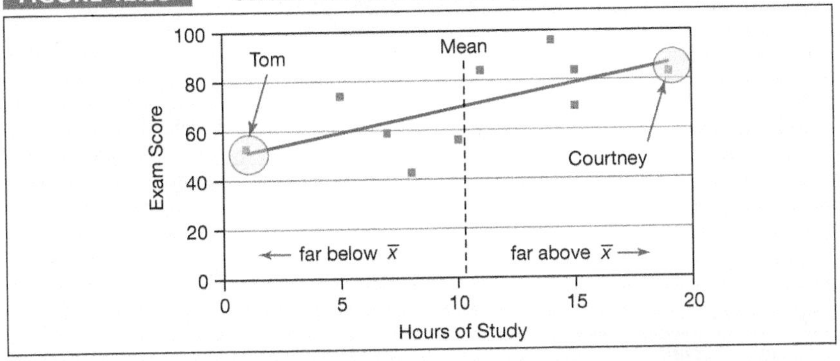

By the quick rule, Tom's leverage exceeds $4/n = 4/10 = .400$, so it appears that his observation is *influential*. Yet, despite his high leverage, the regression fits Tom's actual exam score well, so his residual is not unusual. This illustrates that *high leverage* and *unusual residuals* are two different concepts.

Mini Case 12.5

Body Fat BodyFat

Is waistline a good predictor of body fat? A random sample of 50 men's body fat (percent) and girths (centimeters) was collected. Figure 12.34 suggests that a linear regression is appropriate, and the MegaStat output in Figure 12.35 shows that the regression is highly significant ($F = 97.68$, $t = 9.883$, p-value $= .0000$).

FIGURE 12.34 **Body Fat Regression**

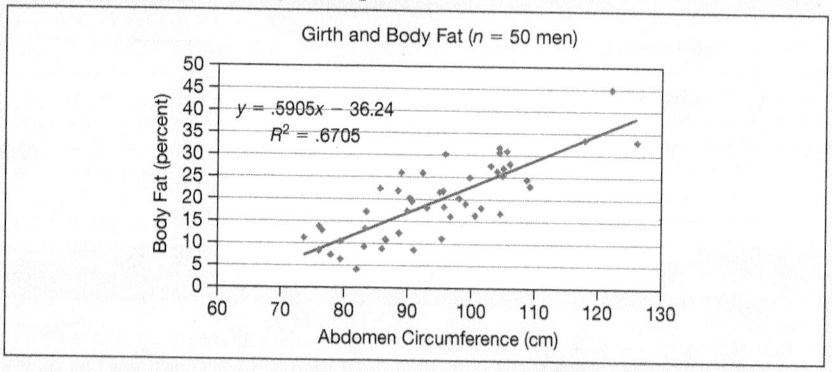

The table of residuals, shown in Figure 12.36, highlights four unusual observations. Observations 5, 45, and 50 have high leverage values (exceeding $4/n = 4/50 = .08$) because their abdomen measurements are far from the mean. Observation 37 has a large studentized deleted residual (actual body fat of 30.20 percent is much greater than the predicted 20.33 percent). "Well-behaved" observations are omitted because they are not unusual according to any of the diagnostic criteria (leverage, studentized residual, or studentized deleted residual).

FIGURE 12.35 **Body Fat Scatter Plot**

Regression Analysis

r^2	0.671	n	50
r	0.819	k	1
Std. Error	5.086	Dep. Var.	Fat% 1

ANOVA table

Source	*SS*	*df*	*MS*	*F*	*p-value*
Regression	2,527.1190	1	2,527.1190	97.68	3.71E-13
Residual	1,241.8162	48	25.8712		
Total	3,768.9352	49			

Regression output

variables	*coefficients*	*std. error*	*t (df= 48)*	*p-value*	*confidence interval 95% lower*	*95% upper*
Intercept	−36.2397	5.6690	−6.393	6.28E-08	−47.6379	−24.8415
Abdomen	0.5905	0.0597	9.883	3.71E-13	0.4704	0.7107

FIGURE 12.36 **Unusual Body Fat Residuals**

Observation	Fat%	Predicted	Residual	Leverage	Studentized Residual	Studentized Deleted Residual
5	33.60	33.44	0.16	0.099	0.033	0.032
37	30.20	20.33	9.87	0.020	1.960	2.022
45	33.10	38.28	−5.18	0.162	−1.114	−1.116
50	45.10	35.86	9.24	0.128	1.945	2.005

SECTION EXERCISES

connect

12.36 An estimated regression for a random sample of observations on an assembly line is *Defects* = 3.2 + 0.045 *Speed*, where *Defects* is the number of defects per million parts and *Speed* is the number of units produced per hour. The estimated standard error is s_e = 1.07. Suppose that 100 units per hour are produced and the actual (observed) defect rate is *Defects* = 4.4. (a) Calculate the predicted *Defects*. (b) Calculate the residual. (c) Standardize the residual using s_e. (d) Is this observation an outlier?

12.37 An estimated regression for a random sample of vehicles is *MPG* = 49.22 − 0.081 *Horsepower*, where *MPG* is miles per gallon and *Horsepower* is the engine's horsepower. The standard error is s_e = 2.03. Suppose an engine has 200 horsepower and its actual (observed) fuel efficiency is *MPG* = 38.15. (a) Calculate the predicted *MPG*. (b) Calculate the residual. (c) Standardize the residual using s_e. (d) Is this engine an outlier?

12.38 A sample of season performance measures for 29 NBA teams was collected for a season. A regression analysis was performed on two of the variables with *Y* = *total number of free throws made* and *X* = *total number of free throws attempted*. Calculate the leverage statistic for the following three teams and state whether or not the leverage would be considered high. Given: SS_{xx} = 999,603 and $\bar{x}$ = 2004.

a. The Golden State Warriors attempted 2,382 free throws.
b. The New Jersey Nets attempted 2,125 free throws.
c. The New York Knicks attempted 1,620 free throws.

12.39 A sample of 74 Noodles & Company restaurants was used to perform a regression analysis with *Y* = *% Annual Revenue Growth* and *X* = *% Revenue Due to Loyalty Card Use*. Calculate the leverage statistic for the following three restaurants and state whether or not the leverage would be considered high. Given: SS_{xx} = 22.285 and $\bar{x}$ = 2.027 percent.

a. Restaurant 21 earned .072 percent of revenue from loyalty card use.
b. Restaurant 29 earned 1.413 percent of revenue from loyalty card use.
c. Restaurant 64 earned 3.376 percent of revenue from loyalty card use.

12.10 OTHER REGRESSION PROBLEMS (OPTIONAL)

Outliers

LO 12-11

Improve data conditioning and use transformations if needed (optional).

We have mentioned outliers under the discussion of non-normal residuals. However, outliers are the source of many other woes, including loss of fit. What causes outliers? An outlier may be an error in recording the data. If so, the observation should be deleted. But how can you tell? Impossible or bizarre data values are *prima facie* reasons to discard a data value. For example, in a sample of body fat data, one adult man's weight was reported as 205 pounds and his height as 29.5 inches (probably a typographical error that should have been 69.5 inches). It is reasonable to discard the observation on grounds that it represents a population different from the other men. An outlier may be an observation that has been influenced by an unspecified "lurking" variable that should have been controlled but wasn't. If so, we should try to identify the lurking variable and formulate a *multiple* regression model that includes the lurking variable(s) as predictors.

Model Misspecification

If a relevant predictor has been omitted, then the model is *misspecified*. Instead of simple regression, you should use *multiple regression*. Such a situation is so common that it is almost a warning against relying on bivariate regression, since we usually can think of more than one explanatory variable. As you will see in the next chapter, multiple regression is computationally easy because the computer does all the work. In fact, most computer packages just call it "regression" regardless of the number of predictors.

Ill-Conditioned Data

Variables in the regression should be of the same general order of magnitude, and most people take steps intuitively to make sure this is the case (**well-conditioned data**). Unusually large or small data (called **ill-conditioned**) can cause loss of regression accuracy or can create awkward estimates with exponential notation. Consider the data in Table 12.5 for 30 randomly selected large companies (only a few of the 30 selected are shown in this table). The table shows two ways of displaying the same data, but with the decimal point changed. Figures 12.37 and 12.38 show Excel scatter plots with regression lines. Their appearance is the same, but the first graph has disastrously crowded axis labels. The graphs have the same slope and R^2, but the first regression has an unintelligible intercept (4E+07).

TABLE 12.5

Net Income and Revenue for Selected Global 100 Companies
Global30

See www.forbes.com and *Forbes* 172, no. 2 (July 21, 2003), pp. 108–110.

Company	*Net Income in Thousands*	*Revenue in Thousands*	*Net Income in Millions*	*Revenue in Millions*
Allstate	1,714,000	30,142,000	1,714	30,142
American Int'l Group	5,493,000	70,272,000	5,493	70,272
Barclays	3,348,000	26,565,000	3,348	26,565
⋮	⋮	⋮	⋮	⋮
Volkswagen Group	2,432,000	84,707,000	2,432	84,707
Wachovia	3,693,000	23,455,000	3,693	23,455
Walt Disney	1,024,000	26,255,000	1,024	26,255

FIGURE 12.37

Ill-Conditioned Data

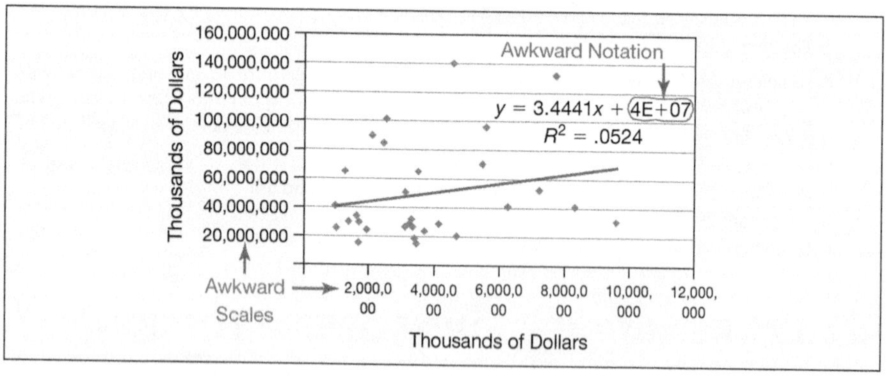

FIGURE 12.38

Well-Conditioned Data

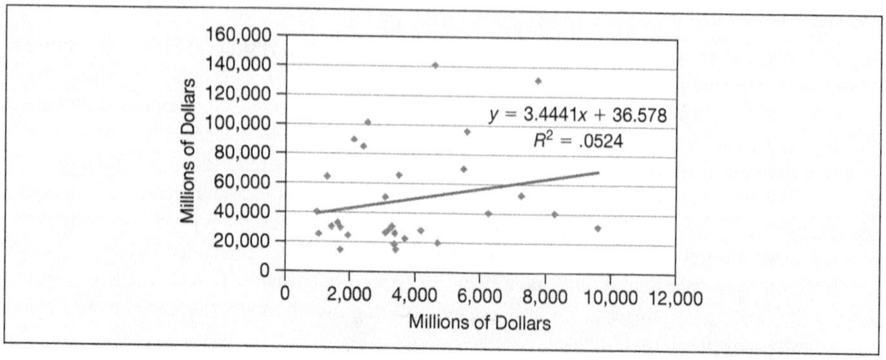

Awkwardly small numbers may also require adjustment. For example, the number of automobile thefts per capita in the United States in 2009 was 0.002588. However, this statistic is easier to work with if it is reported "per 100,000 population" as 258.8. Worst of all would be to mix very large data with very small data. For example, in 2009 the per capita income in New York was $46,957 and the number of active physicians per capita was 0.00391. To avoid mixing magnitudes, we can redefine the variables as per capita income in thousands of dollars (46.957) and the number of active physicians per 10,000 population (39.1).

Scaling Data

Adjust the magnitude of your data *before* running the regression.

Spurious Correlation Prisoners

In a **spurious correlation**, two variables appear related because of the way they are defined. For example, consider the hypothesis that a state's spending on education is a linear function of its prison population. Such a hypothesis seems absurd, and we would expect the regression to be insignificant. But if the variables are defined as *totals* without adjusting for population, we will observe significant correlation. This phenomenon is called the *size effect* or the *problem of totals*. Table 12.6 shows selected data, first with the variables as *totals* and then as adjusted for population.

TABLE 12.6

State Spending on Education and State and Federal Prisoners Prisoners

		Using Totals		Using Per Capita Data	
State	*Total Population (millions)*	*K–12 Spending ($ billions)*	*No. of Prisoners (thousands)*	*K–12 Spending per Capita ($)*	*Prisoners per 1,000 Pop.*
Alabama	4.447	4.52	24.66	1,016	5.54
Alaska	0.627	1.33	3.95	2,129	6.30
⋮	⋮	⋮	⋮	⋮	⋮
Wisconsin	5.364	8.48	20.42	1,580	3.81
Wyoming	0.494	0.76	1.71	1,543	3.47

Source: *Statistical Abstract of the United States, 2001.*

Figure 12.39 shows that, contrary to expectation, the regression on totals gives a very strong fit to the data. Yet Figure 12.40 shows that if we divide by population and adjust the decimals, the fit is nonexistent and the slope is indistinguishable from zero. The spurious correlation arose merely because both variables reflect the size of a state's population. For example, New York and California lie far to the upper right on the first scatter plot because they are populous states, while less populous states like South Dakota and Delaware are near the origin.

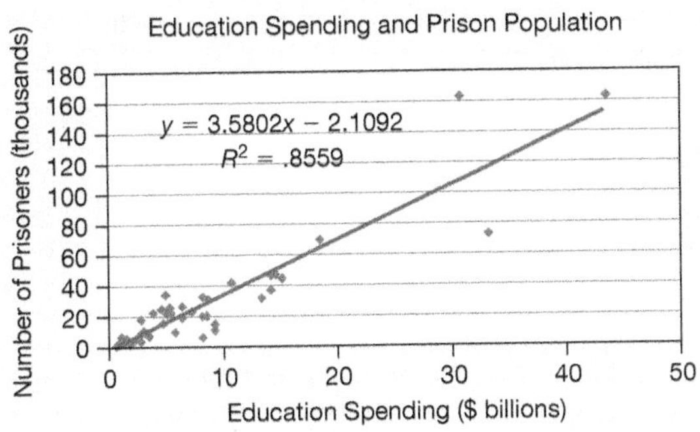

FIGURE 12.39

Spurious Model Using Totals

FIGURE 12.40

Better Model: Per Capita Data

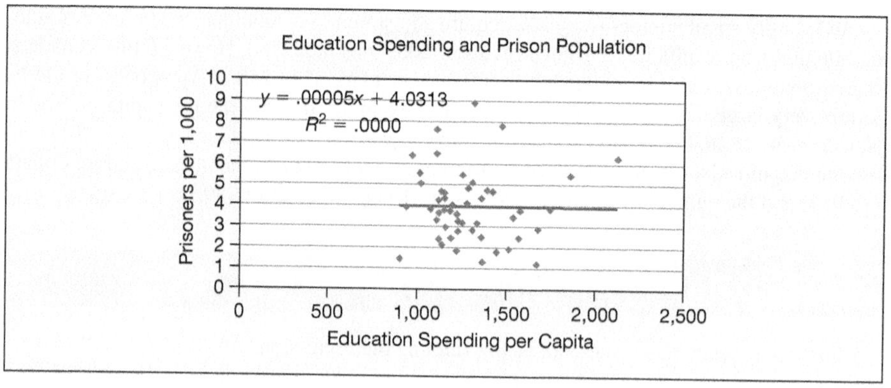

Model Form and Variable Transforms MPG 1

Sometimes a relationship cannot be modeled using a linear regression. For example, Figure 12.41 shows fuel efficiency (city MPG) and engine size (horsepower) for a sample of 93 vehicles with a nonlinear model form fitted by Excel. This is one of several nonlinear forms offered by Excel (there are also logarithmic and exponential functions). Figure 12.42 shows an alternative, which is a linear regression after taking *logarithms* of each variable. These logarithms are in base 10, but any base will do (scientists prefer base *e*). This is an example of a **variable transform**. An advantage of the **log transformation** is that it reduces heteroscedasticity and improves the normality of the residuals, especially when dealing with totals (the *size problem* mentioned earlier). But log transforms will not work if any data values are zero or negative.

FIGURE 12.41

Nonlinear Regression

See Robin H. Lock, *Journal of Statistics Education* 1, no. 1 (1993).

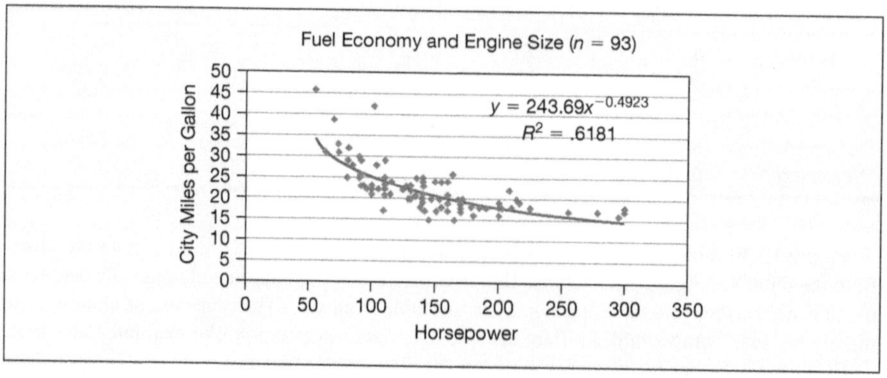

FIGURE 12.42

After Log Transformation

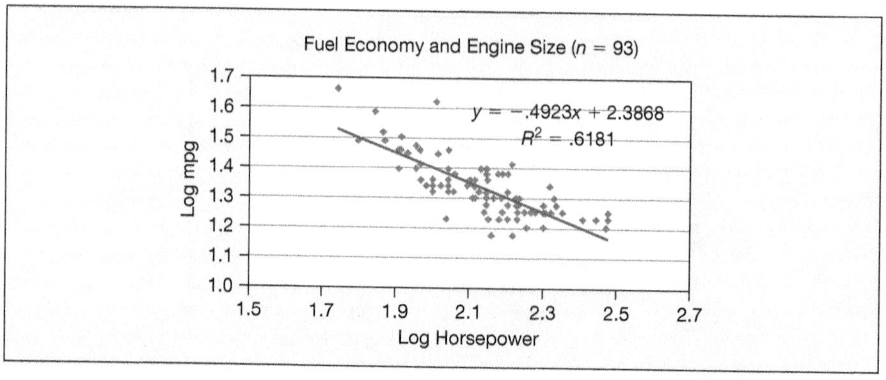

Excel makes it easy to fit all sorts of regression models. But fit is only one criterion for evaluating a regression model. Since nonlinear or transformed models might be hard to justify or explain to others, the principle of *Occam's Razor* (choosing the simplest explanation that fits the facts) favors linear regression, unless there are other compelling factors.

Mini Case 12.6

CEO Compensation CEO

Do highly compensated executives lead their corporations to outperform other firms? Statistics student Greg Burks examined 1-year total shareholder returns in 2001 less the S&P 500 average (i.e., percentage points above or below the S&P average) as a function of total CEO compensation in 2001 for the top 200 U.S. corporations. A scatter plot is shown in Figure 12.43. There appears to be little relationship, but a dozen or so hugely compensated CEOs (e.g., those earning over 50 million) stretch the *X*-axis scale while many others are clustered near the origin. A log transformation of *X* (using base 10) is shown in Figure 12.44. Neither fitted regression is significant. That is, there is little relationship between CEO compensation and stockholder returns (if anything, the slope is negative). However, the transformed data give a clearer picture. An advantage of the log transformation is that it improves the scatter of the residuals, producing a more homoscedastic distribution. In short, a log transformation with skewed data is an excellent option to consider.

FIGURE 12.43 **CEO Compensation and Stock Returns**

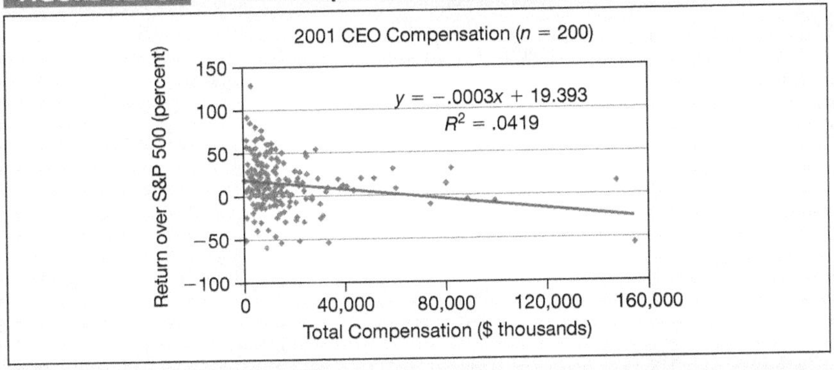

See *The New York Times*, Apr. 4, 2004, pp. 8–9.

FIGURE 12.44 **After Log Transformation**

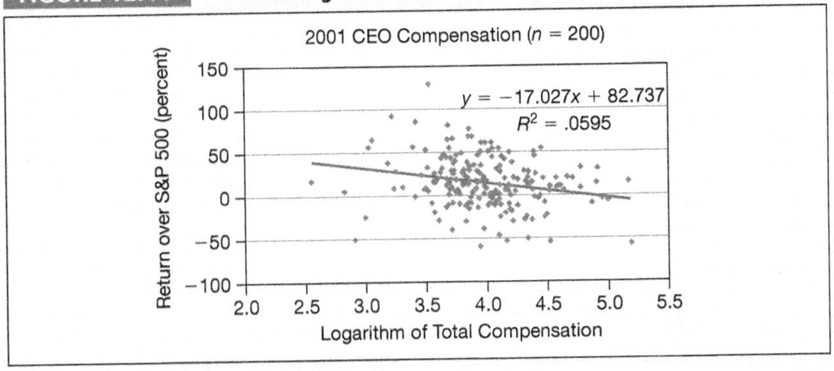

CHAPTER SUMMARY

The **sample correlation coefficient** r measures linear association between X and Y, with values near 0 indicating a lack of linearity while values near -1 (negative correlation) or $+1$ (positive correlation) suggest linearity. The ***t* test** is used to test hypotheses about the **population correlation** ρ. In **simple regression** there is an assumed linear relationship between the independent variable X (the **predictor**) and the dependent variable Y (the **response**). The slope (β_1) and intercept (β_0) are unknown **parameters** that are estimated from a sample. **Residuals** are the differences between **observed** and **fitted** Y-values. The **ordinary least squares** (OLS) method yields **regression coefficients** for the slope (b_1) and intercept (b_0) that minimize the sum of squared residuals. The **coefficient of determination** (R^2) measures the overall fit of the regression, with R^2 near 1 signifying a good fit and R^2 near 0 indicating a poor fit. The ***F* statistic** in the **ANOVA table** is used to test for significant overall regression, while the ***t* statistics** (and their p-values) are used to test hypotheses about the slope and intercept. The **standard error** of the regression is used to create **confidence intervals** or **prediction intervals** for Y. Regression assumes that the errors are normally distributed, independent random variables with constant variance σ^2. **Residual tests** identify possible **violations** of assumptions (**non-normality, autocorrelation, heteroscedasticity**). Data values with high **leverage** (unusual X-values) have strong influence on the regression. Unusual **standardized residuals** indicate cases where the regression gives a poor fit. **Ill-conditioned** data may lead to **spurious** correlation or other problems. **Data transforms** may help, but they also change the **model specification.**

KEY TERMS

autocorrelation
bivariate data
coefficient of determination
confidence interval
error sum of squares
heteroscedastic
homoscedastic
ill-conditioned data
intercept
leverage
log transformation
normal probability plot
ordinary least squares (OLS)
population correlation coefficient, ρ
prediction interval
predictor variable
R^2
regression assumptions
residual
response variable
sample correlation coefficient, r
scatter plot
simple regression equation
slope
spurious correlation
standard error
standardized residuals
studentized residuals
sums of squares
t statistic
variable transform
well-conditioned data

Commonly Used Formulas in Simple Regression

Sample correlation coefficient: $$r = \frac{\sum_{i=1}^{n}(x_i - \bar{x})(y_i - \bar{y})}{\sqrt{\sum_{i=1}^{n}(x_i - \bar{x})^2}\sqrt{\sum_{i=1}^{n}(y_i - \bar{y})^2}}$$

Test statistic for zero correlation: $$t_{\text{calc}} = r\sqrt{\frac{n-2}{1-r^2}} \quad \text{with } d.f. = n - 2$$

True regression line: $$y = \beta_0 + \beta_1 x + \varepsilon$$

Fitted regression line: $$\hat{y} = b_0 + b_1 x$$

Slope of fitted regression: $$b_1 = \frac{\sum_{i=1}^{n}(x_i - \bar{x})(y_i - \bar{y})}{\sum_{i=1}^{n}(x_i - \bar{x})^2} \quad \text{or} \quad b_1 = \frac{SS_{yx}}{SS_{xx}}$$

Intercept of fitted regression d: $$b_0 = \bar{y} - b_1\bar{x}$$

Sum of squared residuals: $$SSE = \sum_{i=1}^{n}(y_i - \hat{y}_i)^2 = \sum_{i=1}^{n}(y_i - b_0 - b_1 x_i)^2$$

Coefficient of determination: $$R^2 = 1 - \frac{\sum_{i=1}^{n}(y_i - \hat{y}_i)^2}{\sum_{i=1}^{n}(y_i - \bar{y})^2} = 1 - \frac{SSE}{SST} \quad \text{or} \quad R^2 = \frac{SSR}{SST}$$

Standard error of the estimate: $$s_e = \sqrt{\frac{\sum_{i=1}^{n}(y_i - \hat{y}_i)^2}{n-2}} = \sqrt{\frac{SSE}{n-2}}$$

Standard error of the slope: $$s_{b_1} = \frac{s_e}{\sqrt{\sum_{i=1}^{n}(x_i - \bar{x})^2}} \quad \text{with } d.f. = n - 2$$

t test for zero slope: $$t_{\text{calc}} = \frac{b_1 - 0}{s_{b_1}} \quad \text{with } d.f. = n - 2$$

Confidence interval for true slope: $$b_1 - t_{\alpha/2}\, s_{b_1} \le \beta_1 \le b_1 + t_{\alpha/2}\, s_{b_1} \quad \text{with } d.f. = n - 2$$

Confidence interval for conditional mean of Y: $$\hat{y}_i \pm t_{\alpha/2}\, s_e \sqrt{\frac{1}{n} + \frac{(x_i - \bar{x})^2}{\sum_{i=1}^{n}(x_i - \bar{x})^2}}$$

Prediction interval for Y: $$\hat{y}_i \pm t_{\alpha/2}\, s_e \sqrt{1 + \frac{1}{n} + \frac{(x_i - \bar{x})^2}{\sum_{i=1}^{n}(x_i - \bar{x})^2}}$$

CHAPTER REVIEW

1. (a) How does correlation analysis differ from regression analysis? (b) What does a correlation coefficient reveal? (c) State the quick rule for a significant correlation and explain its limitations. (d) What sums are needed to calculate a correlation coefficient? (e) What are the two ways of testing a correlation coefficient for significance?
2. (a) What is a simple regression model? (b) State three caveats about regression. (c) What does the random error component in a regression model represent? (d) What is the difference between a regression residual and the true random error?
3. (a) Explain how you fit a regression to an Excel scatter plot. (b) What are the limitations of Excel's scatter plot fitted regression?
4. (a) Explain the logic of the ordinary least squares (OLS) method. (b) How are the least squares formulas for the slope and intercept derived? (c) What sums are needed to calculate the least squares estimates?
5. (a) Why can't we use the sum of the residuals to assess fit? (b) What sums are needed to calculate R^2? (c) Name an advantage of using the R^2 statistic instead of the standard error s_{yx} to measure fit. (d) Why do we need the standard error s_{yx}?
6. (a) Explain why a confidence interval for the slope or intercept would be equivalent to a two-tailed hypothesis test. (b) Why is it especially important to test for a zero slope?
7. (a) What does the F statistic show? (b) What is its range? (c) What is the relationship between the F test and the t tests for the slope and correlation coefficient?
8. (a) For a given X, explain the distinction between a confidence interval for the conditional mean of Y and a prediction interval for an individual Y-value. (b) Why is the individual prediction interval wider? (c) Why are these intervals narrowest when X is near its mean? (d) When can quick rules for these intervals give acceptable results, and when not?
9. (a) What is a residual? (b) What is a standardized residual and why is it useful? (c) Name two alternative ways to identify unusual residuals.
10. (a) When does a data point have high leverage (refer to the scatter plot)? (b) Name one test for unusual leverage.
11. (a) Name three assumptions about the random error term in the regression model. (b) Why are the residuals important in testing these assumptions?

12. (a) What are the consequences of non-normal errors? (b) Explain two tests for non-normality.
13. (a) What is heteroscedasticity? Identify its two common forms. (b) What are its consequences? (c) How do we test for it?
14. (a) What is autocorrelation? Identify two main forms of it. (b) What are its consequences? (c) How do we test for it?
15. (a) Why might there be outliers in the residuals? (b) What actions could be taken?
16. (a) What is ill-conditioned data? How can it be avoided? (b) What is spurious correlation? How can it be avoided?
17. (a) What is a log transform? (b) What are its advantages and disadvantages?

CHAPTER EXERCISES

connect

Instructions: Choose one or more of the data sets *A–J* below, or as assigned by your instructor. The first column is the *X*, or independent, variable and the second column is the *Y*, or dependent, variable. Use a spreadsheet or a statistical package (e.g., MegaStat or MINITAB) to obtain the simple regression and required graphs. Write your answers to exercises 12.40 through 12.55 (or those assigned by your instructor) in a concise report, labeling your answers to each question. Insert tables and graphs in your report as appropriate. You may work with a partner if your instructor allows it.

12.40 Are the variables cross-sectional data or time-series data?

12.41 How do you imagine the data were collected?

12.42 Is the sample size sufficient to yield a good estimate? If not, do you think more data could easily be obtained, given the nature of the problem?

12.43 State your *a priori* hypothesis about the sign of the slope. Is it reasonable to suppose a cause-and-effect relationship?

12.44 Make a scatter plot of *Y* against *X*. Discuss what it tells you.

12.45 Use Excel's Add Trendline feature to fit a linear regression to the scatter plot. Is a linear model credible?

12.46 Interpret the slope. Does the intercept have meaning, given the range of the data?

12.47 Use Excel, MegaStat, or MINITAB to fit the regression model, including residuals and standardized residuals.

12.48 (a) Does the 95 percent confidence interval for the slope include zero? If so, what does this tell you? If not, what does it mean? (b) Do a two-tailed *t* test for zero slope at $\alpha = .05$. State the hypotheses, degrees of freedom, and critical value for your test. (c) Interpret the *p*-value for the slope. (d) Did the sample support your hypothesis about the sign of the slope?

12.49 (a) Based on the R^2 and ANOVA table for your model, how would you assess the fit? (b) Interpret the *p*-value for the *F* statistic. (c) Would you say that your model's fit is good enough to be of practical value?

12.50 Study the table of residuals. Identify as *outliers* any standardized residuals that exceed 3 and as *unusual* any that exceed 2. Can you suggest any reasons for these unusual residuals?

12.51 (a) Make a histogram (or normal probability plot) of the residuals and discuss its appearance. (b) Do you see evidence that your regression may violate the assumption of normal errors?

12.52 Inspect the residual plot to check for heteroscedasticity and report your conclusions.

12.53 Is an autocorrelation test appropriate for your data? If so, perform an eyeball inspection of residual plot against observation order or a runs test.

12.54 Use MegaStat or MINITAB to generate 95 percent confidence and prediction intervals for various *X*-values.

12.55 Use MegaStat or MINITAB to identify observations with high leverage.

DATA SET A **Median Income and Median Home Prices by State (n = 51 states)** HomePrice3

State	Median Income	Median Price
AK	$40,933	$241,750
AL	57,848	128,969
AR	46,896	120,560
⋮	⋮	⋮
WI	42,777	153,935
WV	50,351	129,369
WY	52,201	183,202

Source: *http://www.fhfa.gov and http://www.census.gov.*

DATA SET B **Midterm and Final Exam Scores for Business Statistics Students Fall Semester 2011 (n = 58 students)** ExamScores2

Midterm Exam Score	Final Exam Score
80	78
87	85
72	81
⋮	⋮
80	82
68	70
73	69

DATA SET C **Estimated and Actual Length of Stay in Months (n = 16 patients)** Hospital

Patient	ELOS	ALOS
1	10.5	10
2	4.5	2
3	7.5	4
⋮	⋮	⋮
14	6	10
15	7.5	7
16	3	5.5

Source: Records of a hospital outpatient cognitive retraining clinic.

Note: ELOS used a 42-item assessment instrument combined with expert team judgment. Patients had suffered head trauma, stroke, or other medical conditions affecting cognitive function.

DATA SET D **Single-Engine Aircraft Performance (n = 52 airplanes)** Airplanes

Mfgr/Model	TotalHP	Cruise
AMD CH 2000	116	100
Beech Baron 58	600	200
Beech Baron 58P	650	241
⋮	⋮	⋮
Sky Arrow 650 TC	81	98
Socata TB20 Trinidad	250	163
Tiger AG-5B	180	143

Source: New and used airplane reports in *Flying* (various issues).

Note: Cruise is in knots (nautical miles per hour). Data are for educational purposes only and should not be used as a guide to aircraft performance. *TotalHP* is total horse power.

DATA SET E **Microprocessor Speed (MHz) and Power Dissipation (watts) (n = 14 chips)** Microprocessors

Chip	Speed (MHz)	Power (watts)
1989 Intel 80486	20	3
1993 Pentium	100	10
1997 Pentium II	233	35
1998 Intel Celeron	300	20
1999 Pentium III	600	42
1999 AMD Athlon	600	50
2000 Pentium 4	1300	51
2004 Celeron D	2100	73
2004 Pentium 4	3800	115
2005 Pentium D	3200	130
2007 AMD Phenom	2300	95
2008 Intel Core 2	3200	136
2009 Intel Core i7	2900	95
2009 AMD Phenom II	3200	125

See wikipedia.org and *New Scientist*, 208, no. 2780 (October 2, 2010), p. 41.

DATA SET F **Restaurant Weekly Revenue and Weekly Website Hits (n = 10 restaurants)** WebSiteHits

Restaurant	Website Hits	Weekly Revenue
John's Café	1,213	$12,113
Buccan	1,490	11,409
New City Diner	1,365	14,579
Black Pearl	1,455	11,605
Saratoga	1,269	12,308
Burnt Toast	1,632	12,320
University Seat	1,323	13,225
Jimmy's	1,865	13,652
Maroon and Orange	1,590	13,893
Burger Palace	1,878	13,896

DATA SET G Mileage and Vehicle Weight (n = 73 vehicles) MPG2

Vehicle	Weight	City MPG
Acura TL	3968	20
Audi A5	3583	22
BMW 4 Series 428i	3470	22
⋮	⋮	⋮
Volkswagen Passat SE	3230	24
Volvo S60 T5	3528	21
Volvo XC90	4667	16

Source: Manufacturer websites. Vehicles are a random sample of 2014 vehicles sold in the U.S. All are gas or flex-fuel (no hybrids or electrics). Data are intended for statistical education and should not be viewed as a guide to vehicle performance.

DATA SET H Pasta Sauce per Gram Total Calories and Fat Calories (n = 20 products) Pasta

Product	Fat Cal/gm	Cal/gm
Barilla Roasted Garlic & Onion	0.20	0.64
Barilla Tomato & Basil	0.12	0.56
Classico Tomato & Basil	0.08	0.40
⋮	⋮	⋮
Ragu Roasted Garlic	0.19	0.70
Ragu Traditional	0.20	0.56
Sutter Home Tomato & Garlic	0.16	0.64

Source: Independent project by statistics students Donna Bennett, Nicole Cook, Latrice Haywood, and Robert Malcolm.

Note: Data are intended for educational purposes only and should not be viewed as a nutrition guide.

DATA SET I Temperature and Energy Usage for a Residence (n = 24 months) Electric

Month	Avg Temp (F°)	Usage (kWh)
1	62	436
2	71	464
3	76	446
⋮	⋮	⋮
22	25	840
23	38	867
24	48	606

Source: Electric bills for a residence and NOAA weather data.

DATA SET J U.S. Annual Percent Inflation in Prices of Commodities and Services (n = 47 years) Inflation

Year	Commodities%	Services%
1960	0.9	3.4
1961	0.6	1.7
1962	0.9	2.0
⋮	⋮	⋮
2004	2.3	2.9
2005	3.6	3.3
2006	2.4	3.8

Source: *Economic Report of the President, 2007.*

Note: Data are year-to-year percent changes in the Consumer Price Index (CPI) in these two categories.

12.56 Researchers found a correlation coefficient of $r = .50$ on personality measures for identical twins. A reporter interpreted this to mean that "the environment orchestrated one-half of their personality differences." Do you agree with this interpretation? Discuss.

12.57 A study of the role of spreadsheets in planning in 55 small firms defined Y = "satisfaction with sales growth" and X = "executive commitment to planning." Analysis yielded an overall correlation of $r = .3043$. Do a two-tailed test for zero correlation at $\alpha = .025$.

12.58 In a study of stock prices from 1970 to 1994, the correlation between Nasdaq closing prices on successive days (i.e., with a 1-day lag) was $r = .13$ with a t statistic of 5.47. Interpret this result. (See David Nawrocki, "The Problems with Monte Carlo Simulation," *Journal of Financial Planning* 14, no. 11 [November 2001], p. 96.)

12.59 Regression analysis of free throws by 29 NBA teams during the 2002–2003 season revealed the fitted regression $Y = 55.2 + .73X$ ($R^2 = .874$, $s_{yx} = 53.2$), where Y = total free throws made and X = total free throws attempted. The observed range of X was from 1,620 (New York Knicks) to 2,382 (Golden State Warriors). (a) Find the expected number of free throws made for a team that shoots 2,000 free throws. (b) Do you think that the intercept is meaningful? *Hint:* Make a scatter plot and let Excel fit the line. (c) Use the quick rule to make a 95 percent prediction interval for Y when X = 2,000. FreeThrows

12.60 In the following regression, X = weekly pay, Y = income tax withheld, and $n = 35$ McDonald's employees. (a) Write the fitted regression equation. (b) State the degrees of freedom for a two-tailed test for zero slope, and use Appendix D to find the critical value at $\alpha = .05$. (c) What is your conclusion about the slope? (d) Interpret the 95 percent confidence limits for the slope. (e) Verify that $F = t^2$ for the slope. (f) In your own words, describe the fit of this regression.

R^2	0.202
Std. Error	6.816
n	35

ANOVA table

Source	*SS*	*df*	*MS*	*F*	*p-value*
Regression	387.6959	1	387.6959	8.35	.0068
Residual	1,533.0614	33	46.4564		
Total	1,920.7573	34			

Regression output

					confidence interval	
variables	*coefficients*	*std. error*	*t (df = 33)*	*p-value*	*95% lower*	*95% upper*
Intercept	30.7963	6.4078	4.806	.0000	17.7595	43.8331
Slope	0.0343	0.0119	2.889	.0068	0.0101	0.0584

12.61 In the following regression, X = monthly maintenance spending (dollars), Y = monthly machine downtime (hours), and $n = 15$ copy machines. (a) Write the fitted regression equation. (b) State the degrees of freedom for a two-tailed test for zero slope, and use Appendix D to find the critical value at $\alpha = .05$. (c) What is your conclusion about the slope? (d) Interpret the 95 percent confidence limits for the slope. (e) Verify that $F = t^2$ for the slope. (f) In your own words, describe the fit of this regression.

R^2	0.370
Std. Error	286.793
n	15

ANOVA table

Source	*SS*	*df*	*MS*	*F*	*p-value*
Regression	628,298.2	1	628,298.2	7.64	.0161
Residual	1,069,251.8	13	82,250.1		
Total	1,697,550.0	14			

Regression output

					confidence interval	
variables	*coefficients*	*std. error*	*t (df = 13)*	*p-value*	*95% lower*	*95% upper*
Intercept	1,743.57	288.82	6.037	.0000	1,119.61	2,367.53
Slope	−1.2163	0.4401	−2.764	.0161	−2.1671	−0.2656

12.62 In the following regression, X = total assets ($ billions), Y = total revenue ($ billions), and $n = 64$ large banks. (a) Write the fitted regression equation. (b) State the degrees of freedom for a two-tailed test for zero slope, and use Appendix D to find the critical value at $\alpha = .05$. (c) What is your conclusion about the slope? (d) Interpret the 95 percent confidence limits for the slope. (e) Verify that $F = t^2$ for the slope. (f) In your own words, describe the fit of this regression.

R^2	0.519
Std. Error	6.977
n	64

ANOVA table

Source	*SS*	*df*	*MS*	*F*	*p-value*
Regression	3,260.0981	1	3,260.0981	66.97	1.90E-11
Residual	3,018.3339	62	48.6828		
Total	6,278.4320	63			

Regression output					confidence interval	
variables	*coefficients*	*std. error*	*t (df = 62)*	*p-value*	*95% lower*	*95% upper*
Intercept	6.5763	1.9254	3.416	.0011	2.7275	10.4252
X1	0.0452	0.0055	8.183	1.90E-11	0.0342	0.0563

12.63 Do stock prices of competing companies move together? Below are daily closing prices of two computer services firms (IBM = International Business Machines Corporation, HPQ = Hewlett-Packard Company. (a) Calculate the sample correlation coefficient (e.g., using Excel or MegaStat). (b) At $\alpha = .01$ can you conclude that the true correlation coefficient is not equal to zero? (c) Make a scatter plot of the data. What does it say? (*Source:* finance.yahoo.com.) **StockPrices**

Daily Closing Price ($) of Two Stocks in March and April 2011 ($n = 43$ days)

Date	*IBM*	*HPQ*
3/1/11	159.26	42.83
3/2/11	159.45	43.16
3/3/11	162.75	43.12
⋮	⋮	⋮
4/27/11	169.61	41.04
4/28/11	170.02	40.53
4/29/11	169.82	40.37

NOODLES & COMPANY

12.64 Below are percentages for *annual sales growth* and *net sales attributed to loyalty card usage* at 74 Noodles & Company restaurants. (a) Make a scatter plot. (b) Find the correlation coefficient and interpret it. (c) Test the correlation coefficient for significance, clearly stating the degrees of freedom. (d) Does it appear that loyalty card usage is associated with increased sales growth? **LoyaltyCard**

Annual Sales Growth (%) and Loyalty Card Usage (% of Net Sales) ($n = 74$ restaurants)

Store	*Growth%*	*Loyalty%*
1	−8.3	2.1
2	−4.0	2.5
3	−3.9	1.7
⋮	⋮	⋮
72	20.8	1.1
73	25.5	0.6
74	28.8	1.8

Source: Noodles & Company.

12.65 Below are fertility rates (average children born per woman) in 15 EU nations for 2 years. (a) Make a scatter plot. (b) Find the correlation coefficient and interpret it. (c) Test the correlation coefficient for significance, clearly stating the degrees of freedom. (Data are from the World Health Organization.) **Fertility**

Fertility Rates for EU Nations (n = 15)

Nation	*1990*	*2000*
Austria	1.5	1.3
Belgium	1.6	1.5
Denmark	1.6	1.7
⋮	⋮	⋮
Spain	1.4	1.1
Sweden	2.0	1.4
U.K.	1.8	1.7

12.66 Consider the following Excel regression of perceived sound quality as a function of price for 27 stereo speakers. (a) Is the coefficient of *Price* significantly different from zero at $\alpha = .05$? (b) What does the R^2 tell you? (c) Given these results, would you conclude that a higher price implies higher sound quality? **Speakers**

Regression Statistics

R Square	0.01104
Standard Error	4.02545
Observations	27

Statistic	*Coefficients*	*Std Error*	*t Stat*	*P-value*	*Lower 95%*	*Upper 95%*
Intercept	88.4902	1.67814	52.731	0.0000	85.0340	91.9464
Price	−0.00239	0.00453	−0.528	0.6019	−0.01172	0.00693

12.67 Choose *one* of these three data sets. (a) Make a scatter plot. (b) Let Excel estimate the regression line, with fitted equation and R^2. (c) Describe the fit of the regression. (d) Write the fitted regression equation and interpret the slope. (e) Do you think that the estimated intercept is meaningful? Explain.

Commercial Real Estate (Y = assessed value, \$000; X = floor space, sq. ft.) (n = 15) Assessed

Size	*Assessed*
4,790	1,796
4,720	1,544
5,940	2,094
⋮	⋮
4,880	1,678
1,620	710
1,820	678

Sasnak Co. Salaries (X = employee age; Y = employee salary, $000) ($n$ = 23)
Salaries

Employee	*Age*	*Salary*
Mary	23	28.6
Frieda	31	53.3
Alicia	44	73.8
⋮	⋮	⋮
Marcia	54	75.8
Ellen	44	79.8
Iggy	36	70.2

Poway Big Homes, Ltd. (X = home size, sq. ft.; Y = selling price, $000) ($n$ = 20)
HomePrice2

SqFt	*Price*
3,570	861
3,410	740
2,690	563
⋮	⋮
3,020	720
2,320	575
3,130	785

12.68 Simple regression was employed to establish the effects of childhood exposure to lead. The effective sample size was about 122 subjects. The independent variable was the level of dentin lead (parts per million). Below are regressions using various dependent variables. (a) Calculate the t statistic for each slope. (b) From the p-values, which slopes differ from zero at $\alpha = .01$? (c) Do you feel that cause and effect can be assumed? *Hint:* Do a web search for information about effects of childhood lead exposure. (Data are from H. L. Needleman et al., *The New England Journal of Medicine* 322, no. 2 [January 1990], p. 86.)

Dependent Variable	R^2	*Estimated Slope*	*Std. Error*	*p-value*
Highest grade achieved	.061	−0.027	0.009	.008
Reading grade equivalent	.121	−0.070	0.018	.000
Class standing	.039	−0.006	0.003	.048
Absence from school	.071	4.8	1.7	.006
Grammatical reasoning	.051	0.159	0.062	.012
Vocabulary	.108	−0.124	0.032	.000
Hand-eye coordination	.043	0.041	0.018	.020
Reaction time	.025	11.8	6.66	.080
Minor antisocial behavior	.025	−0.639	0.36	.082

12.69 Below are recent financial ratios for a random sample of 20 integrated health care systems. *Operating Margin* is total revenue minus total expenses divided by total revenue plus net operating profits. *Equity Financing* is fund balance divided by total assets. (a) Make a scatter plot of Y = operating margin and X = equity financing (both variables are in percent). (b) Use Excel to fit the regression, with fitted equation and R^2. (c) In your own words, describe the fit.
HealthCare

Financial Ratios for Selected Health Care Systems (n = 20)

Operating Margin	Equity Financing
3.89	35.58
8.23	59.68
2.56	40.48
⋮	⋮
4.75	54.21
0.00	59.73
10.79	46.21

12.70 Consider the following data on 20 chemical reactions, with Y = chromatographic retention time (seconds) and X = molecular weight (gm/mole). (a) Make a scatter plot. (b) Use Excel to fit the regression, with fitted equation and R^2. (c) In your own words, describe the fit. (Data provided by John Seeley of Oakland University.) **Chemicals**

Retention Time and Molecular Weight (n = 20)

Name	Retention Time	Molecular Weight
alpha-pinene	234.50	136.24
cyclopentene	95.27	68.12
p-diethylbenzene	284.00	134.22
⋮	⋮	⋮
pentane	78.00	72.15
isooctane	136.90	114.23
hexane	106.00	86.18

12.71 A common belief among faculty is that teaching ratings are lower in large classes. Below are MINITAB results from a regression using Y = mean student evaluation of the professor and X = class size for 364 business school classes taught during the 2002–2003 academic year. Ratings are on a scale of 1 (lowest) to 5 (highest). (a) What do these regression results tell you about the relationship between class size and faculty ratings? (b) Is a bivariate model adequate? If not, suggest additional predictors to be considered.

Predictor	Coef	SE Coef	T	P
Constant	4.18378	0.07226	57.90	0.000
Enroll	0.000578	0.002014	0.29	0.774

S = 0.5688 R-Sq = 0.0% R-Sq(adj) = 0.0%

12.72 Below are revenue and profit (both in $ billions) for nine large entertainment companies. (a) Make a scatter plot of profit as a function of revenue. (b) Use Excel to fit the regression, with fitted equation and R^2. (c) In your own words, describe the fit. (Data are from *Fortune* 149, no. 7 [April 5, 2005], p. F-50.) **Entertainment**

Revenue and Profit of Entertainment Companies (n = 9)

Company	Revenue	Profit
AMC Entertainment	1.792	−0.020
Clear Channel Communication	8.931	1.146
Liberty Media	2.446	−0.978
⋮	⋮	⋮
Univision Communications	1.311	0.155
Viacom	26.585	1.417
Walt Disney	27.061	1.267

12.73 Below are fitted regressions based on used vehicle ads. Observed ranges of X are shown. The assumed regression model is $AskingPrice = f(VehicleAge)$. (a) Interpret the slopes. (b) Are the intercepts meaningful? Explain. (c) Assess the fit of each model. (d) Is a bivariate model adequate to explain vehicle prices? If not, what other predictors might be considered? (Data are from *Detroit's AutoFocus* 4, Issue 38 [September 17–23, 2004]. Data are for educational purposes only and should not be viewed as a guide to vehicle prices.)

Vehicle	n	Intercept	Slope	R^2	Min Age	Max Age
Ford Explorer	31	22,252	−2,452	.643	2	6
Ford F-150 Pickup	43	26,164	−2,239	.713	1	37
Ford Mustang	33	21,308	−1,691	.328	1	10
Ford Taurus	32	13,160	−906	.679	1	14

12.74 Below are results of a regression of Y = average stock returns (in percent) as a function of X = average price/earnings ratios for the period 1949–1997 (49 years). Separate regressions were done for various holding periods (sample sizes are therefore variable). (a) Summarize what the regression results tell you. (b) Would you anticipate autocorrelation in this type of data? Explain. (Data are from Ruben Trevino and Fiona Robertson, "P/E Ratios and Stock Market Returns," *Journal of Financial Planning* 15, no. 2 [February 2002], p. 78.)

Holding Period	Intercept	Slope	t	R^2	p
1-Year	28.10	−0.92	1.86	.0688	.0686
2-Year	26.11	−0.86	2.57	.1252	.0136
5-Year	20.67	−0.57	2.99	.1720	.0046
8-Year	24.73	−0.94	6.93	.5459	.0000
10-Year	24.51	−0.95	8.43	.6516	.0000

DO-IT-YOURSELF MINI-PROJECT

12.75 Adult height is somewhat predictable from average height of both parents. For females, a commonly used equation is $YourHeight = ParentHeight - 2.5$ while for males the equation is $YourHeight = ParentHeight + 2.5$. (a) Test these equations on yourself and 9 friends. (b) How well did the equations predict height?

CHAPTER 12 More Learning Resources

You can access these *LearningStats* demonstrations through McGraw-Hill's Connect® to help you understand probability.

Topic	*LearningStats Demonstrations*
Correlation	Overview of Correlation Scatter Plot Simulation
Regression	Overview of Simple Regression Using Excel for Regression
Ordinary least squares estimators	Least Squares Method Demonstration Derivation of OLS Estimators Regression Calculations Effect of *X* Range and Model Form
Confidence and prediction intervals	Confidence vs. Prediction Intervals Regression Calculations Superimposing Many Fitted Regressions
Violations of assumptions	Non-Normal Errors Heteroscedastic Errors Autocorrelated Errors

Key: = PowerPoint = Excel = PDF

INDEX

A

B

D

H

I

Q

S

T

U

V

W

X

Y

Z

Appendices

APPENDIX C-1

STANDARD NORMAL AREAS

Example: $P(0 \leq z \leq 1.96) = .4750$

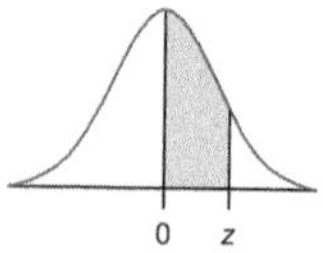

This table shows the normal area between 0 and z.

z	.00	.01	.02	.03	.04	.05	.06	.07	.08	.09
0.0	.0000	.0040	.0080	.0120	.0160	.0199	.0239	.0279	.0319	.0359
0.1	.0398	.0438	.0478	.0517	.0557	.0596	.0636	.0675	.0714	.0753
0.2	.0793	.0832	.0871	.0910	.0948	.0987	.1026	.1064	.1103	.1141
0.3	.1179	.1217	.1255	.1293	.1331	.1368	.1406	.1443	.1480	.1517
0.4	.1554	.1591	.1628	.1664	.1700	.1736	.1772	.1808	.1844	.1879
0.5	.1915	.1950	.1985	.2019	.2054	.2088	.2123	.2157	.2190	.2224
0.6	.2257	.2291	.2324	.2357	.2389	.2422	.2454	.2486	.2517	.2549
0.7	.2580	.2611	.2642	.2673	.2704	.2734	.2764	.2794	.2823	.2852
0.8	.2881	.2910	.2939	.2967	.2995	.3023	.3051	.3078	.3106	.3133
0.9	.3159	.3186	.3212	.3238	.3264	.3289	.3315	.3340	.3365	.3389
1.0	.3413	.3438	.3461	.3485	.3508	.3531	.3554	.3577	.3599	.3621
1.1	.3643	.3665	.3686	.3708	.3729	.3749	.3770	.3790	.3810	.3830
1.2	.3849	.3869	.3888	.3907	.3925	.3944	.3962	.3980	.3997	.4015
1.3	.4032	.4049	.4066	.4082	.4099	.4115	.4131	.4147	.4162	.4177
1.4	.4192	.4207	.4222	.4236	.4251	.4265	.4279	.4292	.4306	.4319
1.5	.4332	.4345	.4357	.4370	.4382	.4394	.4406	.4418	.4429	.4441
1.6	.4452	.4463	.4474	.4484	.4495	.4505	.4515	.4525	.4535	.4545
1.7	.4554	.4564	.4573	.4582	.4591	.4599	.4608	.4616	.4625	.4633
1.8	.4641	.4649	.4656	.4664	.4671	.4678	.4686	.4693	.4699	.4706
1.9	.4713	.4719	.4726	.4732	.4738	.4744	.4750	.4756	.4761	.4767
2.0	.4772	.4778	.4783	.4788	.4793	.4798	.4803	.4808	.4812	.4817
2.1	.4821	.4826	.4830	.4834	.4838	.4842	.4846	.4850	.4854	.4857
2.2	.4861	.4864	.4868	.4871	.4875	.4878	.4881	.4884	.4887	.4890
2.3	.4893	.4896	.4898	.4901	.4904	.4906	.4909	.4911	.4913	.4916
2.4	.4918	.4920	.4922	.4925	.4927	.4929	.4931	.4932	.4934	.4936
2.5	.4938	.4940	.4941	.4943	.4945	.4946	.4948	.4949	.4951	.4952
2.6	.4953	.4955	.4956	.4957	.4959	.4960	.4961	.4962	.4963	.4964
2.7	.4965	.4966	.4967	.4968	.4969	.4970	.4971	.4972	.4973	.4974
2.8	.4974	.4975	.4976	.4977	.4977	.4978	.4979	.4979	.4980	.4981
2.9	.4981	.4982	.4982	.4983	.4984	.4984	.4985	.4985	.4986	.4986
3.0	.49865	.49869	.49874	.49878	.49882	.49886	.49889	.49893	.49896	.49900
3.1	.49903	.49906	.49910	.49913	.49916	.49918	.49921	.49924	.49926	.49929
3.2	.49931	.49934	.49936	.49938	.49940	.49942	.49944	.49946	.49948	.49950
3.3	.49952	.49953	.49955	.49957	.49958	.49960	.49961	.49962	.49964	.49965
3.4	.49966	.49968	.49969	.49970	.49971	.49972	.49973	.49974	.49975	.49976
3.5	.49977	.49978	.49978	.49979	.49980	.49981	.49981	.49982	.49983	.49983
3.6	.49984	.49985	.49985	.49986	.49986	.49987	.49987	.49988	.49988	.49989
3.7	.49989	.49990	.49990	.49990	.49991	.49991	.49992	.49992	.49992	.49992

APPENDIX C-2

CUMULATIVE STANDARD NORMAL DISTRIBUTION

Example: $P(z \leq -1.96) = .0250$

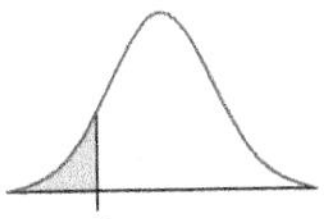

z

This table shows the normal area less than *z*.

z	.00	.01	.02	.03	.04	.05	.06	.07	.08	.09
−3.7	.00011	.00010	.00010	.00010	.00009	.00009	.00008	.00008	.00008	.00008
−3.6	.00016	.00015	.00015	.00014	.00014	.00013	.00013	.00012	.00012	.00011
−3.5	.00023	.00022	.00022	.00021	.00020	.00019	.00019	.00018	.00017	.00017
−3.4	.00034	.00032	.00031	.00030	.00029	.00028	.00027	.00026	.00025	.00024
−3.3	.00048	.00047	.00045	.00043	.00042	.00040	.00039	.00038	.00036	.00035
−3.2	.00069	.00066	.00064	.00062	.00060	.00058	.00056	.00054	.00052	.00050
−3.1	.00097	.00094	.00090	.00087	.00084	.00082	.00079	.00076	.00074	.00071
−3.0	.00135	.00131	.00126	.00122	.00118	.00114	.00111	.00107	.00104	.00100
−2.9	.0019	.0018	.0018	.0017	.0016	.0016	.0015	.0015	.0014	.0014
−2.8	.0026	.0025	.0024	.0023	.0023	.0022	.0021	.0021	.0020	.0019
−2.7	.0035	.0034	.0033	.0032	.0031	.0030	.0029	.0028	.0027	.0026
−2.6	.0047	.0045	.0044	.0043	.0041	.0040	.0039	.0038	.0037	.0036
−2.5	.0062	.0060	.0059	.0057	.0055	.0054	.0052	.0051	.0049	.0048
−2.4	.0082	.0080	.0078	.0075	.0073	.0071	.0069	.0068	.0066	.0064
−2.3	.0107	.0104	.0102	.0099	.0096	.0094	.0091	.0089	.0087	.0084
−2.2	.0139	.0136	.0132	.0129	.0125	.0122	.0119	.0116	.0113	.0110
−2.1	.0179	.0174	.0170	.0166	.0162	.0158	.0154	.0150	.0146	.0143
−2.0	.0228	.0222	.0217	.0212	.0207	.0202	.0197	.0192	.0188	.0183
−1.9	.0287	.0281	.0274	.0268	.0262	.0256	.0250	.0244	.0239	.0233
−1.8	.0359	.0351	.0344	.0336	.0329	.0322	.0314	.0307	.0301	.0294
−1.7	.0446	.0436	.0427	.0418	.0409	.0401	.0392	.0384	.0375	.0367
−1.6	.0548	.0537	.0526	.0516	.0505	.0495	.0485	.0475	.0465	.0455
−1.5	.0668	.0655	.0643	.0630	.0618	.0606	.0594	.0582	.0571	.0559
−1.4	.0808	.0793	.0778	.0764	.0749	.0735	.0721	.0708	.0694	.0681
−1.3	.0968	.0951	.0934	.0918	.0901	.0885	.0869	.0853	.0838	.0823
−1.2	.1151	.1131	.1112	.1093	.1075	.1056	.1038	.1020	.1003	.0985
−1.1	.1357	.1335	.1314	.1292	.1271	.1251	.1230	.1210	.1190	.1170
−1.0	.1587	.1562	.1539	.1515	.1492	.1469	.1446	.1423	.1401	.1379
−0.9	.1841	.1814	.1788	.1762	.1736	.1711	.1685	.1660	.1635	.1611
−0.8	.2119	.2090	.2061	.2033	.2005	.1977	.1949	.1922	.1894	.1867
−0.7	.2420	.2389	.2358	.2327	.2296	.2266	.2236	.2206	.2177	.2148
−0.6	.2743	.2709	.2676	.2643	.2611	.2578	.2546	.2514	.2483	.2451
−0.5	.3085	.3050	.3015	.2981	.2946	.2912	.2877	.2843	.2810	.2776
−0.4	.3446	.3409	.3372	.3336	.3300	.3264	.3228	.3192	.3156	.3121
−0.3	.3821	.3783	.3745	.3707	.3669	.3632	.3594	.3557	.3520	.3483
−0.2	.4207	.4168	.4129	.4090	.4052	.4013	.3974	.3936	.3897	.3859
−0.1	.4602	.4562	.4522	.4483	.4443	.4404	.4364	.4325	.4286	.4247
−0.0	.5000	.4960	.4920	.4880	.4841	.4801	.4761	.4721	.4681	.4641

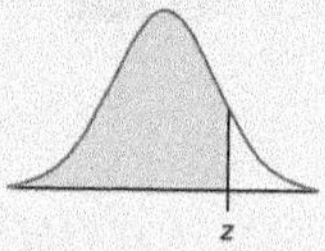

This table shows the normal area less than z.

z	.00	.01	.02	.03	.04	.05	.06	.07	.08	.09
0.0	.5000	.5040	.5080	.5120	.5160	.5199	.5239	.5279	.5319	.5359
0.1	.5398	.5438	.5478	.5517	.5557	.5596	.5636	.5675	.5714	.5753
0.2	.5793	.5832	.5871	.5910	.5948	.5987	.6026	.6064	.6103	.6141
0.3	.6179	.6217	.6255	.6293	.6331	.6368	.6406	.6443	.6480	.6517
0.4	.6554	.6591	.6628	.6664	.6700	.6736	.6772	.6808	.6844	.6879
0.5	.6915	.6950	.6985	.7019	.7054	.7088	.7123	.7157	.7190	.7224
0.6	.7257	.7291	.7324	.7357	.7389	.7422	.7454	.7486	.7517	.7549
0.7	.7580	.7611	.7642	.7673	.7704	.7734	.7764	.7794	.7823	.7852
0.8	.7881	.7910	.7939	.7967	.7995	.8023	.8051	.8078	.8106	.8133
0.9	.8159	.8186	.8212	.8238	.8264	.8289	.8315	.8340	.8365	.8389
1.0	.8413	.8438	.8461	.8485	.8508	.8531	.8554	.8577	.8599	.8621
1.1	.8643	.8665	.8686	.8708	.8729	.8749	.8770	.8790	.8810	.8830
1.2	.8849	.8869	.8888	.8907	.8925	.8944	.8962	.8980	.8997	.9015
1.3	.9032	.9049	.9066	.9082	.9099	.9115	.9131	.9147	.9162	.9177
1.4	.9192	.9207	.9222	.9236	.9251	.9265	.9279	.9292	.9306	.9319
1.5	.9332	.9345	.9357	.9370	.9382	.9394	.9406	.9418	.9429	.9441
1.6	.9452	.9463	.9474	.9484	.9495	.9505	.9515	.9525	.9535	.9545
1.7	.9554	.9564	.9573	.9582	.9591	.9599	.9608	.9616	.9625	.9633
1.8	.9641	.9649	.9656	.9664	.9671	.9678	.9686	.9693	.9699	.9706
1.9	.9713	.9719	.9726	.9732	.9738	.9744	.9750	.9756	.9761	.9767
2.0	.9772	.9778	.9783	.9788	.9793	.9798	.9803	.9808	.9812	.9817
2.1	.9821	.9826	.9830	.9834	.9838	.9842	.9846	.9850	.9854	.9857
2.2	.9861	.9864	.9868	.9871	.9875	.9878	.9881	.9884	.9887	.9890
2.3	.9893	.9896	.9898	.9901	.9904	.9906	.9909	.9911	.9913	.9916
2.4	.9918	.9920	.9922	.9925	.9927	.9929	.9931	.9932	.9934	.9936
2.5	.9938	.9940	.9941	.9943	.9945	.9946	.9948	.9949	.9951	.9952
2.6	.9953	.9955	.9956	.9957	.9959	.9960	.9961	.9962	.9963	.9964
2.7	.9965	.9966	.9967	.9968	.9969	.9970	.9971	.9972	.9973	.9974
2.8	.9974	.9975	.9976	.9977	.9977	.9978	.9979	.9979	.9980	.9981
2.9	.9981	.9982	.9982	.9983	.9984	.9984	.9985	.9985	.9986	.9986
3.0	.99865	.99869	.99874	.99878	.99882	.99886	.99889	.99893	.99896	.99900
3.1	.99903	.99906	.99910	.99913	.99916	.99918	.99921	.99924	.99926	.99929
3.2	.99931	.99934	.99936	.99938	.99940	.99942	.99944	.99946	.99948	.99950
3.3	.99952	.99953	.99955	.99957	.99958	.99960	.99961	.99962	.99964	.99965
3.4	.99966	.99968	.99969	.99970	.99971	.99972	.99973	.99974	.99975	.99976
3.5	.99977	.99978	.99978	.99979	.99980	.99981	.99981	.99982	.99983	.99983
3.6	.99984	.99985	.99985	.99986	.99986	.99987	.99987	.99988	.99988	.99989
3.7	.99989	.99990	.99990	.99990	.99991	.99991	.99992	.99992	.99992	.99992

APPENDIX D

STUDENT'S *t* CRITICAL VALUES

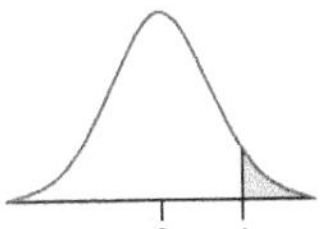

This table shows the *t*-value that defines the area for the stated degrees of freedom (*d.f.*).

	Confidence Level				
	.80	.90	.95	.98	.99
	Significance Level for Two-Tailed Test				
	.20	.10	.05	.02	.01
	Significance Level for One-Tailed Test				
d.f.	.10	.05	.025	.01	.005
1	3.078	6.314	12.706	31.821	63.657
2	1.886	2.920	4.303	6.965	9.925
3	1.638	2.353	3.182	4.541	5.841
4	1.533	2.132	2.776	3.747	4.604
5	1.476	2.015	2.571	3.365	4.032
6	1.440	1.943	2.447	3.143	3.707
7	1.415	1.895	2.365	2.998	3.499
8	1.397	1.860	2.306	2.896	3.355
9	1.383	1.833	2.262	2.821	3.250
10	1.372	1.812	2.228	2.764	3.169
11	1.363	1.796	2.201	2.718	3.106
12	1.356	1.782	2.179	2.681	3.055
13	1.350	1.771	2.160	2.650	3.012
14	1.345	1.761	2.145	2.624	2.977
15	1.341	1.753	2.131	2.602	2.947
16	1.337	1.746	2.120	2.583	2.921
17	1.333	1.740	2.110	2.567	2.898
18	1.330	1.734	2.101	2.552	2.878
19	1.328	1.729	2.093	2.539	2.861
20	1.325	1.725	2.086	2.528	2.845
21	1.323	1.721	2.080	2.518	2.831
22	1.321	1.717	2.074	2.508	2.819
23	1.319	1.714	2.069	2.500	2.807
24	1.318	1.711	2.064	2.492	2.797
25	1.316	1.708	2.060	2.485	2.787
26	1.315	1.706	2.056	2.479	2.779
27	1.314	1.703	2.052	2.473	2.771
28	1.313	1.701	2.048	2.467	2.763
29	1.311	1.699	2.045	2.462	2.756
30	1.310	1.697	2.042	2.457	2.750
31	1.309	1.696	2.040	2.453	2.744
32	1.309	1.694	2.037	2.449	2.738
33	1.308	1.692	2.035	2.445	2.733
34	1.307	1.691	2.032	2.441	2.728
35	1.306	1.690	2.030	2.438	2.724

	Confidence Level				
	.80	.90	.95	.98	.99
	Significance Level for Two-Tailed Test				
	.20	.10	.05	.02	.01
	Significance Level for One-Tailed Test				
d.f.	.10	.05	.025	.01	.005
36	1.306	1.688	2.028	2.434	2.719
37	1.305	1.687	2.026	2.431	2.715
38	1.304	1.686	2.024	2.429	2.712
39	1.304	1.685	2.023	2.426	2.708
40	1.303	1.684	2.021	2.423	2.704
41	1.303	1.683	2.020	2.421	2.701
42	1.302	1.682	2.018	2.418	2.698
43	1.302	1.681	2.017	2.416	2.695
44	1.301	1.680	2.015	2.414	2.692
45	1.301	1.679	2.014	2.412	2.690
46	1.300	1.679	2.013	2.410	2.687
47	1.300	1.678	2.012	2.408	2.685
48	1.299	1.677	2.011	2.407	2.682
49	1.299	1.677	2.010	2.405	2.680
50	1.299	1.676	2.009	2.403	2.678
55	1.297	1.673	2.004	2.396	2.668
60	1.296	1.671	2.000	2.390	2.660
65	1.295	1.669	1.997	2.385	2.654
70	1.294	1.667	1.994	2.381	2.648
75	1.293	1.665	1.992	2.377	2.643
80	1.292	1.664	1.990	2.374	2.639
85	1.292	1.663	1.988	2.371	2.635
90	1.291	1.662	1.987	2.368	2.632
95	1.291	1.661	1.985	2.366	2.629
100	1.290	1.660	1.984	2.364	2.626
110	1.289	1.659	1.982	2.361	2.621
120	1.289	1.658	1.980	2.358	2.617
130	1.288	1.657	1.978	2.355	2.614
140	1.288	1.656	1.977	2.353	2.611
150	1.287	1.655	1.976	2.351	2.609
∞	1.282	1.645	1.960	2.326	2.576

Note: As n increases, critical values of Student's t approach the z-values in the last line of this table. A common rule of thumb is to use z when $n > 30$, but that is *not* conservative.

APPENDIX E

CHI-SQUARE CRITICAL VALUES

Example for *d.f.* = 4

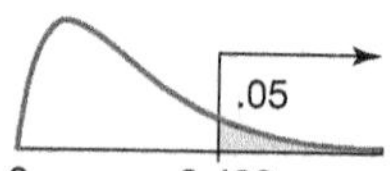

This table shows the critical value of chi-square for each desired right-tail area and degrees of freedom (*d.f.*)

					Area in Upper Tail					
d.f.	***.995***	***.990***	***.975***	***.95***	***.90***	***.10***	***.05***	***.025***	***.01***	***.005***
1	0.000	0.000	0.001	0.004	0.016	2.706	3.841	5.024	6.635	7.879
2	0.010	0.020	0.051	0.103	0.211	4.605	5.991	7.378	9.210	10.60
3	0.072	0.115	0.216	0.352	0.584	6.251	7.815	9.348	11.34	12.84
4	0.207	0.297	0.484	0.711	1.064	7.779	9.488	11.14	13.28	14.86
5	0.412	0.554	0.831	1.145	1.610	9.236	11.07	12.83	15.09	16.75
6	0.676	0.872	1.237	1.635	2.204	10.64	12.59	14.45	16.81	18.55
7	0.989	1.239	1.690	2.167	2.833	12.02	14.07	16.01	18.48	20.28
8	1.344	1.646	2.180	2.733	3.490	13.36	15.51	17.53	20.09	21.95
9	1.735	2.088	2.700	3.325	4.168	14.68	16.92	19.02	21.67	23.59
10	2.156	2.558	3.247	3.940	4.865	15.99	18.31	20.48	23.21	25.19
11	2.603	3.053	3.816	4.575	5.578	17.28	19.68	21.92	24.72	26.76
12	3.074	3.571	4.404	5.226	6.304	18.55	21.03	23.34	26.22	28.30
13	3.565	4.107	5.009	5.892	7.042	19.81	22.36	24.74	27.69	29.82
14	4.075	4.660	5.629	6.571	7.790	21.06	23.68	26.12	29.14	31.32
15	4.601	5.229	6.262	7.261	8.547	22.31	25.00	27.49	30.58	32.80
16	5.142	5.812	6.908	7.962	9.312	23.54	26.30	28.85	32.00	34.27
17	5.697	6.408	7.564	8.672	10.09	24.77	27.59	30.19	33.41	35.72
18	6.265	7.015	8.231	9.390	10.86	25.99	28.87	31.53	34.81	37.16
19	6.844	7.633	8.907	10.12	11.65	27.20	30.14	32.85	36.19	38.58
20	7.434	8.260	9.591	10.85	12.44	28.41	31.41	34.17	37.57	40.00
21	8.034	8.897	10.28	11.59	13.24	29.62	32.67	35.48	38.93	41.40
22	8.643	9.542	10.98	12.34	14.04	30.81	33.92	36.78	40.29	42.80
23	9.260	10.20	11.69	13.09	14.85	32.01	35.17	38.08	41.64	44.18
24	9.886	10.86	12.40	13.85	15.66	33.20	36.42	39.36	42.98	45.56
25	10.52	11.52	13.12	14.61	16.47	34.38	37.65	40.65	44.31	46.93
26	11.16	12.20	13.84	15.38	17.29	35.56	38.89	41.92	45.64	48.29
27	11.81	12.88	14.57	16.15	18.11	36.74	40.11	43.19	46.96	49.64
28	12.46	13.56	15.31	16.93	18.94	37.92	41.34	44.46	48.28	50.99
29	13.12	14.26	16.05	17.71	19.77	39.09	42.56	45.72	49.59	52.34
30	13.79	14.95	16.79	18.49	20.60	40.26	43.77	46.98	50.89	53.67
31	14.46	15.66	17.54	19.28	21.43	41.42	44.99	48.23	52.19	55.00
32	15.13	16.36	18.29	20.07	22.27	42.58	46.19	49.48	53.49	56.33
33	15.82	17.07	19.05	20.87	23.11	43.75	47.40	50.73	54.78	57.65
34	16.50	17.79	19.81	21.66	23.95	44.90	48.60	51.97	56.06	58.96
35	17.19	18.51	20.57	22.47	24.80	46.06	49.80	53.20	57.34	60.27
36	17.89	19.23	21.34	23.27	25.64	47.21	51.00	54.44	58.62	61.58
37	18.59	19.96	22.11	24.07	26.49	48.36	52.19	55.67	59.89	62.88
38	19.29	20.69	22.88	24.88	27.34	49.51	53.38	56.90	61.16	64.18
39	20.00	21.43	23.65	25.70	28.20	50.66	54.57	58.12	62.43	65.48
40	20.71	22.16	24.43	26.51	29.05	51.81	55.76	59.34	63.69	66.77
50	27.99	29.71	32.36	34.76	37.69	63.17	67.50	71.42	76.15	79.49
60	35.53	37.48	40.48	43.19	46.46	74.40	79.08	83.30	88.38	91.95
70	43.28	45.44	48.76	51.74	55.33	85.53	90.53	95.02	100.4	104.2
80	51.17	53.54	57.15	60.39	64.28	96.58	101.9	106.6	112.3	116.3
90	59.20	61.75	65.65	69.13	73.29	107.6	113.1	118.1	124.1	128.3
100	67.33	70.06	74.22	77.93	82.36	118.5	124.3	129.6	135.8	140.2

Note: For *d.f.* > 100, use the Excel function =CHISQ.INV.RT(α,degrees of freedom).

APPENDIX F

CRITICAL VALUES OF $F_{.10}$

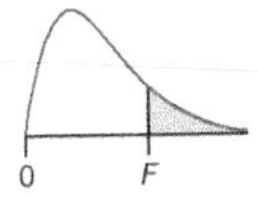

This table shows the 10 percent right-tail critical values of *F* for the stated degrees of freedom (*d.f.*).

Denominator Degrees of Freedom (df_2)	Numerator Degrees of Freedom (df_1)										
	1	2	3	4	5	6	7	8	9	10	12
1	39.86	49.50	53.59	55.83	57.24	58.20	58.91	59.44	59.86	60.19	60.71
2	8.53	9.00	9.16	9.24	9.29	9.33	9.35	9.37	9.38	9.39	9.41
3	5.54	5.46	5.39	5.34	5.31	5.28	5.27	5.25	5.24	5.23	5.22
4	4.54	4.32	4.19	4.11	4.05	4.01	3.98	3.95	3.94	3.92	3.90
5	4.06	3.78	3.62	3.52	3.45	3.40	3.37	3.34	3.32	3.30	3.27
6	3.78	3.46	3.29	3.18	3.11	3.05	3.01	2.98	2.96	2.94	2.90
7	3.59	3.26	3.07	2.96	2.88	2.83	2.78	2.75	2.72	2.70	2.67
8	3.46	3.11	2.92	2.81	2.73	2.67	2.62	2.59	2.56	2.54	2.50
9	3.36	3.01	2.81	2.69	2.61	2.55	2.51	2.47	2.44	2.42	2.38
10	3.29	2.92	2.73	2.61	2.52	2.46	2.41	2.38	2.35	2.32	2.28
11	3.23	2.86	2.66	2.54	2.45	2.39	2.34	2.30	2.27	2.25	2.21
12	3.18	2.81	2.61	2.48	2.39	2.33	2.28	2.24	2.21	2.19	2.15
13	3.14	2.76	2.56	2.43	2.35	2.28	2.23	2.20	2.16	2.14	2.10
14	3.10	2.73	2.52	2.39	2.31	2.24	2.19	2.15	2.12	2.10	2.05
15	3.07	2.70	2.49	2.36	2.27	2.21	2.16	2.12	2.09	2.06	2.02
16	3.05	2.67	2.46	2.33	2.24	2.18	2.13	2.09	2.06	2.03	1.99
17	3.03	2.64	2.44	2.31	2.22	2.15	2.10	2.06	2.03	2.00	1.96
18	3.01	2.62	2.42	2.29	2.20	2.13	2.08	2.04	2.00	1.98	1.93
19	2.99	2.61	2.40	2.27	2.18	2.11	2.06	2.02	1.98	1.96	1.91
20	2.97	2.59	2.38	2.25	2.16	2.09	2.04	2.00	1.96	1.94	1.89
21	2.96	2.57	2.36	2.23	2.14	2.08	2.02	1.98	1.95	1.92	1.87
22	2.95	2.56	2.35	2.22	2.13	2.06	2.01	1.97	1.93	1.90	1.86
23	2.94	2.55	2.34	2.21	2.11	2.05	1.99	1.95	1.92	1.89	1.84
24	2.93	2.54	2.33	2.19	2.10	2.04	1.98	1.94	1.91	1.88	1.83
25	2.92	2.53	2.32	2.18	2.09	2.02	1.97	1.93	1.89	1.87	1.82
26	2.91	2.52	2.31	2.17	2.08	2.01	1.96	1.92	1.88	1.86	1.81
27	2.90	2.51	2.30	2.17	2.07	2.00	1.95	1.91	1.87	1.85	1.80
28	2.89	2.50	2.29	2.16	2.06	2.00	1.94	1.90	1.87	1.84	1.79
29	2.89	2.50	2.28	2.15	2.06	1.99	1.93	1.89	1.86	1.83	1.78
30	2.88	2.49	2.28	2.14	2.05	1.98	1.93	1.88	1.85	1.82	1.77
40	2.84	2.44	2.23	2.09	2.00	1.93	1.87	1.83	1.79	1.76	1.71
50	2.81	2.41	2.20	2.06	1.97	1.90	1.84	1.80	1.76	1.73	1.68
60	2.79	2.39	2.18	2.04	1.95	1.87	1.82	1.77	1.74	1.71	1.66
120	2.75	2.35	2.13	1.99	1.90	1.82	1.77	1.72	1.68	1.65	1.60
200	2.73	2.33	2.11	1.97	1.88	1.80	1.75	1.70	1.66	1.63	1.58
∞	2.71	2.30	2.08	1.94	1.85	1.77	1.72	1.67	1.63	1.60	1.55

Denominator Degrees of Freedom (df_2)	*Numerator Degrees of Freedom (df_1)*										
	15	**20**	**25**	**30**	**35**	**40**	**50**	**60**	**120**	**200**	**∞**
1	61.22	61.74	62.05	62.26	62.42	62.53	62.69	62.79	63.06	63.17	63.32
2	9.42	9.44	9.45	9.46	9.46	9.47	9.47	9.47	9.48	9.49	9.49
3	5.20	5.18	5.17	5.17	5.16	5.16	5.15	5.15	5.14	5.14	5.13
4	3.87	3.84	3.83	3.82	3.81	3.80	3.80	3.79	3.78	3.77	3.76
5	3.24	3.21	3.19	3.17	3.16	3.16	3.15	3.14	3.12	3.12	3.11
6	2.87	2.84	2.81	2.80	2.79	2.78	2.77	2.76	2.74	2.73	2.72
7	2.63	2.59	2.57	2.56	2.54	2.54	2.52	2.51	2.49	2.48	2.47
8	2.46	2.42	2.40	2.38	2.37	2.36	2.35	2.34	2.32	2.31	2.29
9	2.34	2.30	2.27	2.25	2.24	2.23	2.22	2.21	2.18	2.17	2.16
10	2.24	2.20	2.17	2.16	2.14	2.13	2.12	2.11	2.08	2.07	2.06
11	2.17	2.12	2.10	2.08	2.06	2.05	2.04	2.03	2.00	1.99	1.97
12	2.10	2.06	2.03	2.01	2.00	1.99	1.97	1.96	1.93	1.92	1.90
13	2.05	2.01	1.98	1.96	1.94	1.93	1.92	1.90	1.88	1.86	1.85
14	2.01	1.96	1.93	1.91	1.90	1.89	1.87	1.86	1.83	1.82	1.80
15	1.97	1.92	1.89	1.87	1.86	1.85	1.83	1.82	1.79	1.77	1.76
16	1.94	1.89	1.86	1.84	1.82	1.81	1.79	1.78	1.75	1.74	1.72
17	1.91	1.86	1.83	1.81	1.79	1.78	1.76	1.75	1.72	1.71	1.69
18	1.89	1.84	1.80	1.78	1.77	1.75	1.74	1.72	1.69	1.68	1.66
19	1.86	1.81	1.78	1.76	1.74	1.73	1.71	1.70	1.67	1.65	1.63
20	1.84	1.79	1.76	1.74	1.72	1.71	1.69	1.68	1.64	1.63	1.61
21	1.83	1.78	1.74	1.72	1.70	1.69	1.67	1.66	1.62	1.61	1.59
22	1.81	1.76	1.73	1.70	1.68	1.67	1.65	1.64	1.60	1.59	1.57
23	1.80	1.74	1.71	1.69	1.67	1.66	1.64	1.62	1.59	1.57	1.55
24	1.78	1.73	1.70	1.67	1.65	1.64	1.62	1.61	1.57	1.56	1.53
25	1.77	1.72	1.68	1.66	1.64	1.63	1.61	1.59	1.56	1.54	1.52
26	1.76	1.71	1.67	1.65	1.63	1.61	1.59	1.58	1.54	1.53	1.50
27	1.75	1.70	1.66	1.64	1.62	1.60	1.58	1.57	1.53	1.52	1.49
28	1.74	1.69	1.65	1.63	1.61	1.59	1.57	1.56	1.52	1.50	1.48
29	1.73	1.68	1.64	1.62	1.60	1.58	1.56	1.55	1.51	1.49	1.47
30	1.72	1.67	1.63	1.61	1.59	1.57	1.55	1.54	1.50	1.48	1.46
40	1.66	1.61	1.57	1.54	1.52	1.51	1.48	1.47	1.42	1.41	1.38
50	1.63	1.57	1.53	1.50	1.48	1.46	1.44	1.42	1.38	1.36	1.33
60	1.60	1.54	1.50	1.48	1.45	1.44	1.41	1.40	1.35	1.33	1.29
120	1.55	1.48	1.44	1.41	1.39	1.37	1.34	1.32	1.26	1.24	1.19
200	1.52	1.46	1.41	1.38	1.36	1.34	1.31	1.29	1.23	1.20	1.15
∞	1.49	1.42	1.38	1.34	1.32	1.30	1.26	1.24	1.17	1.13	1.00

CRITICAL VALUES OF $F_{.05}$

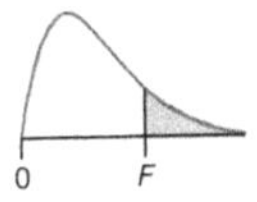

This table shows the 5 percent right-tail critical values of F for the stated degrees of freedom (*d.f.*).

Denominator Degrees of Freedom (df_2)	Numerator Degrees of Freedom (df_1)										
	1	2	3	4	5	6	7	8	9	10	12
1	161.4	199.5	215.7	224.6	230.2	234.0	236.8	238.9	240.5	241.9	243.9
2	18.51	19.00	19.16	19.25	19.30	19.33	19.35	19.37	19.38	19.40	19.41
3	10.13	9.55	9.28	9.12	9.01	8.94	8.89	8.85	8.81	8.79	8.74
4	7.71	6.94	6.59	6.39	6.26	6.16	6.09	6.04	6.00	5.96	5.91
5	6.61	5.79	5.41	5.19	5.05	4.95	4.88	4.82	4.77	4.74	4.68
6	5.99	5.14	4.76	4.53	4.39	4.28	4.21	4.15	4.10	4.06	4.00
7	5.59	4.74	4.35	4.12	3.97	3.87	3.79	3.73	3.68	3.64	3.57
8	5.32	4.46	4.07	3.84	3.69	3.58	3.50	3.44	3.39	3.35	3.28
9	5.12	4.26	3.86	3.63	3.48	3.37	3.29	3.23	3.18	3.14	3.07
10	4.96	4.10	3.71	3.48	3.33	3.22	3.14	3.07	3.02	2.98	2.91
11	4.84	3.98	3.59	3.36	3.20	3.09	3.01	2.95	2.90	2.85	2.79
12	4.75	3.89	3.49	3.26	3.11	3.00	2.91	2.85	2.80	2.75	2.69
13	4.67	3.81	3.41	3.18	3.03	2.92	2.83	2.77	2.71	2.67	2.60
14	4.60	3.74	3.34	3.11	2.96	2.85	2.76	2.70	2.65	2.60	2.53
15	4.54	3.68	3.29	3.06	2.90	2.79	2.71	2.64	2.59	2.54	2.48
16	4.49	3.63	3.24	3.01	2.85	2.74	2.66	2.59	2.54	2.49	2.42
17	4.45	3.59	3.20	2.96	2.81	2.70	2.61	2.55	2.49	2.45	2.38
18	4.41	3.55	3.16	2.93	2.77	2.66	2.58	2.51	2.46	2.41	2.34
19	4.38	3.52	3.13	2.90	2.74	2.63	2.54	2.48	2.42	2.38	2.31
20	4.35	3.49	3.10	2.87	2.71	2.60	2.51	2.45	2.39	2.35	2.28
21	4.32	3.47	3.07	2.84	2.68	2.57	2.49	2.42	2.37	2.32	2.25
22	4.30	3.44	3.05	2.82	2.66	2.55	2.46	2.40	2.34	2.30	2.23
23	4.28	3.42	3.03	2.80	2.64	2.53	2.44	2.37	2.32	2.27	2.20
24	4.26	3.40	3.01	2.78	2.62	2.51	2.42	2.36	2.30	2.25	2.18
25	4.24	3.39	2.99	2.76	2.60	2.49	2.40	2.34	2.28	2.24	2.16
26	4.23	3.37	2.98	2.74	2.59	2.47	2.39	2.32	2.27	2.22	2.15
27	4.21	3.35	2.96	2.73	2.57	2.46	2.37	2.31	2.25	2.20	2.13
28	4.20	3.34	2.95	2.71	2.56	2.45	2.36	2.29	2.24	2.19	2.12
29	4.18	3.33	2.93	2.70	2.55	2.43	2.35	2.28	2.22	2.18	2.10
30	4.17	3.32	2.92	2.69	2.53	2.42	2.33	2.27	2.21	2.16	2.09
40	4.08	3.23	2.84	2.61	2.45	2.34	2.25	2.18	2.12	2.08	2.00
50	4.03	3.18	2.79	2.56	2.40	2.29	2.20	2.13	2.07	2.03	1.95
60	4.00	3.15	2.76	2.53	2.37	2.25	2.17	2.10	2.04	1.99	1.92
120	3.92	3.07	2.68	2.45	2.29	2.18	2.09	2.02	1.96	1.91	1.83
200	3.89	3.04	2.65	2.42	2.26	2.14	2.06	1.98	1.93	1.88	1.80
∞	3.84	3.00	2.60	2.37	2.21	2.10	2.01	1.94	1.88	1.83	1.75

Denominator Degrees of Freedom (df_2)	***Numerator Degrees of Freedom (df_1)***										
	15	***20***	***25***	***30***	***35***	***40***	***50***	***60***	***120***	***200***	***∞***
1	245.9	248.0	249.3	250.1	250.7	251.1	251.8	252.2	253.3	253.7	254.3
2	19.43	19.45	19.46	19.46	19.47	19.47	19.48	19.48	19.49	19.49	19.50
3	8.70	8.66	8.63	8.62	8.60	8.59	8.58	8.57	8.55	8.54	8.53
4	5.86	5.80	5.77	5.75	5.73	5.72	5.70	5.69	5.66	5.65	5.63
5	4.62	4.56	4.52	4.50	4.48	4.46	4.44	4.43	4.40	4.39	4.37
6	3.94	3.87	3.83	3.81	3.79	3.77	3.75	3.74	3.70	3.69	3.67
7	3.51	3.44	3.40	3.38	3.36	3.34	3.32	3.30	3.27	3.25	3.23
8	3.22	3.15	3.11	3.08	3.06	3.04	3.02	3.01	2.97	2.95	2.93
9	3.01	2.94	2.89	2.86	2.84	2.83	2.80	2.79	2.75	2.73	2.71
10	2.85	2.77	2.73	2.70	2.68	2.66	2.64	2.62	2.58	2.56	2.54
11	2.72	2.65	2.60	2.57	2.55	2.53	2.51	2.49	2.45	2.43	2.41
12	2.62	2.54	2.50	2.47	2.44	2.43	2.40	2.38	2.34	2.32	2.30
13	2.53	2.46	2.41	2.38	2.36	2.34	2.31	2.30	2.25	2.23	2.21
14	2.46	2.39	2.34	2.31	2.28	2.27	2.24	2.22	2.18	2.16	2.13
15	2.40	2.33	2.28	2.25	2.22	2.20	2.18	2.16	2.11	2.10	2.07
16	2.35	2.28	2.23	2.19	2.17	2.15	2.12	2.11	2.06	2.04	2.01
17	2.31	2.23	2.18	2.15	2.12	2.10	2.08	2.06	2.01	1.99	1.96
18	2.27	2.19	2.14	2.11	2.08	2.06	2.04	2.02	1.97	1.95	1.92
19	2.23	2.16	2.11	2.07	2.05	2.03	2.00	1.98	1.93	1.91	1.88
20	2.20	2.12	2.07	2.04	2.01	1.99	1.97	1.95	1.90	1.88	1.84
21	2.18	2.10	2.05	2.01	1.98	1.96	1.94	1.92	1.87	1.84	1.81
22	2.15	2.07	2.02	1.98	1.96	1.94	1.91	1.89	1.84	1.82	1.78
23	2.13	2.05	2.00	1.96	1.93	1.91	1.88	1.86	1.81	1.79	1.76
24	2.11	2.03	1.97	1.94	1.91	1.89	1.86	1.84	1.79	1.77	1.73
25	2.09	2.01	1.96	1.92	1.89	1.87	1.84	1.82	1.77	1.75	1.71
26	2.07	1.99	1.94	1.90	1.87	1.85	1.82	1.80	1.75	1.73	1.69
27	2.06	1.97	1.92	1.88	1.86	1.84	1.81	1.79	1.73	1.71	1.67
28	2.04	1.96	1.91	1.87	1.84	1.82	1.79	1.77	1.71	1.69	1.66
29	2.03	1.94	1.89	1.85	1.83	1.81	1.77	1.75	1.70	1.67	1.64
30	2.01	1.93	1.88	1.84	1.81	1.79	1.76	1.74	1.68	1.66	1.62
40	1.92	1.84	1.78	1.74	1.72	1.69	1.66	1.64	1.58	1.55	1.51
50	1.87	1.78	1.73	1.69	1.66	1.63	1.60	1.58	1.51	1.48	1.44
60	1.84	1.75	1.69	1.65	1.62	1.59	1.56	1.53	1.47	1.44	1.39
120	1.75	1.66	1.60	1.55	1.52	1.50	1.46	1.43	1.35	1.32	1.26
200	1.72	1.62	1.56	1.52	1.48	1.46	1.41	1.39	1.30	1.26	1.19
∞	1.67	1.57	1.51	1.46	1.42	1.39	1.35	1.32	1.22	1.17	1.00

CRITICAL VALUES OF $F_{.025}$

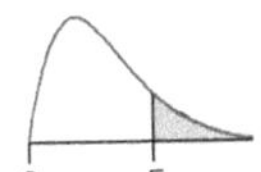

This table shows the 2.5 percent right-tail critical values of F for the stated degrees of freedom ($d.f.$).

Denominator Degrees of Freedom (df_2)	Numerator Degrees of Freedom (df_1)										
	1	2	3	4	5	6	7	8	9	10	12
1	647.8	799.5	864.2	899.6	921.8	937.1	948.2	956.6	963.3	968.6	976.7
2	38.51	39.00	39.17	39.25	39.30	39.33	39.36	39.37	39.39	39.40	39.41
3	17.44	16.04	15.44	15.10	14.88	14.73	14.62	14.54	14.47	14.42	14.34
4	12.22	10.65	9.98	9.60	9.36	9.20	9.07	8.98	8.90	8.84	8.75
5	10.01	8.43	7.76	7.39	7.15	6.98	6.85	6.76	6.68	6.62	6.52
6	8.81	7.26	6.60	6.23	5.99	5.82	5.70	5.60	5.52	5.46	5.37
7	8.07	6.54	5.89	5.52	5.29	5.12	4.99	4.90	4.82	4.76	4.67
8	7.57	6.06	5.42	5.05	4.82	4.65	4.53	4.43	4.36	4.30	4.20
9	7.21	5.71	5.08	4.72	4.48	4.32	4.20	4.10	4.03	3.96	3.87
10	6.94	5.46	4.83	4.47	4.24	4.07	3.95	3.85	3.78	3.72	3.62
11	6.72	5.26	4.63	4.28	4.04	3.88	3.76	3.66	3.59	3.53	3.43
12	6.55	5.10	4.47	4.12	3.89	3.73	3.61	3.51	3.44	3.37	3.28
13	6.41	4.97	4.35	4.00	3.77	3.60	3.48	3.39	3.31	3.25	3.15
14	6.30	4.86	4.24	3.89	3.66	3.50	3.38	3.29	3.21	3.15	3.05
15	6.20	4.77	4.15	3.80	3.58	3.41	3.29	3.20	3.12	3.06	2.96
16	6.12	4.69	4.08	3.73	3.50	3.34	3.22	3.12	3.05	2.99	2.89
17	6.04	4.62	4.01	3.66	3.44	3.28	3.16	3.06	2.98	2.92	2.82
18	5.98	4.56	3.95	3.61	3.38	3.22	3.10	3.01	2.93	2.87	2.77
19	5.92	4.51	3.90	3.56	3.33	3.17	3.05	2.96	2.88	2.82	2.72
20	5.87	4.46	3.86	3.51	3.29	3.13	3.01	2.91	2.84	2.77	2.68
21	5.83	4.42	3.82	3.48	3.25	3.09	2.97	2.87	2.80	2.73	2.64
22	5.79	4.38	3.78	3.44	3.22	3.05	2.93	2.84	2.76	2.70	2.60
23	5.75	4.35	3.75	3.41	3.18	3.02	2.90	2.81	2.73	2.67	2.57
24	5.72	4.32	3.72	3.38	3.15	2.99	2.87	2.78	2.70	2.64	2.54
25	5.69	4.29	3.69	3.35	3.13	2.97	2.85	2.75	2.68	2.61	2.51
26	5.66	4.27	3.67	3.33	3.10	2.94	2.82	2.73	2.65	2.59	2.49
27	5.63	4.24	3.65	3.31	3.08	2.92	2.80	2.71	2.63	2.57	2.47
28	5.61	4.22	3.63	3.29	3.06	2.90	2.78	2.69	2.61	2.55	2.45
29	5.59	4.20	3.61	3.27	3.04	2.88	2.76	2.67	2.59	2.53	2.43
30	5.57	4.18	3.59	3.25	3.03	2.87	2.75	2.65	2.57	2.51	2.41
40	5.42	4.05	3.46	3.13	2.90	2.74	2.62	2.53	2.45	2.39	2.29
50	5.34	3.97	3.39	3.05	2.83	2.67	2.55	2.46	2.38	2.32	2.22
60	5.29	3.93	3.34	3.01	2.79	2.63	2.51	2.41	2.33	2.27	2.17
120	5.15	3.80	3.23	2.89	2.67	2.52	2.39	2.30	2.22	2.16	2.05
200	5.10	3.76	3.18	2.85	2.63	2.47	2.35	2.26	2.18	2.11	2.01
∞	5.02	3.69	3.12	2.79	2.57	2.41	2.29	2.19	2.11	2.05	1.94

Denominator Degrees of Freedom (df_2)	***Numerator Degrees of Freedom (df_1)***										
	15	***20***	***25***	***30***	***35***	***40***	***50***	***60***	***120***	***200***	***∞***
1	984.9	993.1	998.1	1001	1004	1006	1008	1010	1014	1016	1018
2	39.43	39.45	39.46	39.46	39.47	39.47	39.48	39.48	39.49	39.49	39.50
3	14.25	14.17	14.12	14.08	14.06	14.04	14.01	13.99	13.95	13.93	13.90
4	8.66	8.56	8.50	8.46	8.43	8.41	8.38	8.36	8.31	8.29	8.26
5	6.43	6.33	6.27	6.23	6.20	6.18	6.14	6.12	6.07	6.05	6.02
6	5.27	5.17	5.11	5.07	5.04	5.01	4.98	4.96	4.90	4.88	4.85
7	4.57	4.47	4.40	4.36	4.33	4.31	4.28	4.25	4.20	4.18	4.14
8	4.10	4.00	3.94	3.89	3.86	3.84	3.81	3.78	3.73	3.70	3.67
9	3.77	3.67	3.60	3.56	3.53	3.51	3.47	3.45	3.39	3.37	3.33
10	3.52	3.42	3.35	3.31	3.28	3.26	3.22	3.20	3.14	3.12	3.08
11	3.33	3.23	3.16	3.12	3.09	3.06	3.03	3.00	2.94	2.92	2.88
12	3.18	3.07	3.01	2.96	2.93	2.91	2.87	2.85	2.79	2.76	2.73
13	3.05	2.95	2.88	2.84	2.80	2.78	2.74	2.72	2.66	2.63	2.60
14	2.95	2.84	2.78	2.73	2.70	2.67	2.64	2.61	2.55	2.53	2.49
15	2.86	2.76	2.69	2.64	2.61	2.59	2.55	2.52	2.46	2.44	2.40
16	2.79	2.68	2.61	2.57	2.53	2.51	2.47	2.45	2.38	2.36	2.32
17	2.72	2.62	2.55	2.50	2.47	2.44	2.41	2.38	2.32	2.29	2.25
18	2.67	2.56	2.49	2.44	2.41	2.38	2.35	2.32	2.26	2.23	2.19
19	2.62	2.51	2.44	2.39	2.36	2.33	2.30	2.27	2.20	2.18	2.13
20	2.57	2.46	2.40	2.35	2.31	2.29	2.25	2.22	2.16	2.13	2.09
21	2.53	2.42	2.36	2.31	2.27	2.25	2.21	2.18	2.11	2.09	2.04
22	2.50	2.39	2.32	2.27	2.24	2.21	2.17	2.14	2.08	2.05	2.01
23	2.47	2.36	2.29	2.24	2.20	2.18	2.14	2.11	2.04	2.01	1.97
24	2.44	2.33	2.26	2.21	2.17	2.15	2.11	2.08	2.01	1.98	1.94
25	2.41	2.30	2.23	2.18	2.15	2.12	2.08	2.05	1.98	1.95	1.91
26	2.39	2.28	2.21	2.16	2.12	2.09	2.05	2.03	1.95	1.92	1.88
27	2.36	2.25	2.18	2.13	2.10	2.07	2.03	2.00	1.93	1.90	1.85
28	2.34	2.23	2.16	2.11	2.08	2.05	2.01	1.98	1.91	1.88	1.83
29	2.32	2.21	2.14	2.09	2.06	2.03	1.99	1.96	1.89	1.86	1.81
30	2.31	2.20	2.12	2.07	2.04	2.01	1.97	1.94	1.87	1.84	1.79
40	2.18	2.07	1.99	1.94	1.90	1.88	1.83	1.80	1.72	1.69	1.64
50	2.11	1.99	1.92	1.87	1.83	1.80	1.75	1.72	1.64	1.60	1.55
60	2.06	1.94	1.87	1.82	1.78	1.74	1.70	1.67	1.58	1.54	1.48
120	1.94	1.82	1.75	1.69	1.65	1.61	1.56	1.53	1.43	1.39	1.31
200	1.90	1.78	1.70	1.64	1.60	1.56	1.51	1.47	1.37	1.32	1.23
∞	1.83	1.71	1.63	1.57	1.52	1.48	1.43	1.39	1.27	1.21	1.00

CRITICAL VALUES OF $F_{.01}$

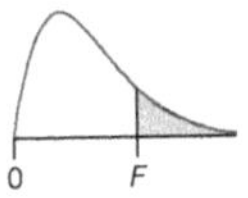

This table shows the 1 percent right-tail critical values of F for the stated degrees of freedom (*d.f.*).

Denominator Degrees of Freedom (df_2)	*Numerator Degrees of Freedom (df_1)*										
	1	**2**	**3**	**4**	**5**	**6**	**7**	**8**	**9**	**10**	**12**
1	4052	4999	5404	5624	5764	5859	5928	5981	6022	6056	6107
2	98.50	99.00	99.16	99.25	99.30	99.33	99.36	99.38	99.39	99.40	99.42
3	34.12	30.82	29.46	28.71	28.24	27.91	27.67	27.49	27.34	27.23	27.05
4	21.20	18.00	16.69	15.98	15.52	15.21	14.98	14.80	14.66	14.55	14.37
5	16.26	13.27	12.06	11.39	10.97	10.67	10.46	10.29	10.16	10.05	9.89
6	13.75	10.92	9.78	9.15	8.75	8.47	8.26	8.10	7.98	7.87	7.72
7	12.25	9.55	8.45	7.85	7.46	7.19	6.99	6.84	6.72	6.62	6.47
8	11.26	8.65	7.59	7.01	6.63	6.37	6.18	6.03	5.91	5.81	5.67
9	10.56	8.02	6.99	6.42	6.06	5.80	5.61	5.47	5.35	5.26	5.11
10	10.04	7.56	6.55	5.99	5.64	5.39	5.20	5.06	4.94	4.85	4.71
11	9.65	7.21	6.22	5.67	5.32	5.07	4.89	4.74	4.63	4.54	4.40
12	9.33	6.93	5.95	5.41	5.06	4.82	4.64	4.50	4.39	4.30	4.16
13	9.07	6.70	5.74	5.21	4.86	4.62	4.44	4.30	4.19	4.10	3.96
14	8.86	6.51	5.56	5.04	4.69	4.46	4.28	4.14	4.03	3.94	3.80
15	8.68	6.36	5.42	4.89	4.56	4.32	4.14	4.00	3.89	3.80	3.67
16	8.53	6.23	5.29	4.77	4.44	4.20	4.03	3.89	3.78	3.69	3.55
17	8.40	6.11	5.19	4.67	4.34	4.10	3.93	3.79	3.68	3.59	3.46
18	8.29	6.01	5.09	4.58	4.25	4.01	3.84	3.71	3.60	3.51	3.37
19	8.18	5.93	5.01	4.50	4.17	3.94	3.77	3.63	3.52	3.43	3.30
20	8.10	5.85	4.94	4.43	4.10	3.87	3.70	3.56	3.46	3.37	3.23
21	8.02	5.78	4.87	4.37	4.04	3.81	3.64	3.51	3.40	3.31	3.17
22	7.95	5.72	4.82	4.31	3.99	3.76	3.59	3.45	3.35	3.26	3.12
23	7.88	5.66	4.76	4.26	3.94	3.71	3.54	3.41	3.30	3.21	3.07
24	7.82	5.61	4.72	4.22	3.90	3.67	3.50	3.36	3.26	3.17	3.03
25	7.77	5.57	4.68	4.18	3.85	3.63	3.46	3.32	3.22	3.13	2.99
26	7.72	5.53	4.64	4.14	3.82	3.59	3.42	3.29	3.18	3.09	2.96
27	7.68	5.49	4.60	4.11	3.78	3.56	3.39	3.26	3.15	3.06	2.93
28	7.64	5.45	4.57	4.07	3.75	3.53	3.36	3.23	3.12	3.03	2.90
29	7.60	5.42	4.54	4.04	3.73	3.50	3.33	3.20	3.09	3.00	2.87
30	7.56	5.39	4.51	4.02	3.70	3.47	3.30	3.17	3.07	2.98	2.84
40	7.31	5.18	4.31	3.83	3.51	3.29	3.12	2.99	2.89	2.80	2.66
50	7.17	5.06	4.20	3.72	3.41	3.19	3.02	2.89	2.78	2.70	2.56
60	7.08	4.98	4.13	3.65	3.34	3.12	2.95	2.82	2.72	2.63	2.50
120	6.85	4.79	3.95	3.48	3.17	2.96	2.79	2.66	2.56	2.47	2.34
200	6.76	4.71	3.88	3.41	3.11	2.89	2.73	2.60	2.50	2.41	2.27
∞	6.63	4.61	3.78	3.32	3.02	2.80	2.64	2.51	2.41	2.32	2.18

Denominator Degrees of Freedom (df_2)	***Numerator Degrees of Freedom (df_1)***										
	15	***20***	***25***	***30***	***35***	***40***	***50***	***60***	***120***	***200***	***∞***
1	6157	6209	6240	6260	6275	6286	6302	6313	6340	6350	6366
2	99.43	99.45	99.46	99.47	99.47	99.48	99.48	99.48	99.49	99.49	99.50
3	26.87	26.69	26.58	26.50	26.45	26.41	26.35	26.32	26.22	26.18	26.13
4	14.20	14.02	13.91	13.84	13.79	13.75	13.69	13.65	13.56	13.52	13.47
5	9.72	9.55	9.45	9.38	9.33	9.29	9.24	9.20	9.11	9.08	9.02
6	7.56	7.40	7.30	7.23	7.18	7.14	7.09	7.06	6.97	6.93	6.88
7	6.31	6.16	6.06	5.99	5.94	5.91	5.86	5.82	5.74	5.70	5.65
8	5.52	5.36	5.26	5.20	5.15	5.12	5.07	5.03	4.95	4.91	4.86
9	4.96	4.81	4.71	4.65	4.60	4.57	4.52	4.48	4.40	4.36	4.31
10	4.56	4.41	4.31	4.25	4.20	4.17	4.12	4.08	4.00	3.96	3.91
11	4.25	4.10	4.01	3.94	3.89	3.86	3.81	3.78	3.69	3.66	3.60
12	4.01	3.86	3.76	3.70	3.65	3.62	3.57	3.54	3.45	3.41	3.36
13	3.82	3.66	3.57	3.51	3.46	3.43	3.38	3.34	3.25	3.22	3.17
14	3.66	3.51	3.41	3.35	3.30	3.27	3.22	3.18	3.09	3.06	3.01
15	3.52	3.37	3.28	3.21	3.17	3.13	3.08	3.05	2.96	2.92	2.87
16	3.41	3.26	3.16	3.10	3.05	3.02	2.97	2.93	2.84	2.81	2.76
17	3.31	3.16	3.07	3.00	2.96	2.92	2.87	2.83	2.75	2.71	2.66
18	3.23	3.08	2.98	2.92	2.87	2.84	2.78	2.75	2.66	2.62	2.57
19	3.15	3.00	2.91	2.84	2.80	2.76	2.71	2.67	2.58	2.55	2.49
20	3.09	2.94	2.84	2.78	2.73	2.69	2.64	2.61	2.52	2.48	2.42
21	3.03	2.88	2.79	2.72	2.67	2.64	2.58	2.55	2.46	2.42	2.36
22	2.98	2.83	2.73	2.67	2.62	2.58	2.53	2.50	2.40	2.36	2.31
23	2.93	2.78	2.69	2.62	2.57	2.54	2.48	2.45	2.35	2.32	2.26
24	2.89	2.74	2.64	2.58	2.53	2.49	2.44	2.40	2.31	2.27	2.21
25	2.85	2.70	2.60	2.54	2.49	2.45	2.40	2.36	2.27	2.23	2.17
26	2.81	2.66	2.57	2.50	2.45	2.42	2.36	2.33	2.23	2.19	2.13
27	2.78	2.63	2.54	2.47	2.42	2.38	2.33	2.29	2.20	2.16	2.10
28	2.75	2.60	2.51	2.44	2.39	2.35	2.30	2.26	2.17	2.13	2.07
29	2.73	2.57	2.48	2.41	2.36	2.33	2.27	2.23	2.14	2.10	2.04
30	2.70	2.55	2.45	2.39	2.34	2.30	2.25	2.21	2.11	2.07	2.01
40	2.52	2.37	2.27	2.20	2.15	2.11	2.06	2.02	1.92	1.87	1.81
50	2.42	2.27	2.17	2.10	2.05	2.01	1.95	1.91	1.80	1.76	1.69
60	2.35	2.20	2.10	2.03	1.98	1.94	1.88	1.84	1.73	1.68	1.60
120	2.19	2.03	1.93	1.86	1.81	1.76	1.70	1.66	1.53	1.48	1.38
200	2.13	1.97	1.87	1.79	1.74	1.69	1.63	1.58	1.45	1.39	1.28
∞	2.04	1.88	1.77	1.70	1.64	1.59	1.52	1.47	1.32	1.25	1.00

Online Supplements

Connect Two-Semester Online Access for Applied Statistics in Business and Economics, Fifth Edition

McGraw-Hill Connect is a digital teaching and learning environment that improves performance over a variety of critical outcomes. With Connect, instructors can deliver assignments, quizzes and tests easily online. Students can practice important skills at their own pace and on their own schedule.

HOW TO REGISTER

Using a Print Book?

To register and activate your Connect account, simply follow these easy steps:

1. **Go to the Connect course web address provided by your instructor or visit the Connect link set up on your instructor's course within your campus learning management system.**
2. **Click on the link to register.**
3. **When prompted, enter the Connect code found on the inside back cover of your book and click Submit. Complete the brief registration form that follows to begin using Connect.**

Using an eBook?

To register and activate your Connect account, simply follow these easy steps:

1. **Upon purchase of your eBook, you will be granted automatic access to Connect.**
2. **Go to the Connect course web address provided by your instructor or visit the Connect link set up on your instructor's course within your campus learning management system.**
3. **Sign in using the same email address and password you used to register on the eBookstore. Complete your registration and begin using Connect.**

**Note: Access Code is for one use only. If you did not purchase this book new, the access code included in this book is no longer valid.*

Need help? Visit mhhe.com/support